Mechanisms
of
inorganic reactions

Mechanisms
of
inorganic reactions

A STUDY OF METAL COMPLEXES IN SOLUTION

Fred Basolo

Professor of Chemistry

Ralph G. Pearson

Professor of Chemistry

NORTHWESTERN UNIVERSITY

NEW YORK · **JOHN WILEY & SONS, INC.**

London

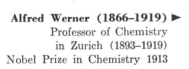

◄ Sophus Mads Jørgensen (1837–1914)
Professor of Chemistry in Copenhagen (1871–1908)

This book is dedicated to S. M. Jørgensen and A. Werner, whose pioneering work laid the foundation for the subject of coordination chemistry. Since these two great adversaries did not meet during their lifetime, it is our pleasure to bring them together here and to acknowledge the debt owed them by all who are interested in the class of compounds dealt with in this volume.

Alfred Werner (1866–1919) ►
Professor of Chemistry
in Zurich (1893–1919)
Nobel Prize in Chemistry 1913

Preface

It is increasingly apparent that in the last two decades there has been what may justifiably be called "the renaissance of inorganic chemistry." In this period the chemistry of non-carbon compounds has escaped from being considered by some a mass of unrelated facts largely confined to the elementary undergraduate courses. It is particularly noteworthy that research activities in inorganic chemistry have vastly increased. With the application of new methods of preparation and separation a great many new substances, often remarkable in their properties, have been prepared. Quantitative data on the properties of these substances have been obtained by the application of new physical methods of study. These data are of such a nature as to lead to a more complete understanding of the fundamental principles underlying them.

Part of this rebirth of interest in inorganic chemistry has been due to the demands of industry and government for new materials with properties unobtainable in organic compounds, e.g., in the areas of nuclear energy, high temperature chemistry, semiconductors, and high energy rocket fuels. Certainly the rise of the atomic age has led to the greatly increased study and use of the less familiar elements. Moreover, it has made many elements available in a useful, radioactive form. These demands and these developments may be expected to expand.

Another part of the interest and growth of inorganic chemistry may be attributed to the rise of theories which make possible the integration and understanding of the large number of facts available. Of these, Professor Linus Pauling's application of quantum mechanics to the chemical bonds holding inorganic compounds together is outstanding. Another more recent approach involves the revitalization of the old electrostatic concept of these compounds by means of the crystal field theory.

The use of physical methods of study in inorganic reactions has passed through three stages: the structural stage, concerned chiefly with the nature of the chemical bonds involved and the stereochemistry of the arrangement of atoms; the thermodynamic stage, concerned with energetics and equilibrium constants; and, most recently, the kinetic and mechanistic study of inorganic reactions. It is with the last stage that this book is chiefly concerned. It is our feeling that enough information is now available to give a reasonably coherent account of what seems to be involved in the chemical reactions of coordination compounds.

We are well aware that the current intense activity in this field will soon make this treatise incomplete. We can only hope that not too many of the views expressed will do violence to the new facts as they are uncovered. Nevertheless the lack of any other convenient reference for many of the topics dealt with here has encouraged us to go on. We hope that research chemists, teachers of chemistry, and graduate students in chemistry can find something of value in these pages.

We need not apologize for restricting ourselves to reactions of coordination compounds. It is generally agreed that an aqueous ion such as iron(II) is in reality $Fe(H_2O)_6^{2+}$, or something similar, and that sodium ion in crystalline sodium chloride, with its neighboring octahedron of chloride ions, is similar to AlF_6^{3-}. Thus, it follows that coordination chemistry includes the greater part of all inorganic chemistry. Without wishing to debate this point further, certainly it can also be said that a knowledge of complex ions is important in many areas other than strictly inorganic chemistry, e.g., biochemistry, analytical chemistry, catalysis, electrochemistry, mineralogy, and radiochemistry, to name several. We regret that limitations both of space and our own knowledge prevent us from discussing such things as gas phase reactions, solid-state reactions, and a host of other important topics in inorganic chemistry. It is indeed a pleasure to note that our neglect of the heaviest elements has been compensated for by the recent appearance of the excellent treatise on *The Chemistry of the Actinide Elements,* by J. J. Katz and G. T. Seaborg.

We assume that our readers are adequately trained in the fundamentals of chemistry. Some prior knowledge of coordination chemistry, stereochemistry, and reaction kinetics is necessary. Nevertheless some introductory material has been included. In particular a rather detailed presentation of the present theories of complexes is given. If, in Chapter 2 and later, we show some bias for the electrostatic approach to these compounds it is partly because we believe that such an approach can be extremely helpful in understanding coordination compounds. Also it is partly because we feel that the valence bond theory of these compounds has been too enthusiastically accepted. The result has been that fact and theory are sometimes rather confusingly intermingled. Perhaps by stressing an alternate viewpoint the assumptions and approximations of both theories can be better accentuated.

In conclusion we would like to thank the following persons who aided in various ways in the writing of this book: A. W. Adamson, A. L. Allred, J. C. Bailar, Jr., C. J. Ballhausen, J. Bjerrum, J. Chatt, R. W. Dodson, F. P. Dwyer, J. Halpern, C. Klixbüll Jørgensen, D. S. McClure, H. M. Neumann, R. S. Nyholm, L. E. Orgel, L. G. Sillén, H. Taube, I. Wender, R. G. Wilkins, our many coworkers, and our wives.

FRED BASOLO
RALPH G. PEARSON

April, 1958
Evanston, Illinois

Contents

1
Introduction

The subject of this treatise is the mechanism of reactions of certain inorganic compounds, usually in homogeneous solution. By *mechanism* is meant all the individual collisional or other elementary processes involving molecules (atoms, radicals, and ions included) that take place simultaneously or consecutively in producing the observed overall reaction.

It is also understood that the mechanism of a reaction should give a detailed stereochemical picture of each step as it occurs. This implies a knowledge of the so-called *activated complex* or *transition state* [1] not only in terms of the constituent molecules but also in terms of the geometry such as interatomic distances and angles.

Kinetic studies and stereochemical studies provide the most powerful methods of investigating detailed reaction mechanisms. However, it is generally not possible to get absolute information. Thus postulated mechanisms are essentially theories devised to explain the facts obtained by experiments. Like other theories mechanisms are subject to change as new information is uncovered, or as new concepts are developed in related areas of science. Nevertheless, the postulation of reaction mechanisms is of the greatest help in understanding and systematizing the study of an area of chemistry.

The area of chemistry concerned in this case is that of *coordination* or *complex compounds*. Such compounds contain a central atom or ion, usually a metal, and a cluster of ions or molecules surrounding it. It is characteristic of the complex that it retains its identity, more or less, even in solution, though partial dissociation may occur. The complex may be non-ionic or a cation or anion depending on the charges carried by the central atom and the coordinated groups. These groups are called *ligands,* and the total number of attachments to the central atom is called the *coordination number.* Other common names for these

1

compounds include complex ions (if electrically charged), Werner complexes, coordination complexes or, simply, complexes.

The historical development of the chemistry of coordination compounds dates back approximately to the end of the eighteenth century. Since the existing valency theory during the early stages of this development could not adequately account for such materials, they were commonly referred to as complex compounds, a term still in common usage but no longer for the same reason. Much of this time the compounds were formulated by writing the generators side by side, e.g., $2KCl \cdot HgCl_2$ and $2KCl \cdot MgCl_2$, as if they were all of the same type. After some investigation it did become apparent that these two are not similar. Aqueous solutions of the two both contain potassium ions, but the former yields only a total of three compared to seven ions per mole for the latter. It is now realized that the first one is a coordination compound with the four chloride ions firmly attached to the mercury, as indicated by the formulation $K_2[HgCl_4]$, whereas the other is a *double salt* and is correctly formulated as written. It is often not possible to distinguish between double salts and coordination compounds on the basis of their behavior in aqueous solution. For example, x-ray data conclusively show [2] that the four chloride ions are tetrahedrally distributed about the cobalt(II) ion in the salt $K_2[CoCl_4]$ and therefore that it is a coordination compound rather than a double salt. However, this complex is labile and immediately reacts with water to yield a pink solution,

$$K_2[CoCl_4] + 6H_2O \rightarrow 2K^+ + Co(H_2O)_6{}^{2+} + 4Cl^- \qquad (1)$$

so that its behavior in solution does in fact resemble that of a double salt.

One other class of coordination compounds are the *metal ammines*. Tassaert [3] reported in 1798 that ammoniacal solutions of cobalt(II) chloride allowed to stand overnight yield an orange-colored crystalline product containing six molecules of ammonia. It was assumed that these compounds were analogous to salt hydrates, and they were designated as ammoniates, $CoCl_3 \cdot 6NH_3$. This analogy is essentially correct for in hydrates, except for interstitial and anion water, the water is coordinated to the central metal ion. However, such information on the structure of salt hydrates became known only after extensive investigations of the properties of metal ammines. The ammonia was found to be very firmly bound in $CoCl_3 \cdot 6NH_3$. This compound shows no loss of ammonia even at 150°C, and a solution of it in dilute sulfuric acid can be refluxed for several hours without the formation of appreciable amounts of ammonium sulfate. Other compounds of cobalt(III) chloride containing fewer than six ammonia molecules per complex were also prepared as shown in Table 1. Observations of the firmness with

Table 1

Cobalt(III) Ammine Chlorides

Compound	Color	Class Name	No. of Ionic Chlorides	Werner's Formulation
$CoCl_3 \cdot 6NH_3$	orange	*luteo* salt	3	$[Co(NH_3)_6]^{3+}3Cl^-$
$CoCl_3 \cdot 5NH_3$	purple	*purpureo* salt	2	$[Co(NH_3)_5Cl]^{2+}2Cl^-$
$CoCl_3 \cdot 4NH_3$	green	*praseo* salt	1	*trans*-$[Co(NH_3)_4Cl_2]^+Cl^-$
$CoCl_3 \cdot 4NH_3$	violet	*violeo* salt	1	*cis*-$[Co(NH_3)_4Cl_2]^+Cl^-$
$CoCl_3 \cdot 3NH_3$	blue green	. . .	0	$[Co(NH_3)_3Cl_3]$

which the ammonia molecules are bound, the wide variations in color, the variations in the numbers of ionic chloride, and the existence of a green and a violet salt of the compound containing four molecules of ammonia suggested that the ammonia must in some way be a definite part of the compound instead of just loosely held in the crystal lattice. Experimental facts of this type were collected on many different systems and were finally correctly interpreted by Werner[4] in 1893.

Werner introduced the concept that, in addition to having a *normal* or *primary* valence, elements may also possess a *residual* or *secondary* valence. Thus cobalt(III) has a normal valence of three but in addition an affinity for six groups, that is, a residual valence or coordination number of six. This concept led to the formulations shown in Table 1, which adequately account for the properties of these compounds. Werner also proposed that the secondary valence bonds are directed in space, and thus that the *praseo* and *violeo* compounds are geometrical isomers. This postulate of directed valency bonds has been of extreme importance in connection with the stereochemistry of these compounds.

G. N. Lewis[5] later put Werner's views of secondary valency or coordination in terms of electrons. Thus the bond between the central ion and each of the attached groups involves a pair of electrons and is represented as a *coordinate* or *dative* bond, $M \leftarrow L$ or $M^{\delta-}:L^{\delta+}$. The electronic configuration of metal ions is often such that they can accommodate as many as twelve electrons, or more, which in turn means that coordination numbers of six and greater are entirely possible. It has been suggested that ions tend to add a sufficient number of electrons by coordination such that the ion in the resulting complex has an *effective atomic number* (E.A.N.) [6] of the next inert gas,

Co^{3+}	contains	24 electrons
$6NH_3$	donate	12 electrons

E.A.N. of Co^{3+} in $Co(NH_3)_6^{3+}$ = 36 electrons (the same as Kr)

This rule can only be given qualitative significance because there are a very large number of exceptions. Furthermore the coordination number of a metal ion may differ depending on the nature of the coordinated groups: nickel(II) forms compounds in which it has coordination numbers of either four, five (Table 2), or six; iron(III) forms FeF_6^{3-} and $Fe(CN)_6^{3-}$ but only $FeCl_4^-$. The polarizability, size, and ability to π-bond of a ligand all seem to play an important role in fixing the coordination number of a metal ion (Chapter 2). Some metal ions are also known to coordinate to a certain number of ligands readily and to an additional number of the same ligand with greater difficulty. For example, mercury(II) forms four-coordinated complexes but two of the ligands are much more readily bound than the other two. Thus, the stepwise formation constants (p. 15) for $HgCl_4^{2-}$ are log K_1 = 7.15, log K_2 = 6.9, log K_3 = 1.0, and log K_4 = 0.7. Bjerrum [7] suggests therefore that mercury(II) be said to have a *characteristic coordination number* of two and a *maximum coordination number* of four. In spite of this, the four chloride ions in $HgCl_4^{2-}$ are probably equivalent.

Much the same behavior is observed with copper(II), which is usually assigned a coordination number of four but which can coordinate to six groups with the formation of a distorted octahedron.[8] Similarly silver(I) has a marked affinity for two ligands but can also exhibit a coordination number of three (Table 2) and four.[9a] In fact a recent study shows that for certain ligands silver(I) does not exhibit a marked affinity for only two groups but instead coordinates readily with either three or four groups.[9b] It is apparent, then, that the assignment of a definite coordination number to a given metal ion must often be done with some reservation.

STEREOCHEMISTRY

The early classical approach to the determination of the structure of coordinated entities was to deduce the structure on the basis of the known geometrical and optical isomers. Square planar, tetrahedral,

and octahedral structures assigned on this basis have since been verified by modern physicochemical methods, the most reliable being x-ray
analysis.[10] Although the coordination number of the central ion for
most compounds is either six or four, examples of compounds are known
which exhibit each of the other numbers up to ten (Table 2).

The four ligands in four-coordinated complexes may be positioned
either at the corners of a tetrahedron, as is true of carbon compounds,
or at the corners of a square plane. For a discussion of other possible
structures and a much more complete treatment of square complexes,
the reader is referred to a review on the subject by Mellor.[11] The first
suggestion that coordination compounds may have a square structure
was made by Werner[4] in an attempt to account for the existence of
α and β forms of $Pt(NH_3)_2Cl_2$. He pointed out that, since there can
only be one form for tetrahedral compounds of this type, MA_2B_2 (individual letters A, B, C, L, X, Y, etc., are used to designate unidentate
ligands), then the isolation of two isomers is an indication of a planar
structure, which can be represented as

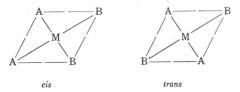

cis   *trans*

This assignment of structure to platinum(II) complexes seemed justified because of the large number of such isomers that had been isolated,
e.g., $Pt(NH_3)_2(NO_2)_2$, $Pt(py)_2(NH_3)_2^{2+}$, $Pt(py)_2Cl_2$, etc. Additional
chemical evidence in support of the planar configuration of platinum(II)
compounds is afforded by the synthesis of two geometrical isomers of
compounds such as $Pt(gly)_2$.[12] Planar compounds of this type, $M(AB)_2$
(a combination of letters in parentheses is used to designate polydentate
ligands, e.g., (AA) is a symmetrical bidentate group such as ethylenediamine, (AB) is an unsymmetrical bidentate group such as glycinate or
benzylmethylglyoximate ions, and (AABBAA) is a sexadentate group
such as ethylenediaminetetraacetate ion), can exist in *cis* and *trans*
forms, neither of which is optically active,

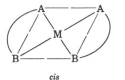   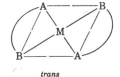

cis   *trans*

However, a tetrahedral structure gives rise to mirror image isomers,

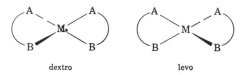

dextro   levo

Chernyaev [13] by an application of the phenomenon of the *"trans effect"* (Chapter 4) was able to prepare three isomeric forms of $Pt(NH_2OH)$- $(py)(NH_3)NO_2^+$. More recently three isomers have also been obtained of the compounds $Pt(C_2H_4)(NH_3)ClBr$ [14] and $Pt(py)(NH_3)ClBr$.[15] A tetrahedral configuration for such compounds, MABCD, would result in an asymmetric central ion and optical activity, but a planar structure predicts the existence of three geometrical isomers. Finally, a very elegant

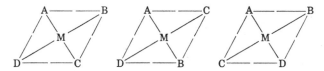

chemical approach to this problem was that of Mills and Quibell,[16] who prepared and resolved isobutylenediamine-*meso*-stilbenediamineplatinum(II) chloride. If the arrangement of the platinum(II) valences is tetrahedral, the complex has a median plane of symmetry and thus cannot be optically active. However, a coplanar arrangement of the two chelate rings does give a dissymmetric cation which can form mirror image isomers:

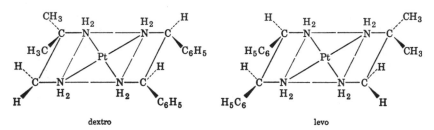

dextro   levo

The structure of four-coordinated platinum(II) compounds has now been determined by many different methods, and there can be no doubt that it is square planar.[11] However, it should be made clear that the chemical approach outlined above cannot be taken as proof of structure unless it is also established that the isomeric forms in question are all monomeric. For example, the synthesis of two substances of composition $(CH_3)_2TeI_2$ was interpreted incorrectly as being due to *cis* (β)

and *trans* (α) isomers of a planar structure.[17] It has since been shown that the β form is dimeric, [$(CH_3)_3TeI$][CH_3TeI_3], and that four-coordinated tellurium is in fact tetrahedral.[18] Furthermore chemical proof of structure must be accompanied by some evidence that the two forms are not different crystal modifications of the same compound. This can be determined by investigations on solutions of the two, e.g., chemical reactions, absorption spectra, dipole moments, etc. The square planar structure has been established for a number of complexes of Pt(II), Pd(II), Ni(II), Ag(II), Cu(II), and Au(III).

Optically active compounds of the type $M(AB)_2$ have been cited as evidence for the tetrahedral structures of B(III), Be(II), Zn(II), and Cu(II) (Chapter 6, Table 9). These compounds racemize rapidly, so that generally the optical activity of the complex was attributed to the observed mutarotation in the presence either of an optically active resolving agent or ligand. This assignment of tetrahedral structure seems justified for complexes of B(III) and Be(II). However, such may not be the case for complexes of Zn(II) and Cu(II) which can have a coordination number of six that might also account for the observed mutarotations. However, on the basis of available physico-chemical evidence, it is possible to assign a tetrahedral configuration to some metal complexes [19] of Cu(I), Ag(I), Au(I), Be(II), Zn(II), Cd(II), Hg(II), B(III), Al(III), Fe(III), Co(II), and Ni(0). Except for complexes such as $FeCl_4^-$, $CoCl_4^{2-}$, $Ni(CO)_4$ (and those such as CrO_4^{2-}, MnO_4^-), there is a noticeable absence of transition metals in this list of metals that form tetrahedral complexes. That this is to be expected on the basis of modern theories of chemical bonding in coordination compounds is discussed in the next chapter.

Except for a very few special cases,[20] substances which contain six groups around a central ion have an octahedral configuration. Werner concluded that the octahedral distribution of groups was correct for six-coordinated compounds because in no case had more than two isomers of either MA_4B_2 or MA_3B_3 been isolated. He pointed out that, if such compounds had either a planar or a trigonal prism structure, then three isomeric forms were possible. However, the geometrical isomers expected for the octahedral structure of compounds of the type MA_4B_2 are

cis   *trans*

more commonly diagramed as used in this book

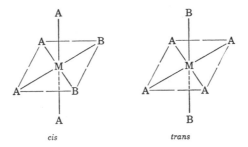

cis   *trans*

but sometimes also designated as

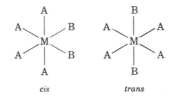

cis   *trans*

For compounds of the type MA_3B_3, the isomers are

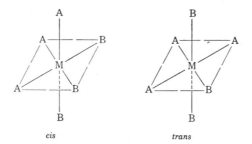

cis   *trans*

That complexes such as $Co(NH_3)_4(NO_2)_2{}^+$, $Co(NH_3)_4Cl_2{}^+$, and $Co(NH_3)_3(NO_2)_3$ had only been isolated in two different forms can only be cited as an indication of structure. That neither the planar nor trigonal prism structure is correct was finally established by the resolution of complexes of the type $M(AA)_3$, which would not be optically active for either of these two structures. The existence of such optically active complexes is, however, consistent with an octahedral structure. Since optical activity was originally associated with only organic compounds, it was necessary for Werner[21] to resolve

$$Co\left(\langle{OH \atop OH}\rangle Co(NH_3)_4\right)_3^{6+}.$$ The only other completely inorganic com-

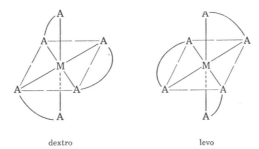

dextro   levo

plex that has been resolved is *cis*-Rh(NHSO$_2$NH)$_2$(H$_2$O)$_2$⁻.[22]   The resolution of six-coordinated complexes of the metal ions Al(III), As(V), Cd(II), Cr(III), Ga(III), Ge(IV), Ir(III), Fe(II), (III), Ni(II), Os(II), (III), Pt(IV), Rh(III), Ru(II), Ru(III), Ti(IV), and Zn(II) has been reported, and examples of some of these are listed in Table 4 (Chapter 6). The octahedral structure has now been amply verified by x-ray analysis and is accepted as the structure of six-coordinated compounds.

Coordination compounds in which the coordination number of the central ion is different from either four or six are much less common. Some examples of other coordination numbers are summarized in Table 2.   In certain cases the structures have been determined by either x-ray analysis or electron diffraction measurements.   However, for several of the complexes the coordination number is known only from data on the stoichiometry of the compounds and their molecular weights.   Stoichiometric data alone are usually not sufficient to establish the coordination number of a compound.   Thus compounds of the composition (NH$_4$)$_3$ZnCl$_5$ and (NH$_4$)$_2$FeCl$_5$·H$_2$O, believed to have a coordination number of five, were shown by x-ray studies to have coordination numbers of four,[36] NH$_4$Cl·(NH$_4$)$_2$[ZnCl$_4$], and of six,[37] (NH$_4$)$_2$[Fe(H$_2$O)Cl$_5$].

A discussion of the stereochemistry of coordination compounds is not complete without a summary of the different types of isomerism (Table 3).   The synthesis, separation, and characterization of these isomers generally follow no set of fixed rules.   However, the *trans*-effect phenomenon (Chapter 4) has been applied with some success to the synthesis of geometrical isomers of platinum(II) complexes.*

---

* A general method for the synthesis of geometric isomers of the types Pt(PR$_3$)$_2$-Cl$_2$ and Pt(AsR$_3$)$_2$Cl$_2$ has been described (see J. Chatt and R. G. Wilkins, *J. Chem. Soc.*, **1951**, 2532. This depends upon the fact that the *cis* isomer is less soluble than the *trans* in benzene and that catalytic amounts of PR$_3$ or AsR$_3$ permit a rapid *cis-trans* equilibration in solution. Thus, upon concentration of the solution in the presence of a catalyst, crystals of the less soluble *cis* isomer are obtained. At equilibrium in solution the mixture is largely the *trans* isomer. If the catalyst is removed by the addition of the dimer [Pt(PR$_3$)$_2$Cl$_2$]$_2$ or [Pt

Table 2

Metal Complexes of Coordination Numbers Other than Four or Six

C.N.	Complex *	Structure [10,19]
2	$Ag(NH_3)_2^+$, $Ag(CN)_2^-$, $Hg(NH_3)_2^{2+}$	linear
3	$M(R_3Y)_2I$;[23] M(I)=Cu, Ag, Au; Y=P, As	probably planar
	$Ag(R_3P)_3^+$, $Ag(R_2S)_3^+$,[24a] $Ag(tu)_3^+$ [24b]	probably planar
5	$Fe(CO)_5$, $M(terpy)Cl_2$;[25] M(II)=Cu, Zn, Cd	trigonal bipyramid

$$(CH_3)_2NC \overset{\displaystyle S \quad NO \quad S}{\diagup \diagdown \mid \diagup \diagdown} M \overset{}{\diagdown \diagup \diagdown \diagup} CN(CH_3)_2; M=V,^{26a}$$
$$\underset{S \qquad\quad S}{}$$

Co is a modified tetragonal pyramid [26c]

Fe,[26b] Co [26a,b]

	$Ni(P(C_2H_5)_3)_2Br_3$,[27] $Ni(DMG)_2Br$,[27] $Ni(tas)Cl_2$ [28a]	probably tetragonal pyramid
	$M(das)_2I$;[28b] M=Ni(II), Pd(II), Au(III)	probably tetragonal pyramid
	$K_3[Co(CN)_5]$,[29a] $Co(CNR)_5^+$,[29b] $Rh(CNR)_4X^+$ [29c]	structures not known
	$V(N(CH_3)_3)_2Cl_3$, $Ti(N(CH_3)_3)_3Cl_2$ [29d]	structures not known
7	ZrF_7^{3-}	pentagonal bipyramid [30]
	NbF_7^{2-}, TaF_7^{2-}	face-centered trigonal prism [31]
8	$Mo(CN)_8^{4-}$	dodecahedral [32]
	TaF_8^{3-}	Archimedean anti-prism [33]
	$M(aeoc)_4$; M(IV)=Zr, Ce, Th, Hf, U, Po [34]	structure not known
	$M(C_2O_4)_4^{4-}$; M(IV)=Zr, Hf, Th, Sn, U [34]	structure not known
9	$Nd(H_2O)_9^{3+}$	face-centered trigonal prism [35]
10	$M_2[M'(CN)_8X_2]\cdot 4H_2O$;[35b] M=Cd, Mn; M'=Mo,W; X=H_2O,NH_3, N_2H_4	structures not known

* The symbols used are: terpy = 2,2',2''-terpyridine; DMG = dimethyl-glyoximate ion; tas = $(CH_3)_2As(CH_2)_3As(CH_3)(CH_2)_3As(CH_3)_2$; das = o-phenyl-enebis(dimethylarsine); X = methanol, ethanol, benzene, or chloroform; aeoc = acetylacetonate ion; tu = thiourea.

Likewise a general method for the preparation of *trans*-platinum(IV) complexes involves the oxidation of the appropriate platinum(II)

$(AsR_3)_2Cl_2]_2$ and the solution evaporated, the product obtained is largely the *trans* isomer. The small amount of *cis* form which also separates is readily removed by extraction with ether (see also p. 251).

Table 3

Types of Isomerism for Coordination Compounds [19]

Isomerism	Examples
Geometrical	*cis-* and *trans-*Pt(NH$_3$)$_2$Cl$_2$
	cis- and *trans-*[Co(NH$_3$)$_4$Cl$_2$]Cl
Optical	*d-* and *l-*bis(benzoylacetonato)beryllium(II)
	d- and *l-*[Cr(en)$_3$]Cl$_3$
Polymerization	Pt(NH$_3$)$_2$Cl$_2$, [Pt(NH$_3$)$_4$][PtCl$_4$],
	[Pt(NH$_3$)$_4$][Pt(NH$_3$)Cl$_3$]$_2$
	and [Pt(NH$_3$)$_3$Cl]$_2$[PtCl$_4$]
Coordination	[Co(NH$_3$)$_6$][Cr(C$_2$O$_4$)$_3$] and [Cr(NH$_3$)$_6$][Co(C$_2$O$_4$)$_3$]
	[Cr(NH$_3$)$_6$][Cr(NCS)$_6$]
	and [Cr(NH$_3$)$_4$(NCS)$_2$][Cr(NH$_3$)$_2$(NCS)$_4$]
	[Pt$^{(II)}$(en)$_2$][Pt$^{(IV)}$Cl$_6$] and [Pt$^{(IV)}$(en)$_2$Cl$_2$][Pt$^{(II)}$Cl$_4$]
Ionization	[Pt(NH$_3$)$_3$Cl]I and [Pt(NH$_3$)$_3$I]Cl
	[Co(en)$_2$(NCS)Cl]NCS and [Co(en)$_2$(NCS)$_2$]Cl
Hydrate	[Cr(H$_2$O)$_6$]Cl$_3$, [Cr(H$_2$O)$_5$Cl]Cl$_2$·H$_2$O
	and [Cr(H$_2$O)$_4$Cl$_2$]Cl·H$_2$O
	[Co(NH$_3$)$_5$H$_2$O](NO$_3$)$_3$ and [Co(NH$_3$)$_5$NO$_3$](NO$_3$)$_2$·H$_2$O
Linkage	[NH$_3$]$_5$Co—NO$_2$](NO$_3$)$_2$ and [(NH$_3$)$_5$Co—ONO](NO$_3$)$_2$
	[(NH$_3$)$_5$Rh—NO$_2$]Br$_2$ and [(NH$_3$)$_5$Rh—ONO]Br$_2$
Coordination position	(R$_3$P)$_2$Pt$\langle^{Cl}_{Cl}\rangle$PtCl$_2$, and ClR$_3$PPt$\langle^{Cl}_{Cl}\rangle$PtPR$_3$Cl
	$\left[(NH_3)_4Co\langle^{OH}_{OH}\rangle Co(NH_3)_2Cl_2 \right]SO_4$
	and $\left[Cl(NH_3)_3Co\langle^{OH}_{OH}\rangle Co(NH_3)_3Cl \right]SO_4$

compound. This results in an expansion of the coordination number from four to six, with the two ligands entering the *trans* positions.[38]

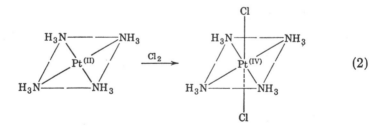

$$(2)$$

This method is applicable mostly to platinum(IV) compounds; *trans* isomers of other six-coordinated compounds are usually obtained not by a specific type of reaction but rather by the crystallization of a slightly soluble salt from a reaction mixture of *cis* and *trans* isomers.

A reaction often used to prepare *cis* isomers, although not always entirely reliable, is one in which a bidentate group is replaced under mild experimental conditions.[39]   Since substitution reactions of six-

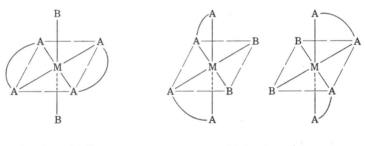

$$\tag{3}$$

coordinated compounds may be accompanied by rearrangements (Chapter 5), there is no assurance that reactions of this type will yield exclusively the *cis* isomer, regardless of experimental conditions.   Reactions such as these have also been used in reverse in attempts to establish the *cis* configuration of a given isomer, but this method suffers from the same criticism.   The only reliable chemical approach to the assignment of *cis* and *trans* structures to geometrical isomers of the type $M(AA)_2B_2$ is the resolution of one form which establishes that it is the *cis* isomer, since the *trans* form is symmetrical and cannot

trans (symmetrical)   *cis* (mirror images)

be optically active.   Reactions of platinum(II) complexes usually take place without rearrangement, which means that chemical techniques can often be used to differentiate between *cis* and *trans* isomers of these compounds.   A large variety of physicochemical methods, e.g., x-ray analysis, dipole moment measurements, absorption spectra, etc., can also be used to establish the configuration of geometrical isomers.

Optical isomerism is not uncommon among coordination compounds. The methods generally employed for the resolution of inorganic complexes are analogous to those used for organic compounds.   The most common procedure is that of converting the racemic mixture into diastereoisomers by means of an optically active resolving agent and the separation of the diastereoisomers by fractional crystallization. Cationic complexes are often resolved by way of d-tartrate, antimonyl d-tartrate, d-camphor-π-sulfonate or α-bromo-d-camphor-π-sulfonate salts, whereas anionic complexes are converted to salts of optically active bases such as brucine, cinchonidine, quinine, strychnine, or d-phenylethylamine.* Subsequent removal of the resolving agent from the desired antipode is then accomplished either by precipitation or extraction, depending upon the property of the individual complex as well as the resolving agent. Non-ionic complexes, for which this method is not applicable, have been resolved by preferential adsorption on optically active quartz [40] and also by the method of configurational activity (p. 285).†

For colored coordination compounds, the magnitude and sign of optical rotation, in the visible region, is often largely dependent upon the wavelength of the light source. This variation in optical rotation with wavelength is referred to as *anomalous rotatory dispersion*. It is therefore necessary that the wavelength of the measurement be designated and furthermore that a zero optical rotation observed at only one wavelength not be taken as proof that the compound is optically inactive, e.g.,

$$[Os(phen)_3](ClO_4)_2 \cdot H_2O, \; [\alpha]_{5896} = 0$$

$$[\alpha]_{5461} = 3670 \; [41]$$

The optical rotation of coordination compounds, at the wavelength of maximum rotation, is generally much greater than that of organic compounds. Werner [42] attempted to relate the generic configurations of analogous complex ions on the assumption that those which form the least soluble diastereoisomers with the same resolving agent have the same generic configuration. His findings agree with later studies made by comparisons of rotatory dispersion curves.[43] It should now be possible to check these two methods by the use of x-ray analysis tech-

---

* It is also of interest to note that optically active complex ions have themselves been used as resolving agents. For example d- and l-Co(en)$_3{}^{3+}$ have been used to resolve dl-Co(EDTA)$^-$ (see F. P. Dwyer, E. C. Gyarfas, and D. P. Mellor, *J. Phys. Chem.*, **59**, 296 (1955).

† Recently the chromatographic separation of optical isomers of complex-ions on starch was reported (H. Krebs, J. Diewald, H. Arlitt, and J. A. Wagner, *Z. anorg. u. allgem. Chem.*, **287**, 98 (1956)).

niques which permit the assignment of absolute configuration of optically active antipodes.[44]

The other types of isomerism listed in Table 3 require no additional comment, except perhaps linkage isomerism. The only known examples of this type of isomerism is that of the nitro (M—NO$_2$) and nitrito (M—ONO) complexes. Investigations relative to the formation and rearrangement of amminenitritocobalt(III) complexes into the more stable corresponding nitro complexes are discussed later (Chapters 3 and 6). It is somewhat surprising that more examples of this type of isomerism are not known since ligands such as $:\ddot{S}:C:::N:^-$, $:C:::N:^-$, and $:C:::O:$ might possibly coordinate through either of two atoms. Apparently the attachment through one of the atoms is so much more energetically favored that its linkage isomer does not exist. Although the bonding in metal cyanides and metal carbonyls is a metal-carbon bond, the cyanide group does form bridges of the type M—C≡N—M,

$$\text{M}\overset{\displaystyle O}{\overset{\displaystyle \|}{-\text{C}-}}\text{M}$$

whereas carbonyl bridges are of the type M—C—M. Sometimes, as in the case of thiocyanate, the point of attachment is different for different metal ions. In cobalt(III) complexes the group is invariably present as isothiocyanato, Co—NCS, and hydrolytic oxidation with chlorine yields the corresponding ammine compounds presumably without a Co—N bond cleavage.[39]

$$\textit{trans-}[(en)_2ClCo-NCS]Cl + 4Cl_2 + 6H_2O \rightarrow$$

$$\textit{trans-}[(en)_2ClCo-NH_3]Cl_2 + CO_2 + H_2SO_4 + 7HCl \quad (4)$$

However, analogous chromium(III) compounds undergo chlorine oxidation to yield the corresponding chloro complex [45a] instead of the ammine:

$$\textit{trans-}[(en)_2Cr-(NCS)_2]Cl + 8Cl_2 + 12H_2O \rightarrow$$

$$\textit{trans-}[(en)_2CrCl_2]Cl + 2CO_2 + 2NH_4HSO_4 + 14HCl \quad (5)$$

Because of this the bonding was assumed to be Cr—SCN, but recent infrared and x-ray studies show that for the Reineckate ion the isorhodanato structure, Cr—NCS, is correct.[45b] The thiocyanato complexes of Hg(II),[8a, 45c] Cu(II),[45d] and Ni(II) [45e] instead are bonded M—SCN.

STABILITY

The electronic concept of coordination compounds indicates that they are formed as a result of Lewis acid–base reactions where the metal ion is the acid (or *acceptor*) and the ligand is the base (or *donor*). It therefore follows that all metal ions will tend to form coordination compounds; this tendency in general increases with increasing electron affinity of the metal ion. It is also true that almost all molecules and ions with at least one free pair of electrons will tend to form complexes with metal ions; the tendency usually increases with increasing proton affinity (base strength) of the ligand. The different types of ligands known are summarized in Table 4.

Table 4

Types of Ligands

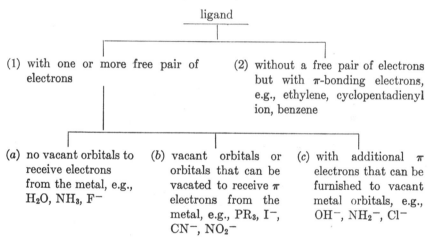

The formation and dissociation of complex compounds, similar to that of polybasic acids, involve the successive equilibria

$$\text{M} + \text{A} \rightleftharpoons \text{MA} \qquad K_1 = \frac{[\text{MA}]}{[\text{M}][\text{A}]} \qquad (6)$$

$$\text{MA} + \text{A} \rightleftharpoons \text{MA}_2 \qquad K_2 = \frac{[\text{MA}_2]}{[\text{MA}][\text{A}]} \qquad (7)$$

$$\cdot \qquad \cdot \qquad \cdot \qquad \cdot$$

$$\text{MA}_n + \text{A} \rightleftharpoons \text{MA}_{n+1} \qquad K_{n+1} = \frac{[\text{MA}_{n+1}]}{[\text{MA}_n][\text{A}]} \qquad (8)$$

Constants $K_1, K_2 \cdots, K_{n+1}$ are designated as stepwise *formation constants*, and the total or overall formation constant K_T is the product of these:

$$M + (n + 1)A \rightleftharpoons MA_{n+1} \qquad K_T = \frac{[MA_{n+1}]}{[M][A]^{n+1}} \qquad (9)$$

The analysis of systems with successive equilibria and the method of evaluating the measurements are described in detail by Bjerrum.[7] There is now a great deal of quantitative information on the stability of co-ordination compounds. Much of this has been summarized and discussed elsewhere,[46, 47] so that only some of the more general trends will be mentioned.

The results of numerous investigations for the first transition series show that, regardless of the nature of the donor group, the so-called *natural order*[48] of the stability of complexes of bivalent transition metals is Mn < Fe < Co < Ni < Cu > Zn. Only in a very few cases have deviations from this order been observed.[47b] Sometimes the difference in stability for successive metals is small. For example the 2,2′,2″-tri-aminotriethylamine complex of Cu(II) is less stable than expected as compared to the stabilities of the Ni(II) or Zn(II) complexes.[49] This is attributed to the fact that the four nitrogen atoms in the tetramine cannot all lie in the same plane as is required by the square planar coordination structure of Cu(II). It has also been observed that the stability of $Fe(phen)_3^{2+}$ is greater than expected and, further, that the value of K_3 for the addition of the third group is larger than either K_1 or K_2.[50] This is attributed to an electronic rearrangement,[47b] for it was shown that the bis complex, $Fe(phen)_2^{2+}$, is paramagnetic, whereas the tris complex, $Fe(phen)_3^{2+}$, is diamagnetic.[51]

There is sufficient experimental evidence on other bivalent metal ions to justify the extension of the above series of relative stabilities approximately as follows: Pt > Pd > Hg > UO_2 > Be > Cu > Ni > Co > Pb > Zn > Cd > Fe > Mn > Ca > Sr > Ba. Univalent and ter-valent ions have not been extensively studied, but data on the systems univalent ions–dibenzoylmethanate ion show the stabilities,[52]

$$Ag > Tl > Li > Na > K > Rb > Cs$$

and for tervalent ions–acetylacetonate ion,[53]

$$Fe > Ga > Al > Sc > In > Y > Pr > Ce > La$$

The complexes of tervalent cobalt and chromium are generally much more stable than those of iron (III). Although much less quantitative data is available on the stabilities of complex ions of the second and third transition metal series, there is little doubt from their general behavior that stabilities increase within any group as one passes from the first to the second to the third transition series. Thus complexes of nickel(II) are least stable, those of palladium(II) more stable, and the corresponding ones of platinum(II) most stable.

Much of the data on stability has been correlated with varying success with ionization potentials of the metals, the (charge)^2/radius ratios for the various ions, and the electronegativities of the metals.[46] Thus in general the stabilities of metal complexes increase with high charge on the central ion, small radius of the central ion, and a large electron affinity of the metal ion. This means that the alkali metal ions have the least tendency to form complexes and that the highly polarizing transition metal ions have the greatest tendency. Still there is ample evidence that even the alkali metal ions do coordinate with certain ligands in solution,[54] and in fact sodium complexes of benzoylacetone and of salicylaldehyde have been isolated.[55]

Among the characteristics of the ligand which are generally recognized as influencing the stability of complexes are: (1) basicity of the ligand, (2) the number of metal chelate rings per ligand, (3) the size of the chelate ring, (4) steric effects, (5) resonance effects, and

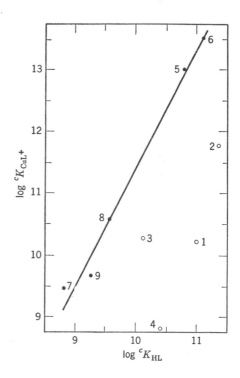

FIG. 1. Concentration formation constants of Cu^{2+} vs. H^+ with oxine derivatives in 50% by volume dioxane-water mixture containing 0.3 M $NaClO_4$ at 20°C. Open circles refer to reagents with a substituent adjacent to the chelating nitrogen atom: (1) 2-methyl-oxine, (2) 1,2,3,4-tetrahydro-10-hydroxyacridine, (3) 8-hydroxy-2,4-dimethylquinazoline, (4) 8-hydroxy-4-methyl-2-phenylquinazoline. Full circles refer to other reagents: (5) oxine, (6) 5-methyloxine, (7) 8-hydroxycinnoline, (8) 8-hydroxyquinazoline, (9) 5-hydroxyquinoxaline. (From reference 47e.)

(6) the ligand atom. No doubt one of the major factors influencing the stability of coordination compounds is the basicity of the ligand. This is to be expected since the role played by the hydrogen ion and metal ions is essentially the same so that the ligand with a large affinity for a proton (strongly basic) may well show the same behavior towards metal ions. Much of the available quantitative data on the formation constants of coordination compounds gives a good linear correlation with the base strength of the ligand. This is illustrated in Fig. 1 for some copper(II) complexes.[47c]

Qualitative observations such as the synthesis of $Co(en)_3^{3+}$ by the reaction of $Co(NH_3)_6^{3+}$ with an excess of ethylenediamine suggests that the greater the number of points of attachment of each ligand to the central metal ion, the greater the stability of the complex. There is now a great deal of quantitative data in support of this observation, e.g., the total formation constants ($\log K_T$) for the complex of copper(II) with four ammonias (unidentate, no chelate rings) is 11.9, with two ethylenediamines (bidentate, two chelate rings) is 20.0, and with one triethylenetetramine (quadridentate, three chelate rings) is 20.5. Likewise the sexadentate ligand ethylenediamine–tetraacetate ion has become known for the unusually stable complexes which it forms with a large variety of metal ions (Table 5). This increase in stability with dentate character is referred to as the *chelate effect*.

Bjerrum and Nielsen [56a] observed that the chelate effect is larger for transition metal ions than for non-transition metal ions. Spike and Parry [56b] (Table 6) found that the chelate effect for non-transition metal ions (Zn^{2+}, Cd^{2+}) is almost entirely an entropy effect, but that for transition metals (Cu^{2+}) it is in part an enthalpy effect. The enthalpy effect may result from the greater crystal field strength of ethylenediamine compared with ammonia which in turn has a greater stabilizing effect on transition metal than on non-transition metal complexes (Chapter 2). It is also of interest that the entropy contribution is approximately constant for all analogous systems. Considerable attention has been devoted to the theoretical treatment of this entropy effect.[46,57] Put in the simplest terms, the entropy contribution means that it is easier, on the basis of probability, to form an aggregate from a few molecules than from many molecules. Furthermore this advantage increases with dilution, the chelates having the greatest relative stability in very dilute solution. The data quoted above for $Cu(NH_3)_4^{2+}$ and $Cu(en)_2^{2+}$ show that the advantage is very large even in concentrated solution.

A

Table 5

Stability Constants of Ethylenediaminetetraacetato Complexes of Some Metal Ions at 20°C

$$(M^{n+} + EDTA^{4-} \rightarrow M(EDTA)^{n-4})$$

Metal Ion	log K	Metal Ion	log K
Li^+	2.8 [a]	Sc^{3+}	23.1 [e]
Na^+	1.7 [a]	V^{3+}	25.9 [f]
Mg^{2+}	8.7 [b]	Fe^{3+}	25.1 [e]
Ca^{2+}	10.7 [b]	Y^{3+}	18.1 [e]
Sr^{2+}	8.6 [b]	La^{3+}	15.5 [e]
Ba^{2+}	7.8 [b]	Ce^{3+}	16.0 [e]
V^{2+}	12.7 [c]	Pr^{3+}	16.4 [e]
Mn^{2+}	13.8 [b]	Nd^{3+}	16.6 [e]
Fe^{2+}	14.2 [d]	Sm^{3+}	17.1 [e]
Co^{2+}	16.1 [d]	Er^{3+}	17.3 [e]
Ni^{2+}	18.5 [d]	Gd^{3+}	17.4 [e]
Cu^{2+}	18.8 [b]	Tb^{3+}	17.9 [e]
Zn^{2+}	16.5 [b]	Dy^{3+}	18.3 [e]
Cd^{2+}	16.5 [b]	Er^{3+}	18.8 [e]
Hg^{2+}	22.1 [b]	Tm^{3+}	19.3 [e]
Pb^{2+}	18.0 [b]	Yb^{3+}	19.5 [e]
Pd^{2+}	18.5 [c]	Lu^{3+}	19.8 [e]
Al^{3+}	16.1 [e]	VO^{2+}	18.8 [e]
Ga^{3+}	20.3 [e]	Th^{4+}	23.2 [e]
In^{3+}	25.0 [e]		

[a] G. Schwarzenbach and H. Ackermann, *Helv. Chim. Acta*, **30**, 1798 (1947).

[b] Quoted in R. W. Schmid and C. N. Reilley, *J. Am. Chem. Soc.*, **78**, 5513 (1956).

[c] W. M. MacNevin and O. H. Kriege, *J. Am. Chem. Soc.*, **77**, 6149 (1955).

[d] Quoted in reference 46.

[e] G. Schwarzenbach, R. Gut, and G. Anderegg, *Helv. Chim. Acta*, **37**, 937 (1954); E. J. Wheelwright, F. H. Spedding, and G. Schwarzenbach, *J. Am. Chem. Soc.*, **75**, 4196 (1953).

[f] Quoted in J. Bjerrum and C. Klixbüll Jørgensen, *Rec. trav. chim.*, **75**, 658 (1956).

Table 6

Differences in Thermodynamic Properties of Chelate and Non-Chelate Complexes at 25°C

Complexes Compared	$\Delta(\Delta F^0)$, kcal	$\Delta(\Delta H^0)$, kcal	$\Delta(T \Delta S^0)$, kcal
$Cd(en)^{2+}$-$Cd(NH_3)_2^{2+}$	1.20	−0.1	−1.3
$Zn(en)^{2+}$-$Zn(NH_3)_2^{2+}$	1.55	−0.1	−1.6
$Cu(en)^{2+}$-$Cu(NH_3)_2^{2+}$	4.30	2.6	−1.7

Although coordination compounds with five- and six-membered chelate rings are the most stable, complexes are known which have chelate ring sizes ranging from four through nine members. Carbonato, $M\langle{}^O_O\rangle C{=}O$, and sulfato, $M\langle{}^O_O\rangle SO_2$, complexes are among the more common four-membered ring compounds. Another large class of such compounds is the bridged complexes of the type $M\langle{}^X_X\rangle M$, where X is OH^-, NH_2^-, Cl^-, NO_2^-, CO, etc. Attempts to isolate chelate compounds from aqueous reaction mixtures of tetramethylenediamine, pentamethylenediamine, or hexamethylenediamine and a variety of metal ions yielded only unidentifiable oils believed to be polymeric electrolytes.[58] However, in alcoholic solution the reaction of tetramethylenediamine with Cu(II), Ni(II), Zn(II), and Cd(II) perchlorates yields seven-membered ring chelate salts. By using alcohol as a solvent, Pfeiffer was also able to prepare the nine-membered ring compound.[59]

That chelation occurs in alcoholic but not aqueous reaction mixtures must result from the greater coordinating property of water being sufficient to prevent the formation of these unstable large chelate rings. The reaction of bis(ethylenediamine)carbonatocobalt(III) ion with succinic acid yields the succinato complex,[60] a seven-membered ring, and with sulfonyldiacetic acid the sulfonyldiacetato complex,[61] an eight-membered ring.

It has been observed that, for a large variety of aliphatic chelate rings, the five- is more stable than the six-membered ring. An interesting illustration of this is afforded by 1,2,3-triaminopropanetetrachloro-

5-membered ring (optically active)   6-membered ring (optically inactive) platinum(IV); the triamine behaves as a bidentate, and, where both five- and six-membered rings are possible, Mann [62] was able to resolve the complex and thus demonstrate that it is the one with the five-membered ring. Thermodynamic data are now available [63a, 64b] on the chelation of ethylenediamine and 1,3-propanediamine with copper(II) and nickel(II) ions (Table 7). These data show that, although 1,3-propane-

Table 7

Thermodynamic Data for the Formation of $Cu(AA)_2^{2+}$ and $Ni(AA)_3^{2+}$ Where AA is Ethylenediamine and 1,3-Propanediamine

(In kcal/g ion)

AA	Copper(II)			Nickel(II)		
	$-\Delta F°$	$-\Delta H°$	$T \Delta S°$	$-\Delta F°$	$-\Delta H°$	$T \Delta S°$
en	27.3	25.4	1.9	24.9	27.9	−3.0
tn	23.4	22.8	0.6	16.4	21.3	−4.9

diamine is a stronger base ($pK_{tnH^+} = 10.63$, $pK_{tnH_2^{2+}} = 8.76$) than ethylenediamine ($pK_{enH^+} = 10.00$, $pK_{enH_2^{2+}} = 7.12$), it does not form the stronger complexes. Furthermore the data show that the greater stability of the five-membered ring complexes is not chiefly due to the entropy [63b] but rather to the enthalpy of formation. This may result from steric strain in the six-membered ring or, as has been suggested,[64] from some steric interaction between the hydrogen atoms on neighboring nitrogen atoms in the six- not present in the five-membered ring. It is finally of interest that for aromatic ligands, or chelates with conjugated linkages, the six-membered chelate ring is often more stable than the five-membered ring. This is perhaps due to the wider bond angles in such groups and also to the requirement of an even number of atoms for resonance in the chelate ring.

Numerous examples of steric inhibition of complex formation have been reported. Most common among these is the type where a bulky group is attached either to the donor atom or near enough to it to cause mutual repulsions between ligands resulting in a weakening of the metal-ligand bonds. This is illustrated by the data in Fig. 1 for the formation constants of substituted 8-hydroxyquinolines (I) and 8-hydroxyquinazolines (II), with copper(II).[47c] Substitution in all positions except 2 shows a good correlation between the stability of the complex and the base strength of the donor ion, but, as represented by

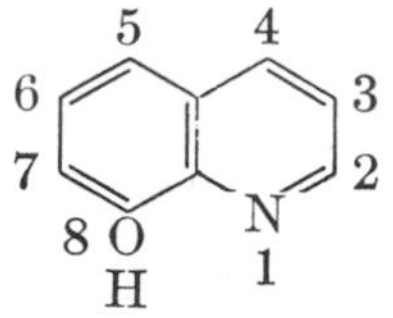

(I) (II)

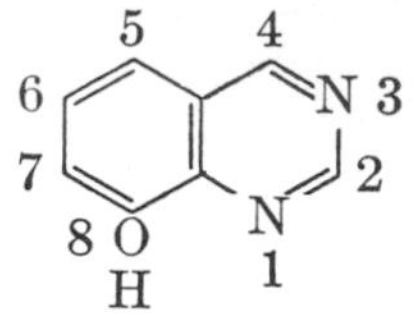

the open circles in Fig. 1, 2-substituted compounds form the least stable complexes. Some other examples of this same type of steric hindrance occur with N-alkylethylenediamines [65] and 6,6'-substituted 2,2'-bipyridines (III).[66]

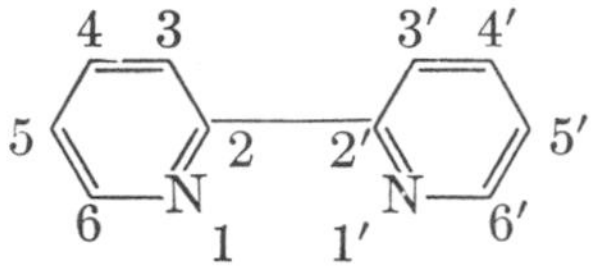

(III)

The steric hindrance observed for 3,3'-disubstituted 2,2'-bipyridine is of a different type.[67] Since here there can be no effect due to repulsions between ligands, it is suggested that the alkyl groups prevent the ligand from assuming a planar configuration and hence interfere with resonance stability in the ligand and introduce strain in the metal-donor bonds. Still another type of steric inhibition of chelation is that already mentioned for the coordination of 2,2',2''-triaminotriethylamine with copper(II).[49] Similar to this is the lower stability of Ag(en)$^+$ compared to Ag(NH$_3$)$_2$$^+$ which is attributed to a strained structure of the chelate ring, since it must distort the usual linear configuration of silver(I) complexes.[68]

The significance of resonance effects in the stability of coordination compounds was demonstrated by Calvin and Wilson.[69] They observed that the stability of copper(II) chelates decreased in the order acetylacetone > 2-hydroxy-1-naphthaldehyde > salicylaldehyde > 2-hydroxy-3-naphthaldehyde, which is also the order of the decrease in the double bond character of the chelate rings. In the acetylacetonate ion the two double bonds are a part of the chelate ring so that it is assigned a bond order of 2. However, for the phenolate ion of salicylaldehyde, one of the double bonds is also part of the resonating benzene ring so that in essence it is in the chelate ring only half the time; thus it is assigned a bond order of 1.5. Similarly because of the resonance structures of naphthalene, one of the double bonds of the naphtholate ion is part of the chelate ring two-thirds of the time for 2-hydroxyl-1-naphthaldehyde giving it a bond order of 1.67, and one-third of the time for 2-hydroxy-3-naphthaldehyde so that its bond order is 1.33. This type of chelate ring resonance stabilization is perhaps also largely responsible for the extreme stability of the metal porphyrins.

Although the trends discussed above are generally applicable to the stability of complexes, it is also necessary to note certain specific behaviors of different donor atoms or ligands. The role of the donor atom in the stability of coordination compounds has been discussed by Sidgwick.[70a] He calls attention to the difference between ligands with oxygen and nitrogen donor atoms. Generally metal ions with an electronic configuration of the preceding inert gas have a greater affinity for oxygen than nitrogen, whereas the reverse is generally true for ions of the non-inert gas type. A similar distinction can be made for the halide complexes. Ahrland [70b] points out that stability data on metal halide complexes in aqueous solution permit a classification of metal ions into two different groups:

Group I (stability order, $F^- \gg Cl^- > Br^- > I^-$):

$$H^+, Fe^{3+}, In^{3+}, Ce^{3+}, U^{4+}, UO_2^{2+}, Zr^{4+}$$

and most probably also

$$Be^{2+}, Cu^{2+}, Zn^{2+}, Sn^{2+}, Al^{3+}, Th^{4+}, Pu^{4+}$$

Group II (stability order, $F^- \ll Cl^- < Br^- < I^-$):

$$Cu^+, Ag^+, Cd^{2+}, Hg^{2+}, Pb^{2+}, Pt^{2+}$$

and most probably also

$$Pd^{2+}, Au^{3+}, Tl^{3+}, Pd^{4+}, Pt^{4+}$$

The metal ions in group II tend to cluster in a "triangular" portion of the periodic table which is known to include metals that form olefin complexes.[70c] For the metal halide complexes the right border-line of this triangle is well defined and runs between the pairs, Cu-Zn, Zn-Cd, Cd-In, In-Tl, and Sn-Pb. However, the left borderline is not well known at present. About all that can be said is that iron is certainly outside, whereas the platinum metals are perhaps all inside, this distorted triangle.

Ligands such as CN^-, CO, C_2H_4, NO_2^-, R_3P, R_3As, R_3Sb, R_2S, R_2Se, and R_2Te, in general, form stable metal complexes primarily with transition metal ions containing some d-orbital electrons. This has been attributed to double bonding (π bonding) of the d-orbital electrons with available vacant orbitals in the ligand atom.[71,72] Thus R_3N which has no vacant orbitals, unlike R_3P and R_3As, does not tend to form stable complexes with transition metals.[73] Likewise, although BF_3 is a strong Lewis acid it does not coordinate with PF_3,[74] whereas Pt(II)[75] and Ni(II),[74] which can form double bonds with PF_3, readily coordinate. The inability of boron to double-bond in these systems does not exclude the possible existence of such compounds, as was demonstrated recently by the synthesis of F_3PBH_3[76a] and F_3PAlCl_3.[76b] It has been suggested that the greater stability of these compounds relative to the fluoride analogs may be due to the larger polarizabilities of the hydride and chloride ions compared to that of the fluoride ion.[76b]

NOMENCLATURE

A comprehensive system of nomenclature of coordination compounds was not possible prior to the coordination theory of Werner. As a result many of the complexes were named according to their color (Table 1), and then later some of the more common terms such as *luteo* and *purpureo* came to be used to mean $M(NH_3)_6$ and $M(NH_3)_5Cl$, without regard to color. One other practice was to name the compound after the person who had first reported it, e.g., NH_4-$[Co(NH_3)_2(NO_2)_4]$, Erdman's salt; $NH_4[Cr(NH_3)_2(NCS)_4]$, Reinecke's salt; $[Pt(NH_3)_4][PtCl_4]$, Magnus's green salt. Werner finally suggested a nomenclature system which, with some modifications, is still employed. One of his suggestions no longer used is that the metal stem be followed by the suffixes -a, -o, -i, and -e to designate the $+1$, $+2$, $+3$ and $+4$ oxidation states of the metal, respectively, e.g., $[Co-(NH_3)_6]Cl_3$, hexamminecobalti chloride; $K_2[PtCl_4]$, potassium tetrachloroplatinoate. The Stock[77] system of using Roman numerals in parentheses to designate oxidation state is now employed.

Recommendations for the nomenclature of coordination compounds made by the Nomenclature Committee of the International Union of Pure and Applied Chemistry[78] have stimulated an interest for a set of fixed rules. The rules listed below are taken largely from a review on the subject by Fernelius.[79]

1. ORDER OF LISTING IONS. The cation is named first, followed by the anion.

2. ENDINGS OF COORDINATED GROUPS. Neutral groups are named as the molecule, positive groups end in -ium, and negative groups end in -o. Exceptions to this are aqua, H_2O, and ammine, NH_3.

$(C_2H_5)_3P$	triethylphosphine
$NH_2NH_3^+$	hydrazinium
$NH_2CH_2CH_2NH_3^+$	2-aminoethylammonium
CH_3COO^-	acetato
$HON{=}C(CH_3)C(CH_3){=}NO^-$	dimethylglyoximato

3. ORDER OF LIGANDS. The order of listing coordinated groups is (1) positive, (2) neutral, and (3) negative, without separation by hyphens. Within each of these categories the groups are listed in order of decreasing complexity.

$[Pt(NH_2NH_3)NH_3Cl_2]NO_3$ *	hydraziniumamminedichloro- platinum(II) nitrate
$[Co(trien)(en)]Cl_3$	triethylenetetramineethylene- diaminecobalt(III) chloride
$[Pt(en)(NH_3)_2NO_2Cl]SO_4$	ethylenediaminediamminenitrochloro- platinum(IV) sulfate

4. NUMERICAL PREFIXES. The prefixes di-, tri-, tetra-, etc., are used before simple expressions, e.g., chloro, oxalato, glycinato, etc. Prefixes bis-, tris-, tetrakis-, etc., are used before complex expressions (chiefly expressions which contain the prefixes mono-, di-, tri-, etc., in the ligand name itself), all of which are enclosed in parentheses, e.g., ethylene-diamine, trialkylphosphine, etc.

5. ENDINGS OF COMPLEXES. The characteristic ending for anionic complexes is -ate, optional -ic if named as an acid. There are no characteristic endings for cationic or neutral complexes.

$K_4[Fe(CN)_6]$	potassium hexacyanoferrate(II)
$H_2[PtCl_6]$	hydrogen hexachloroplatinate(IV) or hexachloroplatinic(IV) acid
$Al(H_2O)_6^{3+}$ *	hexaquaaluminum(III) ion
$Cu(C_5H_7O_2)_2$ †	bis(2,4-pentanedionato)copper(II)

6. OXIDATION STATE. The oxidation state of the central elements is designated by a Roman numeral in parentheses at the end of the name

---

* It has been recommended [80] that the metal be cited last in the formula, e.g., $[(NH_2NH_3)(NH_3)Cl_2Pt]NO_3$. Such, however is not at present the general practice.

† Although the complex is usually enclosed in brackets this system is not followed here except when molecular formulae of salts are written. Brackets will not be used for individual complex ions nor for neutral complexes in order to avoid the confusion which arises with the expression of molar concentrations, e.g., $[[Co(NH_3)_6]^{3+}]$.

of the complex, without a space between the two. The 0 is used for zero, and a minus sign before the Roman numeral is used for negative oxidation states.*

$K_4[Ni(CN)_4]$ potassium tetracyanonickelate(0)
$Na[Co(CO)_4]$ sodium tetracarbonylcobaltate($-$I)

7. BRIDGING GROUPS. Groups that bridge two centers of coordination are preceded by the Greek letter μ, which is repeated before the name of each different kind of bridging group.

$$(C_2O_4)_2Cr \overset{\displaystyle OH}{\underset{\displaystyle OH}{\diagup \diagdown}} Cr(C_2O_4)_2{}^{4-}$$ tetraoxolato-μ-dihydroxodichromate(III) ion

$$(NH_3)_4Co \overset{\displaystyle NH_2}{\underset{\displaystyle NO_2}{\diagup \diagdown}} Co(NH_3)_4{}^{4+}$$ octammine-μ-amido-μ-nitrodicobalt(III) ion

8. POINT OF ATTACHMENT. The point of attachment of a coordinated group is designated by placing the symbols (in italics) of the elements attached after the name of the group, with separation by hyphen. The following optional procedure may be used for $-NO_2{}^-$, nitro; $-ONO^-$, nitrito; $-SCN^-$, thiocyanato; $-NCS^-$, isothiocyanato.

$$K_2\left[Pt\left(\begin{array}{c} S \diagdown \diagup O \\ \diagup S \diagdown \\ O \qquad O \end{array}\right)_2\right]$$ potassium dithiosulfato-O, S-platinate(II)

$$K_2\left[Pt\left(\begin{array}{c} O \diagdown \diagup S \\ \diagup S \diagdown \\ O \qquad O \end{array}\right)_2\right]$$ potassium dithiosulfato-O, O-platinate(II)

* It has been suggested [80] that, because at times it is difficult to assign a definite oxidation state to the central atom, the Stock system should be abandoned in favor of either a designation of the charge on the complex or the use of appropriate prefixes, e.g., $[Co(NH_3)_5Cl]Cl_2$, pentamminechlorocobalt(2+) chloride or pentamminechlorocobalt dichloride. Neither one of these systems is in general usage at the moment.

9. GEOMETRICAL ISOMERS. Geometrical isomers are named either by using numbers, or by the designation *cis* for adjacent positions and *trans* for opposite (180° apart) positions. For square complexes groups 1,3 and 2,4 are in *trans* positions.

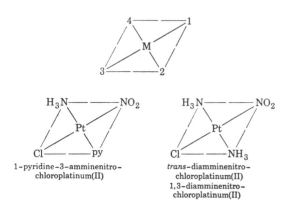

1-pyridine-3-amminenitro-
chloroplatinum(II)

trans-diamminenitro-
chloroplatinum(II)
1,3-diamminenitro-
chloroplatinum(II)

Octahedral complexes are numbered so that the *trans* positions are 1,6; 2,4; 3,5.

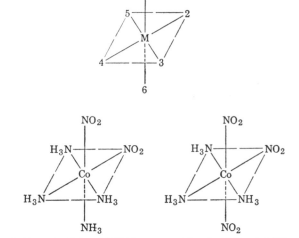

cis-tetramminedinitrocobalt(III) ion
tetrammine-1,2-dinitrocobalt(III) ion

trans-triamminetrinitrocobalt(III)
1,2,6-triamminetrinitrocobalt(III)

Geometrical isomers of polynuclear complexes may be named by this same scheme.

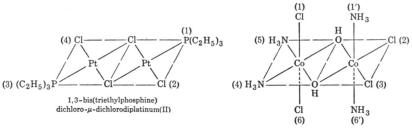

1,3-bis(triethylphosphine)
dichloro-μ-dichlorodiplatinum(II)

4,5-diammine-1',6'-diammine-μ-dihydroxo-
1,6-dichloro-2,3-dichlorodicobalt(III) ion

10. OPTICAL ISOMERS.   Optically active antipodes are designated either by $(+)$ or $(-)$ or by d or l for the dextro- and levorotatory compounds respectively.   Racemic mixtures are designated by $(\pm)$ or dl and inactive forms by *meso*.   The sign of rotation of coordination compounds containing optically active ligands is indicated by D or L and that of the ligands by d or l.   This is somewhat confusing because this same notation has also at times been used to designate relative generic configurations of analogous complexes, without regard to sign of rotation.   Therefore it is suggested that for this latter connotation the capital letters be in italics, D or L.   The types of isomers are specified in the following order: (1) optical and (2) geometrical.

$(+)$- or d-Ni(phen)$_3$$^{2+}$

$(+)$- or d-tris(1,10-phenanthroline)nickel(II) ion

D-Rh(l-cptdin)$_3$$^{3+}$

D-*tris*(l-cyclopentanediamine)rhodium(III) ion

D-Co(l-pn)$_2$Cl$_2$$^+$ (*trans* isomer)

D-*trans*-bis(l-propylenediamine)-dichlorocobalt(III) ion

$$meso\text{-(en)}_2\text{Co} \overset{\text{NH}_2}{\underset{\text{NO}_2}{<\ \ >}} \text{Co(en)}_2{}^{4+}$$

meso-tetrakis(ethylenediamine)-μ-amido-μ-nitrodicobalt(III) ion.

11. METAL-METAL BONDING.   The prefix bi- is used before the name of the metals forming a metal-metal bond.

Cl(C$_2$H$_5$NH$_2$)$_4$Pt—Pt(C$_2$H$_5$NH$_2$)$_4$Cl^{4+}

sym-octakis(ethylamine)dichlorobiplatinum(IV) ion

12. ABBREVIATIONS.   A customary practice in writing formulas of coordination compounds is to use simple abbreviations for complicated molecules.   Except in a few cases such as en, pn, and py, there is no agreement as to the abbreviations for a particular group.   Some of

the abbreviations that have been used and those used in this book are listed below.

2,2′-Bipyridine	bipy
2,3-Butanediamine	bn
trans-1,2-Cyclopentanediamine	cptdin
Diethylenetriamine	dien
Dimethylglyoximato	DMG
Ethylenediamine	en
Ethylenediaminetetraacetato	EDTA, Y
Oxalato	ox
2,4-Pentanedionato (acetylacetonato)	aeoc
1,10-Phenanthroline	phen
1,2-Propanediamine(propylenediamine)	pn
1,3-Propanediamine(trimethylenediamine)	tn
1,2,3-Propanetriamine	ptn
Pyridine	py
Thiourea	tu
2,2′,2″-Triaminotriethylamine	tren
Triethylenetetramine	trien

13. MISCELLANEOUS TERMINOLOGY. Several terms related to coordination compounds that have not yet been introduced will be defined or described. In the case of certain polyfunctional molecules and ions, it is possible for more than one atom of the group to attach itself to the same metal ion. Such a group is called a *multidentate* or a *chelate* group. The adjective chelate was originally used to designate the bidentate character of a group but has been generalized to include all multidentate groups and has been used also as a noun both for the chelate group and for the complex. The preferred usage of the term may be illustrated by the figure, for which the salt is designated as a

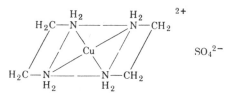

chelate compound, the cation as a *chelate ion*, and the ethylenediamine as a *chelate group*. The latter is also often called a *bidentate* group because it is attached to the central ion through two atoms. A few examples of different types of donor groups are shown in Table 8.

Table 8

Examples of Different Types of Donor Groups

Number of Points of Attachment	Name *	Examples
1	unidentate	H_2O, NH_3, Cl^-, CN^-
2	bidentate	CO_3^{2-}, $C_2O_4^{2-}$, $NH_2CH_2CH_2NH_2$, $NH_2CH_2COO^-$
3	terdentate	$NH(CH_2CH_2NH_2)_2$, $NH(CH_2COO)_2^{2-}$
4	quadridentate	$N(CH_2CH_2NH_2)_3$, $N(CH_2COO)_3^{3-}$

| 5 | quinquidentate | |
| 6 | sexadentate | $[-CH_2N(CH_2COO)_2]_2^{4-}$, |

* It is suggested [81] that names derived solely from Greek or, alternatively, Latin roots be used. Words such as multidentate or polydontate are permissible, but bilingual hybrids such as polydentate or hexadentate are to be avoided.

If the donor atom is attached to two metal ions it is then called a *bridging group* (see rule 7). This results in the formation of a compound which is generally referred to as a "polynuclear complex"; sometimes, also, the name *bridged complex* is applied. The latter term is preferred because the prefix "poly" usually denotes a high molecular weight. Although certain metal complex systems do form high molecular weight species, they are often just dimeric, trimeric, etc. The dimeric complex is the simplest of these because it contains only two

central ions. Generally a donor atom or ion is not coordinated to more than two metal ions, but there are exceptions to this: for example the oxide ion in $Be_4O(C_2H_3O_2)_6$ is attached to each of the four beryllium ions.[82]

REFERENCES

1. S. Glasstone, K. J. Laidler, and H. Eyring, *The Theory of Rate Processes,* McGraw-Hill Book Co., New York, 1941.
2. W. L. Bragg and G. B. Brown, *Z. Krist.,* **63,** 538 (1926); H. M. Powell and A. F. Wells, *J. Chem. Soc.,* **1935,** 359.
3. B. M. Tassaert, *Ann chim. phys.,* **28,** 92 (1798).
4. A. Werner, *Z. anorg. Chem.,* **3,** 267 (1893).
5. G. N. Lewis, *J. Am. Chem. Soc.,* **38,** 762 (1916).
6. N. V. Sidgwick, *The Electronic Theory of Valency,* Clarendon Press, Oxford, 1927.
7. J. Bjerrum, *Metal Ammine Formation in Aqueous Solution,* P. Haase and Son, Copenhagen, 1941.
8. H. Scouloudi, *Acta Cryst.,* **6,** 651 (1953); J. Bjerrum, C. J. Ballhausen, and C. K. Jørgensen, *Acta Chem. Scand.,* **8,** 1275 (1954); S. Kirschner, *J. Am. Chem. Soc.,* **78,** 2372 (1956).
9. (a) C. Brink and H. A. S. Kroese, *Acta Cryst.,* **5,** 433 (1952); C. Brink and A. E. Van Arkel, *ibid.,* **5,** 506 (1952). (b) S. Ahrland, J. Chatt, N. R. Davies, and A. A. Williams, *Nature,* **179,** 1187 (1957); *J. Chem. Soc.,* **1958,** 264, 276.
10. A. F. Wells, *Structural Inorganic Chemistry,* Clarendon Press, Oxford (1945).
11. D. P. Mellor, *Chem. Revs.,* **33,** 137 (1943).
12. F. W. Pinkard, E. Sharratt, W. Wardlaw, and E. G. Cox, *J. Chem. Soc.,* **1934,** 1012.
13. I. I. Chernyaev, *Ann. inst. platine U.S.S.R.,* **6,** 55 (1928).
14. A. D. Hel'man and E. Gorushkina, *Compt. rend. acad. sci. U.R.S.S.,* **55,** 33 (1937).
15. A. D. Hel'man, E. F. Karandashova, and L. N. Essen, *Doklady Akad. Nauk U.S.S.R.,* **63,** 37 (1948).
16. W. H. Mills and T. H. H. Quibell, *J. Chem. Soc.,* **1935,** 839.
17. R. H. Vernon, *ibid.,* **117,** 86, 889 (1920); **119,** 687 (1921).
18. H. D. K. Drew, *ibid.,* **1929,** 560.
19. W. C. Fernelius, *Chemical Architecture* (R. E. Burk and O. Grummitt, eds.), Interscience Publishers, New York, 1948, Chapter III.
20. R. G. Dickinson and L. Pauling, *J. Am. Chem. Soc.,* **45,** 1466 (1923).
21. A. Werner, *Ber.,* **47,** 3087 (1914).
22. F. G. Mann, *J. Chem. Soc.,* **1933,** 412.
23. R. C. Cass, G. E. Coates, and R. G. Hayter, *Chemistry & Industry,* **1954,** 1485; *J. Chem. Soc.,* **1955,** 4007.
24. (a) S. Ahrland and J. Chatt, *Chemistry & Industry,* **1955,** 96. (b) W. S. Fyfe, *J. Chem. Soc.,* **1955,** 1032.
25. D. E. C. Corbridge and E. G. Cox, *J. Chem. Soc.,* **1956,** 594.
26. (a) L. Malatesta, *Gazz. chim. ital.,* **70,** 734 (1940); **71,** 615 (1941). (b) L. Cambi and A. Gagnasso, *Atti accad. nazl. Lincei Mem., Sez. II,* **13,** 254, 404 (1931); L. Cambi, *Z. anorg. u. allgem. Chem.,* **247,** 22 (1941). (c) P. R. H. Alderman and P. G. Owston, *Nature,* **178,** 1071 (1956).
27. K. A. Jensen and B. Nygaard, *Acta Chem. Scand.,* **3,** 474 (1949); *Symposium on Coordination Chemistry,* Danish Chemical Society, p. 117, 1953.

28. (a) G. A. Barclay, *Revs. Pure and Appl. Chem.,* **4,** 77 (1954). (b) C. M. Harris, R. S. Nyholm, and N. C. Stephenson, *Nature,* **179,** 1127 (1956); *J. Chem. Soc.,* **1956,** 4375; *Rec. trav. chim.,* **75,** 687 (1956).

29. (a) A. W. Adamson, *J. Am. Chem. Soc.,* **73,** 5710 (1951). (b) L. Malatesta and A. Sacco, *Atti accad. nazl. Lincei Rend.,* **15,** 93 (1953). (c) L. Malatesta and L. Vallarino, *J. Chem. Soc.,* **1956,** 1867. (d) G. W. A. Fowles and C. M. Pleass, *Chemistry & Industry,* **1955,** 1743.

30. G. C. Hampson and L. Pauling, *J. Am. Chem. Soc.,* **60,** 2702 (1938); W. H. Zachariasen, *Acta Cryst.,* **7,** 792 (1954).

31. J. L. Hoard, *J. Am. Chem. Soc.,* **61,** 1252 (1939).

32. J. L. Hoard and H. H. Nordsieck, *J. Am. Chem. Soc.,* **61,** 2853 (1939).

33. J. L. Hoard, W. G. Martin, M. E. Smith, and J. E. Whitney, *ibid.,* **76,** 3820 (1954).

34. For specific references and additional example of C.N. 8, see L. E. Marchi, W. C. Fernelius, and J. P. McReynolds, *J. Am. Chem. Soc.,* **65,** 329 (1943).

35. (a) L. Helmholz, *ibid.,* **61,** 1544 (1939). (b) W. F. Jakób and Z. L. Jakób, *Roczniki Chem.,* **26,** 492 (1952).

36. H. P. Klug and L. Alexander, *J. Am. Chem. Soc.,* **66,** 1056 (1944).

37. I. Lindquist, *Arkiv Kemi Mineral. Geol.,* **24A,** 1 (1947).

38. N. S. Kurnakow, *Z. anorg. u. allgem. Chem.,* **151,** 264 (1926); F. Basolo, J. C. Bailar, Jr., and B. R. Tarr, *J. Am. Chem. Soc.,* **72,** 2433 (1950).

39. A. Werner, *Ann.,* **386,** 1 (1912).

40. R. Tsuchida, M. Kobayaski, and A. Nokamura, *J. Chem. Soc. Japan,* **56,** 1339 (1935); *Bull. Chem. Soc. Japan,* **11,** 38 (1936).

41. F. P. Dwyer, N. A. Gibson, and E. C. Gyarfas, *J. Proc. Roy. Soc. N. S. Wales,* **84,** 68 (1951).

42. A. Werner, *Ber.,* **45,** 1228 (1912).

43. J. P. Mathieu, *Compt. rend.,* **199,** 278 (1934); **201,** 1183 (1935).

44. J. M. Bijvoet, A. F. Peerdeman, and A. J. van Bommel, *Koninkl. Ned. Akad. Wetenschap. Proc.,* **B54,** 3 (1951); *Nature,* **168,** 271 (1951); Y. Saito, K. Nakatsu, M. Shiro, and H. Kuroya, *Acta Cryst.,* **7,** 636 (1954).

45. (a) P. Pfeiffer, P. Koch, G. Lando, and A. Trieschmann, *Ber.,* **37,** 4255 (1904). (b) Y. Saito, Y. Takeuchi, and R. Pepinsky, *Z. Krist.,* **106,** 4761 (1955); J. Fujita, K. Nakamoto, and M. Kobayashi, *J. Am. Chem. Soc.,* **78,** 3295 (1956). (c) J. W. Jeffery, *Nature,* **159,** 610 (1947). (d) G. Peyronel, *Gazz. chim. ital.,* **73,** 89 (1943). (e) G. Peyronel, *Z. Krist.,* **103,** 157 (1941).

46. A. E. Martell and M. Calvin, *Chemistry of the Metal Chelate Compounds.* Prentice-Hall, New York, 1952.

47. (a) J. Bjerrum, *Chem. Revs.,* **46,** 381 (1950). (b) H. Irving and R. J. P. Williams, *J. Chem. Soc.,* **1953,** 3192. (c) H. Irving and H. Rossotti, *Acta Chem. Scand.,* **10,** 72 (1956).

48. D. P. Mellor and L. E. Maley, *Nature,* **159,** 370 (1947); **161,** 436 (1948); M. Calvin and N. C. Melchior, *J. Am. Chem. Soc.,* **70,** 3270 (1948); H. Irving and R. J. P. Williams, *Nature,* **162,** 146 (1948).

49. J. E. Prue and G. Schwarzenbach, *Helv. Chim. Acta,* **33,** 963 (1950).

50. I. M. Kolthoff, D. L. Leussing, and T. S. Lee, *J. Am. Chem. Soc.,* **72,** 2173, 2348 (1948).

51. F. Basolo and F. P. Dwyer, *ibid.,* **76,** 1454 (1954).

52. L. G. Van Uitert, thesis, The Pennsylvania State University, 1952; W. C. Fernelius and L. G. Van Uitert, *Acta Chem. Scand.,* **8,** 1726 (1954).

53. R. M. Izatt, W. C. Fernelius, C. G. Haas, and B. P. Block, *J. Phys. Chem.*, **59**, 170 (1955).

54. J. R. Van Wazer and D. A. Campanella, *J. Am. Chem. Soc.*, **72**, 655 (1950); N. C. Melchior, *J. Bio. Chem.*, **208** (No. 2), 615 (1954); G. A. Guter and G. S. Hammond, *J. Am. Chem. Soc.*, **78**, 5166 (1956).

55. N. V. Sidgwick and F. M. Brewer, *J. Chem. Soc.*, **127**, 2379 (1925).

56. (a) J. Bjerrum and E. J. Nielsen, *Acta Chem. Scand.*, **2**, 297 (1948). (b) C. G. Spike and R. W. Parry, *J. Am. Chem. Soc.*, **75**, 2726 (1953).

57. M. Calvin and R. N. Bailes, *J. Am. Chem. Soc.*, **68**, 953 (1946); G. Schwarzenbach, *Helv. Chim. Acta*, **35**, 2344 (1952); A. W. Adamson, *J. Am. Chem. Soc.*, **76**, 1578 (1954).

58. A. Werner, *Ber.*, **40**, 15 (1907); L. Tschugaeff, *J. prakt. Chem.*, [2] **75**, 159 (1907); P. Pfeiffer and E. Lubbe, *ibid.*, [2] **136**, 321 (1933).

59. P. Pfeiffer, *Naturwissenschaften*, **35**, 190 (1948).

60. J. C. Duff, *J. Chem. Soc.*, **119**, 385, 1982 (1921); **123**, 560 (1923).

61. T. S. Price and S. A. Brazier, *J. Chem. Soc.*, **107**, 1367 (1915).

62. F. G. Mann, *J. Chem. Soc.*, **1927**, 1224; **1928**, 890.

63. (a) J. Bjerrum and I. Poulsen, *Acta Chem. Scand.*, **9**, 1407 (1955). (b) F. A. Cotton and F. E. Harris, *J. Phys. Chem.*, **59**, 1203 (1955).

64. (a) J. E. Dickens, thesis, Oxford, 1954. (b) H. Irving, R. J. P. Williams, D. J. Ferrett, and A. E. Williams, *J. Chem. Soc.*, **1954**, 3494.

65. F. Basolo and R. K. Murmann, *J. Am. Chem. Soc.*, **74**, 5243 (1952); **76**, 211 (1954); H. Irving and J. M. M. Griffiths, *J. Chem. Soc.*, **1954**, 213.

66. F. H. Burstall, *ibid.*, **1938**, 1662.

67. F. W. Cagle and G. F. Smith, *J. Am. Chem. Soc.*, **69**, 1860 (1947).

68. G. Schwarzenbach, *Helv. Chim. Acta*, **36**, 23 (1953).

69. M. Calvin and K. W. Wilson, *J. Am. Chem. Soc.*, **67**, 2003 (1945).

70. (a) N. V. Sidgwick, *J. Chem. Soc.*, **1941**, 433. (b) S. Ahrland, *Acta Chem. Scand.*, **10**, 723 (1956). (c) I. Leden and J. Chatt, *J. Chem. Soc.*, **1955**, 2936.

71. L. Pauling, *The Nature of the Chemical Bond*, 2nd ed., Cornell University Press, Ithaca, N. Y., 1945, pp. 250–258.

72. A. Kabesh and R. S. Nyholm, *J. Chem. Soc.*, **1951**, 3245; F. H. Burstall and R. S. Nyholm, *ibid.*, **1952**, 3570.

73. J. Chatt and R. G. Wilkins, *J. Chem. Soc.*, **1952**, 4300.

74. J. W. Irvine and G. Wilkinson, *Nature*, **168**, 514 (1951); *Science*, **113**, 742 (1951); *J. Am. Chem. Soc.*, **73**, 5501 (1951).

75. J. Chatt and A. A. Williams, *J. Chem. Soc.*, **1951**, 3061.

76. (a) R. W. Parry and T. C. Bissot, *J. Am. Chem. Soc.*, **78**, 1524 (1956). (b) R. W. Parry and E. Alton, private communication.

77. A. Stock, *Z. angew. Chem.*, **321**, 373 (1919).

78. W. P. Jorissen, H. Bassett, A. Damiens, F. Fichter, and H. Remy, *Ber.*, **73A**, 53 (1940); *J. Chem. Soc.*, **1940**, 1404; *J. Am. Chem. Soc.*, **63**, 889 (1941).

79. W. C. Fernelius, *Advances in Chemistry Ser.*, **8**, 9 (1953).

80. G. H. Cheesman, Inorganic Nomenclature Commission of IUPAC, Stockholm Conference, 1953.

81. F. P. Dwyer, N. S. Gill, E. C. Gyarfas, and F. Lions, *J. Am. Chem. Soc.*, **79**, 1269 (1957).

82. W. H. Bragg and G. T. Morgan, *Proc. Roy. Soc. London*, **A104**, 437 (1923).

2

The theory
of the coordinate bond

There are three theories which are currently used to explain the structures, stabilities, and general properties of coordination compounds. These are (1) the electrostatic theory, including crystal field corrections, (2) the valence bond theory, and (3) the molecular orbital theory. This arrangement is in order of increasing sophistication and generality, though not necessarily of usefulness.[1]

We distinguish between two limiting kinds of chemical bond, the "purely ionic" and the "purely covalent," though recognizing that any actual bond may partake of some of the qualities of each. The ionic bond is concerned only with electrostatic attractions and repulsions due to electric charges, permanent electric dipoles, and induced dipoles. By including van der Waals' repulsions between filled electron shells in a semiempirical manner, it is possible to account completely for the bonding energies of simple compounds such as NaCl both in the crystalline state and in the vapor.[2] This is done without any mention of covalent bonding or any quantum mechanical concept other than the minor one of zero point energy.

In molecular hydrogen the opposite extreme occurs in that, by definition, ionic bonding is absent although electrostatic terms are still the only ones considered in the potential energy of the system.* In this case the bonding results from the greater region in space which has an electric potential positive enough to attract the electron strongly. This greater region allows for a correspondingly smaller value of the kinetic energy for each electron than would otherwise be possible and

---

* The fact that, as shown in the accurate treatment of the hydrogen molecule, there is a considerable chance that both electrons will be near one nucleus at the same time is to be considered a normal attribute of the covalent bond.

a net reduction of total energy equal to the heat of dissociation. Thus in a purely covalent bond the emphasis is on the delocalization of the electrons in a molecule compared to their state in the free atoms. The valence bond theory brings in the delocalization by sharing electrons, usually between two atoms but a greater number can be involved if several resonance structures can be conceived of. The molecular orbital theory also spreads the electrons between two or more atoms, in the limit the entire molecule being involved.

The electrostatic theory, then, essentially excludes this delocalization (or exchange, or resonance) energy, though it is partly included in terms involving induced dipoles since the polarization of one atom or ion by another is equivalent to allowing the electrons of the first ion to move into the field of the second. The valence bond and molecular orbital theories, in turn, can be made to include ionic contributions to any desired extent,[3] though the result is to greatly complicate any attempt at calculations of bond energies. In fact, for anything but the simplest systems, any quantum mechanical approach can be used in only a very approximate way.

In any theory a necessary starting point is some knowledge of the unperturbed atomic orbitals on the central atom, such as would exist in the gas phase in the absence of ligands. Figure 1 shows the conventional boundary contours for the s, p, and d orbitals which will form the basis of further discussion.[4] These contours are only approximate; they indicate roughly the region in space which will contain almost all of the electronic charge of an electron in such an orbital. The plus and minus signs refer to the mathematical sign of the wave function, ϕ, which describes the orbital (it is ϕ^2 which is a measure of the electron density from point to point). The d orbitals are the ones most difficult to visualize and thus require brief comment. The d_{xy}, d_{xz}, and d_{yz} are mutually perpendicular with four alternating positive and negative lobes in each of the respective planes. These three sets of four lobes are situated along a 45° angle between each of the cartesian axes. There are also the $d_{x^2-y^2}$, $d_{x^2-z^2}$, and $d_{y^2-z^2}$, which are mutually perpendicular and each of which lies directly along the respective axes in one of the three different planes. Of these three equivalent orbitals only two are independent. Any pair of them can be used, or, as is usually done, the $d_{x^2-y^2}$ and a hybrid of the other two called d_{z^2} is taken. The d_{z^2} will have large positive lobes along the z axis and smaller negative lobes along both the x and y axes forming in fact a negative sausage-like belt around the z axis symmetric about the xy plane.

Each atomic orbital can hold as many as two electrons, and in the

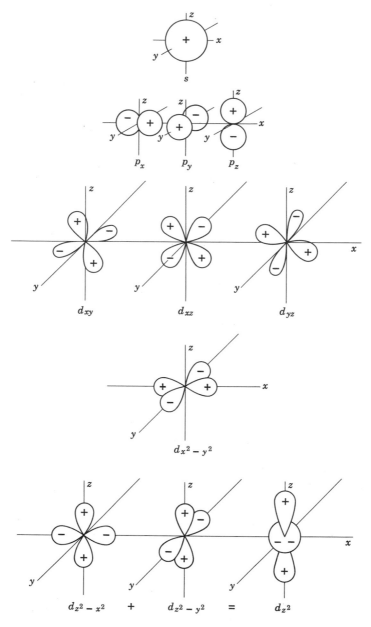

FIG. 1. Atomic orbitals.

gaseous atom electrons fill the orbitals in the order of increasing energy $1s < 2s < 2p < 3s < 3p < 4s \simeq 3d < 4p < 5s \simeq 4d$. All the p orbitals of a given principal quantum number are equal in energy, as are all the d levels. Hund's rules are obeyed. That is, two electrons avoid being in the same orbit if possible, and their spins are parallel if they are in different singly occupied orbits of the same energy.

The three theories mentioned above now diverge in the way in which the approach of the ligands is considered to affect the central atom and its atomic orbitals. The simplest, the electrostatic theory, will be discussed last because of the greater number of illustrative calculations that can be made with it.

THE VALENCE BOND THEORY [5]

One viewpoint is stressed by the valence bond method chiefly developed for complexes by Pauling.[6] In this theory it is considered essential that a number of orbitals on the central metal atom equal to the number of ligands be made available to form coordinate covalent bonds with orbitals on the ligands. Furthermore, by using the criterion that maximum angular overlap of two orbitals forms the strongest covalent bond, it is shown that the original atomic orbitals should be hybridized to form a new set of equivalent bond orbitals with definite directional properties. In this way the familiar set of four tetrahedral orbitals is built up from one s and three p orbitals. For example, Table 1 shows the most important combinations of atomic orbitals

Table 1

Hybrid Orbitals and Directional Properties

Coordination Number	Bond Orbitals	Strength	Shape
1	s	1.00	. . .
1	p	1.73	. . .
2	sp	1.93	linear
3	sp^2	1.99	trigonal
4	sp^3	2.00	tetrahedral
4	dsp^2	2.69	square planar
5	dsp^3, spd^3	. . .	trigonal bipyramid
5	d^2sp^2, spd^3	. . .	square pyramid
6	d^2sp^3	2.92	octahedral

for coordination compounds and their arrangement in space. This spatial arrangement fixes the shape of the resulting complexes. In addition the relative bond strengths according to angular orbital overlap are given. On this scale the non-directional bond formed by an s orbital has a strength equal to unity. In octahedral, or six-coordinated, complexes, the six hybrid orbitals are identical except that they are pointed along the six directions in space given by a set of cartesian axes. The six atomic orbitals used are the s, p_x, p_y, p_z, $d_{x^2-y^2}$, and d_{z^2}. For greatest stability, the d orbitals used are of the next lower principal quantum number than the s or p. Each hybrid orbital accepts a pair of electrons from a ligand, or rather a set of six valence bonds is formed by combining the six hybrid orbitals with six suitable orbitals, one on each of the ligands. Such bonds are called σ *bonds* because the electron density of the bond is symmetrical about the bond axis.

In addition there are the d_{xy}, etc., atomic orbitals on the central atom rotated 45° from the hybrid orbitals. These cannot be used for forming σ bonds. However, they are suitably placed for forming π *bonds* with either p or d orbitals on the ligands. A π bond is one having a nodal plane, or minimum of electron density, along the bond axis. A criterion for π bond formation is that the signs of the wave functions be the same in the regions where they overlap. The second half of a carbon-carbon double bond is also a π bond. Almost always π bonding means double bonding. Another possible kind of bond is a δ *bond* with two nodal planes cutting the bond axis. Such bonds might be formed from two suitably placed d orbitals on different atoms.

It has been postulated by Pauling[7] that, if a ligand has, or can have by resonance, vacant orbitals, and if the central atom has d electrons, π bonding from the metal to the ligand will occur. This will strengthen the coordinate bond (making it a double bond) and help to reduce the negative charge formed on the central atom by the addition of the ligands.

The square planar configuration is formed using s, p_x, p_y, and $d_{x^2-y^2}$ orbitals of the central atom to form σ bonds, thus leaving the p_z and d_{z^2} orbitals projecting above and below the plane of the complex. In addition the d_{xy}, d_{xz}, and d_{yz} can form π-type bonds with any three of the attached groups at one time. The tetrahedral arrangement is shown in Fig. 2 with the same axes used as for Fig. 1. The d_{xy}, etc., orbitals are now poorly situated for π bonding, but the $d_{x^2-y^2}$ and d_{z^2} orbitals can form two such bonds at a time with any two of the four ligands.

Some of the evidence for the existence of π bonding in metal complexes has been reviewed by Chatt and by Nyholm.[8,9] This evidence

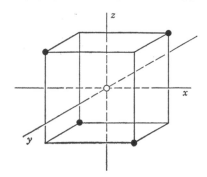

FIG. 2. Location of four groups (dark circles) bonded tetrahedrally to a central atom (open circle).

centers about the relative stabilities of certain complexes, changes in infrared absorption frequencies, and shortening of bond lengths. Thus the stability of carbonyl complexes such as $Ni(CO)_4$, $Fe(CO)_5$, and $Cr(CO)_6$ is hard to understand on any other basis since CO is a very weak base and is not highly polar. Also there is a correlation in these three cases between the reactivity of the compound and the number of d electrons in the metal atom divided by the number of ligands which accept them. It is pointed out by Nyholm and Short[9] that CO in $Ni(CO)_4$ may only be replaced easily by ligands such as R_3As, R_3P and PX_3, whereas a number of ligands such as amines will replace CO from $Cr(CO)_6$ and $Fe(CO)_5$. By using empty d orbitals on P or As, the first set of reagents can form π bonds and accept electrons from the metals.

It is difficult to account for $Ni(CO)_4$ and the non-existence of $Zn(CO)_4^{2+}$ unless double bonding is a factor. The zinc(II) is isoelectronic with nickel(0) and would complex better with anions and polar molecules. However, with an electron acceptor ligand, the positive charge on zinc would make it a poorer donor of d electrons. Theoretical accounts of σ, π, and δ bonding involving d orbitals have been given by Jaffe[10] and others.[11]

In order to account for the different magnetic properties of a given metal ion in various complexes, Pauling[6] postulated that, in the case of strong electron-donating ligands, such as CN^-, covalent bond formation would definitely occur. This would require in many cases the coupling of d electrons to provide the necessary orbitals for hybridization. For weaker ligands, or highly electronegative ones, covalent bond formation would not occur and electrostatic forces only would be involved. Thus a subdivision into "covalent" and "ionic" complexes was made, and the observed magnetic moment was used to decide which kind of complex was at hand (the magnetic criterion of bond type). This criterion is illustrated for some complexes of cobalt(III):

	$3d$	$4s$	$4p$	
Co^{3+} (free ion)	⊙ ⊙ ⊙ ⊙ ⊙	○	○ ○ ○	
$Co(NH_3)_6{}^{3+}$	⊙ ⊙ ⊙ ⊡ ⊙	⊙	⊙ ⊙ ⊙	covalent
$CoF_6{}^{3-}$	⊙ ⊙ ⊙ ⊙ ⊙	○	○ ○ ○	ionic

Complexes in which the number of unpaired electrons is less than in the free ion are called magnetically anomalous or *spin-paired complexes*. The hexamminecobalt(III) ion, being diamagnetic, was considered as a covalent complex and the hexafluoro complex, having a paramagnetism corresponding to four unpaired electrons, as ionic. It was also considered possible that four alternating covalent bonds involving the $4s$ and $4p$ orbitals were formed. Since many of the complexes which are classified as ionic by the magnetic criterion, such as tris(acetylacetonato)iron(III), have what are usually considered covalent properties, such as volatility and solubility in organic solvents,[12] the terminology "ionic" has fallen into disrepute.* The current tendency is to assume that in such cases orbital hybridization occurs between the s, p, and d orbitals of the *same* principal quantum number, sp^3d^2 instead of d^2sp^3. Complexes formed in this way would still be covalent but would allow for electron unpairing in the lower d levels. Further, such complexes would not be as stable as the d^2sp^3 type. Taube[13] uses the terms "inner orbital" and "outer orbital" to differentiate between the kinds of complexes. Burstall and Nyholm[14a] use the term "lower level" and "higher level" covalent bonds. These designations essentially correspond to the terms "penetration" and "normal" complexes introduced earlier by Biltz.[14b]

The more electronegative atoms such as F and O favor outer orbital binding since they concentrate the bonding electrons about themselves. The higher d orbitals from the metal, having greater extension in space, can still overlap appreciably in such a case. Ligands of low electronegativity such as P or As will utilize the lower d orbitals more efficiently. Particularly if π bonding can occur, there will be a greater tendency to use the inner d orbitals and achieve a shorter, stronger bond. Also in the case of the second and third transition groups, it may be assumed that there will be a greater tendency to use the lower orbitals because the upper ones have become too diffuse to bond well.[11]

---

* Actually such properties only give information about intermolecular forces and none at all about intramolecular forces.

Increased positive charge on the central ion will also favor covalent bond formation with the inner orbitals since the increased electronegativity of the central ion will pull the electrons from the ligands.

One unfortunate result of this historical development of the valence bond theory is that the terms "ionic" and "covalent" have come to be used as synonyms for "weak" and "strong" respectively. Thus the incorrect concept has arisen that, in coordination chemistry, covalent bonds have a large dissociation energy and ionic bonds have a small dissociation energy. As we shall see the reverse is generally true except that, if π bonding occurs, this makes the total bond strong since it is a double bond.

THE MOLECULAR ORBITAL THEORY

The application of molecular orbital (M.O.) theory to complex ions was made by Van Vleck.[1] The electrons are assumed to move in molecular orbitals which extend over all the nuclei of the system. The molecular orbitals themselves are taken, for convenience, as linear combinations of atomic orbitals. In the event that a given atomic orbital overlaps appreciably with only one other atomic orbital, the pair may be regarded as forming a localized M.O. holding as many as two electrons. This would correspond to the usual conception of a chemical bond.

When an atomic orbital (A.O.) overlaps several A.O.'s on different nuclei, then a more extended M.O. is obtained. As many M.O.'s will exist as the number of A.O.'s considered. Half of the molecular orbitals will be bonding, i.e., more stable, than the original atomic orbitals, and half will be antibonding, or less stable. In the case of d orbitals on the central atom of a complex, it is clear that extended molecular orbitals will be needed.

Consider a regular octahedral complex of a transition element. The $d_{x^2-y^2}$ orbital would overlap the σ orbitals of the ligands on the x, $-x$, y and $-y$ axes (the ligand σ orbital would be some combination of s and p orbitals projecting in the bond direction). The d_{z^2} orbital would overlap σ orbitals on all six ligands. The allowed M.O.'s formed would be given by the wave functions

Bonding $\begin{cases} \phi_1 = \alpha d_{z^2} + ((1-\alpha^2)/12)^{1/2}[2\sigma_z + 2\sigma_{\bar{z}} - \sigma_x - \sigma_{\bar{x}} - \sigma_y - \sigma_{\bar{y}}] \\ \phi_2 = \alpha d_{x^2-y^2} + ((1-\alpha^2)/4)^{1/2}[\sigma_x + \sigma_{\bar{x}} - \sigma_y - \sigma_{\bar{y}}] \end{cases}$

Antibonding $\begin{cases} \phi_1' = (1-\alpha^2)^{1/2}d_{z^2} - (\alpha^2/12)^{1/2}[2\sigma_z + 2\sigma_{\bar{z}} - \sigma_x - \sigma_{\bar{x}} - \sigma_y - \sigma_{\bar{y}}] \\ \phi_2' = (1-\alpha^2)^{1/2}d_{x^2-y^2} - (\alpha^2/4)^{1/2}[\sigma_x + \sigma_{\bar{x}} - \sigma_y - \sigma_{\bar{y}}] \end{cases}$

Here α^2 is a measure of the degree of mixing of the orbitals, being 0 for a pure ionic complex and 0.5 for a pure covalent complex. Four more bonding and four more antibonding M.O.'s can be formed by combining the central atom's s, p_x, p_y, and p_z orbitals with the same six ligand σ orbitals. Two of the bonding orbitals would be

$$\phi_s = \alpha s + ((1 - \alpha^2)/6)^{1/2}[\sigma_z + \sigma_{\bar{z}} + \sigma_x + \sigma_{\bar{x}} + \sigma_y + \sigma_{\bar{y}}]$$

$$\phi_{p_x} = \alpha p_x + ((1 - \alpha^2)/2)^{1/2}[\sigma_x - \sigma_{\bar{x}}]$$

The number of electrons to be accommodated influences the nature of the interactions and the form of the M.O.'s. For example, in a complex containing many electrons in the antibonding orbitals, it is best if the value of α is close to zero so that the complex is ionic.[15] As the number of antibonding electrons decreases, the value of α will increase since the gain in stabilization energy due to the bonding orbitals being lowered is not outweighed in this case by the antibonding orbitals being raised.

In an analogous way molecular orbitals can be constructed for π bonds [16] formed by combining the d_{xy}, d_{xz}, and d_{yz} orbitals of the central atom with the π orbitals of the ligands (the p orbitals not projecting in the σ-bond direction, or d orbitals). Three bonding and three antibonding orbitals can be constructed, one example of the former being

$$\phi_3 = \beta d_{xz} + ((1 - \beta^2)/4)^{1/2}[\pi_x + \pi_z - \pi_{\bar{x}} - \pi_{\bar{z}}]$$

Figure 3 is a schematic drawing illustrating the formation of M.O.'s in an octahedral complex. For simplicity the value $\beta^2 = 1$ has been chosen so that π bonding is neglected and the d_{xy}-type orbitals considered as non-bonding. The diagram shows the approximate order of increasing energy, but it is not to scale. The orbitals are filled from the bottom up, no more than two electrons per orbital being allowed because of the exclusion principle. The six ligands contribute twelve electrons originally, in their σ orbitals. These fill the six lowest M.O.'s which are the bonding ones. As many as six electrons can be in the non-bonding d_{xy}-type orbitals of the central atom. Then, in addition, as many as four electrons can go in the two antibonding M.O.'s ϕ_1' and ϕ_2'. The antibonding M.O.'s formed from the central atom's s and p orbitals lie too high to be used.

The magnetic properties of complexes can be nicely explained on the basis of such a diagram. Whether or not electron pairing occurs depends on the energy separation of the non-bonding d orbitals and the antibonding molecular orbitals, as well as on the energy required to

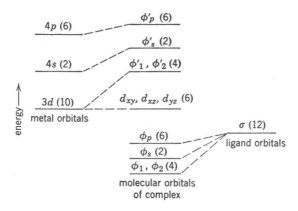

Fɪɢ. 3. Formation of molecular orbitals in a regular octahedral complex. Numbers in parentheses refer to total number of electrons that can be accommodated.

pair electrons originally in singly occupied orbits. Some information is available on these energies since, as a first approximation, the interaction between the ligand σ and the metal d orbitals pushes the M.O.'s formed apart in a symmetrical fashion as shown by the dashed lines in the diagram. [17] Consequently the energy difference, ΔE, between d_{xy} and ϕ_1', for example, is just equal to the bonding energy of a single electron in ϕ_1. It can then be predicted that electron pairing will occur if strong bonds are formed between the central atom and the ligand (ΔE large).

As an illustration consider the paramagnetic octahedral complexes of nickel(II) and the diamagnetic square planar complexes of the same element. The problem in each case is to dispose of the eight d electrons of the metal ion and the several ligand electrons. In the valence bond theory the octahedral complex is considered as follows:

$$\text{Ni(NH}_3\text{)}_6{}^{2+} \quad \odot \ \odot \ \odot \ \odot \ \odot \quad \boxed{\odot \quad \odot \ \odot \ \odot} \quad \odot \ \odot \,|$$

	3d	4s	4p	4d

with outer orbital sp^3d^2 hybridization. The diamagnetic complex would have the electronic arrangement

$$\text{Ni(CN)}_4{}^{2-} \quad \odot \ \odot \ \odot \ \odot \ \boxed{\odot \qquad \odot \qquad \odot \ \odot} \ \bigcirc$$

with inner orbital dsp^2 hybridization.

The molecular orbital theory would put twelve ligand electrons in the six bonding orbitals in $Ni(NH_3)_6^{2+}$. Six electrons are paired up in the three d_{xy}-type non-bonding orbitals, and two electrons are put one each into the two antibonding orbitals derived from $d_{x^2-y^2}$ and d_{z^2}, giving the required paramagnetism. For the square planar $Ni(CN)_4^{2-}$, only four bonding orbitals would be formed involving ligand orbitals and the $3d_{x^2-y^2}$, $4s$, $4p_x$, and $4p_y$ orbitals of nickel. These would contain the eight ligand electrons. There would now be four non-bonding d orbitals, including the d_{z^2}, and these would receive eight electrons all paired. The antibonding orbitals would be unoccupied.

Furthermore it is possible to correlate the energy level diagram with the absorption spectrum (see Chapter 9) of the complex ion.[17,18] This is because the spectral lines in the visible and near ultraviolet would correspond to electronic transitions between the highest filled orbitals and the lowest unfilled ones. With suitable corrections for electron repulsion it is possible to estimate the difference ΔE from spectral data. This has been done for a number of ligands and central atoms. Table 2 shows this quantity, also called $10Dq$, for the aqua complexes of several ions.

Table 2 *

Dq Values ($\Delta E/10$) for Hydrates

(In cm^{-1})

	Ti	V	Cr	Mn	Fe	Co	Ni	Cu	Rh
Divalent	...	1220	1260	780	1050	970	850	1250	...
Trivalent	2040	1900	1770	2100	1400	2000	...	...	2770

* Taken from reference 17 except for Mn(II), Fe(III), and Rh(III).

A more detailed discussion of the significance of these values will be given shortly, but for the moment it can be seen that the bonding energy of a pair of electrons in a divalent ion complex bonding M.O. is about $2 \times 10,000 \ cm^{-1}$ or 60 kcal. For a trivalent ion the corresponding figure is $2 \times 20,000 \ cm^{-1}$ or 120 kcal. The value of ΔE depends on the nature of the ligands, being about 25% greater for NH_3 than for H_2O, for example, and nearly twice as large for cyanide ion as for H_2O. The order of decreasing ΔE from the spectra of regular octahedral complexes is found to be approximately $CN^- >$ 1,10-phenanthroline $> NO_2^- >$ ethylenediamine $> NH_3 > SCN^- > H_2O > F^- > RCO_2^- > OH^- > Cl^- > Br^-$.[19] This is the so-called spectrochemical or Fajans-Tsuchida series.[20]

If the energy separation of the non-bonding and antibonding orbitals is larger than the energy required to couple a pair of electrons, then electrons will be paired to the maximum extent. This is illustrated in Table 3 for some octahedral complexes of iron (II).

Table 3

Magnetic Properties of Some Complexes of Iron (II)

	d_{xy}	d_{zz}	d_{yz}	ϕ_1'	ϕ_2'	Magnetic Moment *
Fe^{2+} (free ion)	⊙	⊙	⊙	⊙	⊙	4.90 B.M.
Fe(H$_2$O)$_6{}^{2+}$	⊙	⊙	⊙	⊙	⊙	4.90
Fe(CN)$_6{}^{4-}$	⊙	⊙	⊙	○	○	0.0
Unknown	⊙	⊙	⊙	⊙	○	2.83

* Magnetic moment in Bohr magnetons calculated by spin only formula. ϕ_1' and ϕ_2' in the gaseous ion correspond to $d_{x^2-y^2}$ and d_{z^2}.

The energy required to pair an electron with another in the same orbit can also be roughly estimated from atomic spectral data.[17,18a] It is largely a property of the central atom only. Since ΔE is a function of the ligands and of the central atom, coupling can be produced by a set of ligands with one central atom but not with another. The pairing energy turns out to be greater for five d electrons than for six (special stability of half-filled shells). Also ΔE is greater for a trivalent ion than for a divalent ion. These factors explain why Co (H$_2$O)$_6{}^{3+}$ is diamagnetic but both Fe(H$_2$O)$_6{}^{2+}$ and Fe(H$_2$O)$_6{}^{3+}$ are paramagnetic with no coupling of electrons in either case.

In passing from the first transition series to the second and third, changes occur in that ΔE gets progressively larger and the pairing energies get smaller. These effects are both due to the greater extension in space of the $4d$ and $5d$ orbitals compared to $3d$. Thus electron pairing is facilitated, and minimum magnetic moments become common. This shows up in the platinum metals, for example, by the complexes having magnetic properties corresponding to one unpaired electron only if an odd number of d electrons is present, or to no unpaired electrons if an even number is present.[21]

It is of interest that some direct evidence for both molecular orbitals and for π bonding exists in the paramagnetic resonance spectrum of IrCl$_6{}^{2-}$ and IrBr$_6{}^{2-}$. The hyperfine structure of the spectrum is due to interaction of the odd electron with both the iridium nucleus and the halogen nuclei.[22] Thus instead of being exclusively in the d_{xy}-type orbital on the metal, the electron spends about 80% of its time near iridium and 3% of the time near each halogen.* An even more remarkable example occurs in the copper(II) complex of tetra(p-chlorophenyl)porphine in which paramagnetic resonance shows interaction of the copper d electron with the chlorine atoms 10 A away.[23] If such π bonding occurs, the non-bonding levels d_{xy}, etc., will become lower in energy and the separation between them and the antibonding orbitals will increase. This should show up in the visible absorption spectrum and presumably accounts for the position of groups such as CN^-, 1,10-phenanthroline and NO_2^- in the spectral series.

Using the criterion of maximum overlapping of the orbitals, it was concluded in the valence bond theory [6] that the relative strengths of tetrahedral, square planar, and octahedral hybrid orbitals were 2.00, 2.60, and 2.92 respectively. In the M.O. theory it is also possible to predict the separation ΔE as a function of the stereochemistry of the complex. This means in turn that the stereochemistry can be predicted with considerable success for systems with different numbers of d electrons. The methods used are those of the crystal field theory and will be discussed under that heading.[24]

It may be mentioned that the same kinds of structures in general are predicted by the molecular orbital method as by the valence bond method.[1] The two theories will not necessarily agree on when the various structures should occur.

It should be also kept in mind that the M.O. theory, although in principle able to calculate actual energies as well as relative changes in energy due to perturbations, is unable to do so in practice for any but the simplest systems. Thus its value lies in the correlation of diverse properties such as spectral, magnetic, and chemical.

THE ELECTROSTATIC THEORY

Van Arkel and DeBoer [25] and, particularly, Garrick,[26] following the pioneering ideas of Kossel, Magnus, and Fajans, showed that a fairly simple electrostatic picture of complexes assuming point charges and dipoles could account for many of their properties. The parameters needed were the charges and sizes of the central ions and the charges, dipole moments, polarizabilities, and sizes of the ligands. Using the

---

* Evidence is also available (M. Tinkham, *Proc. Roy. Soc. London*, **A236**, 535, 549 (1956)) that σ molecular orbitals must exist. Thus the unpaired electrons of Mn^{2+} spend part of their time on coordinated fluoride ions, but the unpaired electrons of Cr^{3+} do not. The latter electrons could only form π bonds, which are not likely in the case of fluoride ion.

ordinary potential energy equations of electrostatics, quantitative calculations could be made for various coordination numbers and stereochemistries.

The results, as we shall show, are remarkably good, allowing calculation not only of relative energies but also of absolute bonding energies in excellent agreement with experiment. From the relative point of view, the theory explains the existence of complexes such as $CuCl_2{}^-$, $CuCl_4{}^{2-}$, and $CuF_6{}^{3-}$ in terms of increasing charge on the metal ion.[27] The existence of $AlF_6{}^{3-}$, but only $AlCl_4{}^-$ and not $AlCl_6{}^{3-}$, can be explained and is a property of the relation between the size of the ligand and the size of the central ion.[26d]

From an absolute point of view Garrick [26d] was able to calculate the energies of formation in the gaseous state of such systems as BF_3, AlF_3, CrF_3, TiF_4, SnF_4, BCl_3, $AlCl_3$, $SiCl_4$, $TiCl_4$, and $SnCl_4$ with errors of less than 6% compared to experimental. Significantly the same electrostatic calculations applied to CF_4, CCl_4, and PCl_5 gave results much smaller than the experimental energies of formation. Thus a model based on purely ionic bonds holding together C^{4+} and $4Cl^-$, for example, is insufficient in these cases, and important covalent bonding must exist.

It could also be easily demonstrated that, for coordination numbers of 2, 4, and 6, linear, tetrahedral, and octahedral complexes respectively should be formed since these structures minimized the electrostatic repulsions of the ligands for each other. However, the existence of square planar complexes is not explicable on the basis of the elementary theory. Also the stability of complexes involving virtually non-polar ligands such as CO was difficult to explain as were the differences in stability between the corresponding complexes of two central ions of the same charge and size, such as iron(III) and cobalt(III). And finally the greater stability of complexes of the second and third transition series metals compared to the first was puzzling since the former metals gave ions of the same charge but greater size than the latter.

Before considering these difficulties further it will be well to show some actual calculations by the electrostatic method. These are largely based on Garrick's method with some simplification in treating repulsive terms in the potential energy function. We will calculate the binding energy in vacuo of a system consisting of a central cation and a number of identical ligands. The zero of energy will be the metal ion and the ligands at infinite separation from each other.

Suppose we have an iron(II) ion surrounded octahedrally by six

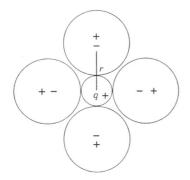

FIG. 4. Electrostatic diagram of symmetrical octahedral complex (two groups not shown) such as $Fe(H_2O)_6{}^{2+}$.

water molecules with the charge on the iron assumed symmetrically disposed around a sphere of radius 0.83 A and the permanent and induced dipoles of the water assumed at the center of a sphere of radius 1.38 A and pointing towards the central ion (see Figure 4). The radius of the ion is the Goldschmidt crystallographic value,[28] and the radius of the water molecule is established from the closest oxygen to oxygen distance in ice.[29] Classically the potential energy of such a system is given by

$$U = -\frac{6q(\mu_o + \mu_i)}{r^2} + \frac{6(1.19)(\mu_o + \mu_i)^2}{r^3} + \frac{6\mu_i^2}{2\alpha} + \frac{6B}{r^9} \tag{1}$$

Here q is the charge on the central ion, μ_o is the permanent dipole moment of water (1.85 debyes), μ_i is the induced dipole moment of water, and r is the distance $0.83 + 1.38 = 2.21$ A. The first term is the attraction between the ion and the dipoles, the second term is the mutual repulsion of the dipoles, the third is the energy required to form the induced dipoles, and the last term represents the van der Waals' repulsions between the six ligands and the central ion. These last are the same as the filled-shell repulsions due to the operation of the Pauli exclusion principle in more modern terms. The common assumption is made that this varies as some large inverse power of the intermolecular distance. B is a constant which will be eliminated by differentiating U with respect to r and setting the differential equal to zero for $r = 2.21$ A.

A value of μ_i is needed. This is obtained from the fundamental relation $\mu_i = \alpha E$ where α is the polarizability of water (1.48 A^3) and E is the electric field at the center of the water molecule directed along the axis. This field is given by

$$E = q/r^2 - \frac{2.37(\mu_o + \mu_i)}{r^3} \qquad (2)$$

where the first term is due to the ion and the last term is the sum of the opposing fields of the other five ligands. Solving for μ_i gives

$$\mu_i = \frac{\alpha(q/r^2 - 2.37\mu_o/r^3)}{(1 + 2.37\alpha/r^3)} \qquad (3)$$

The resulting values of μ_i are 0.67 debye for K^+, 1.74 debyes for Fe^{2+}, and 3.08 debyes for Fe^{3+}, as illustrations of the magnitude (one full electronic charge 1 angstrom from another of opposite sign gives a dipole moment of 4.80 debyes). Simplifying, equation 1 can be written as

$$U = 6\left[\frac{-\mu_o q/r^2 - q^2\alpha/2r^4 + 2.37\mu_o^2/2r^3}{(1 + 2.37\alpha/r^3)}\right] + \frac{6B}{r^9} \qquad (4)$$

and on eliminating the last term by differentiating, the final result is

$$U = 6[-7\mu_o q/9r^2 - 5q^2\alpha/18r^4 + 2.37\mu_o^2/3r^3 - 10(2.37)\mu_o q\alpha/9r^5$$

$$- 4(2.37)q^2\alpha^2/9r^7 + (2.37)^2\alpha\mu_o^2/2r^6] \div (1 + 2.37\alpha/r^3)^2 \qquad (5)$$

An identical equation would be valid for other coordination numbers and geometries except that the factors 6 and 2.37 would be replaced by the new coordination number and by a suitably calculated geometric factor respectively.

All the necessary terms in equation 5 are now known, and the energy can be calculated. The result is shown in the second column of Table 4 as kcal, or the energy of dissociation per bond. Table 4 also shows a number of similar calculations for other complex ions. The mean coordinate bond energy of 50 kcal for iron(II) is made up of 52 kcal due to ion–permanent dipole attraction, 33 kcal ion–induced dipole attraction, 20 kcal dipole-dipole repulsion, and 15 kcal van der Waals' repulsion for each water molecule. The corresponding figures for iron(III) aqua complex are 91 kcal, 107 kcal, 48 kcal, and 43 kcal. The importance of the induced dipole for highly charged cations is obvious. For potassium ion the figures are 17 kcal, 4 kcal, 5 kcal, and 3.5 kcal. The values of r used were 2.05 A for iron(III) and 2.71 A for potassium, the sums of the ionic radii and the radius of the water molecule.

The values of r for the metal ammines were found by taking the radius of the ammonia molecule as 1.40 A. This method is chosen

Table 4

Calculated Coordinate Bond Energies

$$M^{m+} (g.) + nL (g.) \rightarrow ML_n^{m+} (g.)$$

Complex	Energy per Bond	Crystal Field Corrected	Experimental
$Fe(H_2O)_6^{2+}$	50 kcal	52 kcal	58 kcal [a]
$Fe(H_2O)_6^{3+}$	109	109	116 [a]
$K(H_2O)_6^{+}$	13	13	16 [a]
$Cr(H_2O)_6^{3+}$	111	120	122 [a]
$Zn(NH_3)_4^{2+}$	86 [b]	86	89 [a,c]
$Co(NH_3)_6^{3+}$	117	125	134 [a,d]
AlF_6^{3-}	212	212	233 [a,e]
$CrCl_2$	244 [f]	255	272 [g]
$CrCl_3$	378 [h]	392	413 [g]
CrI_2	225 [f]	235	248 [g]

[a] Calculated from heats of hydration of gaseous metal ions, plus heats of reaction in solution and Born heats of hydration of complex ion (see text).

[b] Tetrahedral structure assumed.

[c] C. G. Spike and R. W. Parry, *ibid.*, **75**, 3770 (1953).

[d] K. B. Yatsimirskii, *Doklady Akad. Nauk S.S.S.R.*, **72**, 307 (1950).

[e] W. Latimer and W. L. Jolly, *J. Am. Chem. Soc.*, **75**, 1548 (1953).

[f] Linear structure assumed. Value of $r = 2.40$ A for chloride and 2.70 for iodide.

[g] From heats of formation in the vapor state, ionization potentials of metal atoms, and electron affinities of halogen atoms. T. L. Allen, *J. Am. Chem. Soc.*, **78**, 5476 (1956).

[h] Trigonal planar structure assumed. Value of $r = 2.30$ A.

because it gives figures for the metal-oxygen and metal-nitrogen distances such as are found in the solid state for hydrates and ammines.[30] For the fluoro complex also the value of r used was equal to the sum of the ionic radii (as given in Table 9). This procedure will not work for the chloride and iodide systems, however, the distances actually used being about 0.2 A less than the sum of the ionic radii and being about 0.1 A larger than what Pauling [31] would call the sum of the "covalent bond radii" of the metal and halogen atoms. Such covalent bond radii are, of course, a set of numbers chosen empirically to reproduce experimental distances in complex compounds as closely as possible. Their applicability does not depend in any way upon whether or not the bond in question is covalent or not.

From an electrostatic viewpoint it is necessary to affirm that atomic and ionic sizes are not constants but are simply a result of balanced forces of attraction and repulsion. For strong forces of attraction, the observed interatomic distances will be less. Hence the "size" of an ion will be a function of the compound in which it occurs. The size of a halide ion in an alkali halide crystal will not be suitable for use in a compound in which the halide is very near a small, highly charged cation. The variation in size will be most important for the more polarizable iodide and bromide ions.

The theoretical calculation of the proper value for r in different cases is not impossible but would be difficult. Garrick,[26a, b] for example, treated the van der Waals' repulsion in equation 1 in a more detailed manner. The coefficient B was evaluated by considering each ion and molecule in the complex to be similar to the nearest inert gas molecule. For these gases the magnitude of the repulsion term in the intermolecular potential energy function is known from a study of the second virial coefficient.[32] If B is known, it is possible to solve for the value of r which makes the potential energy a minimum. This was done graphically by Garrick. This method agrees very well with the method used above for hydrates and gives slightly larger values of r for ammoniates. The easiest procedure is to find the proper value of the intermolecular distance to use from published data on distances between atoms for the compound in question or some close analog. This will rarely be exact since the required distances are in the gas phase and experimental data are usually for the solid state.

In any event the model used is very crude, and further refinements might be considered such as the inclusion of the London attraction forces,[2] which would add about 2 kcal to each bond energy. Or a more elaborate representation of the water or ammonia molecule than the point dipole model might be used.[33] The major need, however, is to refine the picture of the central ion since it is seen in Table 4 that $Fe(H_2O)_6^{3+}$ and $Cr(H_2O)_6^{3+}$ differ but little in stability according to the calculation. This is not in agreement with the observation that the iron complex exchanges its waters rapidly with the solvent, as judged by oxygen 18 experiments, whereas the chromium ion does not.[34] Also a calculation of the energy of $Fe(NH_3)_6^{3+}$ would predict the same stability as for $Co(NH_3)_6^{3+}$, again at variance with the properties of these two ions.*

* Ammonia has a lower dipole moment than water, 1.40 debyes, but a higher polarizability, 2.26 A.[3] Hence with small, highly charged ions it would form somewhat more stable complexes than does water.

THE CRYSTAL FIELD THEORY

The necessary correction lies in the crystal field theory first proposed by Bethe [35] and applied to the magnetic properties of the transition metal ions by Schlapp and Penney [36] and by Van Vleck.[37] Recently this theory has been widely used to explain the so-called d-d spectra of complexes in the visible region (see Chapter 9). Orgel [17, 38] was the first to call attention to the consequences of the theory on the stability of coordination compounds of the transition elements.

The essence of the theory is that the five d orbitals, which are degenerate and equal in energy in the gaseous metal ion, become differentiated in the presence of the electrostatic field due to the ligands (the crystal field). It is the symmetry of this field, or its regular geometric properties, which gives the theory its name. Though originally applied to crystalline solids, it is equally applicable to any orderly arrangement of electrically interacting particles such as a single complex. In particular those orbitals lying in the direction of the ligands are raised in energy with respect to those lying away from the ligands. By preferentially filling the low-lying levels the d electrons can stabilize the system compared to the case of random filling of the d orbitals. The gain in bonding energy achieved in this way may be called the *crystal field stabilization energy* (C.F.S.E.). It is caused by the distribution of charge around the central atom of the complex not being symmetrical as assumed in the earlier electrostatic calculation. If the d orbitals were occupied equally, the resulting electron density would have spherical symmetry.

For example, in an octahedral complex, the $d_{x^2-y^2}$ and d_{z^2} orbitals are clearly raised in energy relative to the d_{xy}, d_{yz}, and d_{xz} orbitals. The first three d electrons will then go into the lower set (for six equal ligands these are all equal in energy). The next few electrons will either fill the higher pair of levels (also equal in energy for the symmetrical case) or pair up and occupy the lower levels doubly. Again, as in the M.O. theory, the choice will depend on the splitting between the upper and lower levels and on the pairing energy required. If the splitting is large (strong crystal field), then pairing will occur and a reduced magnetism will result. If the splitting is small (weak crystal field), then the electrons will occupy different orbitals and the maximum paramagnetism will be observed (magnetically normal or *spin-free* complexes).

The separation between the energy levels can be obtained in two ways: as before in the M.O. theory, the visible spectrum of a complex is believed to involve just the transitions between the various energy levels that the d electrons can occupy. Hence the energy difference between d_{xy} and $d_{x^2-y^2}$, say, may be estimated from the absorption bands of the complex ion. (This would be the same as the difference between the non-bonding and antibonding orbitals in the M.O. picture.) However, a more absolute calculation can also be made using a combined quantum mechanical and electrostatic model.[39]

This involves assuming a set of hydrogen-like or Slater-type.[40] d wave functions, and calculating by the first-order perturbation theory for degenerate levels [41] the new energies and wave functions produced by the electric field of the ligands. These are idealized as point charges or dipoles. The result is a set of energy levels which can be characterized in terms of one or more parameters. In a regular octahedral complex only a single parameter occurs. The quantity $10Dq$ is defined as the energy separation between the lower and upper levels. Since, from symmetry considerations, the d_{xy}, d_{xz}, and d_{yz} are equal in energy, as are the $d_{x^2-y^2}$ and d_{z^2} levels, an assignment can be made of $-4Dq$ for the energy of the former and $+6Dq$ for the latter. These numbers follow because of the rule that the energy (C.F.S.E.) must be zero if all levels are equally occupied.

A definite value is given for $10Dq$ in terms of the perturbation calculation discussed above. The result is approximately [42]

$$10Dq \simeq \frac{5eq\overline{a^4}}{3r^5} \quad \text{or} \quad 10Dq \simeq \frac{5e\mu\overline{a^4}}{r^6}$$

where e is the charge on the electron, q or μ is the charge or dipole moment of one ligand, r is the distance from the center of the ion to the center of the ligand and $\overline{a^4}$ is the average value of the fourth power of the radius of the d electrons.

As an example, consider $Co(H_2O)_6^{3+}$, in which r is about 2 A and μ is about 5 debyes, counting the quite large induced dipole (see the remarks on $Fe(H_2O)_6^{3+}$ given earlier). Since the cyrstallographic radius of Co^{3+} is about 0.65 A, it might be expected that $\overline{a^4}$ would be less than unity. However, to give agreement with the spectral value of $10Dq$ (Table 2), a value of $\overline{a^4}$ equal to 1 A^4 is needed. As an order of magnitude calculation, the result is very satisfactory.

Also the fact that $10Dq$ is less for divalent ions than trivalent ions may be partly correlated with the larger values of the induced dipoles for the latter, changes in $\overline{a^4}$ and r^6 tending to compensate. The greater values of $10Dq$ found for the second and third transition series are accounted for in part on the basis of $\overline{a^4}$ becoming quite large in these cases, and in part because such ions also behave as if their charges were greater. This matter will be discussed in more detail later.

The crystal field strengths produced by various ligands can be obtained from the spectra of symmetrical complexes. The order of decreasing Dq, or weaker crystal fields, is that of the spectrochemical series given (p. 44). There are some obvious difficulties in rationalizing the order found on the basis of the simple electrostatic model used for the ligands. Thus the position of hydroxide ion with respect to water is anomalous since it has both a higher charge and a higher polarizability. Also the large Dq values for large, unsaturated amines such as 2,2'-bipyridine and 1,10-phenanthroline are unreasonable.

These difficulties for the most part disappear as soon as allowance is made for π bonding. This, being a covalent, or delocalization, phenomenon, is outside the scope of the simple crystal field theory. However, if it is allowed, then it is clear that ligands can be divided into three classes based on their π-bonding behavior: (1) those that receive electrons from the metal ion; (2) those that donate electrons to the metal ion; and (3) non-π-bonders. As already discussed under molecular orbital theory, the first kind of π bonding stabilizes the d orbital that donates the electrons. In octahedral and square planar complexes these will be members of the d_{xy} set. Also removal of electrons from the central atom is equivalent to increasing its positive charge. Both of these factors will cause an increase in the $10Dq$ of energy separation. Contrariwise, electron donation from the ligand to the metal will decrease the charge on the central ion. This will cause a decrease in the magnitude of $10Dq$. However, the effect is probably small compared to another which is best discussed from the localized M.O. point of view. The d orbital on the central atom and a π orbital on the ligand will form both a low energy bonding M.O. and a high energy antibonding M.O. If the ligand does not occupy the low level with a pair of electrons, the central atom will. But, if the ligand has a pair of π electrons, the central atom has available for its use only the high energy, antibonding orbital. Thus there will be a repulsive interaction between the electrons in the ligand's π orbital and the central atom's d_{xy} orbital. This will raise the energy of the d_{xy} orbital, making the energy separation $10Dq$ less.

Thus, in addition to the effect of the charges and dipole moments of the ligands, the energy separation can also be increased if π bonding to unsaturated ligands occurs, and can be decreased if π bonding from an electron-rich ligand occurs.   These considerations help explain the order in the spectral series.

For structures other than that of a regular octahedron, perturbation calculations can also be made and the energies of the various d orbitals can be found.   Except for the tetrahedral case, more than one parameter is needed to express the results; in particular the ratio $\overline{a^2}/r^4$ occurs in some terms instead of $\overline{a^4}/r^6$ as in the octahedral system.   In what follows a reasonable factor of about three has been used to convert the first of these ratios into the second.   This enables us to calculate the crystal field stabilization of systems with various numbers of d electrons and with various structures.   Table 5 shows the appropriate theoretical

Table 5

The d-Orbital Energy Levels in Crystal Fields of Different Symmetries

C.N.	Structure	$d_{x^2-y^2}$	d_{z^2}	d_{xy}	d_{xz}	d_{yz}
1	... [a]	$-3.14Dq$	$5.14Dq$	$-3.14Dq$	$0.57Dq$	$0.57Dq$
2	linear [a]	-6.28	10.28	-6.28	1.14	1.14
3	trigonal [b]	5.46	-3.21	5.46	-3.86	-3.86
4	tetrahedral	-2.67	-2.67	1.78	1.78	1.78
4	square planar [b]	12.28	-4.28	2.28	-5.14	-5.14
5	trigonal bipyramid [c]	-0.82	7.07	-0.82	-2.72	-2.72
5	square pyramid [c]	9.14	0.86	-0.86	-4.57	-4.57
6	octahedron	6.00	6.00	-4.00	-4.00	-4.00
7	pentagonal bipyramid [c]	2.82	4.93	2.82	-5.28	-5.28

[a] Bonds lie along z axis.
[b] Bonds in the xy plane.
[c] Pyramid base in xy plane.
Only electrostatic perturbations are considered.

single electron energies of the several d orbitals of a central atom for a number of the important geometries found in coordination compounds. These are obtained from the papers by Ballhausen and Klixbüll Jørgensen [43] with the assumption mentioned above (in the terminology of Ballhausen and Klixbüll Jørgensen this assumption is that $B_2 = 2B_4$).

Figure 5 shows some of the energy levels in a schematic manner. To avoid confusion it must be recalled that, when ligands are added to a gaseous ion, the total energy of the system goes down.   However, because of the negative charge of the ligands, the energy of all the d

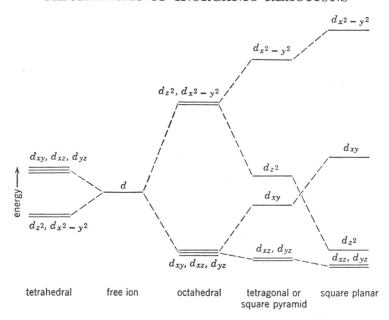

Fig. 5. Crystal field splittings of the d orbitals of a central ion in regular complexes of various structures.

orbitals must go up. The energy of some will go up more than that of others. It is only the relative changes in energy of the set of d orbitals in any given complex which are shown correctly in Fig. 5.

The energy levels again obey the rule that, if they are all equally filled, the total energy is zero. We may now proceed to calculate the stabilization energies of atoms with any number of d electrons by filling up the levels in order. Actually this can only be done in a rather approximate manner since the levels shown in Table 5 are correct for a single d electron only (or, with inversion, nine d electrons). Systems with d^n electrons have more complicated total energies because of electron interaction.[18, 19] Also in such cases a choice must be made between pairing the electrons in the lower levels or keeping the electrons unpaired and moving on to higher levels. In some cases again it is possible to estimate the pairing energy required from atomic spectral data.[17, 18]

In spite of these difficulties valuable information as to relative stabilizations can still be obtained. Table 6 shows the crystal field stabilization energies for d^n systems calculated from Table 5 for regular

Table 6

Crystal Field Stabilization Energies for d^n Complexes

	Examples	Octahedral Weak Field	Octahedral Strong Field	Square Planar Weak Field	Square Planar Strong Field
d^0	Ca^{2+}, Sc^{3+}	$0Dq$	$0Dq$	$0Dq$	$0Dq$
d^1	Ti^{3+}, U^{4+}	4	4	5.14	5.14
d^2	Ti^{2+}, V^{3+}	8	8	10.28	10.28
d^3	V^{2+}, Cr^{3+}	12	12	14.56	14.56
d^4	Cr^{2+}, Mn^{3+}	6	16 (1)	12.28	19.70 (1)
d^5	Mn^{2+}, Fe^{3+}, Os^{3+}	0	20 (2)	0	24.84 (2)
d^6	Fe^{2+}, Co^{3+}, Ir^{3+}	4	24 (2)	5.14	29.12 (2)
d^7	Co^{2+}, Ni^{3+}, Rh^{2+}	8	18 (1)	10.28	26.84 (1)
d^8	Ni^{2+}, Pd^{2+}, Pt^{2+}, Au^{3+}	12	12	14.56	24.56 (1)
d^9	Cu^{2+}, Ag^{2+}	6	6	12.28	12.28
d^{10}	Cu^+, Zn^{2+}, Cd^{2+}, Ag^+, Hg^{2+}, Ga^{3+}	0	0	0	0

The figures in parentheses are the number of electrons that must be paired in going from the weak field case to the strong field case.

octahedral and square planar complexes. Two sets of values are found, for the "weak field" approximation and the "strong field" approximation, that is, no electron pairing beyond that in the free ion and maximum electron pairing. In the latter case the number of extra electrons to be paired is also shown.

It can be seen from Table 6 that the spin-free complex $Fe(H_2O)_6^{3+}$ has zero crystal field stabilization, whereas the spin-paired (diamagnetic) complexes of cobalt(III) have considerable C.F.S.E. This amounts to $24Dq$ in octahedral complexes, less the energy required to pair two electrons. Since the value of $10Dq$ from the spectrum is about 56 kcal for water ligands and about 25% greater for amine ligands, the crystal field energy is considerable (about 135–170 kcal). The electron-pairing energy is less certain but appears to be about 85–100 kcal for two electrons,[44, 18a] leaving a net gain of about 40 kcal for $Co(H_2O)_6^{3+}$. Further, complexes of chromium(III) are stabilized by $12Dq$ in weak or strong fields and no electron pairing is necessary. From the spectrum $10Dq$ is 17,400 cm^{-1} corresponding to a crystal field energy of 57 kcal for $Cr(H_2O)_6^{3+}$. The octahedral d^8 systems are also strongly stabilized without electron pairing being required. In the case of complexes of nickel(II), the stabilization is about half that of chromium(III) because of the smaller value of Dq for divalent ions.

APPLICATIONS OF THE CRYSTAL FIELD THEORY

Table 6 may be used to explain the existence of square planar complexes in preference to octahedral ones. The comparison of the C.F.S.E.'s as so many Dq is not enough since two other factors must be considered: (1) the numerical value of Dq is not the same for a given central atom and ligands for the two structures, being greater for the square planar complexes,[45] and (2) the electrostatic energy holding the four groups is greater per group than that holding six groups (stronger bonds in planar systems). Both of these factors result from the same cause: the fact that the mutual repulsion of four ligands is less than that of six. Hence larger induced dipoles and closer distances of approach are possible. Working in the opposite direction is the fact that the total bonding energy of six ligands is greater than that of four unless the mutual repulsions are very large.

Nevertheless Table 6 clearly indicates that square planar complexes will be formed more easily from d^8 and d^9 systems than others in strong fields with d^7 systems next. This is in good agreement with the properties of the nickel(II) triad and copper(II) and gold(III) complexes. In fact with the higher transition series, where electron pairing occurs readily, systems with six or less d electrons form octahedral complexes most commonly and systems with more than six generally are square planar.[24] In weak fields d^4 systems should form square planar complexes, but there is little evidence to support this conclusion. However, one other factor must be considered.

Because of the rapid falling off of the crystal field with the distance r, it is possible to have the stabilization of a square planar structure and still have a coordination number of six. Thus a system with tetragonal symmetry, with four ligands close in and with two others *trans* to each other and further away, will give essentially the crystal field of the four closer ligands only. This is undoubtedly what happens in a very large number of complexes. In fact it can be stated that the *Jahn-Teller* [46] *effect* in general will occur. This is the result of a theorem which states that, if a system such as a complex has several total energy levels which are equal in the ground state, a distortion of the system will occur to remove the degeneracy and make one level the most stable. Essentially it means that the best energy for a complex even with six equal ligands will not usually be that of a regular octahedron. Depending on the number of d electrons, the best arrangement will be tetragonal or even rhombic for all systems except d^3, diamagnetic d^6, paramagnetic d^8, uncoupled d^5, and, of course, d^0 and d^{10}.

Thus x-ray and other evidence shows that for copper(II) four groups lie in a plane close to the copper ion and two groups perpendicular to the plane lie further away.[47] If the four groups lie in the xy plane, it is the $d_{x^2-y^2}$ orbital which is half-filled, giving extra stability to the complex.[45] The same structure is anticipated for d^4 systems.* For square planar complexes of nickel, palladium, and platinum, a simple consideration of energetics leads one to expect that two other groups will be above and below the plane at a distance great enough not to change the crystal field. Evidence for these two extra groups has been provided in a number of cases [48] (see also Chapter 4).

Because of the symmetrical nature of the d orbitals, a ligand on the $+x$ axis has the same effect on the energies as when on the $-x$ axis. Hence the square pyramid structure with C.N. five gives C.F.S.E.'s intermediate between the regular octahedral and the square planar structures. This arrangement is particularly favored by cobalt(II), which is a d^7 system. Known examples include $Co(CN)_5^{3-}$ and Co-(triarsine)I_2 (see Table 2, Chapter 1). Nickel(III) in the compound $Ni(Et_3P)_2Br_3$[49] also has this structure. Table 5 provides some theoretical justification for these facts since good stability is obtained in a square pyramid with the $d_{x^2-y^2}$ level empty and the d_{z^2} half-filled. The d-orbital energy levels of the square pyramid may also serve as a good approximation to those of a tetragonal system in some cases.

The crystal field theory may also be used to predict the occurrence of tetrahedral complexes. It will only be necessary to compare the stabilization energies with those of octahedral complexes for the case of weak fields. For strong fields, tetrahedral structures for the transition elements are improbable.† The reason for this is that the theoretical splittings in the tetrahedral case are small, being only $\frac{4}{9}$ of the octahedral, other factors being equal, as shown in Table 5.

However, in some cases it may be that four ligands are better than six (ligand repulsion large). It may then be argued that systems with no crystal field stabilization and non-transition elements, d^0, d^5, and d^{10} systems, will form tetrahedral complexes most readily. This is borne out in the case of $FeCl_4^-$, $Zn(NH_3)_4^{2+}$, $AlCl_4^-$, $Cd(NH_3)_4^{2+}$,

---

* Evidence for the tetragonal structure of Mn(III) complexes has become available (L. E. Orgel and J. D. Dunitz, *Nature*, **179**, 462 (1957); M. A. Hepworth, K. H. Jack, and R. S. Nyholm, *ibid.*, 211 (1957)).

† However, it is likely that the diamagnetic d^4 systems, $ReCl_4^-$ and Re_2Cl_6, are tetrahedral.[24]

$HgI_4{}^{2-}$, $MnO_4{}^-$, $CrO_4{}^{2-}$, $SO_4{}^{2-}$, and many others. The ready formation of tetrahedral complexes such as $CoX_4{}^{2-}$, where X is a halogen or pseudohalogen, also finds some justification from Table 7 since the loss of C.F.S.E. is small for d^7.

Table 7

Weak Field Stabilization of d^n Systems

	Tetrahedral	Octahedral
$d^1\ d^6$	$2.67Dq$	$4Dq$
$d^2\ d^7$	5.34	8
$d^3\ d^8$	3.56	12
$d^4\ d^9$	1.78	6
$d^0\ d^5\ d^{10}$	0	0

It seems unlikely that nickel(II) will form tetrahedral complexes, since the loss of stabilization energy would be large. It has long been considered that the paramagnetic complexes of nickel with coordination number four were tetrahedral.[50] An example would be the bis(acetylacetonato)nickel(II). However, tetrahedral structures have rarely been proved for such systems. In solution, for example, the spectra of such complexes are what one would expect for tetragonal systems and quite unlike that which crystal field theory predicts for a d^8 tetrahedral structure.[50b] Furthermore x-ray examination of the acetylacetonate complex in the solid state reveals a peculiar trimer structure in which nickel is actually six-coordinated.[51] Since other groups are always available in the solid state and solvent molecules are available in solution, it follows that an assignment of tetrahedral structure only on the basis of an apparent coordination number of four can never be made with certainty.*

Another kind of prediction that may be made with the aid of the general theory is that metals which can have considerable crystal field stabilization will react preferentially with ligands of large Dq values. Since ammonia and the amines in general have larger Dq values than water and ligands in which the bonding atom is oxygen, it is expected

---

* In the vapor state nickel(II) acetylacetonate has a square planar configuration (S. Shibata, M. Kishita, and M. Kubo, *Nature*, **179**, 320 (1957)). Recently (L. M. Venanzi, International Conference on Coordination Chemistry, Rome, September, 1957) it was reported that paramagnetic complexes of the type $Ni(P(C_6H_5)_3)_2X_2$ are tetrahedral. Because of steric hindrance the metal ion cannot be six-coordinated, and because of the weak crystal field strength of $P(C_6H_5)_3$ the complexes are not square planar.

that the transition metals will bond preferentially to N compared to O. The non-transition metals, the rare earths, iron(III), and manganese(II), on the other hand, will have a greater tendency to bond to O over N. This is in good agreement with experience. Again, other factors may come in since Cu(I), Ag(I), Au(I), Cd(II), Zn(II), and Hg(II) also prefer N to O even though crystal field stabilization is not involved. This is an expected property of linear and tetrahedral structures since, because of the large induced dipole moments, NH_3-NH_3 repulsions can be greater than H_2O-H_2O. The ligand repulsion is minimized in linear and tetrahedral structures.

Even though Cr(III) and Co(III) are both strongly stabilized by crystal field effects and form good complexes to nitrogen ligands, there is a definite tendency for cobalt to prefer N over O more than chromium does.[52] This may be correlated with the stabilization energy of $24Dq$ for cobalt compared to $12Dq$ for chromium, the electron-pairing energy required for cobalt being about the same regardless of the nature of the ligands.

Crystal field theory may be used to help correlate oxidation-reduction potentials of certain complex ions. For example, Table 8 shows

Table 8

Some Iron(II)-Iron(III) Couples

Electrode Reaction	Potential, E^0, volts
$Fe(H_2O)_6^{2+} \rightleftharpoons Fe(H_2O)_6^{3+} + e$	-0.77
$FePO_4^- + PO_4^{3-} \rightleftharpoons Fe(PO_4)_2^{3-} + e$	-0.61
$Fe(CN)_6^{4-} \rightleftharpoons Fe(CN)_6^{3-} + e$	-0.36
$Fe(bipy)_3^{2+} \rightleftharpoons Fe(bipy)_3^{3+} + e$	-1.10
$Fe(phen)_3^{2+} \rightleftharpoons Fe(phen)_3^{3+} + e$	-1.14

the standard oxidation potentials of several iron(II)-iron(III) systems. Taking the aqua ions as standards, it is seen that negative ion ligands stabilize the trivalent state as might be expected since electrostatic repulsion will favor the removal of an electron from the iron(II). However, neutral unsaturated ligands stabilize the divalent state. This inversion is partly due to the greater crystal field stabilization of a d^6 system compared to a d^5 one in strong fields (see Table 6). The stabilization of $24Dq$ for d^6 compared to $20Dq$ for d^5 must be weighted with the relative values of Dq for each ion since they will not be the same. For a ligand which owes its crystal field effect largely to π bonding, there will be a smaller difference in Dq between a divalent ion and a trivalent ion than indicated in Table 2. This follows since a divalent cation can donate electrons more easily than a trivalent cation.

Other factors influence the E^0 values for the couples chosen. In the first two cases, the ferric ion is stabilized by the phenomenon of special stability of half-filled shells, being a d^5 system. This is a property of the free gaseous ion and has nothing to do with chemical bonding. It can be estimated that the required coupling energy for spin-paired iron(III) is some 30–40 kcal greater than for iron(II) because of this effect.[17,18a] In strong crystal field complexes where electron pairing is complete, this is equivalent to a destabilization of the trivalent iron compared to the situation in the aqua ions. One final factor is the change in solvation energy on oxidation. For cationic species, this always favors the trivalent state and does so most when the ions involved are small, i.e., the aqua iron(III) is stabilized more than the tris(2,2'-bipyridine)iron(III) ion.

Closely related to changes in E^0 for various couples are the stabilizations of valence states by complexation. The classic example of this is, of course, cobalt(III) which forms stable complexes with ligands of good crystal fields but forms an unstable complex with water. Other examples are the stabilization of silver(II) and silver(III) with unsaturated ligands that form square planar complexes.[53] Similarly we have the stabilization of nickel(IV) in octahedral complexes with C.N. six.[50a]

As a final example of the use of the crystal field and electrostatic approach, the paramagnetic and diamagnetic complexes of nickel will be considered again. The distribution of the eight nickel electrons would be

	d_{xy}	d_{xz}	d_{yz}	d_{z^2}	$d_{x^2-y^2}$
$Ni(NH_3)_6^{2+}$	⊙	⊙	⊙	⊙	⊙
$Ni(CN)_4^{2-}$	⊙	⊙	⊙	⊙	○

with the $d_{x^2-y^2}$ orbital empty in the last case because, lying in the plane of the four ligands, it is very high in energy with respect to d_{z^2}. All of the orbitals are considered as atomic orbitals on nickel only. The electrons of the ligands are considered to be localized also in orbitals belonging only to the ligands.

THE COORDINATE BOND ENERGY

Having developed the theory of the coordinate bond in the preceding sections, it is necessary to see what experimental evidence is available to quantitatively test these theories. Most of the data that can be found has to do with formation constants and heats of reaction in aqueous solution. The formation constants can be converted into free energies but these differ from the energy or enthalpy differences by $T \Delta S$. This latter term may be as large as ΔH in solution in some cases.

Actually if we wish information about the absolute dissociation energy of a coordinate bond, it is necessary to have heat of formation data in the gas phase

$$M^{m+} \text{ (g.)} + L \text{ (g.)} \rightarrow ML^{m+} \text{ (g.)} \tag{6}$$

The reason for this is that heats measured in aqueous solution merely give differences in bond energy between water and some other ligand.

$$M(H_2O)^{m+} \text{ (aq.)} + L \text{ (aq.)} \rightarrow ML^{m+} \text{ (aq.)} + H_2O \text{ (aq.)} \tag{7}$$

Also it can be seen that the heats of hydration of the ligand and of water enter in, as well as the heats of hydration of the aqua complex and the ligand complex. Very often these last four terms may all approximately cancel. Also for an overall reaction

$$M^{m+} + nL \rightarrow ML_n^{m+} \tag{8}$$

in either the gas phase or solution, the energy of adding the nth ligand is not the same as for $n - 1$, $n - 2$, and so on.

There are few cases in which the coordinate bond energy can be found directly in the gas phase. The heat of dissociation of $(CH_3)_3B{-}N(CH_3)_3$ is measurable and is 17.6 kcal per mole.[54] For $F_3B{-}N(CH_3)_3$ the corresponding value is 28.5 kcal. Also the heat of the reaction

$$L \text{ (g.)} + H^+ \text{ (g.)} \rightarrow LH^+ \text{ (g.)} \tag{9}$$

can be evaluated by straightforward thermal cycles in simple cases. This negative heat is called the proton affinity and is characteristic of the base L.[55] When L is NH_3, the value is 202 kcal.[56] When L is Cl^-, the proton affinity is 328 kcal.[55] These are the energies of the coordinate bond to hydrogen ion in each case.

From the heats of formation of the metal carbonyls and the heat of vaporization of the solid metal, it is possible to calculate the average bond energy of $Ni(CO)_4$ as 33 kcal, for $Fe(CO)_5$ as 30 kcal, and for $Cr(CO)_6$ as 29 kcal.[57] However, these are for the reaction

$$M \text{ (g.)} + nCO \text{ (g.)} \rightarrow M(CO)_n \text{ (g.)} \tag{10}$$

in which the metal atom is in the normal state $3d^84s^2$ for nickel, $3d^64s^2$ for iron, and $3d^54s^1$ for chromium. A fairer calculation would be one in which the metal atoms are first converted to $3d^{10}$, $3d^8$, and $3d^6$. This requires 42 kcal for nickel, making the average bond energy 44 kcal, and 169 kcal for chromium, making this bond energy 57 kcal. The excitation energy for iron is 152 kcal, so that the bond energy is 60 kcal.[*][57]

In the case of metallic ions there is no direct way of measuring or calculating the heat of reaction in the gas phase. However, the heats of hydration of a number of gaseous ions are known from various thermochemical measurements

$$M^{m+} \text{ (g.) } \rightarrow M^{m+} \text{ (aq.)} \tag{11}$$

It is possible to use these data to calculate the heat of the reaction

$$M^{m+} \text{ (g.) } + 6H_2O \text{ (g.) } \rightarrow M(H_2O)_6{}^{m+} \text{ (g.)} \tag{12}$$

with the aid of two reasonable assumptions. One is that the coordination number towards water is known and is generally taken as six, but some other number could be used if evidence supported it. The second is that the heat of hydration can be broken down into two parts, one due to the interaction of the central ion with the first coordination sphere and the second due to the interaction of the ion plus its first coordination sphere with the rest of the solvent. This procedure is essentially that used by Verwey [58] to calculate the hydration energies to the alkali metal ions.

The second part of the heat of hydration, the heat of hydration of the aqua complex, may be estimated from the familiar Born equation [59] and the variation of the dielectric constant of water with temperature. This should be valid for large, spherically symmetric ions.

$$\Delta F_B = \frac{-q^2}{2r}\left(1 - \frac{1}{D}\right) \tag{13}$$

$$\Delta S_B = \frac{q^2}{2Dr}\left(\frac{\partial \ln D}{\partial T}\right)_p \tag{14}$$

$$\Delta H_B = \Delta F_B + T\,\Delta S_B \tag{15}$$

Here q is the charge on the ion and r is the radius of the central ion plus 2.76 A, the diameter of a water molecule. D is 78 for water at 25°C

* The excitation energies for iron and chromium are estimated by H. A. Skinner and F. H. Sumner, *J. Inorg. Nuclear Chem.*, **4**, 245 (1957).

and $(\partial \ln D/\partial T)_p$ is -0.0046. The heat of vaporization of water, which is 10.4 kcal/mole at 25°C, is also needed.

As examples, the Born heat of hydration for $Fe(H_2O)_6{}^{2+}$ is calculated to be -186 kcal, and for $Fe(H_2O)_6{}^{3+}$ the result is -437 kcal. For a univalent ion such as $K(H_2O)_6{}^+$ the value is -39 kcal.

Table 9 gives a number of heats of hydration for ions of interest in coordination chemistry.[60] Also given are the total ionization potentials to form the ion, that is, the energy for the reaction

$$M \text{ (g.)} \rightarrow M^{m+} \text{ (g.)} + me \text{ (g.)} \tag{16}$$

The ionic radii according to Goldschmidt are also listed. There are several sets of ionic radii available (Pauling and Kordes) which may differ by as much as 0.1 A for a given ion. None of them is completely reliable, but the Goldschmidt values are more directly related to experiment and furthermore show the irregularities in the radii of the first transition series which are predicted because of the crystal field of the neighboring anions in the solid state.[61]

From the total heat of hydration of iron(II) ion we calculate the heat of reaction 6 as $186 - 62 - 468$ or -344 kcal. This corresponds to an average coordinate bond energy of 56 kcal. For iron(III) the result is -697 kcal for the heat of reaction to form $Fe(H_2O)_6{}^{3+}$ in the vapor state. This gives a mean bond energy of 116 kcal. These values are fairly characteristic of the divalent and trivalent cations of the transition metals.

Furthermore by using data on heats of reactions such as 7 in solution it is also possible to calculate the bonding energies for ligands other than water. Again it is necessary to estimate the Born heat of hydration of the complex ion to get bond energies in the gas phase. This procedure has been followed for the complexes listed in Table 4. Yatsimirskii has developed a somewhat different method of calculating bond dissociation energies, consisting of measuring the heat of solution of a solid complex and calculating the lattice energy of the solid by an approximate method.[62] He obtains for the negative heats of the reaction

$$M^{2+} \text{ (g.)} + 3 \text{ ethylenediamine (g.)} \rightarrow M(en)_3{}^{2+} \text{ (g.)} \tag{17}$$

342 kcal for iron, 372 for cobalt, 383 for nickel, 372 for zinc, and 323 for cadmium.

Dividing these figures by six to get energies per bond, values from 54 to 64 kcal are found. From this it would appear that the energy per bond is not too different for water and ethylenediamine. This is

Table 9

Some Properties of Common Metal Ions

Ion	Radius	Total Ionization Potential [a]	−Heat of Hydration [b]
H^+	...	313.4 kcal	263 kcal
Li^+	0.78 A	124.3	125
Na^+	0.95	118.5	100
K^+	1.33	100.1	79
Rb^+	1.49	96.3	75
Cs^+	1.65	89.8	68
Cu^+	0.93 [c]	178	139
Ag^+	1.13	175	116
Au^+	1.37 [c]	213	154
Tl^+	1.49	141	80
Mg^{2+}	0.78	523	464
Ca^{2+}	0.99	414	382
Sr^{2+}	1.27	385	350
Ba^{2+}	1.43	351	316
Ti^{2+}	0.85 [c]	471	446 [d]
V^{2+}	0.82 [c]	483	453
Cr^{2+}	0.80 [c]	541	460
Mn^{2+}	0.91	532	445
Fe^{2+}	0.83	556	468
Co^{2+}	0.82	583	497
Ni^{2+}	0.78	596	507
Cu^{2+}	0.72 [c]	646	507
Zn^{2+}	0.83	631	492
Ru^{2+}	0.81 [c]	558	448
Rh^{2+}	0.80 [c]	596	486
Pd^{2+}	0.85 [c]	651	505
Ag^{2+}	0.93 [c]	681	411
Cd^{2+}	1.03	597	437
Sn^{2+}	1.10 [c]	506	374
Os^{2+}	0.88 [c]	539	444
Ir^{2+}	0.92 [c]	582	477
Pt^{2+}	1.24 [c]	652	523
Hg^{2+}	1.12	673	441
Pb^{2+}	1.32	518	359
Al^{3+}	0.57	1228	1122
Sc^{3+}	0.83	1022	947 [d]
Ti^{3+}	0.64 [c]	1105	1027 [d]
V^{3+}	0.69 [c]	1094	1053 [d]
Cr^{3+}	0.65	1259	1105 [d]
Mn^{3+}	0.66 [c]	1328	1098 [d]

Table 9   (Continued)

Ion	Radius	Total Ionization Potential [a]	−Heat of Hydration [b]
Fe^{3+}	0.67	1261	1072 [d]
Co^{3+}	0.65	1365	1126 [d]
Ga^{3+}	0.62 A	1319 kcal	1124 kcal
In^{3+}	0.81	1214	995
La^{3+}	1.22	835	793
Ce^{3+}	1.18	890	837
Tl^{3+}	1.05	1299	984
Ce^{4+}	1.01	1737	1542
Sn^{4+}	0.71	2152	1827
F^-	1.36	80	117
Cl^-	1.81	86	85
Br^-	1.95	81	74
I^-	2.16	72	61

[a] At 0°K.
[b] At 25°C.
[c] Largely estimated; see reference 60a.
[d] From reference 67.

borne out by measurements of the heats of reaction of aqua complexes with amines. The reactions are usually exothermic by about 5 kcal per bond for divalent cations.[63]   Also for most ligands the heat effect on replacing water is rarely as much as 10 kcal per bond (see Table 2 in Chapter 9). Even though anions are held more firmly than ligands like water or ammonia in the gas phase (see Table 4, p. 50), this does not hold true in solution. The extra solvation energy of the free anion compared to a neutral ligand just compensates for the firmer bonding in the complex.

The methods for getting bond energies in the vapor state discussed above are probably reliable for symmetrical complexes. However, for unsymmetrical complexes, such as $Co(NH_3)_5Cl^{2+}$, the charge distribution is such as to create a dipole moment as well as a net charge in the molecule. This will affect the lattice energy as well as the Born heat of hydration. It should be possible to make more reliable calculations in such cases by using the methods developed by Kirkwood [64] for solvation energies of spherical and ellipsoidal molecules with arbitrary charge distributions. For very irregularly shaped complexes, however, no reliable calculation can be made.

The hydration energies of Table 9 show indisputable evidence for the crystal field stabilization effect.[38a]   Thus in examining the divalent

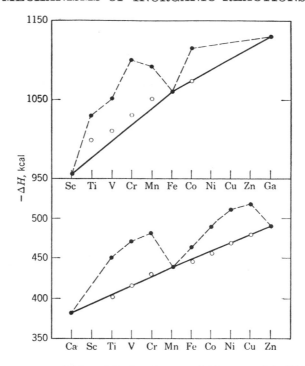

Fɪɢ. 6. The uncorrected (dotted line) and crystal field corrected (solid line) hydration energies of the divalent (lower) and trivalent (upper) ions of the first transition series. (After O. G. Holmes and D. S. McClure, *J. Chem. Phys.*, **26**, 1686 (1957).)

and trivalent ions of the first transition series, including Ca(II) to Ga(III), the heats vary in an irregular manner. However, if the estimated crystal field corrections are subtracted from the total heats, the residual values fall on a smooth curve. This is shown in Fig. 6. It can also be seen that the so-called "natural order" of stability for complexes, which is Mn < Fe < Co < Ni < Cu > Zn,[65] can be explained on the same basis. The order is due to a constantly increasing electronegativity up to and including zinc, and a crystal field correction (greater for almost all good ligands than for water) increasing to a maximum at nickel and copper and falling off abruptly to zero for zinc. In agreement with this explanation, the increased stability for Cu(II) and Ni(II) and the drop at Zn(II) is greatest for ethylenediamine, intermediate for glycine, and very small for oxalate ion.[65] This is the order of decreasing crystal field strength of these ligands.

Table 10 shows the successive formation constants for the ethylene-diamine complexes of some of the common divalent ions. The total

Table 10

Formation Constants for Ethylenediamine Complexes,
1 N KCl at 30°C

	Mn	Fe	Co	Ni	Cu	Zn
log K_1	2.73	4.28	5.89	7.52	10.55	5.71
log K_2	2.06	3.25	4.83	6.28	9.05	4.66
log K_3	0.88	1.99	3.10	4.26	−1.0	1.72
log K_T	5.67	9.52	13.82	18.06	18.60	12.09
Expected	5.67	6.95	8.24	9.52	10.80	12.09
Difference	0	2.57	5.58	8.54	7.80	0

Data from reference 65.

constant, K_T, as found and as calculated by assuming a linear inter-polation between manganese and zinc, which have no crystal field stabilization (d^5 and d^{10} systems), is given. The difference between the experimental values and the interpolated ones is due to crystal field effects.[45, 66] The results for nickel are in good agreement with theory in that Dq for the hydrate of nickel(II) is 850 cm^{-1} and Dq for tris-(ethylenediamine)nickel(II) ion is 1160 cm^{-1} from the spectra.[14] The excess crystal field energy over the hydrate for an octahedral complex should be 12 ΔDq or 10 kcal (see Table 6). The experimental increase is RT ln 8.54 or 12.3 kcal (free energy). For copper(II) it is seen that the advantage lies only in the first two ethylenediamine molecules added. This is in agreement with the tetragonal structure which favors $Cu(en)_2(H_2O)_2{}^{2+}$. Furthermore the increase in stability for the first two constants is considerably greater than would be calculated on the basis of a strictly octahedral configuration.*

An examination of Table 9 shows a very marked correlation between the total ionization potential of an ion and its hydration energy. This is very reasonable since adding electrons either as such or through ligands should be influenced in a similar way by the size and effective charge of the ion. As pointed out by Orgel,[45] the correlation is even better if the ionization potentials are corrected to correspond to a stand-ard configuration, i.e.,

---

* The data on the EDTA complexes of the rare earths shown on p. 19 demon-strate that crystal field effects, though smaller, also occur for the 4f orbitals.[24]

$$M(3d)^n(4s)^2 \rightarrow M^{2+}(3d)^n + 2e \qquad (18)$$

This correction occurs for chromium atom, which has a ground state $(3d)^5(4s)$, and for copper atom, which is $(3d)^{10}(4s)$. It is possible to find the appropriate change in ionization potential from atomic spectroscopy, the energies 7750 cm^{-1} for chromium and 11,200 cm^{-1} for copper then being subtracted from the values given in Table 9. Figure 7 shows the corrected ionization potentials plotted against the heats of hydration corrected for C.F.S.E. The overall change in ionization potential from Ca(II) to Zn(II) is about 50%. The corresponding change in hydration energy is only 25%.

The lattice energies of the transition metal halides also reveal several points of interest. These are plotted in Fig. 8 for the first series. It is evident that there are strong crystal field effects as in the hydration energies. These amount to as much as 40 kcal per mole for divalent ions and 80 kcal for trivalent ions.[24, 67] The minima in the lattice energies at manganese(II) and iron(III) are as predicted by theory.

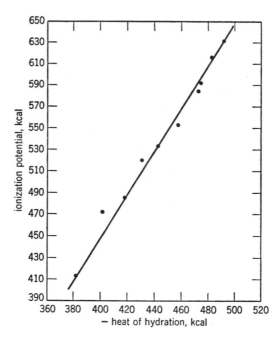

FIG. 7.   Corrected ionization potential $(M(3d)^n(4s)^2 \rightarrow M^{2+}(3d)^n + 2e)$ plotted against crystal field corrected heat of hydration, divalent cations of first transition series.

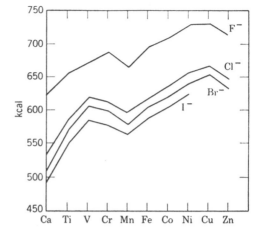

Fig. 8. Lattice energies of divalent halides of first transition series. (From reference 45).

After correcting for C.F.S.E. there is still a steady increase of about 15% in the lattice energy in going from calcium(II) to zinc(II).

Theoretical calculations of the lattice energies of ionic solids using electrostatic potential energy, such as we have used for complexes, work very well for the alkali halides as already mentioned. London dispersion energies replace the induced dipole attractions because in the solid the electric field at each ion is nearly zero due to symmetry. Similar calculations for the halides of copper and silver give theoretical lattice energies which are about 10% lower than the experimental.[68] CuCl has a larger experimental lattice energy than NaCl, though the interionic distances are very similar.

The variation of the heat of hydration with ionic radius is also worth noting. Within a non-transition group, the heat of hydration varies inversely with the ionic radius as might be anticipated. The transition metals give considerable variation as shown by the fact that Cu(I), which has virtually the same size and charge as Na(I), has a higher heat of hydration by 40%. Also Au(I), which is larger than either of the others, has the highest heat of the three. The ionization potentials are also anomalous, being 118.5 kcal for Na, 178 for Cu(I), and 213 for Au(I). The same difficulties are encountered with the divalent and trivalent ions of the non-transition and transition metals.

All these phenomena are disturbing in view of the electrostatic theory by which we earlier calculated bond energies. Use was made of a potential function which varied from one metal to another only in the value of q, the charge on the central atom, and r, the ion size. One set of corrections has been made in that, for the d electrons, it was shown that the use of a uniform distribution of charge over the central atom was incorrect. Instead the d electrons, if possible, concentrated in the regions of less negative potential. This correction will not help for the case of Cu(I) and Au(I) mentioned above since here we have filled d shells which must be spherically distributed.

It has become customary to attribute all of the evidence for stronger bonding in compounds of the transition metals, and for bonding which is not an obvious function of the ionic charge and size, to covalent character in these bonds. Thus AgCl is said to be considerably more covalent than NaCl, $ZnCl_2$ much more covalent than $CaCl_2$, and the complexes of platinum(II), for example, more covalent than the corresponding complexes of nickel(II). Although it is probably true that these statements are qualitatively correct, there is considerable doubt that the energy differences which exist are primarily due to this increased covalency.

CONCEPT OF THE EFFECTIVE IONIC CHARGE

It is necessary to refine the electrostatic theory still further by taking into account the structure of the central atom, which consists of a positive nucleus and extended clouds of negative charge representing the electrons. We define the "effective ionic charge," q', by the statement that the potential acting on a test charge at a given point at a distance r from the nucleus of the central atom, exclusive of any potentials due to ligands or solvent molecules, is given by q'/r. The effective charge, thus defined, is a function of r. For a test charge far removed from the nucleus, q' will be equal to q, the ordinary ionic charge. However, as the test charge approaches the nucleus, q' will increase.

The reason for this is shown in Fig. 9. It is derived from the classical electrostatic result that an amount of electric charge dq uniformly distributed over a thin spherical shell of radius a has a potential equal to dq/r for points outside the sphere and a potential equal to dq/a for points inside the sphere.[69] The electron clouds of a real atom represent an infinite number of such thin spherical shells of varying values of a ranging from zero to infinity and with dq a function of a, falling off in magnitude more or less rapidly with increasing a.

For large values of r, all of the negative charge will be closer to the nucleus than the test charge. Hence it will act as if it is all concentrated at the center, and the potential will be the expected q/r, q being

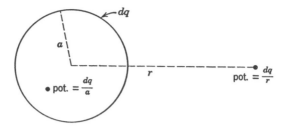

F<small>IG</small>. 9. Potential due to a spherical shell distribution of charge for a point inside and outside the shell.

the difference between the nuclear charge and the total number of electrons. Each electron may be said to have a shielding coefficient of one. As the test charge moves in closer, some electron charge will become exterior to it and begin to exert a potential proportional to $1/a$. Since a is greater than r, the net potential on the test charge will become more positive and q' will be greater than q. The outermost electrons will have shielding coefficients of less than one. The maximum value of q' will be right at the nucleus. For example, a nickel(II) ion will have $q' = 2+$ at a large distance and q' greater·than $7.5+$ at the nucleus. This last figure is the value used for the effective nuclear charge in a Slater-type atomic orbital.[40]

In making electrostatic calculations of the bonding energies of complexes, it is necessary to use the effective ionic charge instead of the usual charge q. The correct q' must be evaluated at the distance to which the ligand has approached. It is clearly only the outermost electrons of the central atom which produce any significant difference between q and q' at such distances. Now it is just the characteristic of the transition metals that they have large numbers of electrons (the d electrons) which are in rather extended orbitals in space (see Fig. 1). Furthermore, for the higher transition metals there is only a small separation in energy, and hence distance from the nucleus, for all of the outermost electrons. Particularly after filling the $4f$ level, the third transition series has a large number of electrons which are relatively far from the nucleus.

Thus there will be a greater positive potential on a test charge a given short distance from Cu^+ than from Na^+. This will increase the electron affinity of the ion, the heat of hydration, and the lattice energy of its salts. The gradual increase in all of these properties in going from Ca(II) to Zn(II) is explicable in terms of an increasing number of d electrons and consequent poorer shielding. The third transition series will have the largest values of q' in spite of their somewhat greater size. It is thus possible to account for all the phenomena mentioned at the outset in terms of this one concept of effective ionic charge.

The greater variation in the ionization potentials than in the hydration energies for the series Ca(II) to Zn(II) is due largely to a higher value of q' for the ionization potential than for hydration. This in turn arises because even an outer shell electron penetrates to the nucleus moderately often. The electrons of a ligand would be expected to get as far as the nucleus of another atom very infrequently. Both the ionization potentials and the solvation energies vary approximately as $(q')^2$.

It would be highly desirable to be able to calculate the correct value of the effective ionic charge to use for each distance of approach. This would require using assumed wave functions for the outermost electrons of the central atom. The wave functions available for polyelectronic atoms are not very reliable at present for this purpose. There is also the complication that the presence of the ligands influences the wave functions of the central atom considerably.[11, 70] Another approach is to evaluate q' empirically from one set of data, such as the ionization potentials, and correct it to other values of r, either empirically or theoretically. Data on the stabilities of complex ions indicate that the increase in q to obtain q' is about 10% at most for the first transition series and 20% for the third transition series.

THEORETICAL COORDINATION NUMBERS

If, after suitable refinements, the quantitative aspects of the electrostatic theory are really valid, it should be possible not only to correlate certain geometries with certain coordination numbers, as has already been done, but also to predict the coordination numbers of various systems. Thus the preference for C.N. four in some cases, the prevalence of C.N. six, and the rarity of C.N.'s five and seven should be explicable. In the valence bond theory, the latter point is associated with the special stability of d^2sp^3 hybrid bonds.* It must be empha-

---

* In fact the custom is prevalent of using the terms "dsp^2," "sp^3," and "d^2sp^3" as synonomous with square planar, tetrahedral, and octahedral respectively. This usage is very questionable. Similarly, it is far better to use the operational terms spin-free and spin-paired rather than the commonly used "ionic" and "covalent" to describe the magnetic properties of complexes (see R. S. Nyholm, reference 48).

sized that in the electrostatic theory there is no mention of valence bonds or hybrid orbitals. Only non-directional electrostatic energies are invoked, and it must be shown by calculation that one arrangement of all the particles of the system is more stable than any other and that this arrangement agrees with what is experimentally observed.

To illustrate this, the potential energy function developed earlier has been used to calculate bonding energies for several systems assuming other coordination numbers than those generally agreed on. This has been done both for the gas phase and also in solution using the Born approximation for the hydration energy of the complex ion. For low coordination numbers this begins to be difficult since the ions do not approximate to spherical symmetry. Even for the tetrahedral case it is probable that water molecules can approach the tetrahedral faces more closely, so that the effective radius of the complex is somewhat less than that of the central ion plus the diameter of one ligand. Coordination numbers less than four will not be discussed.

For a seven-coordinated complex, an unsymmetrical structure has been assumed. There are two axial ligands with the same value of r as for the octahedral case. The other five ligands lie in a plane and form a regular pentagon. In order to do this it is necessary to increase the metal ligand distance to r' since otherwise there is not room for five groups. The r' chosen is such that the five groups just touch, assuming a radius of 1.40 A for ammonia and 1.36 A for fluoride ion. It is about 0.3 A larger than r. The Born hydration energy is calculated by using a value for the radius of the complex which is an average, $(r + 2r')/3$. Probably there are fairly large van der Waals' repulsions developed between the ligands, but these have not been included in the calculation. They are balanced in part by van der Waals'-London attractions but may still be considered to make the complex of C.N. seven less stable than otherwise indicated.

In the case of the square pyramid structure for C.N. five, the hydration energy can be calculated in two ways. First, an average radius can be calculated, e.g., $(5r + r_i)/6$, where r_i is the crystallographic radius of the central ion. Second, it can be assumed that the radius for the square pyramid is the same as for the octahedron. This is equivalent to excluding solvent from the region vacated by the missing ligand. The difference in the two Born hydration energies calculated with these radii is found to be almost the same as if a water molecule had been added to the coordination sphere to form $Co(NH_3)_5H_2O^{3+}$, for example, from $Co(NH_3)_5^{3+}$.

This is, of course, very reasonable and suggests that the hydration energies of linear and square planar complexes could be found by adding water molecules to complete the octahedral configuration and calculating the Born heat of hydration in the usual way. The potential energy of the original system plus the added water molecules would then be calculated by the electrostatic theory. The distances of the added water molecules from the central ion would be larger than usual, presumably.

Table 11 shows the results of a number of calculations of the bonding energies of complexes presented in terms of the energy required to form

Table 11

Theoretical Energies Required to Change Configurations and Coordination Numbers of Some Complexes

	ΔH; kcal
$Zn(NH_3)_4{}^{2+}$ (g.) + $2NH_3$ (g.) → $Zn(NH_3)_6{}^{2+}$ (g.)	36 [a]
$Zn(NH_3)_4{}^{2+}$ (aq.) + $2NH_3$ (aq.) → $Zn(NH_3)_6{}^{2+}$ (aq.)	52 [a]
$Fe(H_2O)_6{}^{2+}$ (g.) → $Fe(H_2O)_4{}^{2+}$ (g.) + $2H_2O$ (g.)	73 [a]
$Fe(H_2O)_6{}^{2+}$ (aq.) → $Fe(H_2O)_4{}^{2+}$ (aq.) + $2H_2O$ (aq.)	53 [a,b]
$Fe(H_2O)_6{}^{2+}$ (g.) → $Fe(H_2O)_5{}^{2+}$ (g.) + H_2O (g.)	35 [b,c]
$Fe(H_2O)_6{}^{2+}$ (aq.) → $Fe(H_2O_5)^{2+}$ (aq.) + H_2O (aq.)	25 [b,c]
$AlF_6{}^{3-}$ (g.) + F^- (g.) → $AlF_7{}^{4-}$ (g.)	182 [d]
$AlF_6{}^{3-}$ (aq.) + F^- (aq.) → $AlF_7{}^{4-}$ (aq.)	10 [d]
$AlF_6{}^{3-}$ (g.) → $AlF_5{}^{2-}$ (g.) + F^- (g.)	−59 [c]
$AlF_6{}^{3-}$ (aq.) → $AlF_5{}^{2-}$ (aq.) + F^- (aq.)	39 [c]
$Co(NH_3)_6{}^{3+}$ (g.) + NH_3 (g.) → $Co(NH_3)_7{}^{3+}$ (g.)	77 [d,e]
$Co(NH_3)_6{}^{3+}$ (aq.) + NH_3 (aq.) → $Co(NH_3)_7{}^{3+}$ (aq.)	103 [d,e]
$Co(NH_3)_6{}^{3+}$ (g.) → $Co(NH_3)_5{}^{3+}$ (g.) + NH_3 (g.)	131 [c,f]
$Co(NH_3)_6{}^{3+}$ (aq.) → $Co(NH_3)_5{}^{3+}$ (aq.) + NH_3 (aq.)	121 [c,f]
$Co(NH_3)_6{}^{3+}$ (g.) → $Co(NH_3)_5{}^{3+}$ (g.) + NH_3 (g.)	105 [g]
$Co(NH_3)_6{}^{3+}$ (aq.) → $Co(NH_3)_5{}^{3+}$ (aq.) + NH_3 (aq.)	6–94 [g,h]

[a] Tetrahedral for C.N. four.

[b] Loss of 3 kcal crystal field energy included.

[c] Trigonal bipyramid for C.N. five.

[d] Pentagonal bipyramid for C.N. seven.

[e] Loss of 47 kcal crystal field energy included.

[f] Loss of 64 kcal crystal field energy included.

[g] Square pyramid for C.N. five; loss of 22 kcal crystal field energy included.

[h] Higher value goes with assumption in note g. Lower value is calculated for $Co(NH_3)_5H_2O^{3+}$.

certain trial configurations from the stable ones. The energies in solution are always positive, which means that the accepted configurations of these complex ions can be justified in terms of the electrostatic theory.

In the gas phase trigonal AlF_5^{2-} is more stable than octahedral AlF_6^{3-}. In solution this is changed by the greater Born heat of hydration of the triple negative ion.[71] The near stability of AlF_7^{4-} in solution is due to a very large Born heat of hydration (752 kcal) and may be greatly in error since this calculated value is not very reliable.

The energies of the cobalt ammine systems have been considered in detail because of the bearing on the mechanism of substitution reactions in these complexes. The results depend very much on crystal field stabilization energies which favor the octahedral structure. Fairly reliable values for this loss in crystal field energy are available from Table 5 and spectral data. A very considerable loss in C.F.S.E. occurs in going from the octahedral to either a trigonal or pentagonal bipyramid. This is because, if the xy plane is chosen for the pyramid base, there is a disappearance of the energy difference between the d_{xy} and $d_{x^2-y^2}$ orbitals. Also for the square pyramid case, the energy has been calculated in two ways: in one case hydration of the empty position giving $Co(NH_3)_5H_2O^{3+}$ is assumed; in the other case a hole has been left in the sixth position and solvent approach excluded. This is, of course, a very unreal situation, but it puts an upper limit on the energy required to remove one ammine group.

CRITIQUE OF THE THREE THEORIES

In the previous pages we have mentioned the three chief theories, valence bond, molecular orbital, and electrostatic, used to describe coordination compounds currently. Most of the detail was developed for the latter theory, including its refinements such as the crystal field. It is desirable next to give an estimate of the relative usefulness and general merit of each of the three approaches.[1] To begin with, certainly we are dealing in each case with an approximation which cannot be complete. All three approaches have their uses, and one or the other may be most convenient in any one application. All three can account for the main features of complexes, such as coordination numbers, structures, and magnetic properties, in a qualitative way.

When it comes to quantitative calculations, the electrostatic plus crystal field theory is well in the lead. In fact it is difficult to find another theory anywhere in chemistry which is so simple and still gives so many numbers which are almost correct.* Using the same

---

* For a further illustration, it is possible to calculate the vibration frequencies of metal-ligand bond stretching from the electrostatic potential energy function. This

kind of model that successfully calculates the lattice energies of the alkali halides, it is possible to account for 90% or more of the binding energy of water, ammonia and halide complexes after suitable corrections for the splitting of the d orbital energy levels. No directed bonds are formed between the ligands and the central atom.

It is true that polarization, which plays a large part in the electrostatic theory, is similar to covalent bond formation. But it is the classical polarizability as measured by the weak electric fields due to light waves (refractive index measurements) which is used. As the electrons are distorted from the ligand towards the central ion, there is no requirement that there be an atomic orbital present to receive them. Admittedly it is helpful if there is *not* an atomic orbital occupied by electrons in the direction towards which the electrons are distorted. There is also the possibility that weak field polarizabilities are not the correct ones to use for the intense electric fields surrounding a positive ion. This is true but theory indicates that the strong field polarizability is somewhat greater than the weak field value.[73] A more serious problem is the anisotropy of the polarizability of the ligand which is averaged in the case of weak fields but not in strong fields.

Nevertheless there is no real reason to believe that covalent bond formation does not occur to some extent even for complexes with electronegative ligands. The contribution to the energy would seem to be small in such cases, however. In systems in which delocalization energy is important, the electrostatic theory will fail badly. This will most commonly be for complexes in which π bonding occurs, since this is essentially a delocalization method of lowering the energy. For unsaturated ligands in general and ligands which have unfilled d orbitals, such as $P(C_2H_5)_3$, $S(C_2H_5)_2$, and the like, the electrostatic viewpoint must be replaced or supplemented with the molecular orbital or valence bond approach. It is significant that in the metal carbonyls, even though the coordinate bond is believed to be a double bond, the bond energy is rather small compared to even a moderate electrostatic bond.

In connection with the metal carbonyls, the fact that iron carbonyl has a greater bond energy than nickel carbonyl has been used as an ar-

is done by setting the second derivative of U with respect to r equal to k, the force constant, $(\partial^2 U/\partial r^2) = k$. Using the relationship $\nu = \sqrt{k/4\pi^2 m}$, where ν is the frequency and m the reduced mass of the oscillation, one can then calculate infrared and Raman frequencies as far as orders of magnitude are concerned. For typical complexes the result is in the range of 500 cm^{-1}. For a given coordination number, a trivalent ion should have frequencies about 50% greater than for a divalent ion. The predicted value agrees with the magnitude of those reported in the literature for various complexes.[72]

gument that π bonding does not occur in these compounds since nickel with ten electrons and only four bonds to share them over should be more π-bonded than the iron complex with eight electrons and five CO groups to share them.[57a] This conclusion is not warranted, however, because a tetrahedral structure can form only two π bonds of any reasonable strength (with the $d_{x^2-y^2}$ and d_{z^2} orbitals of the metal). A trigonal bipyramid structure, such as $Fe(CO)_5$ has, can form four π bonds (to all d orbitals of the metal except the d_{z^2}). It is of interest that this ratio of four π-bonding orbitals to eight metal atom electrons can account for the coordination number and structure of iron carbonyl. For $Cr(CO)_6$, the structure is that predicted by the crystal field theory for a d^6 system. It is also satisfactory in that three π bonds can be formed in an octahedral complex. For nickel carbonyl with ten d electrons, the choice of the tetrahedral structure can only mean that lack of an empty d orbital limits the coordination number. Hence covalent bonding for even the σ bond is a reality.

The molecular orbital theory, in principle at least, is the most powerful of the three theories. It includes the electrostatic theory as a special case (no mixing of metal orbitals with ligand orbitals) and can be extended to include any degree of covalent bonding, including π bonding. Furthermore, with a reasonable selection of atomic orbitals to begin with, the theory automatically includes all of the interactions which in the valence bond theory would require the inclusion of a large number of resonance forms.

Also the crystal field theory is not an exclusive property of the electrostatic method but can be incorporated into the molecular orbital theory, as was, in fact, done in the discussion. It has been pointed out [19b] that the important requirement in the crystal field theory is that the d orbitals be split into groups of different energies. Qualitatively this splitting is a function only of the symmetry of the five d orbitals and the symmetry of the ligands surrounding the central atom. The result is the same whether the splitting is done by electrostatic fields or by covalent bond formation. The term *ligand field theory* * has been proposed for the combined M.O. and crystal field approach.[24]

The chief defects of the M.O. theory are (1) the usual one of any quantum mechanical approach to complex systems, that quantitative calculations of the energy cannot be made, and (2) the disappearance of the nice pictures of chemically bonded atoms so useful to the chemist.

Thus in the description of the unusual coordination compounds such

---

* This name has also been proposed for all aspects of the crystal field theory when applied to single molecules or ions (reference 45).

as ferrocene,[74] bis(π-cyclopentadienyl)iron(II), and dibenzenechromium(0),[75] the molecular orbital [76] description below (a) is probably more accurate. However, this is much more complicated to visualize or to describe than the valence bond picture (b) of six octahedral bonds formed from the twelve π electrons of two benzene rings to the metal atom. Two resonance structures are needed, of course,

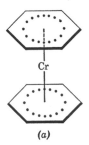
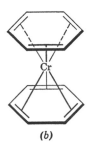

(a)   *(b)*

for the two Kekule structures of benzene. The bonds are assumed to center on the double bonds of the benzene ring. This picture is in poor agreement with the fact that more ligands can be added to the metal in some cases, e.g., $Ti(C_5H_5)_2Cl_2$. The M.O. theory, which binds the aromatic rings to the metal by one bond per ring, can easily allow for the addition of further groups. It is of interest that bis(cyclopentadienyl)magnesium(II) also has the "sandwich" configuration. This compound is usually considered to be ionic because of its lability.[77]

The valence bond theory, in spite of its great service in the development of the theory of coordination compounds, now seems to do the poorest job of the three theories. A number of inconsistencies and failures of the theory will be discussed in detail below but the following generalizations can be made:

1. The theory is limited to qualitative explanations only.

2. It cannot interpret the spectra of complexes.

3. It cannot account for magnetic properties in detail.

4. It cannot give even relative energies of different structures and different coordination numbers.

5. It cannot be extended easily to include splittings of the d energy levels (for the d orbitals not used in forming bonds).

6. The classification, by the magnetic criterion, into ionic and covalent bonds is misleading.

7. Its chief virtues are the chemically satisfying pictorial representations of the bonded atoms and the familiarity and simplicity of its basic rules and tenets.

Under point 1, the same difficulty mentioned for other quantum mechanical methods applies in that actual energies cannot be calculated.* Also there is an even greater scarcity than usual of any quantitative detail in the theory. The only numbers that the theory has to work with are those concerned with the criterion of angular overlap, and these will be shown to be unreliable. Under points 2 and 3, both of the other theories can give considerable information and correlation since the energy levels in the two cases are very similar and of a nature suitable for discussing physical properties. The energy levels in the valence bond theory are not of the same kind and are not suitable for understanding these properties nor for describing the experimental facts.

This holds true not only for the visible and ultraviolet spectra as discussed in Chapter 9 but also for soft x-ray absorption spectra.[78] Thus it has been possible to observe the transition of an electron from a $1s$ orbital to the $4p$ and $4s$ orbitals in a number of complexes of the first transition series upon irradiation with soft x-rays of increasing energy. This would be difficult to account for on the basis of the valence bond theory since the $4s$ and $4p$ orbitals are already occupied by the electrons of the ligands. Evidence that it is indeed the $4p$ orbital which is involved is obtained by comparing the splittings observed in the x-ray absorption spectrum with those calculated from crystal field theory. For a tetragonal complex, such as $Cu(NH_3)_4$ $(H_2O)_2^{2+}$, it can be seen by inspection that the energy of the $4p_x$ or $4p_y$ orbitals should be different from that of the $4p_z$ (the water molecules are assumed to be on the z axis). The energy difference can be calculated by the usual electrostatic crystal field methods and comes out to be of the order of 100 kcal in agreement with experiment. Also the energy required for the $1s \rightarrow 4p$ transition and the difference in energy between the $1s \rightarrow 4s$ and $1s \rightarrow 4p$ transitions are in agreement with expected values as deduced from the spectra of the gaseous zinc(II) ion as a suitable reference.

It is of interest that in the cyanide complex $Co(CN)_6^{3-}$ the transition $1s \rightarrow 4p$ cannot be observed.[79] In the case of $Ni(CN)_4^{2-}$ the observed x-ray spectrum shows only weak $1s \rightarrow 4p$ and strong $1s \rightarrow 5p$ transitions [80] and not the $1s \rightarrow 4s$. These results indicate that two out of the three $4p$ orbitals for nickel and all three $4p$ orbitals for cobalt are already sufficiently occupied by electrons. This may be interpreted as evidence for considerable covalent σ bonding in these cases. Figure 10 shows the experimental x-ray absorption spectrum for the Ni

* See, however, T. L. Allen, *J. Chem. Phys.*, **26**, 1644 (1957).

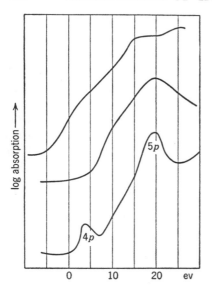

FIG. 10. Soft x-ray absorption curves for nickel metal (top), $Ni(C_5H_5)_2$ (middle), and $K_2[Ni(CN)_4]$ (bottom). (From reference 80.)

$(CN)_4{}^{2-}$ complex, as well as bis(π-cyclopentadienyl)nickel(II), which also shows evidence for the $4p$ orbitals being already occupied.

As an example of the failure of the valence bond theory from an energetic point of view, consider the hydration energies of the transition metal ions. The theory would predict very considerably larger heats of hydration for d^0, d^1, d^2, and d^3 systems since these would form inner orbital complexes even with water ligands (no electron pairing required). Except for cobalt(III), the other hydrates would be less stable since they would be outer orbital or ionic complexes. This is not at all what is found. The hydration energies of d^0, d^1, and d^2 systems are less than those of any of the other ions of a given series. For d^3 a considerable stabilization is found, but this exception is readily accounted for by the crystal field theory.

Also, from the criterion of maximum angular overlap of the wave functions, it is predicted by the valence bond method that octahedral bonds are stronger than tetrahedral bonds by a factor of 2.92 to 2.00. In fact, as shown in Table 4, tetrahedral bonds are stronger than octahedral bonds for positively charged central atoms and electronegative ligands such as $Zn(NH_3)_4{}^{2+}$. This is expected in the electrostatic theory because of the smaller repulsion of four ligands than six.

There is, of course, no definite assurance that an ion such as $Zn(NH_3)_4{}^{2+}$ is tetrahedral in solution since it may be tetragonal with two water molecules occupying octahedral positions. In the solid state zinc(II) does form a hexammine.[81] The complex $HgCl_4^{2-}$ is indicated to be tetrahedral by x-ray studies in aqueous solution.[82] It has a large experimental binding energy of 175 kcal per bond in the gas phase.[83] Even if the assumed structure in solution is incorrect and a linear $HgCl_2$ molecule with two other loosely attached chloride ions is pictured,[84] the valence bond theory is in difficulty. This is because the linear sp hybrid is presumed even weaker than the tetrahedral by 1.93 to 2.00. It may be mentioned that Raman spectra rather definitely prove that $ZnCl_4^{2-}$, as well as $GaCl_4^-$, is tetrahedral in solution.[82b]

If a simple electrostatic calculation of $HgCl_4^{2-}$ is made to obtain the theoretical bond energy, the bonding energy comes out to be only 128 kcal/mole. This is done assuming a tetrahedral structure and a metal-ligand distance of 2.60 A, which is the average Hg-Cl distance in the solid state (the solid consists essentially of a $HgCl_2$ molecule with four chloride ions further away [85]). This calculation illustrates the difficulty of applying the simple theory to a third transition series metal as previously mentioned. On the other hand, to get agreement with experiment it is necessary to use an effective ionic charge, q', of 2.39 instead of 2. There is probably also some π-bond contribution to the total energy (see Chapter 4).

These remarks about the strengths of various bonds are only intended to point out the weakness of the angular overlap rule for bond strengths and not to disprove the existence of covalent bonding in these systems. It has already been shown [86] that a much better criterion of the strength of covalent bonding is the total overlap of the two wave functions, one on each atom, which combine to form the valence bond. That is to say, both the radial and angular parts of the wave function must be included in the calculation and not just the angular part. If this is done,[11] there is very little indicated superiority of an octahedral bond over a tetrahedral one. It may be pointed out also that theoretical calculations of the total overlap integral show that π bonding with d orbitals is quite feasible since the overlap is large for even rather wide variations in the nature of the assumed d wave function.[11] For σ bonding the overlap is uncertain since it is rather sensitive to such parameters as the effective nuclear charge used in the wave function and the principal quantum number of the orbital. For the methide ion as a ligand, it has been calculated that the σ-bond overlap decreases in going from the first, to the second, to the third transition series.[87] A strongly basic ligand such as an alkide ion will tend to form the most covalent bonds with a given central ion. Hence the instability of conventional organometallic compounds of the transition metals can be understood in terms of a reluctance to form covalent σ bonds using d orbitals.[10]

To reconcile the square planar, or the tetragonal, structure of copper(II) complexes with their stability, in the valence bond theory it is necessary to promote one $3d$ electron to the empty $4p$ orbital. This is a process that would require 340 kcal in the gas phase [88] and would presumably still require a goodly fraction of this energy in the complex. Where the energy comes from to balance this is not easily seen. Further, on this basis copper(II) should be exceedingly easy to oxidize to copper(III), contrary to experience. The similar postulation that, in complexes of cobalt(II) involving electron pairing, promotion of an electron to a $5s$ orbital occurs is equally unlikely. In the gaseous state, again, this would take 485 kcal of energy.[88]

It is rather instructive to look at some of the energies required to promote an electron from one orbit in a gaseous metal ion or atom to another. Table 12 shows a small sampling of data taken from reference 88. These are given in terms of the energy required to make the transition from the ground state to the lowest of the indicated excited states. Of interest is the fact that, for a neutral metal atom in the first transition series, it is the $4s$ orbit which is obviously filled first and then the $3d$. However, for ionized atoms, the energy levels begin to be reversed so that for doubly charged cations it is the $3d$ level which is the lowest. Furthermore as the atomic number increases, in going from titanium ion to zinc ion, the separation between the $3d$ and $4s$ increases steadily. Also the $4p$ is always definitely above the $4s$, the separation increasing with increasing ionic charge and also in going across the periodic table. This means that a $3d$ electron in copper(II) is several hundred kcal more stable than a $4p$.

This is for the gaseous ion, however, and it is likely that complex formation reduces the energy separation. That is, addition of electrons from the ligands is similar to reducing the ion back to the neutral metal. The extent to which this occurs is not known. It is estimated that, if the intense absorption shown by all complexes at about 2000 A is partly due to a $d \rightarrow p$ transition, the energy separation has been cut about in half from the free ion value.[89] The $4d$ level lies so far above the $3d$ level in energy that the benefit of using this orbital to permit covalent bond formation in the so-called outer orbital complexes (see p. 40) begins to be very doubtful.

This is particularly so when the extent of participation of even available inner $3d$ orbitals in the formation of most complexes is open to

Table 12

Transition Energies for Some Gaseous Metal Atoms and Ions

Atom or Ion	Level	Energy, cm^{-1}	Atom or Ion	Level	Energy, cm^{-1}
Ti	$3d^24s^2$	0	Fe^{2+}	$3d^6$	0
	$3d^34s^1$	6,556		$3d^54s^1$	30,089
	$3d^24s^14p^1$	15,877		$3d^54p^1$	82,001
	$3d^24s^14d^1$	41,194	Fe^{3+}	$3d^5$	0
Ti^+	$3d^24s^1$	0		$3d^44p^1$	189,893
	$3d^3$	908	Mn^{3+}	$3d^4$	0
	$3d^24d^1$	64,884		$3d^34s^1$	111,502
Ti^{2+}	$3d^2$	0	Cu	$3d^{10}4s^1$	0
	$3d^14s^1$	38,063		$3d^{10}4p^1$	30,535
	$3d^14p^1$	75,197	Cu^+	$3d^{10}$	0
	$3d^14d^1$	129,096		$3d^94s^1$	21,928
Ti^{3+}	$3d^1$	0		$3d^94p^1$	66,418
	$4s^1$	80,378		$3d^95s^1$	108,014
Fe	$3d^64s^2$	0		$3d^94d^1$	115,569
	$3d^74s^1$	6,928	Cu^{2+}	$3d^9$	0
	$3d^64s^14p^1$	19,350		$3d^84s^1$	60,804
Fe^+	$3d^64s^1$	0		$3d^84p^1$	118,864
	$3d^7$	7,955		$3d^85s^1$	193,369
				$3d^84d^1$	193,519

1000 cm^{-1} equals 2.86 kcal.

debate.   It will be recalled that the crystal field theory ignored this possibility.   If the premise is adopted that the forces holding complexes of at least electronegative ligands and cations together are chiefly electrostatic, then the exact importance of covalent bonding becomes difficult to assess.[90]   For example recent infrared studies [91] of complexes of carboxylic acid anions reveal that the C=O stretching frequency of

$$\overset{\text{O}}{\overset{\|}{\text{the group C—O—M}}}$$

the group C—O—M, where M is a cation, is rather close to that for the free carboxylate ion and much further from that of a relatively covalent

$$\overset{\text{O}}{\overset{\|}{\text{carboxyl group, C—OH,}}} \qquad \overset{\text{O}}{\overset{\|}{\text{or an ester group, C—OCH}_3.}}$$

carboxyl group, C—OH, or an ester group, C—OCH$_3$.   Hence the bond between the metal ion and the carboxylate ion is ionic. This is true even when M is a species like cobalt(III), in which magnetic evidence tells us that the bond would be called covalent according to the valence bond theory. However, the exact frequencies, to cite one case, of 1745 cm^{-1} for the carboxyl, 1604 cm^{-1} for the free carboxylate, and 1650 cm^{-1} for the metal-carboxylate group do not allow any per cent of ionic character to be assigned. Intense electrostatic interactions as well as covalent bonding certainly affect the frequencies.

In the event that the covalent contribution to the bonding is small, a theory which puts prime emphasis on the providing of suitable orbitals for covalent bond formation is likely to prove a poor guide. In such a case it is not necessary to have one orbital for each partially covalent bond to be formed. A three-center bond [92] may be formed, for example, in which a single p_x orbital on the central atom can be used to provide room for delocalizing the ligand electrons on both the $+x$ and $-x$ axes. This would correspond, in the valence bond method, to resonance between L—M L^- and L^- M—L and becomes similar to Pauling's original suggestion concerning ionic bonds.

In the molecular orbital theory such a three-center bond has as solutions to the simple L.C.A.O. (linear combination of atomic orbitals) approximation, two wave functions of low energy. The most stable of these is centered on all three nuclei (M, L, and L) and the other centered only on L and L. Putting the four ligand electrons into these two orbitals would correspond to two L—M bonds which are very polar with the negative charge piled up on the ligands, but which still have considerable delocalization energy.

It is important also to remember that the degree of ionic character in a bond depends on differences in electronegativity of the bonded atoms. Taking as a measure of electronegativity the effective ionic potential, q'/r, for an ion, it can be seen that ions of large charge and small size will be in a much better position to compete with an electronegative ligand for the electrons of the coordinate bond. Hence covalent bonding will be more pronounced in such cases as SF_6, CrO_4^{2-}, MnO_4^-, $GeCl_4$, $PtCl_6^{2-}$, etc.

One final point worth commenting on is a recent demonstration [93] that in the square pyramid complex bis (N,N-dimethyldithiocarbamato)-nitrosylcobalt(III), $Co(S_2CNMe_2)_2NO$, the cobalt atom lies slightly above the square plane containing the four sulfur atoms. The sulfur-cobalt-nitric oxide bond angle is 104.5° instead of the 90° expected for a true square pyramid. The point of interest is that such a distorted structure is predicted by quantum mechanical arguments.[94]

The procedure is to consider that there are five unpaired electrons occupying initially an s, three p, and one d hydrogenic orbitals. A determinantal form of the total wave function for the system satisfying the Pauli exclusion principle is then constructed, and the positions of maximum electron density are found. They correspond in this case to the five positions defining a trigonal bipyramid. However, another set only slightly less favorable can be found which corresponds almost exactly to the structure determined for the cobalt compound mentioned earlier.

This method of finding positions of maximum probability for various groups of electrons will predict nearly all of the common geometries found for various coordination numbers.[94, 95] However, it turns out that the use of simple electrostatic repulsion of the electrons will predict exactly the same structures as we have already seen. Even in the case of the square pyramid it is clear that repulsion of the four planar ligands for the one above the plane will tend to distort the system in the direction that is observed (this means that some of our energy calculations based on the more regular structure are slightly in error, the calculated bonding energy not being quite large enough). Thus the same result ensues whether we imagine that electrons repel each other because of coulomb forces or because of the operation of the Pauli principle.

REFERENCES

1. J. H. Van Vleck, *J. Chem. Phys.*, **3**, 803, 807 (1935).
2. For solids, see a discussion on lattice energies such as that by M. L. Huggins, *ibid.*, **5**, 143 (1937). For vapors, see E. J. W. Verwey and J. H. DeBoer, *Rec. trav. chim.*, **55**, 431 (1936); E. S. Rittner, *J. Chem. Phys.*, **19**, 1030 (1951).
3. (a) H. Eyring, J. Walter, and G. E. Kimball, *Quantum Chemistry*, John Wiley & Sons, New York, 1944, p. 207. (b) R. G. Pearson, *J. Chem. Phys.*, **17**, 969 (1949).
4. For a fuller discussion see C. A. Coulson, *Valence,* Oxford University Press, London, 1952, Chapter II.
5. For a review see R. S. Nyholm, *Revs. Pure and Appl. Chem.*, **4**, 15 (1954).
6. L. Pauling, *The Nature of the Chemical Bond,* Cornell University Press, Ithaca, 1940, Chapter III.
7. *Ibid.,* Chapter VII.
8. J. Chatt and A. A. Williams, *J. Chem. Soc.*, **1952**, 3061; J. Chatt and R. G. Wilkins, *ibid.*, p. 273; see also W. Hieber, R. Nast, and J. G. Floss, *Z. anorg. u. allgem. Chem.*, **283**, 188 (1956).
9. R. S. Nyholm and L. N. Short, *J. Chem. Soc.*, **1953**, 2670.
10. H. H. Jaffe and G. O. Doak, *J. Chem. Phys.*, **21**, 196 (1953); **22**, 1462 (1954); H. H. Jaffe, *J. Phys. Chem.*, **58**, 185 (1954).

11. D. P. Craig, A. Maccoll, R. S. Nyholm, L. E. Orgel, and L. E. Sutton, *J. Chem. Soc.*, **1954**, 332; H. H. Jaffe, *J. Chem. Phys.*, **21**, 156, 258 (1953).
12. S. Sugden, *J. Chem. Soc.*, **1943**, 328.
13. H. Taube, *Chem. Revs.*, **50**, 69 (1952).
14. (a) H. F. Burstall and R. S. Nyholm, *J. Chem. Soc.*, **1952**, 3570. (b) W. Biltz, *Z. anorg. allgem. Chem.*, **164**, 245 (1927).
15. R. J. P. Williams, *J. Chem. Soc.*, **1956**, 8.
16. See p. 227 of reference 3a and K. W. H. Stevens, *Proc. Roy. Soc. London*, **A219**, 542 (1953).
17. L. E. Orgel, *J. Chem. Phys.*, **23**, 1819 (1955).
18. (a) J. S. Griffith, *J. Inorg. Nuclear Chem.*, **2**, 1, 229 (1956). (b) J. Owen, *Proc. Roy. Soc. London*, **A227**, 183 (1955).
19. (a) C. J. Ballhausen and C. Klixbüll Jørgensen, *Kgl. Danske Videnskab. Selskab Mat. fys. Medd.*, **29** (No. 14), (1955). (b) L. E. Orgel, *J. Chem. Phys.*, **23**, 1004 (1955).
20. R. Tsuchida, *Bull. Chem. Soc. Japan*, **13**, 388, 435, 471 (1938).
21. R. S. Nyholm, *Quart. Revs. London*, **7**, 377 (1953).
22. J. H. E. Griffiths and J. Owen, *Proc. Roy. Soc. London*, **A226**, 96 (1954).
23. D. J. E. Ingram, J. E. Bennett, P. George, and J. M. Goldstein, *J. Am. Chem. Soc.*, **78**, 3545 (1956).
24. P. George, D. S. McClure, J. S. Griffith, and L. E. Orgel, *J. Chem. Phys.*, **24**, 1269 (1956).
25. A. E. Van Arkel and J. H. DeBoer, *Rec. trav. chim.*, **47**, 593 (1928); *ibid.*, *Die Chemische Bindung als elektrostatische Erscheinung*, Leipzig, 1931.
26. F. J. Garrick, *Phil. Mag.*, (a) **9**, 131 (1930); (b) **10**, 71, 76 (1930); (c) **11**, 741 (1931); (d) **14**, 914 (1932).
27. W. Klemm and E. Huss, *Z. anorg. Chem.*, **258**, 221 (1949).
28. V. M. Goldschmidt, *Skrifter Norske Videnskaps-Akad. Oslo*, **8**, 69 (1926); *Ber.*, **60**, 1263 (1927).
29. J. Morgan and B. E. Warren, *J. Chem. Phys.*, **6**, 670 (1938).
30. R. W. G. Wyckoff, *Crystal Structures*, Interscience Publishers, New York, Vols. I–III, 1951–1953.
31. L. Pauling, *op. cit.*, Chapter V.
32. J. E. Lennard-Jones, *Proc. Roy. Soc. London*, **A106**, 463 (1924); J. O. Hirschfelder, F. T. McClure, and I. F. Weeks, *J. Chem. Phys.*, **10**, 201 (1942).
33. A. Duncan and J. Pople, *Trans. Faraday Soc.*, **49**, 217 (1953); the model used by W. H. Kleiner, *J. Chem. Phys.*, **20**, 1784 (1952), is not a very good one since the lone pairs of electrons on oxygen are not in a position to attract the central ion strongly.
34. H. L. Friedman, J. P. Hunt, and H. Taube, *J. Chem. Phys.*, **18**, 759 (1950).
35. H. Bethe, *Ann. Physik*, [5] **3**, 133 (1929).
36. R. Schlapp and W. G. Penney, *Phys. Rev.*, **42**, 666 (1932).
37. J. H. Van Vleck, *Theory of Electric and Magnetic Susceptibilities*, Oxford University Press, London, 1932; for a recent review of the crystal field theory, see B. Bleaney and W. K. Stevens, *Repts. Progr. in Phys.*, **16**, 108 (1953).
38. (a) L. E. Orgel, *J. Chem. Soc.*, **1952**, 4756. (b) J. Bjerrum and C. Klixbüll Jørgensen, *Acta Chem. Scand.*, **9**, 180 (1955).
39. F. E. Ilse and H. Hartmann, *Z. physik. Chem.*, **197**, 239 (1951).
40. J. C. Slater, *Phys. Rev.*, **36**, 67 (1930).

41. Page 96 of reference 3a.
42. (a) J. H. Van Vleck, *J. Chem. Phys.*, **7**, 72 (1939). (b) D. Polder, *Physica*, **9**, 709 (1942).
43. Reference 19a and also C. J. Ballhausen, *Kgl. Danske Videnskab. Selskab Mat. fys. Medd.*, **29** (No. 4) (1954).
44. C. J. Ballhausen, private communication.
45. L. E. Orgel, Tenth Solvay Conference, Brussels, May, 1956.
46. J. H. Van Vleck, *J. Chem. Phys.*, **7**, 61, 72 (1939).
47. N. V. Sidgwick, *Chemical Elements and Their Compounds,* Oxford University Press, London, 1950, p. 156ff; S. Kirschner, *J. Am. Chem. Soc.*, **78**, 2372 (1945); H. Scoulondi, *Acta Cryst.*, **6**, 651 (1953); J. Bjerrum, C. J. Ballhausen, and C. Klixbüll Jørgensen, *Acta Chem. Scand.*, **8**, 1275 (1954).
48. (a) R. S. Nyholm, Tenth Solvay Conference, Brussels, May, 1956. (b) R. S. Nyholm, E. M. Harris, and N. C. Stephenson, *Rec. trav. chim.*, **75** (1956).
49. K. A. Jensen and B. Nygaard, *Acta Chem. Scand.*, **3**, 474 (1949).
50. (a) The evidence for the tetrahedral structure is reviewed by R. S. Nyholm, *Chem. Revs.*, **53**, 263 (1953), and also (b) C. J. Ballhausen, *Rec. trav. chim.*, **75**, 665 (1956).
51. G. J. Bullen, *Nature*, **177**, 537 (1956). For metal-metal bonding in the solid state between square planar complexes, see R. E. Rundle, *J. Am. Chem. Soc.*, **76**, 3101 (1954); S. Yamada and R. Tsuchida, *Bull. Chem. Soc. Japan*, **29**, 421 (1956).
52. Quantitative data on both Co(III) and Cr(III) complexes of the same kind are scarce. D. Banerjea, N. N. Ghosh, and P. Rây, *J. Indian Chem. Soc.*, **29**, 157 (1952), have shown that, for the first two stages of dissociation of the trisbiguanide complexes, cobalt is more stable than chromium by 6 kcal of free energy.
53. D. Sen, P. Rây, and N. N. Ghosh, *J. Indian Chem. Soc.*, **27**, 619 (1950).
54. H. C. Brown, H. Bartholomay, and M. D. Taylor, *J. Am. Chem. Soc.*, **66**, 435 (1944).
55. G. Briegleb, *Naturwissenschaften*, **28**, 436, 469 (1942); *Z. Elektrochem.*, **53**, 350 (1949).
56. A. P. Altshuller, *J. Am. Chem. Soc.*, **77**, 3480 (1955).
57. (a) F. T. King and E. R. Lippincott, *J. Am. Chem. Soc.*, **78**, 4192 (1956), and also (b) J. W. Cable and R. K. Sheline, *Chem. Revs.*, **56**, 1 (1956), and F. A. Cotton, A. K. Fischer, and G. Wilkinson, *J. Am. Chem. Soc.*, **78**, 5168 (1956).
58. E. J. W. Verwey, *Rec. trav. chim.*, **61**, 127 (1942).
59. M. Born, *Z. Physik*, **1**, 45 (1920).
60. Data taken from (a) L. Brewer, L. A. Bromley, P. W. Gilles, and N. L. Lofgren, *Chemistry and Metallurgy of Miscellaneous Materials,* edited by L. L. Quill, McGraw-Hill Book Co., New York, 1950, p. 165ff. (b) See also K. B. Yatsimirskii, *J. Gen. Chem. U.S.S.R.*, **17**, 169 (1947).
61. J. W. van Santen and J. S. van Wieringen, *Rec. trav. chim.*, **71**, 420 (1952).
62. K. B. Yatsimirskii and N. Astasheva, *Zhur. Obshchei Khim.*, **20**, 2139 (1950); K. B. Yatsimirskii, *Doklady Akad. Nauk S.S.S.R.*, **72**, 307 (1950); see also L. I. Katzin and J. R. Ferraro, *J. Am. Chem. Soc.*, **74**, 6040 (1954).
63. (a) C. G. Spike and R. W. Parry, *J. Am. Chem. Soc.*, **75**, 2726, 3770 (1953). (b) T. Davies, S. S. Singer, and L. A. K. Staveley, *J. Chem. Soc.*, **1954**, 2304, (c) I. Poulsen and J. Bjerrum, *Acta Chem. Scand.*, **9**, 1407 (1955).

64. J. G. Kirkwood, *J. Chem. Phys.*, **2**, 351 (1934).
65. H. Irving and R. J. P. Williams, *J. Chem. Soc.*, **1953**, 3192.
66. J. Bjerrum and C. Klixbüll Jørgensen, *Rec. trav. chim.*, **75**, 658 (1956).
67. D. S. McClure, private communication.
68. J. E. Mayer, *J. Chem. Phys.*, **1**, 327 (1933); J. E. Mayer and R. B. Levy, *ibid.*, p. 647.
69. See any standard text on electrostatics.
70. D. P. Craig and E. A. Magnusson, *J. Chem. Soc.*, **1956**, 4895.
71. Garrick (reference 26d) calculated AlF_6^{3-} in solution to be 30 kcal more stable than AlF_5^{2-} and 150 kcal more stable than AlF_8^{5-}.
72. G. M. Barrow, R. H. Krueger, and F. Basolo, *J. Inorg. and Nuclear Chem.*, **2**, 340 (1956); D. B. Powell and N. Sheppard, *J. Chem. Soc.*, **1956**, 3108.
73. L. E. Sutton, C. A. Coulson, and A. Maccoll, *Trans. Faraday Soc.*, **48**, 106 (1952).
74. For a review, see P. L. Pauson, *Quart. Revs. London*, **9**, 391 (1955).
75. E. O. Fischer and W. Pfab, *Z. Naturforschung*, **7B**, 377 (1952); E. O. Fischer and W. Hafner, *ibid.*, **10B**, 665 (1955).
76. W. Moffitt, *J. Am. Chem. Soc.*, **76**, 3386 (1954); J. D. Dunitz and L. E. Orgel, *J. Chem. Phys.*, **23**, 954 (1955); E. Ruch and E. O. Fischer, *Z. Naturforsch.*, **7B**, 676 (1952).
77. F. A. Cotton and T. L. Reynolds, *J. Am. Chem. Soc.*, **80**, 269 (1958).
78. G. Mitchell and W. W. Beeman, *J. Chem. Phys.*, **20**, 1298 (1952); F. A. Cotton and C. J. Ballhausen, *ibid.*, **25**, 617 (1956); F. A. Cotton and H. P. Hanson, *ibid.*, p. 619.
79. Y. Cauchois, quoted in reference 48a; *J. chim. phys.*, **51**, 76 (1954).
80. E. O. Fischer, *Angew. Chem.*, **67**, 475 (1955).
81. W. Biltz, *Z. anorg. u. allgem. Chem.*, **130**, 93 (1923).
82. (a) C. L. V. P. van Eck, H. B. M. Wolters, and W. J. M. Jaspers, *Rec. trav. chim.*, **75**, 802 (1956); (b) L. A. Woodward and A. A. Nord, *J. Chem. Soc.*, **1956**, 3721.
83. J. A. V. Butler, *Electrocapillarity*, Methuen, London, 1940, p. 54.
84. L. G. Sillen, *Acta Chem. Scand.*, **3**, 539 (1949).
85. A. F. Wells, *Structural Inorganic Chemistry*, Oxford Press, London, 1945, p. 514.
86. R. S. Mulliken, *J. Phys. Chem.*, **56**, 295 (1952).
87. H. H. Jaffe, *J. Chem. Phys.*, **22**, 1462 (1954).
88. C. E. Moore, "Atomic Energy Levels," *Nat. Bur. Standards U. S. Cir.* 467, 1949 and 1952.
89. A. D. Liehr and C. J. Ballhausen, *Phys. Rev.*, **106**, 1161 (1957).
90. See C. H. Townes and B. P. Dailey, *J. Chem. Phys.*, **23**, 118 (1955), and W. Gordy, *Discussions Faraday Soc.*, **19**, 14 (1955), for relationships between per cent ionic character in a bond and other properties.
91. D. N. Sen, S. Mizushima, C. Curran, and J. V. Quagliano, *J. Am. Chem. Soc.*, **77**, 211 (1955); M. L. Morris and D. H. Busch, *ibid.*, **78**, 5178 (1956).
92. R. E. Rundle, *ibid.*, **69**, 1327 (1947); C. A. Coulson and G. R. Lester, *J. Chem. Soc.*, **1956**, 3650.
93. P. R. H. Alderman and P. G. Owston, *Nature*, **178**, 1071 (1956).
94. C. E. Mellish and J. W. Linnett, *Trans. Faraday Soc.*, **50**, 657, 665 (1954).
95. H. K. Zimmerman, Jr., and P. Van Rysselberghe, *J. Chem. Phys.*, **17**, 598 (1949).

Substitution reactions
of octahedral complexes

THE NATURE OF SUBSTITUTION REACTIONS

In any attempt to cover the reactions of coordination compounds in a systematic manner, classification into types of reaction is necessary. We have divided these reactions into three main categories: substitution reactions, electron transfer or oxidation-reduction reactions, and isomerization and racemization reactions. The latter are usually only special cases of substitution reactions, but it is convenient to discuss them separately.

Substitution reactions include the replacement of one ligand by another in a complex, or one metal ion by another. Following the very convenient terminology developed by Hughes and Ingold in describing organic reactions, these can be called S_N and S_E reactions respectively.[1] The terms refer to *nucleophilic substitution* and *electrophilic substitu-*

$$Y + M—X \rightarrow M—Y + X \qquad S_N \qquad (1a)$$

$$M' + M—X \rightarrow M'—X + M \qquad S_E \qquad (1b)$$

tion. A *nucleophilic reagent* is one which donates electrons to an atomic nucleus in a reaction. An *electrophilic reagent* is one which acquires electrons from a nucleophilic reagent. In coordination chemistry, the central atom is an electrophilic reagent and the ligands are nucleophilic reagents.

The strict definition makes all reducing agents also nucleophilic reagents and all oxidizing agents electrophilic. This usage, however, has not been fruitful, and the terms in practice are restricted to reagents which react by partial transfer and acceptance of a pair of electrons. With this restriction the terms become nearly synonomous with base and acid respectively in the broadest meaning of these latter terms: the definition given by G. N. Lewis.[2]

The newer terms have an added meaning in that they are used to describe kinetic processes and not equilibrium situations. Thus a good nucleophilic reagent is one which reacts rapidly with electrophilic reagents.[3] It may or may not be a strong base. Certain reagents such as thiourea and iodide ion may be excellent nucleophilic reagents in that they react rapidly, even though the stability of the compounds formed by them may be less than for other, more basic, reagents.

The terms base and acid refer more to thermodynamic properties in that a good base or a good acid forms a stable product. It must not be inferred, however, that a single scale of basicity, such as that relative to hydrogen ion in aqueous solution, will be valid for all of the generalized acids with which a series of bases will react. Edwards[4] has proposed a two-parameter equation which correlates a large amount of kinetic and thermodynamic data for reactions of both organic and inorganic systems.

$$\log (k/k_0) = \alpha E + \beta H \qquad (2)$$

In this equation (k/k_0) is a rate or equilibrium constant relative to that of water, E is a nucleophilic constant characteristic of the base, and H is the logarithm of the ordinary base constant relative to water $(H = pK_a + 1.74)$.

The coefficients α and β must be determined for each type reaction. For rate constants in organic reactions α is large and β small, for complex ion formation constants involving a small, highly charged central cation, α is small and β is large. Table 1 lists a number of values for E and H for nucleophilic reagents. It is of considerable interest that the E values are calculated, when possible, from the standard electrode potential of the reaction $(E = E^0 + 2.60)$.

$$2X^- \rightleftharpoons X_2 + 2e \qquad (3)$$

Not too much confidence can be placed in some of the values of E, however, since in some cases they have been evaluated only from the data of a single reaction. Also the applicability of these constants in estimating rates of reaction of metal ion complexes must not be taken as established. Correlation with available rate data will be discussed in later sections.

From what has been said it is clear that substitution reactions involve the fundamental acid-base reaction

$$A + :B \rightleftharpoons A:B \qquad (4)$$

Table 1

Electron Donor Constants

Donor	E	H
F^-	-0.27	4.90
H_2O	0.00	0.00
NO_3^-	0.29	(0.40)
Picrate	0.50	2.0
SO_4^{2-}	0.59	3.74
$ClCH_2COO^-$	0.79	4.54
CH_3COO^-	0.95	6.46
Pyridine	1.20	7.04
Cl^-	1.24	(-3.00)
HCO_3^-	1.46	9.37
HPO_4^{2-}	1.46	8.53
$C_6H_5O^-$	1.46	11.74
Br^-	1.51	(-6.00)
N_3^-	1.58	6.46
OH^-	1.65	17.48
NO_2^-	1.73	5.09
Aniline	1.78	6.28
SCN^-	1.83	(1.00)
NH_3	1.84	11.22
CN^-	2.04	10.88
I^-	2.06	(-9.00)
SH^-	2.10	9.50
Thiourea	2.18	0.80
$S_2O_3^{2-}$	2.52	3.60
SO_3^{2-}	2.57	9.00
S^{2-}	3.08	14.66

Data taken from references 3 and 4, except those for CN^-, which are from E. M. Kosower, *J. Am. Chem. Soc.*, **78**, 3497 (1956). Values of H in parentheses are estimated.

The forward reaction of 4 is called coordination, and the reverse reaction *heterolytic or ionic dissociation*. The second method of breaking a chemical bond is called *homolytic or free radical dissociation:*

$$A : B \rightleftharpoons A \cdot + B \cdot \tag{5}$$

Such a process is characteristic of some oxidation-reduction reactions (atom or group transfer). The reverse of reaction 5 is called *colligation.*

Mechanistically a substitution reaction is more complicated than is shown in equation 4. There are at least two fundamentally different pathways that can be conceived. These are the *displacement* and *dissociation mechanisms* called S_N2 (or S_E2) and S_N1 (or S_E1) by Hughes and Ingold. An S_N2 reaction is one involving a bimolecular rate-determining step in which one nucleophilic reagent displaces another

$$Y + M—X \rightarrow Y\text{---}M\text{---}X \rightarrow Y—M + X \qquad (6)$$

An S_E2 reaction would have one electrophilic reagent displacing another, the transition state being $M\text{---}X\text{---}M'$.* In these bimolecular processes the coordination number of the metal ion or of the ligand increases by one in the transition state. There is presumably a fairly definite stereochemical orientation of all of the groups concerned.

An S_N1 or S_E1 reaction goes by a two-step mechanism in which the first step is a slow unimolecular heterolytic dissociation

$$M—X \rightleftharpoons M + X \qquad (7)$$

followed by a rapid coordination reaction of either M or X with a second reagent

$$M + Y \rightarrow M—Y \qquad (8)$$

$$X + M' \rightarrow M'—X \qquad (9)$$

In this sequence the coordination numbers of both the ligand and the metal ion decrease by one in the rate-determining step. Furthermore there exists as an intermediate the metal ion of reduced coordination number.

It is not correct to assume that a bimolecular reaction will show second-order kinetics and a unimolecular reaction first-order kinetics.[5] This may or may not be the case depending on the relative concentrations, the experimental conditions, and the complexities of the overall mechanism. Hence the observed kinetics of a substitution reaction rarely give the mechanism unambiguously.[6] The problem of deciding from kinetics and other data what the probable mechanism is will be the subject of large sections of the pages to follow.

The detection in some manner of the intermediate of reduced coordination number is the best diagnosis of the S_N1 or S_E1 mechanism.

---

* A reaction may be simultaneously S_N2 and S_E2 in that X is both pushed away and pulled away from M. If the influence of the solvent on stabilizing X as it is liberated is considered, all reactions are S_E2. We shall not adhere to this point of view, however, and we consider only the cases where M' is another potential central atom of a coordination compound.

The view may be taken that, from an operational standpoint, unless such an intermediate can be demonstrated, the reaction is automatically to be considered S_N2 or S_E2. However, this approach can be misleading because the intermediate may be of such a nature as to escape detection even by the most refined means. For example, by its very nature it may be extremely short-lived, not enduring beyond the first collision with a potential ligand.

In such a case it seems reasonable to establish other criteria for a displacement mechanism. In an S_N2 reaction, for example, the rate of substitution should be dependent on the nucleophilic character of the incoming ligand Y in equation 6. In an S_E2 reaction the rate should be dependent on the electrophilic character of the incoming metal ion, M′. If a dependence is found on the nature of the reagent, then it must also follow that a dependence on the concentration of the reagent must exist. This may not be true for all ranges of concentration, however.

Another criterion of mechanism that has been widely used is that of stereochemistry. It can be seen that the S_N2 and S_N1 paths may give rise to quite different stereochemical results. However, it is not necessary that they do this, nor can the expected stereochemistry in each case be predicted beforehand without further assumptions. As a rough guide, it is common to believe that S_N2 reactions will be more stereospecific than S_N1 reactions. This follows by analogy with organic chemistry, and its validity for reactions of coordination compounds will be examined later.

Other mechanistic criteria include the effect on the rate of structural changes in M—X, including changes in M, X, and in the other groups attached to M, and the effect on the rate of changes in the reaction medium. This last includes changes in solvent and added components in the solvent such as ionic species. It might also include catalytic materials present in small amount. Finally, reference will often be made to the use of isotopic labeling to determine specific pieces of information about the reaction mechanism.

It must always be borne in mind that, no matter how much evidence can be supplied which supports a particular reaction mechanism, it can never be said to prove it. The reason for this is that mechanisms, particularly detailed stereochemical mechanisms, are essentially theories and as such are not capable of proof. Like other theories, mechanisms should be capable of expansion and revision to include new experimental facts. A choice between alternative mechanisms is usually made on the basis of the simplest one that accommodates all of the facts.

One of the great complicating factors in assigning mechanisms to substitution reactions is the existence of borderline or intermediate mechanisms between S_N1 and S_N2.[7] That is, an assignment made on the basis of pure S_N1 and pure S_N2 reactions is one that is possible only sometimes in practice. Frequently reactions occur by a mechanism which is intermediate between the two extremes. This does not mean a reaction proceeding by a mixture of S_N1 and S_N2 steps, which might occur also, but one in which the extent of participation by the external reagent Y (or M′) is small. Thus Y, which may be the solvent, is in the transition state but at such a distance from M that its influence on the energetics of the system is small. In such a case it becomes experimentally impossible in most instances to tell the difference between an S_N2 reaction and an S_N1 reaction (Y completely absent).

A recent suggestion has been made to subdivide organic substitution reactions into three classes: [8] S_N1, in which the rate-determining step involves only bond breaking as in the M—X bond; S_N2, in which the rate step involves about equal bond breaking in M—X and bond making in Y—M; S_N2 (lim) in which the rate step involves only bond making as in Y—M. The last category is believed to be involved in the hydrolysis of systems such as some esters, amides, anhydrides, and acid halides. Such a classification of reaction types may prove useful in inorganic chemistry as well. A further subdivision of the unimolecular reactions into S_N1 (lim) and S_N1 may also be of value. The definition of an S_N1 (lim) *mechanism* to be used here will be one in which definite evidence for the existence of the intermediate of reduced coordination number can be found. An S_N1 mechanism will mean one in which such evidence cannot be presented but which otherwise satisfies the requirements of a dissociation mechanism and fails the requirements of a displacement mechanism. It is recognized that examples in which Y exists in the activated complex for the reaction, but interacting only weakly, will also be counted as S_N1 by this definition. These classifications are shown schematically in Table 2.

THEORETICAL APPROACH TO SUBSTITUTION MECHANISMS

According to the transition state theory of reaction rates,[9] we can make a good estimate of the speed with which a chemical reaction occurs by knowing something about the properties of the activated complex. The *activated complex* consists of the aggregate of several reactant molecules in the configuration of highest potential energy, that is, in the act of passing over the activation energy barrier for the

Table 2

Classification of Nucleophilic Substitution Reactions

S_N1 (lim)	S_N1	S_N2	S_N2 (lim)
	Degree of Bond Breaking in Rate Step		
Large	large	appreciable	none
	Degree of Bond Making in Rate Step		
None	none to small	appreciable	·large
	Evidence for Intermediate of Reduced C.N.		
Definite	indefinite	none	none
	Evidence for Intermediate of Expanded C.N.		
None	none	indefinite	definite

reaction. The region at the top of such an energy barrier is called a *transition state* and the activated complex is in the transition state. The less the energy required to form the activated complex, the faster the reaction will proceed as a rule, though special non-energy factors can sometimes slow down a reaction. The entropy of activation, $\Delta S^\ddagger$, which is the difference in entropy between the activated complex and the reactants, is such a factor.

The implication is that, if we can estimate the total potential energy of the activated complex for several possible mechanisms, a choice may be made between them as to which is most probable. Such calculations can be made in a few cases (for symmetrical systems) using the electrostatic method developed in the last chapter. In fact Table 6 in that chapter has several results that may be used. Consider an exchange reaction of the ligand in a symmetrical complex such as Co-$(NH_3)_6{}^{3+}$. The transition state for an S_N2 mechanism may resemble the pentagonal bipyramid containing five ammonia molecules symmetrically placed in a plane and two other molecules above and below this plane. This is, of course, not the only possible structure for a seven-coordinated system. Another plausible arrangement would have the seventh group attached to one of the octahedral faces of a hypothetical C.N. six progenitor. If the seventh group is on one of the back faces of the octahedron, then it is not easy to visualize how such an arrangement can lead to a net reaction. However, if it adds to a front face, a reasonable transition state would be formed in which the group being displaced also moves down to the front face diagonal to the entering group. This movement is required because the principle of microscopic reversibility (see p. 239) demands that the incoming group and the leaving group occupy identical positions within the activated complex.

At any rate the energy calculated for the pentagonal bipyramid gives some idea of the stability of a possible intermediate for the S_N2 path. In a similar way the energy of a five-coordinated species such as $Co(NH_3)_5^{3+}$ gives an idea of the possibility of an S_N1 mechanism since its energy of formation from $Co(NH_3)_6^{3+}$ is the minimum activation energy for the S_N1 (lim) process in which the intermediate of C.N. five becomes completely free. The data of Table 11 (Chapter 2) predict, then, activation energies in solution of 103 kcal for the S_N2 mechanism, 121 kcal for the S_N1 mechanism with a trigonal bipyramid structure, and 6–94 kcal for the S_N1 mechanism with a square pyramid structure. The last figure represents limits for the extreme cases where the vacated position in the coordination sphere is occupied by solvent and where it is left completely vacant (solvent excluded).

Now the exchange reaction of $Co(NH_3)_6^{3+}$ with NH_3 is very slow and is not observed unless a heterogeneous catalyst is added (see p. 356). However, the exchange of water with the solvent in $Co(NH_3)_5H_2O^{3+}$ has been studied.[10] It has a half-life of about one day at room temperature and an activation energy of 27 kcal.[11] From the difference in heats of formation of $Co(NH_3)_6^{3+}$ and $Co(NH_3)_5H_2O^{3+}$ it can immediately be computed that about 7 kcal more would be required to dissociate an ammonia ligand than a water ligand to form the same five-coordinated species. Thus a reasonable value for the activation energy for NH_3 exchange is 34 kcal. Only one of the theoretical values quoted above lies near this figure.

Thus it appears that the most favorable path is one involving an S_N1 mechanism with a square pyramid structure for the intermediate. It must, however, be a solvated square pyramid to reduce the activation energy to a reasonable figure, and, as previously stated in Chapter 2, the intermediate in this case becomes difficult to distinguish from $Co(NH_3)_5H_2O^{3+}$. The conclusion is that ligand exchange of $Co(NH_3)_6^{3+}$ would proceed by loss of an NH_3 molecule in a dissociation step, followed by instantaneous pickup of a water molecule. The water molecule in turn would be lost in a dissociation process to be replaced by another water, and this is also lost, until finally an NH_3 molecule from the solution would become coordinated. At this stage exchange would have occurred.

In such a case the energy difference between $Co(NH_3)_6^{3+}$ and

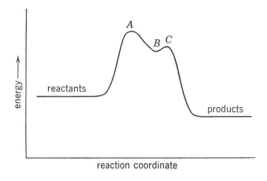

FIG. 1. Potential energy diagram for a chemical reaction showing location of activated complexes (at A and C) and of transient intermediate (at B).

$Co(NH_3)_5H_2O^{3+}$ (6–7 kcal) is not the activation energy for exchange since the latter compound is not an activated complex but an intermediate of some stability. An activated complex is a species that exists at a maximum in a potential energy diagram. An intermediate is a species that exists at a minimum in the potential energy diagram. Figure 1 shows the distinction between the two. The shallowness of the minimum determines the reactivity of the intermediate. To calculate the activation energy it is necessary to consider the stage of transition between $Co(NH_3)_6^{3+}$ and $Co(NH_3)_5H_2O^{3+}$ which is the hardest to achieve and hence highest on the energy curve.

The easiest way in which this could happen would be by an ammonia molecule beginning to dissociate by a lengthening of its coordinate bond distance, and then by a water molecule entering in alongside of it when the bond is sufficiently extended. For minimum repulsion from the other ligands, these two groups would take up a position twisted away from the original plane of four ligands. In this case it becomes identical, except for distances, with a very good structure for an S_N2 mechanism. Figure 2 shows the activated complex for such a procedure as well as for the S_N2 mechanism. Five groups are close to the central atom, and two are further away. The coordination number might be called either five or seven depending on whether the five closely attached groups or the seven groups all told are being emphasized. For the same reason the path could be said to correspond to either an S_N1 mechanism (C.N. five) or an S_N2 mechanism (C.N. seven). The reaction mechanism is borderline, and a decision as to how best describe it depends upon the extent and manner in which the water molecule coming in lowers the energy of the system. If the energetic interaction is great and if the nature of the interaction is specific and markedly dependent on the properties of the water mol-

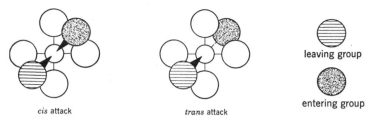

cis attack   *trans* attack

leaving group

entering group

F<small>IG</small>. 2. Arrangement of ligands in an octahedral complex in the transition state for approach at front octahedral face (*cis* attack) and back octahedral face (*trans* attack). One of the inert ligands is not shown.

ecule, then an S_N2 label is best. If the energy interaction is small or of such a nature as to be provided by any molecule to a reasonably similar degree, then an S_N1 label is most fitting.

There is undoubtedly an energy effect of substantial magnitude since the activation energy must be reduced from the 94 kcal predicted for no interaction to the 34 or so kcal expected for this reaction. Because of the unsymmetrical nature of this complex, it is not too easy to calculate the potential energy in the usual way. However, the fact that 34 kcal lies between the limits of no interaction and complete interaction of the solvent makes the energy requirement seem a reasonable one. The question still remains as to how specific the interaction is and whether it is best classified as a solvation effect or as a chemical reaction of water.

Now the reactions of cobalt(III) complexes have been extensively studied, and the example discussed was deliberately picked to throw light on the reactions of cobalt(III). This cannot be regarded as a very typical case, however, because the energy of various arrangements of ligands about cobalt(III) is very dependent on crystal field stabilization. Included in the activation energies for the S_N2 pentagonal bipyramid path and the S_N1 trigonal bipyramid and square pyramid paths were substantial changes in C.F.S.E. It will be recalled that the stabilization amounted to $24Dq$ for a regular octahedron in a d^6 system, and was a result of the six electrons being in the d_{xy}, d_{xz}, and d_{yz} orbitals out of the way of the six ligands.

If a seventh group is added along any edge of the original octahedron, then it can readily be seen that it must be forced in directly towards one of those filled and previously stable d orbitals. In the same way, if a group is lost and the three remaining ligands in a plane rearrange to a trigonal form, they can do so only by moving over and interfering seriously with the filled d orbital. The least disturbance is caused by simply removing one group and leaving five ligands in a square pyramid. Even this is accompanied by some loss of C.F.S.E. since, after all, it is the ligands which cause the original energy separation, leading to stabilization. All of these effects on the energies of the possible intermediates can be approximately calculated using the energy levels for various structures given on p. 55. Thus a pentagonal bipyramid with six d electrons has a C.F.S.E. of $15.5Dq$. The loss compared to the octahedral case is $8.5Dq$ or about 47 kcal. A regular trigonal bipyramid has only $12.5Dq$ stabilization energy, the loss on formation being about 64 kcal.

A square pyramid with five equal ligands has C.F.S.E. of $20Dq$, or only 22 kcal less than the octahedral. It is this consideration which made the most plausible intermediate for the exchange reaction one with five groups left undisturbed and the entering and leaving groups both relatively far away. The dependence of the crystal field effect on distance is large enough so that this arrangement would essentially have the C.F.S.E. of a square pyramid. The C.F.S.E. of a seven-coordinated transition state with two groups closer in and lying in two of the original octahedral faces cannot easily be calculated. However, since the six d electrons are avoided by ligands on the faces, the energy loss would be less than for a pentagonal bipyramid.

Suppose we repeated the calculations previously made to apply to the exchange of water in $Fe(H_2O)_6^{3+}$. Since iron(III) in this complex has five spin-uncoupled electrons, there is no crystal field stabilization, or loss thereof, to consider. We would then calculate activation energies for a pentagonal bipyramid S_N2 path of about 50 kcal and the same for a trigonal bipyramid S_N1 mechanism. A square pyramid S_N1 path would have an activation energy between 0 and 70 kcal. In fact, if 22 kcal for the loss in C.F.S.E. is subtracted from the 27 kcal observed for $Co(NH_3)_5H_2O^{3+}$, we see that water exchange in $Fe(H_2O)_6^{3+}$ by the same mechanism is already down to such a low activation energy that it would be very rapid. This is in agreement with the facts (see p. 51). One of the obvious variables that we have to consider in discussing the rates of substitution reactions of complexes, then, is the loss of crystal field stabilization energy in systems with different numbers of d electrons and different coordination numbers.

Before taking up this topic in detail, let us use the simple coulombic picture to consider the effect of other variables on the rates of substitution reactions of coordination compounds. Imagine, for simplicity, a system with completely empty or completely filled d shells so that crystal field effects are not a factor. The variables of importance are the size and charge of the central atom and the sizes and charges of the entering and leaving groups.

Without going into numerical calculations it is easy to see that the lower the charge and the greater the size of either the central atom or the leaving group, the more rapid its reactions will be by a dissociation type of mechanism.* Thus $Fe(H_2O)_6^{2+}$ will be expected to exchange water more rapidly than $Fe(H_2O)_6^{3+}$ and $Co(NH_3)_5Br^{2+}$ to react more rapidly than $Co(NH_3)_5Cl^{2+}$. Furthermore, in an S_N2 process, the smaller the size and the greater the charge of the entering group, the faster the reaction should be. For a good estimate of the relative reactivities of various reagents in a displacement mechanism, one could use the relative stabilities of the complexes formed by that reagent with the central atom to which it becomes attached in the transition state. Thus Table 1 in Chapter 9 is a measure of the expected nucleophilic efficiency of several anions in S_N2 reactions. It will be noted that $F^- > Cl^- > Br^-$, that CNS^- and N_3^- are good, and OH^- is expected to be best of all. Other small, strongly basic anions are also expected to be effective. Although SO_4^{2-} may be a good reagent because of its charge, its greater size may prevent its entering into C.N. seven as easily.

The effect of increased charge on the central atom is not clearly defined for an S_N2 process. Whereas bond breaking is made more difficult, bond making is made easier. The net effect will depend on the relative contributions of the two energy effects. However, a very clear prediction can be made as to the probability of an S_N2 mechanism compared to an S_N1 mechanism. As the positive charge and size of the central atom increase, the chance of an S_N2 mechanism will increase. As the positive charge of the central atom increases, size being constant, the chance of an S_N1 mechanism diminishes.

As far as the effect of the nature of the leaving group is concerned, lower charge and greater size will lead to rapid reactions, but by either mechanism as a first approximation. In the limit of a very small, highly charged ligand, it may be argued that an S_N1 mechanism becomes impossible and, other factors not being prohibitive, an S_N2 mechanism will be required to release such a group. Similarly for very large groups to be displaced an S_N2 mechanism may become difficult for steric reasons and an S_N1 mechanism favored. This latter effect will be easier to demonstrate, however, if several of the ligands

* The assumption is made that interaction of the ligand with the central atom is greater than the interaction of the ligand with the solvent.

on the central atom, including those which are not labile, become very large. These other ligands can also affect the course of the reaction by their electric charge. Thus a greater negative charge on the non-reacting ligands will favor an S_N1 mechanism by repelling the reactive ligand. An S_N2 process will be discouraged because of repulsion of the incoming ligand. All of these predictions based on electrostatic considerations and the sizes of the groups involved are summarized in Table 3.

Table 3

Effect of Sizes and Charges on Rates of S_N1 and S_N2 Reactions

	S_N1 (lim) and S_N1 Rate	S_N2 Rate	S_N2 (lim) Rate
Increased positive charge of central atom	decrease	opposing effects	increase
Increased size of central atom	increase	increase	increase
Increased negative charge of entering group	no effect	increase	increase
Increased size of entering group	no effect	decrease	decrease
Increased negative charge of leaving group	decrease	decrease	decrease
Increased size of leaving group	increase	opposing effects	decrease
Increased negative charge of other ligands	increase	opposing effects	decrease
Increased size of other ligands	increase	decrease	decrease

This approach is oversimplified and cannot be expected to be complete. For example, no account of π bonding has been taken. It may be anticipated that in certain cases unsaturated ligands will be effective as displacing reagents because of the chance of increased bonding in the transition state. Such double bonded ligands will also be difficult to displace when already present in the coordination sphere. Also for complexes where covalent bonding is an especially important factor, an electrostatic picture will not be very reliable.

THE EFFECT OF THE ELECTRONIC STRUCTURE OF THE CENTRAL ATOM

It has already been pointed out that it is necessary to consider not only the size and charge of the central atom but also its d electron structure in predicting the rates of substitution reactions. Before doing this in terms of the crystal field theory, it is of interest to consider the application of the valence bond theory to the same problem. Much of what follows is taken from a review by Taube.[12]

The term *labile* is applied to very reactive complexes, whereas less reactive complexes are called *inert*. There is, of course, no sharp division between these two classes, but rather there exists a continuous gradation. Taube has defined labile to mean systems where reactions are complete within the time of mixing (1 min, room temperature, about 0.1 M solutions). The term inert is used for reactions that are either too slow to measure or reactions that are slow enough to follow at ordinary conditions by conventional techniques.

The mòst direct and least ambiguous test of lability is to measure the rate of exchange for a reaction of the type

$$MA_6 + *A = MA_5*A + A \qquad (10)$$

The equilibrium state corresponds to an almost statistical distribution of the A groups. Since the equilibrium is favorable for exchange, a labile complex will undergo immediate exchange upon mixing with tagged *A. The recent availability of radioactive isotopes has greatly enhanced studies of this type (Table 5, Chapter 9). Data are also available on the rate of exchange of the central ion between complexes as in a reaction of the type

$$MA_6 + *M(H_2O)_6 = *MA_6 + M(H_2O)_6 \qquad (11)$$

A rapid rate of exchange of the central ions is good evidence that the two complexes are labile, but a slow exchange does not necessarily mean they are inert.* Reactions where there is a net chemical change as in 1 are very common but not entirely satisfactory as an estimate of lability. Failure to react cannot be taken as proof of an inert complex; it may merely be the result of an unfavorable equilibrium. Furthermore some apparently simple substitution reactions may not be "simple," and the rate-determining step may not be a measure of the lability of the metal ligand bond. However, it does follow that the rate of substitution will be at least as rapid as the overall rate, and thus a very fast reaction is a reliable indication of a labile complex.

Additional information on the reactivity of complexes is available from studies on the isomerization of these substances. The very existence of geometric isomers and the fact that these persist in solution at

* Although investigations of complex lability are best carried out by ligand exchange studies for the highest member in the coordination series, e.g., MA_6, studies of metal exchange are best for the lowest member, e.g., MA (p. 397).

non-equilibrium concentrations are good indications that the complexes involved are inert. It would appear that a similar observation for optical isomers should also be indicative of an inert complex. However, it is reported that racemic complexes of aluminum(III), beryllium(II), cadmium(II), gallium(III), iron(III), and zinc(II) have been resolved (Chapter 6). Since these complex ions are known to be labile, one must conclude that each substitution is not accompanied by racemization. Therefore it would appear to follow that each substitution also need not lead to isomerization so that the isolation of geometric isomers is not proof that the complex is inert. Furthermore, because of the possibility of intramolecular rearrangement (Figs. 10 and 11, Chapter 6), failure to isolate geometric isomers or to separate optical isomers cannot be accepted as absolute proof that the metal complex in question is labile.

The term inert must not be confused with the term stable. One has kinetic meaning and the other thermodynamic. It is true that often thermodynamically stable substances are slow to react, whereas unstable compounds react rapidly. There is no absolute requirement that this be so, however. Table 4 illustrates the lack of correlation in the

Table 4

Exchange Rate and Stability of Some Cyano Complexes

Complex	Dissociation Constant	Exchange Rate *
$Ni(CN)_4^{2-}$	10^{-22}	very fast
$Mn(CN)_6^{3-}$	10^{-27}	measurable
$Fe(CN)_6^{4-}$	10^{-37}	very slow
$Hg(CN)_4^{2-}$	10^{-42}	very fast
$Fe(CN)_6^{3-}$	10^{-44}	very slow

* With labeled cyanide ion. Data from reference 21.

case of some cyano complexes, between lability and stability. Although these complexes may be considered as quite stable, yet two are labile. By contrast $Co(NH_3)_6^{3+}$ in the presence of an acid solution is thermodynamically completely unstable (either to NH_4^+ and $Co(H_2O)_6^{3+}$, or to NH_4^+, $Co(H_2O)_6^{2+}$, and N_2) but will persist unchanged for several weeks in such a medium.

Taube [12] suggests that much of the available data pertaining to the lability of coordination compounds can be explained on the basis of their electronic configuration as given by the valence bond theory. In general the labile complexes are either of the *outer orbital* type or of the *inner orbital* type with at least one vacant lower d orbital. Some metal ions that form labile and inert complexes and their representative electronic configurations are shown in Table 5. These are inner orbital or d^2sp^3 complexes.

Table 5

Inner Orbital Six-Coordinate Complexes

Labile Complexes

Electronic Configuration			Central Metal Ions
d	s	p	
○ ○ ○ ⊙ ⊙	⊙	⊙ ⊙ ⊙ *	Sc(III), Y(III), rare earths(III), Ti(IV), Zr(IV), Hf(IV), Ce(IV), Th(IV), Nb(V), Ta(V), Mo(VI), W(VI)
⊙ ○ ○ ⊙ ⊙	⊙	⊙ ⊙ ⊙ *	Ti(III), V(IV), Mo(V), W(V), Re(VI)
⊙ ⊙ ○ ⊙ ⊙	⊙	⊙ ⊙ ⊙ *	Ti(II), V(III), Nb(III), Ta(III), Mo(IV), W(IV), Re(V), Ru(VI)

Inert Complexes

d	s	p	Central Metal Ions
⊙ ⊙ ⊙ ⊙ ⊙	⊙	⊙ ⊙ ⊙ *	V(II), Cr(III), Mo(III), W(III), Mn(IV), Re(IV)
⊙ ⊙ ⊙ ⊙ ⊙	⊙	⊙ ⊙ ⊙	$Cr(CN)_6^{4-}$, $Cr(bipy)_3^{2+}$, $Mn(CN)_6^{3-}$, Re(III), Ru(IV), Os(V)
⊙ ⊙ ⊙ ⊙ ⊙	⊙	⊙ ⊙ ⊙	$Cr(bipy)_3^{1+}$, $Mn(CN)_6^{4-}$, Re(II), $Fe(CN)_6^{3-}$, $Fe(phen)_3^{3+}$, $Fe(bipy)_3^{3+}$, Ru(III), Os(III), Ir(IV)
⊙ ⊙ ⊙ ⊙ ⊙	⊙	⊙ ⊙ ⊙	$Mn(CN)_6^{5-}$, $Fe(CN)_6^{4-}$, $Fe(phen)_3^{2+}$, $Fe(bipy)_3^{2+}$, Ru(II), Os(II), Co(III) (except CoF_6^{3-}), Rh(III), Ir(III), Ni(IV), Pd(IV), Pt(IV)

* These electronic configurations are assigned on the assumption that if lower d orbitals are vacant they will be used in bond formation. Magnetic data here will not distinguish between d^2sp^3 and sp^3d^2.

It is indeed striking how the line of demarcation between labile and inert complexes falls precisely at the point where the inner d orbitals all become at least singly occupied. For example, the d^1 complexes of molybdenum(V) and tungsten(V) are labile, whereas those of Mo(III) and W(III) are inert. Since the first two have a higher positive charge on the central atom, it would be predicted that they would react more slowly by a dissociation mechanism and not necessarily react more rapidly by a displacement mechanism on electrostatic grounds alone. In the same way vanadium(II) complexes appear inert (a d^3 system), whereas vanadium(III) complexes appear labile. (Often the evidence on which lability or inertness is assigned in Table 5 is only qualitative.)

A reasonable assumption is that all of these complexes are reacting by an $S_N 2$ mechanism in which a seventh group must be added to the coordination sphere, and, in keeping with the valence bond theory, such a process is greatly aided if an empty lower d orbital is available to the incoming group. If such an orbital is not available, then the seventh group must add by using an outer d orbital of lower stability. This reaction is slower because a higher activation energy is required.*

Outer orbital complexes have the electronic configuration $sp^3 d^2$ where the order indicates that d orbitals of the same principal quantum number as the s and p orbitals are used. In general, outer orbital complexes are labile, e.g., Mn(II), Fe(II), Fe(III), Co(II), Zn(II), Cd(II), Hg(II), Al(III), Ga(III), In(III), and Tl(III). For a given isoelectronic series, the lability decreases with increasing charge on the central ion, e.g., $AlF_6^{-3} > SiF_6^{-2} > PF_6^- > SF_6$. Hence outer orbital complexes can become inert as in SF_6, SiF_6^{2-}, PF_6^-, and $SbCl_6^-$.

Since the outer d orbitals are less stable than the inner d orbitals, it follows that bonds involving them are less stable. Hence it should be relatively easy to have a dissociation into a complex of C.N. five, since one of the unstable orbitals can now be left out of the hybridization. However, as the positive charge on the central atom increases, the bond strength increases so that eventually the compounds become inert. It may be noted at this time that the assumption, inherent in the valence bond theory, that coordinate bonds in the complexes classified as outer orbital are weaker than they would otherwise be is completely unjustified. There is experimental evidence, as discussed in Chapter 2, that the bond strengths are very much the same for "inner orbital" and "outer orbital" complexes of a given type. The variations that exist are explicable on the crystal field theory but not on valence bond theory. This seriously weakens the explanation for the lability of the so-called outer-orbital-type complexes given by the valence bond theory. The other chief objection to the kinetic application of the theory is that, as always, it is purely qualitative. For example, any differences that exist, say, between a d^1 and a d^2 system, or between an inner orbital d^3 or d^4 system, cannot be predicted. Similarly all outer orbital systems are lumped together except insofar as the charge and size of the central atom are varied. No distinction based on the number of d electrons is made.

* An $S_N 1$ mechanism might be invoked if it is assumed that $d^3 sp$ forms more stable bonds than $d^2 sp^2$.

KINETIC APPLICATION OF CRYSTAL FIELD THEORY

The importance of crystal field stabilization in determining the rates of reaction of coordination compounds was pointed out in a qualitative way by Orgel [13] and by Klixbüll Jørgensen.[14] Orgel noted that the reactivity of d^0, d^1, and d^2 systems compared to d^3 could be accounted for on the basis of an S_N2 mechanism in which the entering group entered the plane in which the low energy d orbital was empty. Thus, if the d_{xy} orbital was unoccupied, the seventh group would be added to the xy plane. In this way losses in C.F.S.E. would be minimized. This would not be possible for d^3 and higher systems. Klixbüll Jørgensen noted that, because of the large crystal field stabilizations of d^3, diamagnetic d^6, and d^8 systems in octahedral complexes, any reaction, whether going by C.N. five or C.N. seven would inevitably lead to a considerable loss of energy and hence be slow.

These ideas can be put in more quantitative terms by the use of the energy values of Table 5, Chapter 2. The procedure is to calculate the C.F.S.E. for various numbers of d electrons for a regular octahedral complex in weak or strong fields, and also for a regular square pyramid and a pentagonal bipyramid. The latter two are used as approximations to the activated complexes for S_N1 and S_N2 mechanisms respectively. It may be noted that a trigonal bipyramid is always less favorable than a square pyramid as far as crystal field effects are concerned.

Tables 6 and 7 show the results of such calculations. The difference between the original octahedral and final C.F.S.E. is considered as a contribution, ΔE_a, to the total activation energy for each reaction. A large value of ΔE_a implies a slow reaction by that particular path. A negative value of ΔE_a is essentially a zero value since it implies that a better C.F.S.E. could be obtained by distorting the octahedron. In such a case, the original state of the system would be a distorted, and not a regular, octahedron. It may be noted also that the electrons are kept in the same orbitals that they occupied in the original octahedron in passing over to the square pyramid or pentagonal bipyramid. In some cases it might be favorable to rearrange the electrons prior to reaction.

The immediate conclusion on scanning Tables 6 and 7 is that d^3, spin-coupled d^6, and d^8 are indeed the systems which are most affected, as far as crystal field energies are concerned, by the formation of a transition state by either an S_N1 or an S_N2 mechanism. In special

Table 6

Crystal Field Activation Energies for Dissociation Mechanism

Octahedral → square pyramid

System	Strong Fields			Weak Fields		
	Octahedral	Square Pyramid	ΔE_a	Octahedral	Square Pyramid	ΔE_a
d^0	$0Dq$	$0Dq$	$0Dq$	$0Dq$	$0Dq$	$0Dq$
d^1	4	4.57	−0.57	4	4.57	−0.57
d^2	8	9.14	−1.14	8	9.14	−1.14
d^3	12	10.00	2.00	12	10.00	2.00
d^4	16	14.57	1.43	6	9.14	−3.14
d^5	20	19.14	0.86	0	0	0
d^6	24	20.00	4.00	4	4.57	−0.57
d^7	18	19.14	−1.14	8	9.14	−1.14
d^8	12	10.00	2.00	12	10.00	2.00
d^9	6	9.14	−3.14	6	9.14	−3.14
d^{10}	0	0	0	0	0	0

Table 7

Crystal Field Activation Energies for Displacement Mechanism

Octahedral → pentagonal bipyramid

System	Strong Fields			Weak Fields		
	Octahedral	Pentagonal Bipyramid	ΔE_a	Octahedral	Pentagonal Bipyramid	ΔE_a
d^0	$0Dq$	$0Dq$	$0Dq$	$0Dq$	$0Dq$	$0Dq$
d^1	4	5.28	−1.28	4	5.28	−1.28
d^2	8	10.56	−2.56	8	10.56	−2.56
d^3	12	7.74	4.26	12	7.74	4.26
d^4	16	13.02	2.98	6	4.93	1.07
d^5	20	18.30	1.70	0	0	0
d^6	24	15.48	8.52	4	5.28	−1.28
d^7	18	12.66	5.34	8	10.56	−2.56
d^8	12	7.74	4.26	12	7.74	4.26
d^9	6	4.93	1.07	6	4.93	1.07
d^{10}	0	0	0	0	0	0

circumstances a number of other systems are also predicted to react slowly because of a loss of C.F.S.E. The systems d^0, d^1, and d^2, as well as d^{10}, on the other hand, never lose any C.F.S.E. by either mechanism. It is accordingly predicted that they will react fast compared to any corresponding complexes in which ΔE_a is positive.

In strong fields, which correspond to "inner orbital" complexes for systems from d^0 to d^6, it is predicted that reactions will be fast for d^0, d^1, and d^2 and slow for d^3, d^4, d^5, and d^6, with the order of rates decreasing as $d^5 > d^4 > d^3 > d^6$ by either S_N1 or S_N2 mechanisms. In weak fields which correspond to outer orbital complexes for systems from d^4 to d^{10}, the only case which is predicted to be slow by either mechanism is that of d^8.

Thus there is agreement between the valence bond theory and the crystal field theory in predicting rapid reactions for complexes in which an empty lower d orbital is available. The reasons, however, are quite different in the two theories. The valence bond theory favors an S_N2 mechanism and stresses the availability of an orbital for covalent bond formation. The crystal field theory, as usual, ignores covalent bonding and orbital requirements and notes only that a transition state with either an increased or decreased coordination number can be formed without any decrease in C.F.S.E. This prediction is made regardless of mechanism. Note that it is not valid to conclude that, since complexes with an empty d orbital react rapidly, an S_N2 mechanism is required.

There is also agreement between the two theories in predicting that non-transition elements, the rare earths, and d^{10} systems will react rapidly. Again, different reasons are advanced. There is agreement that d^3 and spin-coupled d^4, d^5, and d^6 systems will be slow and that spin-free d^4, d^5, d^6, d^7, and d^9 systems will be fast. A major point of disagreement is spin-free d^8 octahedral complexes, for which the valence bond theory predicts the same lability as for spin-free d^4, d^5, d^6, d^7, and d^9 and the crystal field theory predicts inertness equal to that of a d^3 corresponding complex.

Where the theories agree, the correspondence to experiment is perfect. In fact it may be stated now that it is very difficult to observe a slow substitution reaction in a metal complex which is not crystal field stabilized. To do so it is necessary to go to such specialized systems as ethylenediaminetetraacetatoiron(III) which will be discussed later, or magnesium in chlorophyll which has a rigid quadridentate structure.* Also the inertness of complexes of chromium(III), and spin-coupled complexes of iron(II), (III), cobalt(III), rhodium(III), osmium(III), and iridium(III), is well known.

Where the theories disagree, in the case of d^8, the evidence is definitely on the side of the crystal field theory. Virtually the only examples which can be used as a test are the paramagnetic complexes of nickel(II). The diamagnetic nickel(II), palladium(II), platinum(II), and gold(III) are planar structures which are to be discussed in Chapter 4 and whose reaction mechanisms are different. Now the spin-free complexes of nickel(II) are often considered as labile, and the rapidity of many of their reactions justifies this assignment. But what is predicted by the theories just discussed is not the absolute rate of these reactions but the relative rates for systems with different numbers of d electrons. The absolute rate is determined largely by the charge on the central atom, the nature of the ligands, etc. Certainly in comparison with the complexes of trivalent chromium or cobalt the reactions of divalent nickel will be faster.

In comparison with corresponding complexes of manganese(II), cobalt(II), copper(II), and zinc(II), the reactions of nickel(II) are slow. Thus the rates of dissociation of the tris complexes of 1,10-phenanthroline, 2,2'-bipyridine, and even ethylenediamine of nickel(II) are measurable,[15] as are the rates of formation and dissociation of the mono 1,10-phenanthroline complex.[16] In contrast the same complexes for manganese(II), cobalt(II),[17] copper(II),[18] and zinc(II) [18] are either observed qualitatively to be extremely labile or are shown more conclusively by exchange studies to be very much faster. Also the EDTA complex of nickel(II) is slow to exchange, but those of iron(II) and cobalt(II) are labile.[19]

A number of qualitative studies have been made by Bjerrum and Poulsen [20] by working at low temperatures ($-75°C$) in methanol solution, with the general conclusion that the aqua complexes of Mn(II), Zn(II), and Cu(II) react fast, and those of Fe(II), Co(II), and Ni(II) react more slowly. Table 7 in Chapter 4 shows more detailed comparison of the ethylenediamine complexes of Ni(II) and Cu(II) in which the slower reaction of the nickel complexes is very evident.

---

* Another group of inert compounds which are not crystal field stabilized is such organometallics as $Hg(CH_3)_2$, $Ge(C_2H_5)_4$, etc. These compounds are best considered as covalent. Their bonds are stable towards heterolytic dissociation because of the instability of simple carbanions.

An indirect method [21] has been used to estimate rates of reaction of aqua cations with the anion of thenoyltrifluoracetone (TTA), e.g.,

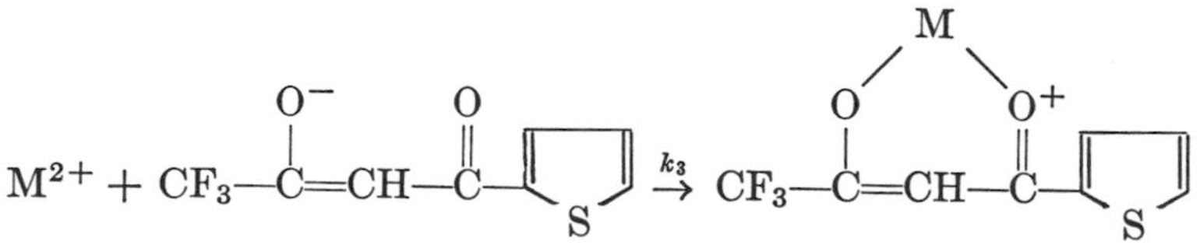

$$(12)$$

The method involves competition of the metal ion with hydrogen ion

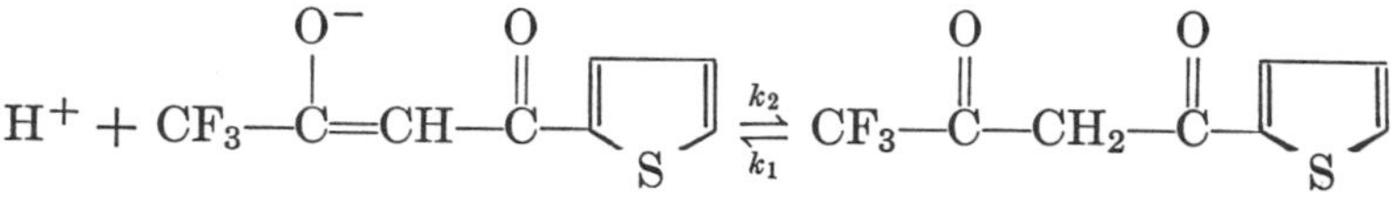

$$(13)$$

for the carbanion. Since the ionization constant of TTA is known and the rate of ionization, k_1, can be measured, it is possible to calculate k_2. For certain conditions it was found that the rate of ionization of the diketone, k_1, was rate determining for the formation of the TTA complex of the metal ion. In other cases the rate step involved the concentration of the metal ion. A division could be made of the metal ions into two classes as shown in Table 8 with rate constants, k_3, falling into two limiting categories, those greater than 10^8 M^{-1} min^{-1} and those less than 10^6 M^{-1} min^{-1}.

Table 8

Rates of Complex Formation with TTA for Some Metal Aqua Ions in Water at 25°C

Ion	Radius	q^2/r	k_3, M^{-1} min^{-1}
Zn^{2+}	0.74 A	5.4	
Cu^{2+}	0.74	5.4	
Mg^{2+}	0.70	5.7	
La^{3+}	1.18	7.6	greater than 10^8
Ce^{3+}	1.18	7.6	
Sc^{3+}	0.82	11.0	
Be^{2+}	0.32	12.5	
Cr^{3+}	0.64	14.1	less than 10^6
Fe^{3+}	0.60	15.0	
Al^{3+}	0.50	18.0	

An inverse correlation was found for the rates of reaction with the magnitude of (ionic charge)^2/ionic radius. This is a clear indication of the importance of coulombic effects for these reactions. It shows that the critical feature is the tightness of binding of the hydration sphere to the cation. The strongly solvated ion must be freed in part from the first layer of water molecules before reaction with another ligand can occur. It may also be concluded from the rate with which copper(II) complexes usually react that pentagonal bipyramid S_N2 mechanisms are not often followed. Table 7 shows a crystal field activation energy by such a route. The predicted value of ΔE_a would be even larger if the tetragonal structure of the original complex were taken into account. This would make its C.F.S.E. about 9 instead of 6, and the loss about $4Dq$ in an S_N2 reaction.

The crystal field theory makes predictions as to the relative rates of the inert complexes as well. For example, it follows from Tables 6 and 7 that the reaction of a nickel(II) complex should be faster than that of an iron(II) complex in strong fields. This is observed for the spin-coupled 2,2'-bipyridine complex of iron(II) compared to that of nickel(II). However, the rates of dissociation of the 1,10-phenanthroline complexes of iron and nickel are abnormal in that the iron compound reacts faster even though spin coupled. The reason for this is that the theory only predicts changes in activation energies due to crystal field effects, and other factors can influence the rates. For $Fe(phen)_3^{2+}$ the activation energy for dissociation is 32 kcal and for $Ni(phen)_3^{2+}$ only 25 kcal, in good agreement with theory which predicts a difference of $2Dq$ for a dissociation (S_N1) mechanism. The iron compound reacts faster, however, because of an abnormally large positive entropy of activation (see Table 5, Chapter 6). The corresponding prediction that d^6 systems react more slowly than d^3 in the case of cobalt(III) and chromium(III) is usually obeyed. This will be discussed in more detail later.

In the case of cyanide complexes, the following orders of lability have been observed:[12, 23] $V(CN)_6^{3-} > Mn(CN)_6^{3-} \gg Cr(CN)_6^{3-} > Fe(CN)_6^{3-} \sim Co(CN)_6^{3-}$; and $Cr(CN)_6^{4-} > V(CN)_6^{4-} \sim Mn(CN)_6^{4-} > Fe(CN)_6^{4-}$; also $V(CN)_6^{3-} > V(CN)_6^{4-}$. The last fact is in agreement with both crystal field theory and valence bond theory because of the empty d orbital in vanadium(III). The crystal field explanation has the advantage of also correlating the greater stability of certain complexes of vanadium(II) compared to vanadium(III), by the same concept of C.F.S.E. Thus the complex $V(phen)_3^{2+}$ is more stable[22] than the complex $V(phen)_3^{3+}$.

The theoretical order of reactivity $d^5 > d^4 > d^3 > d^6$ is not obeyed, however, for the cyanide complexes as the d^4 systems $Mn(CN)_6^{3-}$ and

$Cr(CN)_6^{4-}$ react the fastest. An explanation of the reactivity has been offered [23a] in terms of an S_N2 mechanism in which the four electrons are paired off in two orbitals, leaving one orbital free for covalent bond formation. It is true that magnetic data on d^4 complexes show that the ground state is diamagnetic in strong field complexes.[24] This does not necessarily mean that two d orbitals are doubly occupied, however, since spin-orbital coupling is probably responsible. It is possible, however, by a distortion of the octahedral structure to tetragonal to make two orbitals lower in energy (see Table 5, Chapter 2). In such a case it is probably fairly easy to obtain double occupancy of these two lowest levels. With one empty d_{xy} orbital, it is then possible to have a facile reaction to form either a square pyramid or pentagonal bipyramid intermediate. No great loss in C.F.S.E. will be involved.

The exchange reaction of $Mn(CN)_6^{3-}$ with labeled CN^- is a first-order process independent of cyanide ion concentration (half-life about 6 minutes at 25°C).[23a] The activation energy is small, 8.5 kcal, and if calculated as a unimolecular process the entropy of activation * is −44 entropy units. This large negative entropy value was considered evidence for an S_N2 reaction, with water necessarily being the second reactant. The crystal field theory, however, makes an S_N1 mechanism just as likely as an S_N2 mechanism. The experimental activation energy and entropy include the energy requirement and the probability of the electron promotion process.

MECHANISM OF SUBSTITUTION REACTIONS OF COMPLEXES OF COBALT(III)

After this largely theoretical survey, it is necessary to consider the experimental evidence available in detail. As might be expected the greatest amount of kinetic study has been made on the robust complexes of cobalt(III), chromium(III), and a few of their related elements in the periodic table. Because of the great variety of complexes of cobalt(III) that can be prepared, it is anticipated that the most information on the intimate mechanism of reaction can be obtained in this case.[25] The substitution reactions have been subdivided into

---

* The entropy of activation, $\Delta S^{\ddagger}$, is obtained from the equation

$$k = \frac{RTe}{Nh} e^{-Ea/RT} e^{\Delta S^{\ddagger}/R}$$

from the transition state theory of reaction rates.[9]

several categories for convenience, and each of them will be reviewed in turn.

Acid hydrolysis. The substitution reaction most extensively investigated by kinetic methods is that commonly referred to as *aquation* and illustrated by the typical equation

$$MA_5X^n + H_2O \rightarrow MA_5H_2O^{n+1} + X^- \tag{14}$$

Likewise of common usage in the literature is the term *hydrolysis* with reference to reactions of the type

$$MA_5X^n + OH^- \rightarrow MA_5OH^n + X^- \tag{15}$$

Since both of these are essentially reactions of complex ions with water, it is suggested that both be called *hydrolysis reactions*. If the reaction product is an aqua complex (14) the reaction is termed *acid hydrolysis,* whereas, if the product is a hydroxo complex (15) the reaction is called *base hydrolysis.* Depending upon the pH of the reaction mixture and the acidity of the aqua complex, it follows that the reaction product can be an acid-base equilibrium mixture of the aqua and hydroxo complexes with both present in appreciable amounts. In such a case the reaction is simply referred to as *hydrolysis* with no specification as to acid or base hydrolysis. This terminology will be used here as it is believed to be more informative than the older terms, aquation and hydrolysis.

An appreciable amount of data is available on the rates of acid hydrolysis reactions. These studies, made in aqueous solutions, give a linear plot for first-order kinetics. This result is to be expected, since the concentration of the reactant and solvent does not change during the reaction. The rate is therefore dependent only on the concentration of the complex and is first order or pseudo first order. This observation by itself furnishes no information as to the role played by the water and does not tell anything about the molecularity of these reactions.

Nevertheless the way in which the rate constant is affected by various changes in the nature of the complex ion is expected to give us information about the mechanism. Table 9 contains the observed data on the acid hydrolysis of a number of cobalt(III) chloroammines. These data permit two conclusions to be drawn. One is that increasing chelation, such as replacing two NH_3 ligands by one ethylenediamine, slows down the rate of acid hydrolysis in a progressive manner. The

Table 9

Rates of Acid Hydrolysis of Some Pentamminechloro and Tetramminedichloro Cobalt(III) Complexes at pH 1 *

Ion	$k \times 10^4$, min^{-1}	Ion	$k \times 10^4$, min^{-1}
cis-Co(NH$_3$)$_4$Cl$_2{}^+$	very fast	Co(NH$_3$)$_5$Cl^{2+}	4.0
cis-Co(en)$_2$Cl$_2{}^+$	150	cis-Co(en)$_2$NH$_3$Cl^{2+}	0.85
cis-Co(trien)Cl$_2{}^+$	90	cis-Co(trien)NH$_3$Cl^{2+}	0.40
$trans$-Co(NH$_3$)$_4$Cl$_2{}^+$	1100	Co(en)(dien)Cl^{2+}	0.31
$trans$-Co(en)(NH$_3$)$_2$Cl$_2{}^+$	130	Co(tetraen)Cl^{2+}	0.15
$trans$-Co(en)$_2$Cl$_2{}^+$	19		

* Dichloro complexes at 25°C and chloro complexes at 35°C. Data from R. G. Pearson, C. R. Boston, and F. Basolo, *J. Phys. Chem.*, **59**, 304 (1955). Substitution of first chlorine only for dichloro complexes.

second is that, allowing for the first effect, the divalent monochloro complexes react about 100 times slower than the univalent dichloro complexes. This is also borne out by the fact that the acid hydrolysis of the latter complexes occurs in two steps:

$$Co(AA)_2Cl_2{}^+ + H_2O \rightarrow Co(AA)_2(H_2O)Cl^{2+} + Cl^- \quad (16a)$$

$$Co(AA)_2(H_2O)Cl^{2+} + H_2O \rightarrow Co(AA)_2(H_2O)_2{}^{3+} + Cl^- \quad (16b)$$

with the second reaction about 100 times slower than the first.[26] Table 9 reports only the rate constant for 16a.

The interpretation of the effect of the positive charge of the complex on the rate is straightforward. Separation of negative charge in the form of the chloride ion is more difficult the greater the remaining charge on the complex. This immediately tells us that bond breaking is important and that we are not dealing with an S_N2 (lim) mechanism in any event. If the reactions are going by displacement mechanisms, then the reagent is water and the interaction of the charge of the complex with the dipole of water will be less than with the electric charge of the chloride ion. Hence an S_N2 process cannot be excluded, though the relative order "bond breaking more important than bond making" is established.

The interpretation of the effect of chelation is more ambiguous. Certainly it may be possible that a displacement mechanism acting on the opposite side of the complex from the halide ion to be displaced *

* The convenient term "backside attack" is esthetically unsatisfactory. It is therefore suggested that the terms *"cis* attack" and *"trans* attack" be used to

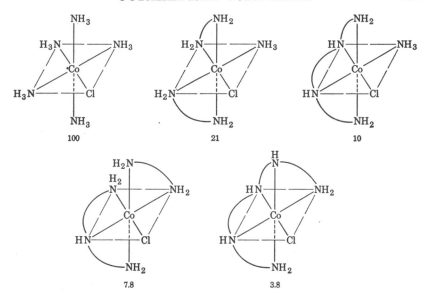

Fig. 3. Relative rates of acid hydrolysis for a series of chloropentammine complexes of cobalt(III) with different degrees of chelation. (C. R. Boston, Ph. D. thesis, Northwestern University, 1953.)

is being hindered. Figure 3 illustrates how chelation ties up the back of the complex and makes an attack by a reagent more difficult. In fact in the case of $Co(en)(dien)Cl^{2+}$ and $Co(tetraen)Cl^{2+}$ it would appear that such a mechanism is virtually excluded. The fact that these complexes react only slightly more slowly than some of the others is an argument against an S_N2 *trans* attack.

It is possible that the inductive effect of the chelate amines compared to ammonia is responsible for the rates. Data on the acid dissociation constants of the monoprotonated onium ions are as follows: NH_4^+ 9.28, enH^+ 9.93, $dienH^+$ 9.98, $trienH^+$ 9.92.[27] Thus NH_3 is a somewhat weaker base. This means that it does not give its electrons up as completely towards the cobalt(III) ion. But if this is true then the chloride ion would be held more firmly by the more positive cobalt and reaction would be slow. This is opposite to what is observed.

An explanation can be given based upon another kind of electro-

designate the relationship of the incoming group and leaving group in a displacement reaction (see p. 219).

static argument. As the chloride ion is lost from the original complex, an additional solvation by the water molecules making up the secondary coordination sphere is needed. That is, a trivalent cation is more intensely solvated than a divalent cation. From the Born equation it can be seen that the solvation energy is also greater the smaller the size of the ion. One effect of replacing NH_3 molecules by polyamines is certainly to increase the size of the complex. The larger the ion, the less its solvation energy will be and the less easily it can be formed. These arguments will also hold for a transition state in which the chloride ion is only partly lost. Thus the rate is slowed down by chelation because of reduced stability of the transition state due to less efficient solvation. In agreement with this view, the logs of the rate constants in Table 9 give a linear plot versus the number of chelate rings, or number of N—H bonds, for the chloro or *trans*-dichloro complexes. The log of the rate constant is proportional to the free energy of activation. This solvation theory, if true, does not distinguish between an S_N1 and an S_N2 mechanism. All it does is again call attention to the importance of ionic bond breaking in the transition state.

Another series of cobalt(III) complexes whose rates of acid hydrolysis have been measured is given in Table 10. Again only the

Table 10

Rates of Acid Hydrolysis of *trans*-$Co(AA)_2Cl_2^+$ at 25°C and pH 1

$$Co(AA)_2Cl_2^+ + H_2O \rightarrow Co(AA)_2(H_2O)Cl^{2+} + Cl^-$$

Diamine	Symbol	$k \times 10^3$, min^{-1}
1. NH_2—CH_2—CH_2—NH_2	en	1.9
2. NH_2—CH_2—$CH(CH_3)$—NH_2	pn	3.7
3. dl-NH_2—$CH(CH_3)$—$CH(CH_3)$—NH_2	dl-bn	8.8
4. $meso$-NH_2—$CH(CH_3)$—$CH(CH_3)$—NH_2	m-bn	250
5. NH_2—CH_2—$C(CH_3)_2$—NH_2	i-bn	130
6. NH_2—$C(CH_3)_2$—$C(CH_3)_2$—NH_2	tetrameen	instantaneous
7. NH_2—CH_2—CH_2—$NH(CH_3)$	meen	1.0
8. NH_2—CH_2—CH_2—$NH(C_2H_5)$	eten	3.6
9. NH_2—CH_2—CH_2—$NH(n\text{-}C_3H_7)$	n-pren	7.1
10. NH_2—CH_2—CH_2—CH_2—NH_2	tn	600 *
11. NH_2—CH_2—CH_2—NH_2, NH_2—CH_2—CH_2—CH_2—NH_2	(en)(tn)	26.0
12. NH_2—CH_2—$C(CH_3)_2$—CH_2—NH_2	dan	180

* At 10°C. Data from R. G. Pearson, C. R. Boston, and F. Basolo, *J. Am. Chem. Soc.*, **75**, 3089 (1953).

rates of reaction of the first chlorine are reported. In this group of compounds, two effects are studied. For the first nine compounds, the change in structure involves C or N alkyl substitution on ethylenediamine. For a single methyl substituent on nitrogen, the rate is diminished by a factor of two. This is in agreement with the solvation theory previously proposed. Except for this, every increase in the number or size of the alkyl groups in place of hydrogen atoms leads to an increase in the rate of acid hydrolysis. Thus in the case of the tetramethylethylenediamine complex, hydrolysis is instantaneous on solution in water.*

Such an acceleration in rate upon increased substitution is strongly suggestive of a dissociation mechanism. Certainly increasing the crowding about the cobalt atom would not be conducive to an S_N2 mechanism in which an increase in coordination number to seven is required. On the other hand such an increase in the size of the inert ligands is expected to favor an S_N1 mechanism in which the coordination number decreases to five. The explanation would be that a sterically crowded complex is unstable because of repulsion and distortion of the ligands. Upon losing one group, a chloride ion in this case, an expansion and rearrangement of the remaining five groups could occur to relieve the steric strain. Accelerations in reaction rate due to excessive crowding of groups in the reactant have been observed in bulky organic halides.[28] That steric strain in the original complex is responsible for the rate is evidenced by the observation that the rates of hydrolysis are correlated with the dissociation constants of the nickel complexes of the same series of diamines.[29]

For example the 30-fold increase in the rate of acid hydrolysis of the meso-butylenediamine compared to the dl-butylenediamine complex corresponds to a 740-fold decrease in the total stability constant of $Ni(AA)_3^{2+}$. When the two methyl groups are on the same side of the five-membered chelate ring, as in the meso compound, there is considerable interference between them. Similarly there is a 60-fold increase in the rate of acid hydrolysis of meso-stilbenediamine complex, $Co(m\text{-stien})_2Cl_2^+$, compared to the corresponding l-stilbenediamine complex in 50% methanol. The dissociation constants of the bis nickel complexes $Ni(AA)_2^{2+}$ differ by 10^5.

The last three complexes of Table 10 show the effect on the rate

* The *trans* complex salts are all green and their solutions are green, changing to pink or red upon hydrolysis. The half-life of the hydrolysis corresponds closely to a colorless stage, which makes possible an estimation of the rate even if very rapid.

of expanding the size of the chelate ring from five members to six by using trimethylenediamine instead of ethylenediamine. The rate is increased by 1000-fold for such a change. Again this increase in rate is connected to the observation that complexes with six-membered chelate rings are much less stable than those with five-membered rings, unless part of an aromatic system.[30] An examination of the reason for the instability shows that it lies in the 90° bond angles which are necessarily formed by the metal chelate bonds. Release of one group from the octahedron and expansion of this bond angle will relieve the strain in the complex with a six-membered ring. A peculiar result is that methyl substitution in the six-membered ring (compound 12) leads to a decrease in rate rather than an increase.

Before accepting the rate data in Table 10 as evidence for a dissociation mechanism, it is necessary to consider the possible influence of inductive effects further. This is because the base-strengthening character of the alkyl group with respect to hydrogen will lead to increased negative charge near the cobalt atom and an increased rate as observed. To test the influence of inductive effects it is desirable to prepare a series of compounds in which only inductive factors are varied and not steric or other factors. Table 11 shows some rate data

Table 11

Rates of Acid Hydrolysis of $Co(en)_2(X\text{-}py)Cl^{2+}$ at 50°C

X-py	pK_a	$k \times 10^5$, sec^{-1}
Pyridine	5.18	1.1
3-Methylpyridine	5.81	1.3
4-Methylpyridine	6.08	1.4
4-Methoxypyridine	6.47	1.5

Rates of Acid Hydrolysis of $trans\text{-}Co(X\text{-}py)_4Cl_2^+$ at 25°C

Pyridine	5.18	0.82
3-Methylpyridine	5.81	2.50
4-Methylpyridine	6.08	1.50
2,2'-Bipyridine *	4.40	very rapid

* $trans$-Co(bipy)$_2$Cl$_2^+$. Data from F. Basolo, J. G. Bergmann, R. E. Meeker, and R. G. Pearson, *J. Am. Chem. Soc.*, **78**, 2676 (1956).

on a series of complexes $Co(en)_2(X\text{-}py)Cl^{+2}$ in which X-py stands for a pyridine substituted in the *meta* or *para* position.

Assuming that steric factors are nearly the same, it is seen that an increase in base strength of the pyridine molecule (increase in pK_a)

leads to an increased rate of acid hydrolysis as expected. The factor is very small since a 20-fold increase in base strength leads to only a 40% increase in rate overall. Since the base strengths of the substituted ethylenediamines shown in Table 10 do not change by more than a factor of 1.5 over the entire range,[31] it may safely be concluded that the increased rates with alkyl substitution observed for these complexes are not due to inductive effects. They also cannot be due to solvation effects for the reasons previously presented. Table 11 also has some data on several tetrapyridine complexes and a bis(-2, 2'-bipyridine) complex. The latter hydrolyzes in a fraction of a second on solution in water. The pyridine complexes follow the order of base strengths in their reactivity except for the 3-methyl compound. It is possible that steric strain is again responsible for the higher rate in this case. The four pyridine rings must be pitched, like the blades of a propeller, to get the four ligand nitrogen atoms into a plane about the cobalt. It is impossible to do this in the case of the reactive 2,2'-bipyridine complex. Another possibility is that resonance in the bipyridine system stabilizes the transition state for reaction. 2,2'-Bipyridine is the weakest base by far of all those included in the table.

Up to now there has been no evidence for the effect on the rates of hydrolysis of changing the nature of the group which is replaced. Table 12 has some data for a number of complexes in which this group is varied. In agreement with the previous conclusion that bond breaking is important, it is seen that the rates vary markedly with the nature of the group being replaced. The general order of reactivity is $HCO_3^- >$ $NO_3^- > I^- > Br^- > H_2O > Cl^- > SO_4^{2-} > F^- > CH_3COO^- >$ $NCS^- > NO_2^-$. In comparisons in which the inert ligands are kept constant, the rates of hydrolysis are generally greatest for those complexes for which the thermodynamic stability is lowest.[32] The stability is measured, in this case, by the heat of formation of the aqueous complex ion from the aqueous ligands and $Co(H_2O)_6^{3+}$.

Also included in Table 12 are most of the relatively few observations available on chromium, rhodium, and iridium complexes. It is seen that chromium complexes react faster than analogous cobalt compounds and that the activation energies run about two kilocalories lower for chromium. The activation energies plus the rates are a more reliable guide than the rates alone, since one compound with a higher activation energy than another will accelerate its rate more with increasing temperature. In fact it is possible that it may react more slowly than the other compound at low temperature and more rapidly at high temperatures. This will only be possible, however, if the frequency factor A,

Table 12

Rates of Acid Hydrolysis of Some Cobalt(III) and Related Complexes at 25°C

Ion	k, min^{-1}	E_a, kcal
$Co(NH_3)_5HCO_3^{2+}$	$\sim 10^{-1}$	... [a]
$Co(NH_3)_5NO_3^{2+}$	1.6×10^{-3}	26 [b]
$Co(NH_3)_5I^{2+}$	5×10^{-4}	... [c]
$Co(NH_3)_5Br^{2+}$	3.8×10^{-4}	24
$Co(NH_3)_5H_2O^{3+}$	4×10^{-4}	27 [d]
$Co(NH_3)_5Cl^{2+}$	1.0×10^{-4}	24
$Co(NH_3)_5SO_4^{+}$	0.7×10^{-4}	19 [e]
$Co(NH_3)_5OOCCH_3^{2+}$	$\sim 10^{-6}$	... [f]
$Co(NH_3)_5NCS^{2+}$	1.7×10^{-7}	27
$Co(NH_3)_5NO_2^{2+}$	very slow	... [g]
cis-$Co(en)_2Cl_2^{+}$	1.5×10^{-2}	22 [h]
$trans$-$Co(en)_2Cl_2^{+}$	1.9×10^{-3}	24 [h]
cis-$Co(en)_2(OH)Cl^{+}$	7.8×10^{-1}	... [i]
$trans$-$Co(en)_2(OH)Cl^{+}$	8.4×10^{-2}	... [i]
cis-$Co(en)_2(NO_2)Cl^{+}$	2.2×10^{-4}	22 [j]
$trans$-$Co(en)_2(NO_2)Cl^{+}$	2.2×10^{-3}	20 [j]
$trans$-$Co(en)_2Br_2^{+}$	8.4×10^{-3}	... [k]
$trans$-$Co(en)_2(NCS)Cl^{+}$	3×10^{-6}	30 [l]
cis-$Co(en)_2F_2^{+}$	5×10^{-4}	... [k]
$trans$-$Co(en)_2F_2^{+}$	6×10^{-5}	... [k]
$Cr(NH_3)_5Br^{2+}$	3×10^{-3}	22
$Cr(NH_3)_5Cl^{2+}$	5×10^{-4}	22
$Cr(NH_3)_5NCS^{2+}$	6×10^{-6}	25
$Cr(H_2O)_5NCS^{2+}$	5.5×10^{-7}	28 [m]
cis-$Cr(en)_2Cl_2^{+}$	2.1×10^{-2}	... [n]
$trans$-$Cr(en)_2Cl_2^{+}$	2.3×10^{-3}	... [n]
$Rh(NH_3)_5Br^{+}$	$\sim 10^{-5}$	26 [o]
$Ir(NH_3)_5Br^{+}$	$\sim 10^{-7}$	... [p]

Data from A. W. Adamson and R. G. Wilkins, *J. Am. Chem. Soc.*, **76**, 3379 (1954), except as noted.

[a] A. B. Lamb and R. G. Stevens, *ibid.*, **61**, 3229 (1939).

[b] J. N. Brønsted, *Z. physik. Chem.*, **122**, 383 (1926).

[c] Estimated from data at 45°C by R. G. Yalman, *ibid.*, **75**, 1842 (1953).

[d] Rate of water exchange, reference 10.

[e] B. Adell, *Z. anorg. u. allgem. Chem.*, **249**, 251 (1942); H. Taube and F. A. Posey, *J. Am. Chem. Soc.*, **75**, 1463 (1953).

[f] F. Basolo, J. G. Bergmann, and R. G. Pearson, *J. Phys. Chem.*, **56**, 22 (1952).

[g] From qualitative observations.

[h] J. P. Mathieu, *Bull. soc. chim.*, **3**, 2152 (1936) for activation energies; rates from Table 9.

[i] R. G. Pearson, R. E. Meeker, and F. Basolo, *J. Am. Chem. Soc.*, **78**, 2673 (1956).

[j] S. Asperger and C. K. Ingold, *J. Chem. Soc.*, **1956**, 2862, for activation energies; rates from F. Basolo, B. D. Stone, J. G. Bergmann, and R. G. Pearson, *J. Am. Chem. Soc.*, **76**, 3039 (1954).

[k] F. Basolo, W. R. Matoush, and R. G. Pearson, *ibid.*, **78**, 4883 (1956); difluoro complex reactions are acid catalyzed, minimum rate reported.

[l] C. K. Ingold, R. S. Nyholm, and M. L. Tobe, *J. Chem. Soc.*, **1956**, 1691. Chloride ion is released in reaction.

[m] C. Postmus and E. L. King, *J. Phys. Chem.*, **59**, 1217 (1955).

[n] R. G. Pearson, R. A. Munson, and F. Basolo, *J. Am. Chem. Soc.*, **80**, 504 (1958).

[o] A. B. Lamb, *J. Am. Chem. Soc.*, **61**, 3229 (1939); rate extrapolated from data at 64 and 84°C.

[p] A. B. Lamb and L. T. Fairhall, *ibid.*, **45**, 378 (1923), from data at 80 and 95°C.

in the expression $k = Ae^{-E_a/RT}$ is greater for the first compound. Unfortunately activation energies are usually known less accurately than rate constants.

This greater rate and lower value of E_a for a d^3 system compared to a d^6 ion is what is predicted on the basis of the crystal field theory. The difference in energy is not as great as might have been anticipated. Removing a chloride ion ligand completely in a pentammine complex causes a change in C.F.S.E. which may be estimated in the following way: the value of Dq for Cl^- is only somewhat more than half of that for NH_3. Hence the C.F.S.E. of $Co(NH_3)_5Cl^{2+}$ is estimated as $22Dq$, where Dq is the value for NH_3. On forming a square pyramid with C.N. five, the C.F.S.E. drops to $20Dq$. The loss in stabilization energy is thus about $2Dq$ or 12 kcal. For $Cr(NH_3)_5Cl^{2+}$, the loss would be half of this or 6 kcal. The expected difference is 6 kcal. For an S_N2 mechanism the difference would be at least this great for a frontside approach to one of the octahedral faces, and considerably greater, perhaps 30 kcal, for a pentagonal bipyramid transition state.

The slower rate of $Rh(NH_3)_5Br^{2+}$ and the still slower reaction of $Ir(NH_3)_5Br^{2+}$ are as expected. The chief difference is probably not because of crystal field effects, which are in the observed order since Dq is greater for Ir(III) than for Co(III), but in stronger binding due to the increased effective charge of the higher transition elements. For iridium it is also observed that the rates vary as $NO_3^- > I^- > Br^- > Cl^-$.[33] This decrease in rates is again in the order of increasing stability as measured by the equilibrium constant for the reaction

$$Ir(NH_3)_5X^{2+} + H_2O \rightleftharpoons Ir(NH_3)_5H_2O^{3+} + X^- \qquad (17)$$

The chloro complex is the most stable of those studied.

Table 13 contains some rate data for acid hydrolysis of a series of substituted pentammineacetato complexes of cobalt(III). A somewhat different kind of information is available from these rates than from those found in Table 12. True enough, the expected trend is found, in that the complexes in which the acetato group is only weakly basic hydrolyze the fastest. Thus the trifluoroacetato group, CF_3COO^-, has the least affinity for Co(III) just as it has the least affinity for H^+. The parallelism between the rates and the acid ionization constants of the corresponding substituted acetic acid is indeed very good. More important than this is the fact that steric factors seem to play a very minor role in the reaction. For example trichloroacetato and trimethylacetato, which are very bulky groups, seem to react at about the right rates, considering their K_a values, without

Table 13

**Rates of Acid and Base Hydrolyses of Some Pentammineacetato
Complexes of Cobalt(III), $Co(NH_3)_5X^{2+}$**

X^-	K_a for HX	k_{H_2O}, min^{-1}	k_{OH^-}, $M^{-1}min^{-1}$
1. CF_3COO^-	5×10^{-1}	3.3×10^{-3}	4.4
2. CCl_3COO^-	2×10^{-1}	3.2×10^{-3}	4.3
3. $CHCl_2COO^-$	5×10^{-2}	9.6×10^{-4}	1.6
4. CH_2ClCOO^-	1.4×10^{-3}	3.5×10^{-4}	2.5×10^{-1}
5. CH_2OHCOO^-	1.5×10^{-4}	. . .	7.0×10^{-2}
6. CH_3COO^-	1.8×10^{-5}	4.9×10^{-4}	4.2×10^{-2}
7. $CH_3CH_2COO^-$	1.5×10^{-5}	1.9×10^{-4}	2.7×10^{-2}
8. $(CH_3)_2CHCOO^-$	1.5×10^{-5}	1.6×10^{-4}	3.4×10^{-2}
9. $(CH_3)_3CCOO^-$	1.0×10^{-5}	2.6×10^{-4}	1.8×10^{-2}

Rates in acid at 70°C, and rates in base at 25°C.   Data from F. Basolo, J. G.
Bergmann, and R. G. Pearson, *J. Phys. Chem.*, **56**, 22 (1952).

any slowing down due to steric hindrance.   An examination of molecular models reveals that access to the front side of the complexes becomes progressively more difficult as the size of the groups attached to
carboxyl increases.   Hence this rate evidence is against a mechanism
which involves an S_N2 displacement by water from the same side of
the complex as the acetato group.   An S_N2 mechanism from the opposite side is not excluded, and an S_N1 mechanism is also in agreement
with the facts.   The intermediate type of mechanism depicted in Fig. 2
is also possible since, as the acetato group is moved out, sufficient
room for a water molecule to move in becomes available.

BASE HYDROLYSIS OF COBALT(III) COMPLEXES

Up to now, nothing has been said about the effect of the nature of
the incoming ligand on the rate of a substitution reaction.   The reason
for this is very simple: with the single exception of hydroxide ion,
there is no evidence for any direct reaction of a nucleophilic reagent
with a cobalt(III) complex in water solution.   Thus, in every example
that has been studied, the reaction mechanism for the substitution
of X by Y has gone through the intermediate formation of an aqua
complex as shown, for example,

$$Co(NH_3)_5X^{2+} + H_2O \rightleftharpoons Co(NH_3)_5H_2O^{3+} + X^- \qquad (18)$$

$$Co(NH_3)_5H_2O^{3+} + Y^- \rightarrow Co(NH_3)_5Y^{2+} + H_2O \qquad (19)$$

Since the order of the reaction in which X^- is liberated is always zero with respect to Y^-, there is no way to test the effect of the nature of Y^- on the rates.

The first example of the mechanism shown in 18 and 19 was provided by Ettle and Johnson,[34] who found that the rate of exchange of radioactive chloride ion with cis-$Co(en)_2Cl_2^+$ went through the aqua stage.

$$Co(en)_2Cl_2^+ + H_2O \rightarrow Co(en)_2(H_2O)Cl^{2+} + Cl^- \quad (20)$$

$$Co(en)_2(H_2O)Cl^{2+} + {}^*Cl^- \rightarrow Co(en)_2{}^*Cl_2^+ + H_2O \quad (21)$$

Furthermore the rate of the reaction leading to exchange was independent of the concentration of chloride ion so that no direct replacement of Cl^- by ${}^*Cl^-$ occurred.

Similar observations on the effect of added anions on the rate of hydrolysis of $Co(NH_3)_5Cl^{2+}$ were made by Garrick.[35] Except for small increases or decreases to be attributed to ion interaction effects (see p. 383), the rates were unaffected by NO_3^-, ClO_4^-, and SO_4^{2-} Nor does the presence of more strongly basic anions have any different result. Thus the rates of chloride ion release in cis- and trans-$Co(en)_2$-$(NO_2)Cl^+$ are independent of $[N_3^-]$ up to 0.5 M and of $[NO_2^-]$ up to 1.0 M, provided the solutions are buffered to keep $[OH^-]$ at a low value.[36] Thiocyanate ion, which is a good reagent for organic halides, is ineffective for the chloronitro complexes. Also the exchange reactions of $Cr(NH_3)_5NCS^{2+}$, $Co(NH_3)_5NCS^{2+}$, and $Co(en)_2(NCS)_2^+$ with ${}^*NCS^-$ proceed by the hydrolysis mechanism of 20 and 21 with no direct reaction.[37] At high concentrations of thiocyanate ion there is a small increase in the rate of hydrolysis of $Co(NH_3)_5NCS^{2+}$, but this is ascribed to ion-pair formation (p. 383).

In alkaline buffer solutions containing borate ion, acetate ion, or trimethylamine as the basic component, the increased rate of hydrolysis compared to acid conditions is due only to the hydroxide ion present.[38] If one plots the observed rate constant for the release of chloride ion from trans-$Co(en)_2Cl_2^+$ in acetic acid–acetate buffers as a function of the reciprocal of the acetic acid concentration at constant acetate ion concentration, a straight line is obtained.[39] Upon extrapolation to infinite acetic acid concentration, the rate becomes the same as that observed in a nitric acid solution of pH 1. Hence acetate ion has no effect on the rate. cis- and trans-$Cr(en)_2Cl_2^+$ also hydrolyze at a rate independent of acetate ion concentration.

This independence of reaction rate on the nature and concentration of external reagents is not only characteristic of cobalt(III) and chromium(III) but also of the metals which form octahedral complexes in general, at least in the divalent and trivalent state. Thus the exchange reactions, involving exchange with a ligand, which have rates slow enough to measure are almost always independent of the concentration of the external ligand. This is true, for example, in the exchanges of $Ni(en)_3^{2+}$ with ethylenediamine,[18] of $Ni(phen)_3^{2+}$ with 1,10-phenanthroline,[15b] and of $Cr(CN)_6^{3-}$, $Fe(CN)_6^{4-}$, and $Co(CN)_6^{3-}$ with cyanide ion.[23b]

As mentioned, hydroxide ion falls into a special category. It is necessary to appreciate the great influence of even low concentrations of hydroxide ion on the rate of release of halide ion and other labile ligands from ammine complexes of cobalt(III). Under alkaline conditions hydrolysis is very rapid, for many complexes the half-life being less than 1 sec for 0.001 M reactants at 25°C. Flow techniques can be used to study such very rapid reactions,[38] or they can be studied in buffer solutions of suitable pH. In a few cases, such as for $Co(NH_3)_5$-Cl^{2+}, conventional techniques for kinetic studies can be used.

In all cases in which a reaction with hydroxide ion can be detected, the reactions have been found to be second order overall, first order in the complex, and first order in [OH$^-$]. Table 13 also shows a number of the second-order rate constants for the base hydrolysis of the cobalt complexes that are listed there. There is the same trend in rates as for acid hydrolysis, the weakest base again being the one most easily replaced. Figure 4 shows that there is a linear relationship between the logarithms of the rate constant for base hydrolysis and the logarithm of the acid ionization constant of the corresponding substituted acetic acid. The difference between the base and acid hydrolysis results lies in the much greater rate of the former (factor of 10^5 allowing for temperature difference) and in the somewhat greater spread of rates for base hydrolysis. Thus for a total change of 10^4 in

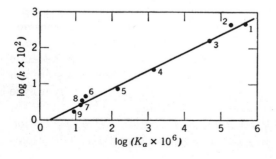

FIG. 4. Rates of base hydrolysis of $Co(NH_3)_5X^{2+}$ compared to the acid strength of HX. Ions numbered as in Table 13. (From F. Basolo, J. G. Bergmann, and R. G. Pearson, *J. Phys. Chem.*, **56**, 22 (1952).)

the acid ionization constants there is only a spread of 10 for the rates of acid hydrolysis, but of 100 for base hydrolysis.

These results could be interpreted as showing a common mechanism for acid and base hydrolysis, such as a displacement process. As indicated previously the incoming group must then approach from the back because both sets of rates are independent of the size of the acetato ligand. The greater spread in rates for a reaction with OH^- acting as a nucleophile compared to H_2O is reasonable, since the inductive effect of a strongly acid group such as CF_3COO^- would be more efficient in promoting the approach of a negative ion than of a negative end of a dipole. This would be a rate increasing factor in addition to that of the weaker cobalt-oxygen bond in the strong acid complex. Similarly the fact that the ratio of rates for acid hydrolysis and for base hydrolysis of $Co(NH_3)_5Cl^{2+}$, $Co(NH_3)_5Br^{2+}$, and $Co(NH_3)_5NO_3{}^{2+}$ is constant suggests a common, presumably S_N2, mechanism for both reactions.[40] Furthermore the ratios of the rate constants of 10^5 can be rationalized by considering the following equilibrium,

$$Co(NH_3)_4XH_2O^{2+} + OH^- \rightleftharpoons Co(NH_3)_4XOH^+ + H_2O \qquad (22)$$

which gives the relative stabilities of a hydroxo complex and an aqua complex similar to the transition states for the substitution reaction. The equilibrium constant for 22 is simply K_a/K_w, where K_w is 10^{-14} and K_a is the acid ionization constant of a divalent cobalt complex. From a study of the acid strengths of cobalt(III) complexes (see pp. 387–388) it can be concluded that K_a is the order of 10^{-8}. This makes the equilibrium constant for 22 about 10^6, and this should be the upper limit for the ratio of base and acid hydrolysis rates (an upper limit because bonding is less in a transition state than in a normal molecule).

An examination of rate data for other ions reveals that such a unified mechanism cannot be correct. Table 14 gives a further group of base hydrolysis rates for cobalt(III) complexes. A comparison of the acid hydrolysis rates of these same compounds given in the earlier tables shows that the ratio of rates is by no means constant. In fact in three series of compounds the opposite trend is found for base hydrolysis and for acid hydrolysis. For example, the first seven compounds show the effect of increased chelation, which slows down acid hydrolysis but increases base hydrolysis (by very large factors in the case of the *cis* isomers). A smaller effect is shown by the substituted pyridinechloro complexes (21 to 24 in the table) in which a base-strengthening substituent increases acid hydrolysis but slows down base hydrolysis. In compounds 7 to 17 the effect of alkyl substituents on ethylenediamine

Table 14

Rates of Base Hydrolysis, k_{OH^-}, for Some Complexes of Cobalt(III) Compared to Rates of Acid Hydrolysis, k_{H_2O}, at 25°C

Ion	k_{OH^-}, M^{-1} sec^{-1}	k_{H_2O}, sec^{-1}
1. $Co(NH_3)_5Cl^{2+}$	8.5×10^{-1}	1.7×10^{-6}
2. $cis\text{-}Co(en)_2NH_3Cl^{2+}$	5.4×10^{1}	4.7×10^{-7} a
3. $cis\text{-}Co(trien)NH_3Cl^{2+}$	1.6×10^{2}	2.2×10^{-7} a
4. $cis\text{-}Co(en)_2Cl_2^+$	1×10^{3}	2.5×10^{-4}
5. $cis\text{-}Co(trien)Cl_2^+$	2×10^{5}	1.5×10^{-4}
6. $trans\text{-}Co(NH_3)_4Cl_2^+$	1.8×10^{3}	1.8×10^{-2}
7. $trans\text{-}Co(en)_2Cl_2^+$	3.0×10^{3}	3.2×10^{-5}
8. $trans\text{-}Co(pn)_2Cl_2^+$	2.3×10^{3}	6.2×10^{-5}
9. $trans\text{-}Co(dl\text{-}bn)_2Cl_2^+$	2.1×10^{3}	1.5×10^{-4}
10. $trans\text{-}Co(m\text{-}bn)_2Cl_2^+$	9.8×10^{3}	4.2×10^{-3}
11. $trans\text{-}Co(i\text{-}bn)_2Cl_2^+$	9.8×10^{3}	2.2×10^{-3}
12. $trans\text{-}Co(N\text{-}meen)_2Cl_2^+$	1.1×10^{4}	1.7×10^{-5}
13. $trans\text{-}Co(N\text{-}pren)_2Cl_2^+$	2.1×10^{4}	1.2×10^{-4}
14. $trans\text{-}Co(en)_2Br_2^+$	1.2×10^{4}	1.4×10^{-4}
15. $trans\text{-}Co(en)_2F_2^+$	6.4×10^{1}	1×10^{-6}
16. $trans\text{-}Co(dan)_2Cl_2^+$	1.7×10^{4}	3×10^{-3}
17. $trans\text{-}Co(en)_2(NCS)Cl^+$	1.3×10^{1}	5×10^{-8} b
18. $trans\text{-}Co(en)_2(OH)Cl^+$	2×10^{2}	1.4×10^{-3}
19. $cis\text{-}Co(en)_2(NO_2)Cl^+$	3.2×10^{-2}	3.6×10^{-6} c
20. $trans\text{-}Co(en)_2(NO_2)Cl^+$	8.0×10^{-2}	3.6×10^{-5} c
21. $Co(en)_2(py)Cl^{2+}$	1.6×10^{3}	1.1×10^{-5} d
22. $Co(en)_2(3\text{-}mepy)Cl^{2+}$	1.3×10^{3}	1.3×10^{-5} d
23. $Co(en)_2(4\text{-}mepy)Cl^{2+}$	1.3×10^{3}	1.4×10^{-5} d
24. $Co(en)_2(4\text{-}meopy)Cl^{2+}$	1.2×10^{3}	1.5×10^{-5} d

Data taken from R. G. Pearson, R. E. Meeker, and F. Basolo, *J. Am. Chem. Soc.*, **78**, 709 (1956), except as indicated.

a Corrected from rates at 35°C by dividing by three.

b C. K. Ingold, R. S. Nyholm, and M. L. Tobe, *J. Chem. Soc.*, **1956**, 1691.

c Rates of acid and base hydrolysis at 0°C, S. Asperger and C. K. Ingold, *J. Chem. Soc.*, **1956**, 2862.

d F. Basolo, J. G. Bergmann, R. E. Meeker, and R. G. Pearson, *J. Am. Chem. Soc.*, **78**, 2676 (1956). Acid hydrolysis rates at 50°C.

is quite different for the two kinds of hydrolysis. Thus C alkylation slows down, or has only a small accelerating effect on, the rates of base hydrolysis compared to the large accelerations of acid hydrolysis. Also N alkylation produces the greatest increase in the rate of base hydrolysis, whereas, in the case of N—CH$_3$, acid hydrolysis is actually retarded.

It would seem that different mechanisms for acid and base hydrolysis are required. Further the probability that the reaction with OH^- is a bimolecular displacement process is lessened considerably by the facts that increased chelation and increased steric crowding about the cobalt atom do not greatly reduce the rates of these reactions. Nevertheless it is necessary to account for the unusual and specific reactivity of hydroxide ion in some manner.

Such a specific mechanism has been given by Garrick,[41] inspired by the earlier work of Brønsted.[42] Brønsted noted that the hydrolysis of $Co(NH_3)_5NO_3{}^{2+}$ is independent of pH below 3; however, that of $Co(NH_3)_4(H_2O)NO_3{}^{2+}$ was dependent on H^+ even below pH 3. The explanation he gave was that the aqua complex dissociated to a hydroxo complex which reacted more rapidly.

$$Co(NH_3)_4(H_2O)NO_3{}^{2+} + H_2O \xrightarrow{slow} Co(NH_3)_4(H_2O)_2{}^{3+} + NO_3{}^-$$

$$(23)$$

$$Co(NH_3)_4(H_2O)NO_3{}^{2+} \underset{}{\overset{fast}{\rightleftharpoons}} Co(NH_3)_4(OH)NO_3{}^+ + H^+$$

$$(24)$$

$$Co(NH_3)_4(OH)NO_3{}^+ + H_2O \xrightarrow{fast} Co(NH_3)_4(OH)H_2O^{2+} + NO_3{}^-$$

$$(25)$$

The acid-base equilibrium in 24 would be rapidly established. As Table 12 shows, a hydroxo group has a labilizing influence on a replaceable ligand so that 25 would be fast. The concentration of the reactive hydroxo complex would be inversely proportional to $[H^+]$, and the rate should show the same inverse proportionality. This is in agreement with the observations. A similar explanation holds for the second-order dependence on $[OH^-]$ of the rate of hydrolysis [43] of $Cr(H_2O)_5Cl^{2+}$. The reactive species is chiefly $Cr(H_2O)_3(OH)_2Cl$.

Garrick's mechanism involves the formation, in a rapid acid-base equilibrium step, of the conjugate base or amido complex of the original ammine complex. This then dissociates rapidly and eventually forms the hydroxo complex, in which 27, although rapid, is the rate-

$$Co(NH_3)_5Cl^{2+} + OH^- \overset{fast}{\rightleftharpoons} Co(NH_3)_4NH_2Cl^+ + H_2O \quad (26)$$

$$Co(NH_3)_4(NH_2)Cl^+ \xrightarrow{slow} Co(NH_3)_4NH_2{}^{2+} + Cl^- \quad (27)$$

$$Co(NH_3)_4NH_2{}^{2+} + H_2O \xrightarrow{fast} Co(NH_3)_5OH^{2+} \quad (28)$$

determining step. Such a mechanism may be conveniently called an S_N1CB *mechanism* [1] (substitution, nucleophilic, unimolecular, conjugate base).

In order to agree with the observed second-order kinetics (first order in OH^-) it is necessary that reaction 26 occur, but only to a small extent even in 0.01 M alkali. Otherwise all of the chloro complex would be converted to the conjugate base form at some particular value of the pH, and for further increases in $[OH^-]$ no further increase in rate could happen. Furthermore, in order to agree with the observation that only hydroxide ion affects the rate and that other bases are ineffective as such, it is necessary that reaction 26 be established as an equilibrium more rapidly than the rapid overall reaction. The necessity for this arises from the certainty of a general base catalysis otherwise.[44] A proton could be removed from the original complex by any base, and the resultant amido compound could rapidly react. In such a case the rate equation for hydrolysis would be

$$\text{Rate} = k[\text{complex}][\text{base}] \tag{29a}$$

or rather a sum of such terms for every base in solution. Only if 26 is an equilibrium will the equation for the rate be

$$\text{Rate} = k[\text{conjugate base}] = \frac{kK_a}{K_w}[\text{complex}][OH^-] \tag{29b}$$

These requirements are fulfilled apparently since cobalt ammines are acidic enough to exchange deuterium with D_2O even in acid solution,[45] but are too weak as acids to measure experimentally (see p. 388). Also in the case of $Co(NH_3)_5Cl^{2+}$ in basic solution it has been shown that exchange with D_2O occurs more rapidly than the net release of the chloride ion.[46]

The S_N1CB mechanism can be used to rationalize most, but not all, of the data in Table 14. From equation 29b it can be seen that the observed second-order rate constant for base hydrolysis is equal to kK_a/K_w, where k is the rate constant for the dissociation of the conjugate base as in 27 and K_a is the acid constant of the amine group. It may be postulated that the rate constant will vary for a series of compounds in the same manner as the rate constant for acid hydrolysis, assuming the latter reaction also goes by a dissociation mechanism. Hence a tentative rule can be formulated that *rates of base hydrolysis should parallel rates of acid hydrolysis for a series of complex ions of cobalt(III) unless a marked change occurs in the acidities of some of the members of the series.* That is, changes in K_a can influence the rate of base hydrolysis.

On this basis it can be explained why increasing chelation increases the rate of base hydrolysis. It is known that the K_a values for the complexes $Pt(NH_3)_6{}^{4+}$, $Pt(en)(NH_3)_4{}^{4+}$, and $Pt(en)_3{}^{4+}$ are 1.2×10^{-8}, 7.1×10^{-7}, and 3.5×10^{-6} respectively.[47] Also the rate of deuterium exchange [45] is greater for $Co(en)_3{}^{3+}$ than for $Co(NH_3)_6{}^{3+}$. Hence increasing chelation increases the acidity of the remaining N—H bonds and, in accordance with the S_N1CB mechanism, should increase the rate of base hydrolysis. The rate constants for C alkylation are also understandable in terms of the inductive effect weakening the acidity of the ammine portion and partially compensating for the increased rate of dissociation due to steric crowding.

The high rates of base hydrolysis of the N-alkyl complexes are also a result of increased acidity as judged from such indirect evidence as the pK_a of $Co(en)_2(H_2O)_2{}^{3+}$ equal to 5.28, and that of $Co(N\text{-meen})_2$-$(H_2O)_2{}^{3+}$ equal to 4.71 (for the aqua groups).[38] These somewhat unexpected results of groups such as CH_3 and $NH_2CH_2CH_2$ being acid strengthening are apparently due to solvation effects such as have been used to explain the acidity of $(CH_3)_3NH^+$ and are discussed in more detail in Chapter 9.

There is a critical test possible for the S_N1CB mechanism. Obviously to be operative, it is required that the coordination compound contain a moderately acidic proton. It is predicted, then, that complexes without acidic protons will not react rapidly with hydroxide ion. This is true for the complexes $Co(CN)_5Br^{3-}$ and $Co(CN)_5I^{3-}$, which hydrolyze at a rate independent of pH over the alkaline range.[46] It is also true for complexes such as $Fe(CN)_5NH_3{}^{3-}$ and $Fe(CN)_5SO_3{}^{5-}$, which hydrolyze in a first-order process independent of alkali.[49] In these cases of negatively charged ions, the failure to react with hydroxide ion may be due to electrostatic repulsion and hence is not conclusive. A better example is in the *trans*-tetrapyridinedichloro complexes shown in Table 11. These compounds without acidic protons react at a rate independent of pH up to 9.18,[48] from which it may be safely concluded that the rate of reaction with hydroxide ion is very small compared to most of those shown in Table 14. Unfortunately higher pH solutions cause complete decomposition of these compounds.

Another example [48] is the *trans*-bis(-2,2'-bipyridine)dinitrocobalt(III) ion which reacts in a first-order process independent of alkali over the range of $[OH^-]$ equal to 10^{-4} to 10^{-3} M. The corresponding dichloro complex is very labile (Table 11), and hence the more inert dinitro complex was used. The extreme lability conferred by the 2,2'-bipyridine group offers the possible explanation that perhaps an S_N1 mechanism is greatly promoted for this compound and the normal S_N2 mechanism of hydroxide ion is too small to detect.[92]   This argument will not hold for the case of $trans$-Co$((C_2H_5)_2PCH_2CH_2P(C_2H_5)_2)_2Cl_2^+$. Because of π bonding it is expected that the cobalt atom in this complex will be more positive than usual.   Accordingly, it should react very slowly by an S_N1 mechanism and better by an S_N2 mechanism.   It is found that chloride ion release is very slow in acid solution and largely due to decomposition.   In alkaline solution the complex reacts somewhat faster, but at a rate independent of the hydroxide ion concentration in the pH range 9 to 11. [50]

$$Co(tep)_2Cl_2^+ + OH^- \xrightarrow{\text{slow}} Co(tep)_2OHCl^+ + Cl^- \qquad (30)$$

Thus this compound behaves as expected if the rapid reactions of ammine complexes are due to an S_N1CB mechanism.   There is no evidence for a direct chloride ion displacement by hydroxide ion in any of the compounds tested which have acidic protons.

π BONDING IN DISSOCIATION REACTIONS OF OCTAHEDRAL COMPLEXES

If the conjugate base of the original complex is the reactive species in base hydrolysis, it is necessary to see if the great rapidity of such reactions is an expected result of the nature of the conjugate base. As mentioned, the observed second-order rate constant is the product of an equilibrium constant, K_a/K_w, and a unimolecular rate constant for dissociation. K_a cannot be measured for cobalt(III) complexes if the acidity is in an N—H bond.   However, it may be demonstrated that it must be less than 10^{-18} (see Chapter 9), and it is convenient to arbitrarily assign a maximum value of 10^{-14} to all the complexes discussed so far.   This procedure ignores the undoubted difference in electrical charge effects and substituent effects, but the point is that K_a is 10^{-14} or smaller for all of the systems studied.

With this value of K_a, the observed rate constant for base hydrolysis becomes equal to the rate constant for dissociation of the conjugate base which we shall call k_{CB}.   If K_a is less than 10^{-14}, k_{CB} will be correspondingly greater.   Table 15 gives some typical data on the ratio of k_{CB} to k_{H_2O}, the latter being the rate constant for acid hydrolysis.   It can be seen that there is a very large factor of the order of 10^5 to 10^8 in favor of the conjugate base in every case but that of the chloronitro complex.   Furthermore these ratios will be even larger if K_a is less

Table 15

Ratio of Rate Constants for Dissociation of Conjugate Bases and Their Parent Complexes

Ion	k_{CB}/k_{H_2O}	Ion	k_{CB}/k_{H_2O}
$Co(NH_3)_5Cl^{2+}$	5×10^5	trans-$Co(en)_2Cl_2^+$	9.0×10^7
cis-$Co(en)_2NH_3Cl^{2+}$	1.1×10^8	trans-$Co(en)_2Br_2^+$	8.6×10^7
cis-$Co(trien)NH_3Cl^{2+}$	7.3×10^8	trans-$Co(en)_2F_2^+$	6.4×10^7
cis-$Co(en)_2Cl_2^+$	4×10^6	trans-$Co(en)_2NCSCl^+$	2.6×10^8
trans-$Co(NH_3)_4Cl_2^+$	1.0×10^6	trans-$Co(en)_2NO_2Cl^+$	2.2×10^3

than 10^{-14}. This large difference in rates is unexpected. It is true that the conjugate base has a lower positive charge by one unit than its parent. This would facilitate release of a negative ion. However, inspection of the divalent ions in Table 9 compared to the univalent ions shows that this factor is expected to be only about 10^2. This figure is also in agreement with calculations based on electrostatic theory and with other experimental data on the effect of electrical charges on rates of reaction.[51]

Thus there is an unexplained factor of 10^3 to 10^6, and perhaps even larger, favoring the reaction rate of the conjugate base. Since these all contain an amido group with an unshared pair of electrons, it is proposed that the increased rate of dissociation is due to π bonding in the reaction intermediate or in the transition state.[52] This π bonding is of the type in which electrons move from ligand to metal. The movement will aid in the loss of halide ion and also stabilize the five-coordinated species after dissociation,

$$\begin{array}{c}
\diagdown\;\diagup\;NH_2 \\
Co \\
\diagup\;\diagdown\;X
\end{array}
\rightarrow
\begin{array}{c}
\diagdown\; \\
Co\!=\!NH_2^+ + X^- \\
\diagup\;
\end{array}
\qquad (31)$$

If such π bonding is responsible for the unusual reactivity of amido complexes, it should be noticeable with other ligands containing an unshared pair of electrons. The magnitude of the effect should depend on the tendency of the ligand to release electrons and in particular should increase in the series $Cl^- < OH^- < NH_2^-$. The data in Table 12 shows that the acid hydrolyses of chlorohydroxo complexes of cobalt(III) are faster than those of the corresponding dichloro complexes by a factor of 40 to 50 in spite of the statistical factor of two in favor of the dichloro ions. Thus the expected trend is observed.

It is not necessary to postulate such π bonding to explain the relative reactivities. Another explanation could be based on the inductive effects of the ligands involved. It is known that the base-strengthening effects of these ligands increase in the order $Cl^- < OH^- < NH_2^-$ and that base-strengthening ligands would increase the rate. However, this kind of effect appears to be too small to be a satisfactory explanation (see Table 11). The situation is similar to what is encountered in organic chemistry in explaining the high solvolytic reactivity of α-haloethers. The accepted explanation for this reactivity is that resonance, involving π bonding from the oxygen atom's unshared electron pairs, stabilizes the carbonium ion formed.

$$CH_3OCH_2Cl \rightarrow Cl^- + CH_3-O-CH_2^+$$
$$CH_3-\overset{\uparrow}{O}{}^+{=}CH_2 \tag{32}$$

In this case it is known that the proper geometry can be reached so that π bonding can occur. It is necessary to consider the situation in octahedral complexes more closely to see what geometric considerations are involved. This has been done in terms of the valence bond theory [52] but the crystal field approach is easier to visualize.

In an earlier section (p. 54) ligand to metal π bonding was mentioned in connection with the crystal field theory. It was pointed out that π-electron-donating ligands would raise the energy of the d_{xy}-type orbitals if these orbitals were already occupied by metal atom electrons. This is the case for cobalt(III) and chromium(III). Although this would make an amido complex less stable, it is not greatly changed by the dissociation of one of the other ligands in the system. Thus it is an interaction which would make the amido complex harder to form (lower K_a), but not one that will increase its lability. Another orbital interaction which is present is that between the ligand π orbital and a p orbital on the central atom. This would be a $4p$ orbital in the case of cobalt or chromium, which, in the crystal field theory, is unoccupied. Hence the interaction would be a stabilizing one in that the ligand π electrons would gain delocalization energy (or resonance energy) by spreading over somewhat to the p orbital. The interaction would be small because of the relatively high energy of the metal atom p orbital. By removing one of the negative ligands, the energy of the p orbital is lowered, however, and the interaction energy would be greater. Accordingly this is a factor which could cause an amido complex to be reactive in an S_N1 process.

If the ligand is removed from, say, the x axis, it is the p_x orbital

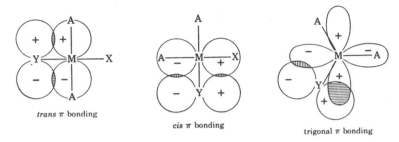

FIG. 5. pp-π bonding involving electron transfer from a ligand *trans* or *cis* to a replaceable group X. pd-π bonding after departure of X and rearrangement to a trigonal bipyramid.

which is lowered most in energy relative to the p_y and p_z orbitals. Now only a ligand which is *cis* to the removed ligand can form a π bond to the p_x orbital. The *trans* ligand can only π-bond to p_y or p_z. The conclusion is that an electron-donating ligand in the *cis* position to a reactive group should labilize it more than when in the *trans* position. The situation is illustrated in Fig. 5. The data in Table 13 show that it is true that *cis*-dihalo and *cis*-chlorohydroxo complexes are more reactive to acid hydrolysis than their *trans* counterparts by a factor of about ten. This is in agreement with the theory. The relative effect of *cis*- and *trans*-amido is not known since all of the compounds studied in base hydrolysis have an ammine group *cis* to the reactive ligand.

Conceivably this greater reactivity might be due to electrostatic repulsions of the negative ligands which would appear to be greater in the *cis* position than in the *trans* because of the smaller distance of separation. There are reasons why this is probably not true. One is that the superiority of *cis* over *trans* vanishes in the case of base hydrolysis for the dichloro complexes. This is because amido π bonding, *cis* for both complexes, supersedes halogen π bonding. This same explanation will hold for the relatively low rate of base hydrolysis of *trans*-$Co(en)_2(OH)Cl^+$ compared to its large rate of acid hydrolysis.

Also for non-electron-donating negative ligands such as nitro, the reverse is found in that *trans*-$Co(en)_2(NO_2)Cl^+$ is more reactive than *cis*-$Co(en)_2(NO_2)Cl^+$ in both acid and base hydrolysis. Also indirect evidence shows that the sulfito group, like nitro, is more activating when in the *trans* position than in the *cis* position. In the synthesis of the isomers of $Co(en)(NH_3)_2Cl_2{}^+$, the key step is the replacement of two NH_3 groups *trans* to two $SO_3{}^{2-}$ groups, leaving two NH_3 groups *cis* to SO_3^{2-} untouched.[53] The acid ionization constants of *cis-* and *trans-*$Co(en)_2(H_2O)_2^{3+}$ as well as of *cis-* and *trans-*$Cr(en)_2(H_2O)_2^{3+}$ also show that electrostatic repulsion, in the case of two protons, is greater when in the *trans* position than in the *cis* position.[54] Thus in these cases the *trans* isomer is the stronger acid, and the difference in the successive ionization constants is greater for the *trans* isomer than for the *cis*. Finally, the examples in this paragraph are generally cited as examples of the *trans* effect, which states that a negative ligand *trans* to a reactive ligand will activate it. This rule, which is valid and very valuable for the square complexes of platinum(II), is discussed in detail in Chapter 4. If the π-bonding hypothesis for the reactions of octahedral complexes such as cobalt(III) and chromium(III) is valid, this rule will not work for such complexes in the case of ligands which form π bonds by electron donation to the central atom.

There is another prediction that can be made based on the π-bonding concept. If a group dissociates completely leaving an intermediate of C.N. five, there will be a great tendency for the square pyramid structure to rearrange into a trigonal bipyramid structure. The basis for this is that, by such a rearrangement, π bonding can now take place between the ligand and the empty $d_{x^2-y^2}$ orbital in the trigonal plane (Fig. 5). Since this orbital is lower in energy than the p_x orbital, the new π bonding will lead to a greater stabilization of the system. Such a rearrangement will have important stereochemical consequences for the products of a substitution reaction. These will be discussed in Chapter 5. It will be recalled that, on the basis of crystal field effects, rearrangement to a trigonal bipyramid is strongly forbidden, unless other factors such as π bonding are involved.

There is some further evidence that suggests that such rearrangement to a trigonal bipyramid will occur during the base hydrolysis of metal ion complexes if an S_N1CB mechanism is involved. Table 16 shows the data on the few other systems besides cobalt(III) where the rates of reaction with hydroxide ion are known. The remarkable result is that the ratio of base hydrolysis rates to acid hydrolysis rates for chromium(III) is only of the order of 10^2 compared to 10^7 to 10^8 for analogous cobalt complexes. The rate of reaction with hydroxide ion is very small for the chromium complexes. This is unexpected on the basis of an S_N2 mechanism, either by the crystal field theory, which definitely would predict that chromium would react faster than cobalt, or by the valence bond theory. In the latter theory a path for reaction by a displacement mechanism could involve coupling one pair of d electrons in one orbital, thus emptying an orbital and making it available for nucleophilic attack.[12, 37]

Table 16

Rates of Base Hydrolysis of Some Chromium(III) and Other Complexes at 25°C

Ion	k_{OH^-}, M^{-1} sec^{-1}	k_{H_2O}, sec^{-1}
cis-Cr(en)$_2$Cl$_2$$^+$	2.72×10^{-2} [a]	3.5×10^{-4}
trans-Cr(en)$_2$Cl$_2$$^+$	3.68×10^{-2} [a]	3.9×10^{-5}
cis-Co(en)$_2$Cl$_2$$^+$	1×10^3	2.5×10^{-4}
trans-Co(en)$_2$Cl$_2$$^+$	3.0×10^3	3.2×10^{-5}
Rh(NH$_3$)$_5$Br^{2+}	9.2×10^{-1} [b]	5.2×10^{-5} [b]
Co(NH$_3$)$_5$Br^{2+}	6.1 [c]	6.5×10^{-6}

[a] R. G. Pearson, R. A. Munson, and F. Basolo, *J. Am. Chem. Soc.*, **80**, 504 (1958).

[b] At 84°C; data from reference 59.

[c] J. N. Brønsted and R. Livingston, *J. Am. Chem. Soc.*, **49**, 435 (1927).

A slow rate of reaction in a conjugate base dissociation mechanism may be due to a low acidity of the ammine complex or to a small reactivity of the conjugate base. The former is not likely to be true for chromium(III) compared to cobalt(III) because, for corresponding aqua complexes, the acidity of the two elements is very similar (see p. 387). If the overall slowness of the reaction with hydroxide ion is due to a lack of reactivity of the conjugate base, then it follows that the greater the number of d electrons on the central metal atom, the faster its conjugate base must react (cobalt faster than chromium). This is not unreasonable since it was pointed out earlier that the interaction of the π-bonding electrons of an amido or hydroxo group with a filled d_{xy}-type orbital was repulsive. Since removal of a chloro group alone would not diminish this repulsion, it must be postulated that removal of the chloro group is accompanied by rearrangement to a trigonal bipyramid. This would greatly reduce the interaction with the occupied d orbitals of the metal atom. The driving force for such rearrangement would be greater for cobalt than for chromium.

Such an explanation may also make reasonable the rather low rate of reaction of the chloronitro complexes of cobalt(III) with base. If π bonding occurs in which the d_{xy} electrons of cobalt are drawn into the nitro group, this would stabilize the conjugate base as far as the repulsive interactions of π electrons from an amido group on the x or y axes are concerned. It is also seen from Table 16 that the ratio of base hydrolysis to acid hydrolysis of a rhodium(III) ion is somewhat less than for a cobalt(III) ion. The opposite might be expected since Dq for rhodium is expected to be larger than for cobalt, and accordingly all crystal field effects would be magnified. The data for rhodium are at 84°C and those for cobalt are at 25°C, which may have some effect. The activation energies for the reaction of $Co(NH_3)_5Br^{2+}$ with water and with OH^- are about the same,[46] so that the ratio of rates would be nearly constant over a range of temperature in this case.

Other evidence can be cited for the type of π bonding proposed in which electrons from the ligand move in to the metal atom. The binuclear complex $(NH_3)_5Cr—O—Cr(NH_3)_5^{4+}$ has a paramagnetism corresponding to two unpaired electrons instead of the six expected for two chromium(III) atoms. This and other evidence [55] suggests that two electrons from each chromium and four electrons from oxygen are paired in occupying four three-center molecular orbitals centered on Cr—O—Cr. These would be formed from the d_{xy} and d_{xz} orbitals of each chromium and from the p_y and p_z orbitals of oxygen, for example. The complex $Cl_5Ru—O—RuCl_5^{4-}$ is diamagnetic instead of having four unpaired electrons and seems to have the same kind of orbital hybridization.[56] In this case x-ray evidence shows that the Ru—O—Ru bond is linear as is required for the proposed explanation. It may be expected that π bonding from ligands with unshared pairs of electrons to central atoms which have, or can be made to have, a stable vacant orbital is a general phenomenon in coordination chemistry.

REACTIONS INVOLVING THE REPLACEMENT OF COORDINATED WATER

The replacement of water from an aqua complex is the reverse of an acid hydrolysis reaction and is sometimes called the anation reaction.

$$Co(NH_3)_5H_2O^{3+} + X^- \rightarrow Co(NH_3)_5X^{2+} + H_2O \qquad (33)$$

Kinetic studies of these reactions in aqueous solutions after suitable corrections are found to be second order with a rate dependent on $[X^-]$.[57] However, from this information alone it cannot be concluded that these reactions are bimolecular. The same second-order kinetics would be observed for a unimolecular process such as

$$Co(NH_3)_5H_2O^{3+} \underset{\substack{+H_2O \\ \text{fast}}}{\overset{\substack{\text{slow} \\ -H_2O}}{\rightleftharpoons}} Co(NH_3)_5^{3+} \overset{\substack{+X^- \\ \text{fast}}}{\longrightarrow} Co(NH_3)_5X^{2+} + H_2O$$

$$(34)$$

In such a scheme a pseudoequilibrium exists between the aqua complex and the five-coordinated intermediate. Since group X^- must compete with the solvent water for the active intermediate, it follows that the rate of formation of $Co(NH_3)_5X^{2+}$ can be dependent upon the concentration of X^-. On the other hand, there should be some high concentration of the reactant, X^-, where the rate of replacement of water would no longer be dependent upon the concentration of X^-. The rate of formation of $Co(NH_3)_5X^{2+}$ at this concentration should be equal to the rate of formation of $Co(NH_3)_5^{3+}$ and also equal to the rate of water exchange between the aqua complex and the solvent. Such a reaction scheme may be formalized by the use of the *steady-state approximation* [58] which we can apply to the set of reactions

$$A \underset{k_2}{\overset{k_1}{\rightleftharpoons}} B \tag{35}$$

$$B + C \overset{k_3}{\rightarrow} D \tag{36}$$

The rate of formation of B is given by the equation

$$\frac{d[B]}{dt} = k_1[A] - k_2[B] - k_3[C][B] \tag{37}$$

Since [B] is a very reactive intermediate, the steady-state approximation assumes that its concentration remains small and constant during the reaction and allows the formulation $d[B]/dt = 0$, at the steady state. Equation 37 becomes equal to zero and gives the steady-state concentration of B as

$$[B] = \frac{k_1[A]}{k_2 + k_3[C]} \tag{38}$$

Therefore the rate of formation of the final product D is given by

$$\frac{d[D]}{dt} = k_3[B][C] = \frac{k_1k_3[A][C]}{k_2 + k_3[C]} \tag{39}$$

Two limiting cases of 39 are of interest. One is where $k_2 \gg k_3[C]$ so that

$$\frac{d[D]}{dt} = \frac{k_1k_3}{k_2}[A][C] \tag{40}$$

Under these conditions a second-order reaction would be observed, dependent on [C]. In the example where A is $Co(NH_3)_5H_2O^{3+}$ and C is X^-, this would correspond to what is observed for the anation reaction. The other limiting case is when $k_3[C] \gg k_2$, which gives

$$\frac{d[D]}{dt} = k_1[A] \tag{41}$$

This shows that a limiting rate is reached which is first order and independent of [C], or [X$^-$]. Furthermore, the first-order constant k_1 will be equal to the rate constant for dissociation of the aqua complex. It should, for example, be equal to the rate of water exchange in isotopically labeled systems.[10] Furthermore, if the symbol X$^-$ represents a number of reagents, the same limiting rate should be reached for all at sufficiently great concentration.

Attempts have been made to discover such indications of an S_N1 mechanism for the water replacement reaction. They have not met with success, however, because of the complications introduced by the fact that the reactants are charged particles and very sensitive to their environment. For example in studying the reversible reactions

$$Rh(NH_3)_5H_2O^{3+} + Br^- \rightleftharpoons Rh(NH_3)_5Br^{2+} + H_2O \tag{42}$$

Lamb [59] found that both the forward and reverse reactions followed a first-order law under conditions where the [Br$^-$] was of the same order as [Rh(NH$_3$)$_5$H$_2$O^{3+}]. However, adding excess bromide ion, or increasing the total concentration, increased the first-order rate constants. The explanation for the first-order constant for the forward reaction is that the activity coefficients change with changing ionic strength during the course of the reaction. Thus the reaction is actually second order overall, first order in aqua complex and first order in bromide ion. According to the Brønsted-Bjerrum-Christiansen law [60] for reactions between oppositely charged ions, decreasing ionic strength increases the rate of such a reaction. Accordingly, as bromo complex is formed, with a drop in ionic strength as charges are neutralized, the second-order rate constant increases. This compensates partly for the normal decrease in rate for a second-order process so that the net effect is close to that for a first-order process.

In going to higher concentrations of X$^-$ other problems arise in that changes in activity coefficients cannot be controlled even by the principle of constant ionic strength. This is because at high concentrations particular ions have specific effects and are not interchangeable. Furthermore definite species, ion pairs, are formed which have different rates of reaction from the original reactants (see Chapter 9). Thus in studying the rate of reaction of cis-Co(en)$_2$(NO$_2$)H$_2$O^{2+} with azide ion and thiocyanate ion, the rate continuously increased with increasing concentration of the entering anion, being approximately first order in this concentration.[36] A limiting rate was not reached at 2 M NCS$^-$ nor at 3.2 M N$_3^-$. Since evidence for ion pairs was obtained, these results cannot be used as an indication of either an S_N1 or an S_N2 reaction.

Similarly the rate of the reaction

$$Co(NH_3)_5H_2O^{3+} + SO_4^{2-} \rightarrow Co(NH_3)_5SO_4^+ + H_2O \qquad (43)$$

gradually increases with increasing sulfate ion concentration.[61] The dependence on [SO$_4^{2-}$] is less than first order and diminishes with increasing [SO$_4^{2-}$], but even at 2.9 M Na$_2$SO$_4$ there is no sign of reaching a limiting rate. In this case an ion pair, $Co(NH_3)_5H_2O^{3+}$, SO_4^{2-}, was definitely detected, and its equilibrium constant for formation studied (see p. 383). Even after sufficient SO$_4^{2-}$ was added so that all of the aqua complex was converted to ion pair, the rate of sulfation continued to increase with further addition of sulfate ion. Also in a solution as concentrated as 2 M Na$_2$SO$_4$ and 3 M NaHSO$_4$, the rate of formation of the sulfato complex was less than the rate of water exchange under the same conditions. However, the rate of water exchange is less in the presence of sulfate ion than in its absence.[10] This would suggest that there is a competition between SO$_4^{2-}$ and H$_2$O for the intermediate, whatever its nature.

A study has been made of the reaction [62]

$$Cr(H_2O)_6^{3+} + NCS^- \rightleftharpoons Cr(H_2O)_5NCS^{2+} + H_2O \qquad (44)$$

in which it is found that the forward rate law is first order in [NCS$^-$] up to the highest concentration studied, 0.1 M. There is an expected pH dependence showing that $Cr(H_2O)_5OH^{2+}$ and $Cr(H_2O)_4(OH)_2^+$ are also reacting with thiocyanate ion. Furthermore the rate increases for the three reacting species as the positive charge diminishes. Thus the hydroxide ligand is labilizing for the replacement of water just as it is for replacement of chloride ion. Since, in an S_N2 reaction, it would be expected that the more positive ion would react faster with the negative thiocyanate ion, these opposite results are indicative of an S_N1 mechanism. In agreement with this, the net rate of reaction 44 is only 4% of the rate of water exchange at the highest concentration studied.

REACTIONS IN NON-AQUEOUS SOLVENTS

Mechanistic studies of complex ions have usually been made in aqueous solution. This is a result of the general interest in the be-

havior of such systems in the medium where reactions in a preparative
sense are usually carried out, and also because of the lack of solubility
of complex ions in other solvents. It has been seen that direct replacement of one ligand by another is not common in water because of the
formation of aqua compounds. In a solvent with poorer coordinating
properties, it might be possible to demonstrate a direct substitution and
hence find an S_N2 mechanism. A suitable solvent would be methanol,
since complexes such as $Co(NH_3)_5CH_3OH^{3+}$ are very unstable. Thus
at equilibrium a chloro complex in methanol remains almost completely
the chloro complex, though racemization, isomerization, and exchange
reactions may occur.

Brown and Ingold [63] have investigated the kinetics of substitution
of a chloro group in cis-$Co(en)_2Cl_2{}^+$ by several anions in the solvent
methyl alcohol using polarimetric, spectroscopic, chemical, and radio-
chemical methods. Experimentally these substitutions proceed directly
without any intermediate formation of a methyl alcohol complex. It
was observed that some of the reagents, all weakly nucleophilic, react at
the same rate, whereas other reagents react more rapidly and at different rates relative to their nucleophilic power, as shown schematically in
Fig. 6. It was suggested that the substitutions by $NO_3{}^-$, $*Cl^-$, Br^-,
or NCS^- proceed by an S_N1 mechanism. In agreement with this, the
rates were found to be independent of the concentration of the entering
anion.

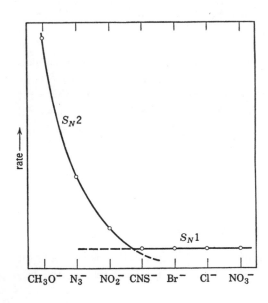

FIG. 6. Schematic representation of relative rates and
assumed mechanisms for
various anions reacting with
cis-$Co(en)_2Cl_2{}^+$ in methanol. (From reference 63.)

The fact that these reagents all react at the same rate is in itself good evidence of a dissociation mechanism. The rate-determining step in all cases is the rate of formation of the five-coordinated intermediate,

$$\text{Co(en)}_2\text{Cl}_2{}^+ \xrightarrow[-\text{Cl}^-]{\text{slow}} \text{Co(en)}_2\text{Cl}^{2+} \xrightarrow[+\text{X}^-]{\text{fast}} \text{Co(en)}_2\text{ClX}^+ \qquad (45)$$

Other observations further support this assignment of an S_N1 mechanism to these reactions. The rate of reaction is the same as the rate of racemization if optically active cis-Co(en)$_2$Cl$_2{}^+$ is used, which would be true providing the active intermediate is either symmetrical or has sufficient time to rearrange prior to reaction. Finally a mass-law retardation was observed, which is usually the most diagnostic kinetic evidence for a unimolecular mechanism.

The mass-law retardation effect has been successfully applied to mechanistic studies of organic reactions.[28b] The example presented here has to do with the reaction

$$\text{Co(en)}_2\text{Cl}_2{}^+ + \text{NCS}^- \rightarrow \text{Co(en)}_2(\text{NCS})\text{Cl}^+ + \text{Cl}^- \qquad (46)$$

It is found that the rate constant for the formation of Co(en)$_2$(NCS)Cl$^+$ decreases as the extent of the reaction progresses. Such behavior is attributed to the reaction scheme

$$\text{Co(en)}_2\text{Cl}_2{}^+ \underset{k_{\text{Cl}^-}}{\overset{k_{\text{diss}}}{\rightleftharpoons}} \text{Co(en)}_2\text{Cl}^{2+} + \text{Cl}^- \qquad (47)$$

$$\text{Co(en)}_2\text{Cl}^{2+} + \text{NCS}^- \xrightarrow{k_{\text{NCS}^-}} \text{Co(en)}_2(\text{NCS})\text{Cl}^+ \qquad (48)$$

It is seen that, owing to the reversibility of the initial heterolysis 47, the developed chloride ion will return to the cation from which it separated to an increasing degree as reaction progresses, thereby retarding the thiocyanate substitution 48. It is also found that, as the initial excess of thiocyanate ion is increased, the progressive retardation is lessened until it becomes inappreciable at the largest excesses employed (Fig. 7). The polarimetric rate constants are presumed to be for the rates of dissociation, k_{diss}, the changing values being due to salt effects. It is then apparent from Fig. 7 that at high [NCS$^-$]/[Cl$^-$] ratios the rate of formation of Co(en)$_2$(NCS)Cl$^+$ is the same as that of dissociation. Applying the steady-state approximation to this system, it follows that the rate of formation of Co(en)$_2$(NCS)Cl$^+$ is

$$\begin{aligned} \text{Rate} &= k_{\text{NCS}^-}[\text{Co(en)}_2\text{Cl}^{2+}][\text{NCS}^-] \\ &= \frac{k_{\text{diss}}k_{\text{NCS}^-}[\text{Co(en)}_2\text{Cl}_2{}^+][\text{NCS}^-]}{k_{\text{Cl}^-}[\text{Cl}^-] + k_{\text{NCS}^-}[\text{NCS}^-]} \end{aligned} \qquad (49)$$

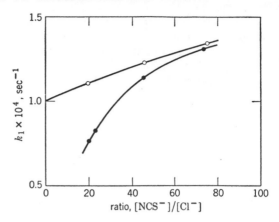

FIG. 7. Rates of racemization (open circles) and substitution by NCS⁻ (filled circles) for *cis*-Co-(en)₂Cl₂⁺ in methanol at 35.8°C. (From reference 63.)

At the limit of high concentration of thiocyanate equation 49 becomes

$$\text{Rate} = k_{\text{diss}}[\text{Co(en)}_2\text{Cl}_2{}^+] \tag{50}$$

In spite of the excellent agreement of all of these results with the predictions of an S_N1 mechanism, it turns out on closer examination that they are equally in agreement with an S_N2 mechanism involving the solvent methanol as the nucleophilic reagent. As soon as it is demonstrated that the methanol complex that would be formed in such a process is unstable,* then the S_N1 and S_N2 mechanisms become kinetically indistinguishable. The reaction sequence is identical with those shown in equations 47 and 48 except that the reactive intermediate is not $\text{Co(en)}_2\text{Cl}^{2+}$ but $\text{Co(en)}_2(\text{CH}_3\text{OH})\text{Cl}^{2+}$, formed by reversible reactions such as

$$\text{CH}_3\text{OH} + \text{Co(en)}_2\text{Cl}_2{}^+ \rightleftharpoons \text{Co(en)}_2(\text{CH}_3\text{OH})\text{Cl}^{2+} + \text{Cl}^- \tag{51}$$

There would, of course, be a mass-law retardation, and racemization could happen directly in 51, or more likely through several rapid exchange reactions such as

$$\text{CH}_3\text{OH}' + \text{Co(en)}_2(\text{CH}_3\text{OH})\text{Cl}^{2+} \rightleftharpoons$$

$$\text{Co(en)}_2(\text{CH}_3\text{OH}')\text{Cl}^{2+} + \text{CH}_3\text{OH} \tag{52}$$

each producing partial racemization.

* The methoxy complex can be formed by the action of sodium methoxide on $\text{Co(en)}_2\text{Cl}_2{}^+$. Upon acidification it immediately reverts to the dichloro complex.[63] However, the green *trans*-dichloro is formed even if the *cis*-dichloro is the starting material. On standing in neutral solution in methanol the purple *cis* complex forms the more stable *trans* isomer.

It is seen in Fig. 6 that the reagents NO_2^-, N_3^-, and CH_3O^- react more rapidly than do the reagents just discussed. These three reagents substitute according to a roughly second-order law, and it has been suggested that they proceed by an S_N2 mechanism.[63] If correct, this is of extreme interest because of the difficulty of finding evidence in support of such a process for substitutions in octahedral complexes. It is found that, at a common temperature, the second-order rates of reaction for CH_3O^-, N_3^-, and NO_2^- stand approximately in the ratio 30,000 :100 :1.

It may immediately be pointed out, however, that the data with methoxide ion can also be explained by an S_N1CB mechanism, reasoning by analogy with the hydroxide ion in water. Carrying the analogy further, if a solution of sodium azide or of sodium nitrite in water were used as a reagent for cis-$Co(en)_2Cl_2^+$, there would also be a reaction more rapid than that observed in an acid solution of the same complex. In this case the increased reaction would be due entirely to hydroxide ion produced by the hydrolysis of these basic anions. Because of the enormous factor for base hydrolysis over acid hydrolysis, 10^6 to 10^8, it is necessary to study acid hydrolysis in water at a pH of 3 or less. Even at pH 7 the hydroxide ion reaction may be ten times the rate of acid hydrolysis alone. Hence it is necessary to use buffered solutions to study the effect of a basic anion per se.

In line with this reasoning a series of studies on a number of complexes of cobalt(III) in methanol have recently been made using buffered solutions whenever basic anions were involved.[64] In each case the acid component of the buffer was increased until the rate was no longer affected by further acid or, by plotting the data for several acid concentrations, a limiting rate was calculated.

In the case of several ions of the type trans-$Co(AA)_2Cl_2^+$ it is found that unbuffered solutions of basic anions such as azide, nitrite, and acetate caused a very rapid release of chloride ion. However, buffering the solutions greatly inhibited these reactions. Table 17 shows some rate constants obtained with trans-$Co(en)_2Cl_2^+$ and acetate ion, including the extrapolated value obtained by plotting the observed pseudo first-order constant against the reciprocal of the acetic acid concentration. This plot is shown in Fig. 8. The extrapolated value is indistinguishable from the rate of radioactive chloride exchange and the rate of reaction with NCS^- for the same complex. The last two rates are independent of the concentration of radioactive chloride ion and of thiocyanate ion, as was found for the

Table 17

Rate Constants for Release of Chloride Ion from *trans*-Co(en)$_2$Cl$_2^+$ in Acetate-Acetic Acid Buffers in Methanol at 25°C

[HOAc]	$k \times 10^3$, min^{-1}	[HOAc]	$k \times 10^3$, min^{-1}
None	~100	0.01	1.77
0.003 M	5.00	0.02	0.79
0.004	3.68	0.05	0.42
0.005	2.99	∞	0.35

[OAc$^-$] = 0.05 M.

corresponding *cis* complex, except for ionic strength effects. It is demonstrated by this series of experiments that there is no direct reaction with acetate ion in this case, the accelerations in rate being caused by the methoxide ion generated by the reaction

$$OAc^- + CH_3OH \rightleftharpoons CH_3O^- + HOAc \tag{53}$$

Since the equilibrium constant for reaction 53 is known,[65] it is possible to calculate the rate of reaction of *trans*-Co(en)$_2$Cl$_2^+$ with methoxide ion as well. The ionization constant of methanol is 2.2×10^{-17}, and K_a for acetic acid in methanol is 2.2×10^{-10}. The rate constant for reaction with CH$_3$O$^-$ is calculated from the slope of Fig. 8. Similar experiments with the other members of the series *trans*-Co(AA)$_2$Cl$_2^+$ give the results shown in Table 18. There seems to be little doubt that the hydroxide ion reaction in water and the methoxide ion reaction in methanol are essentially the same reaction.

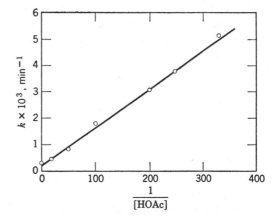

F$_{IG}$. 8. Rate of release of chloride ion from *trans*-Co-(en)$_2$Cl$_2^+$ in 0.05 M acetate ion solution in methanol at 25°C as a function of methoxide ion concentration. Value shown at zero is the rate of chloride ion exchange. (From reference 64.)

Table 18

Rate Constants for Some Reactions of _trans_-Co(AA)₂Cl₂⁺ in Methanol and in Water at 25°C

AA	k_{CH_3OH},[a] min^{-1}	k_{H_2O},[b] min^{-1}	$k_{CH_3O^-}$, $M^{-1}\,sec^{-1}$	k_{OH^-}, $M^{-1}\,sec^{-1}$
$NH_2CH_2CH_2NH_2$	3.2×10^{-4}	1.9×10^{-3}	4.5×10	3.0×10^3
$NH_2CHCH_3CH_2NH_2$	4.0×10^{-4}	3.7×10^{-3}	5.5×10	2.3×10^3
dl-$NH_2CHCH_3CHCH_3NH_2$	7.5×10^{-4}	8.8×10^{-3}	8×10	2.1×10^3
$NH_2C(CH_3)_2CH_2NH_2$	115×10^{-4}	130×10^{-3}	29×10	9.8×10^3
$NH_2C(CH_3)_2C(CH_3)_2NH_2$	instant.	instant.	. . .	. . .
$CH_3NHCH_2CH_2NH_2$	0.4×10^{-4}	1.0×10^{-3}	90×10	11×10^3
$NH_2CH_2CH_2NH_2$ [c]	20 [d] $\times 10^{-4}$	15×10^{-3}	$\sim 2 \times 10$	1×10^3
Triethylenetetramine [c]	13×10^{-4}	9×10^{-3}	. . .	200×10^3

[a] From rates of radiochloride exchange, reaction with thiocyanate ion, and intercept of rates in buffered acetate solutions.

[b] Rates of acid hydrolysis.

[c] _cis_-Dichloro isomer.

[d] Data from reference 63.

In the same manner the acid hydrolysis reaction in water is the same as that first-order process which leads to radiochloride exchange and reaction with thiocyanate and other ions in methanol. Whatever the mechanism of either of these reactions in water, it is most likely that the same mechanism holds in methanol. The chief difference in the observed results is that an aqua complex is stable, whereas a methanol complex is not. The slower rate of the acid reaction in methanol by a factor of ten is reasonable in view of the lower dielectric constant compared to water, since a separation of charge in the transition state is certainly involved.

Furthermore, within the limits of experimental error, no reaction with acetate ion can be found for the _trans_ complexes listed in Table 18, so methoxide ion is specific in methanol for these compounds. This is not true for the _cis_ complexes. Table 19 shows the pseudo first-order rate constants obtained for the release of chloride ion in the case of _cis_-Co(en)₂Cl₂⁺ and buffers of acetate ion and acetic acid in methanol. With acetate ion in sufficient excess, linear first-order plots are obtained for these reactions if it is assumed that both chlorides are released in the first step but not if it is assumed that one chloride ion only is released. Because of the reactivity of Co(en)₂-

Table 19

Rate Constants for Release of Chloride Ion in Acetate-Acetic Acid Buffers for cis-Co(en)$_2$Cl$_2^+$ in Methanol at 25°C

[OAc$^-$]	[HOAc]	$k \times 10^3$,[a] min^{-1}	$k \times 10^3$ [b]
0.0192 M	none	45.5	...
0.0192	0.0022	13.2	...
0.0192	0.0048	11.7	...
0.0192	0.0096	11.5	4.7
0.0096	0.0048	9.5	4.2
0.0048	0.0024	8.1	3.6
0.0024	0.0012	7.0	3.3
0.0012	0.0006	6.1	3.0
0.0006	0.0003	4.8	2.3
...	...	2.0 [c]	2.0 [c]

Concentration of complex is $6.0 \times 10^{-4} M$.

[a] Initial rates only assuming one chloride ion released in first step.

[b] Assuming both chlorides released in first step.

[c] Rate of dissociation from reference 63.

(OH)Cl$^+$ it is reasonable that Co(en)$_2$(CH$_3$CO$_2$)Cl$^+$ would also be very reactive.* Hence the sequence would be

$$\text{Co(en)}_2\text{Cl}_2{}^+ + \text{OAc}^- \xrightarrow{\text{slow}} \text{Co(en)}_2\text{(OAc)Cl}^+ + \text{Cl}^- \quad (54)$$

$$\text{Co(en)}_2\text{(OAc)Cl}^+ + \text{OAc}^- \xrightarrow{\text{fast}} \text{Co(en)}_2\text{(OAc)}_2{}^+ + \text{Cl}^- \quad (55)$$

The rate constants determined on this assumption are given in the fourth column of Table 19.

It is seen that buffering, as expected, reduces the rate of reaction in the presence of a fixed concentration of acetate ion. Nevertheless a residual reaction remains which is definitely greater than the rate of reaction of the same complex ion with such weakly basic anions as NO$_3^-$ and NCS$^-$, or the rate of chloride exchange. Also this residual rate is a function of acetate ion concentration, increasing with higher concentrations. Similar results are obtained with azide ion and nitrite ion in buffered media. Figure 9 shows the residual rate constant (methoxide ion reaction eliminated by buffering) as a function of concentration in the case of azide ion (the rate constant in this case is calculated for one chloride ion only being released). There is not a simple first-order dependence on the concentration of N$_3^-$.

* The alternative explanation for the linear kinetic plots is that both chloride ions are released at identical rates. This seems unlikely.

Fig. 9. Rate of release of chloride ion from *cis*-Co-(en)$_2$Cl$_2^+$ in solutions of sodium azide in methanol at 25°C. Value at zero is the rate of chloride ion exchange from reference 63. (Other data from reference 64.)

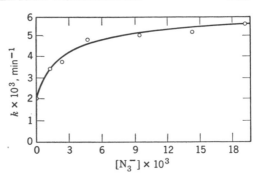

The detailed shape of the curve in Fig. 9 can be reproduced by superimposing the effects of ion-pair formation between the reactants, and ionic strength effects on the magnitude of the ion-pair formation constant.[64] The ionic strength effects are approximated by the Debye-Hückel theory for the activity coefficients of ions (see p. 377). The mechanism would be in outline

$$\text{Co(en)}_2\text{Cl}_2{}^+ + \text{X}^- \overset{\text{fast}}{\rightleftharpoons} \text{Co(en)}_2\text{Cl}_2{}^+, \text{X}^- \qquad (56)$$

$$\text{Co(en)}_2\text{Cl}_2{}^+, \text{X}^- \overset{\text{slow}}{\longrightarrow} \text{Co(en)}_2\text{ClX}^+ + \text{Cl}^- \qquad (57)$$

with reaction 57 perhaps going directly as shown (S_N2) or perhaps in steps such as (S_N1)

$$\text{Co(en)}_2\text{Cl}_2{}^+, \text{X}^- \overset{\text{slow}}{\longrightarrow} \text{Co(en)}_2\text{Cl}^{2+}, \text{X}^- + \text{Cl}^- \qquad (58)$$

$$\text{Co(en)}_2\text{Cl}^{2+}, \text{X}^- \overset{\text{fast}}{\longrightarrow} \text{Co(en)}_2\text{ClX}^+ \qquad (59)$$

The equation for the observed first-order rate constant would be

$$k_{\text{obs}} = \frac{k_1 + k_2 K[\text{X}^-]}{1 + K[\text{X}^-]} \qquad (60)$$

where k_1 is the rate constant for dissociation of free Co(en)$_2$Cl$_2^+$, k_2 is the rate constant for step 57, and K is the equilibrium constant for the formation of ion pairs as in 56.

The evidence for ion pairs is indirect since it can be shown in the case of *cis*-Co(en)$_2$Cl$_2^+$ with Cl$^-$ and Br$^-$ that ion pairs are formed.[64] The method of detection is the shift in the near-ultraviolet spectrum of the complex that results. Also *trans*-Co(en)$_2$Cl$_2^+$ does not form ion pairs with Cl$^-$ as judged by this criterion of changing spectrum. It is plausible that the ion pair is formed in the case of the *cis* isomer but not the *trans* because of the net dipole moment of the former, the charges being equal. Then the negative ion must be held at the side of the complex away from the chloride ligands for electrostatic reasons. The failure to show reaction with acetate ion and the failure to form ion pairs is thus related in *trans*-Co(en)$_2$Cl$_2$$^+$.

Ion-pair formation is not a sufficient cause for an increased rate of reaction since the *cis* complex forms ion pairs with chloride and bromide ion, but the rate of reaction is not accelerated by increasing concentrations of these ions under conditions where ion-pair formation is not complete.[63] Nor is the rate different from that with NO$_3$$^-$ and NCS$^-$, or from the rate of racemization. Only basic anions increase the rate. Pyridine, which would not form an associated pair with the complex, does not cause an accelerated rate. Since the nucleophilic character of an anion towards metal complexes is expected to parallel basicity towards hydrogen ion, it is certainly possible that the ion pair reacts by an S_N2 displacement process.

This is not the only explanation for the reactivity, however. Another possible mechanism is that there is a strong interaction of a basic anion with the acidic protons of the complex in an ion pair. Such interaction, which is indeed expected on electrostatic grounds, would permit the electrons of the N—H bond to behave at least somewhat like the electrons of an amido group. That is, they would perhaps be labilized enough to form a partial π bond to the cobalt atom and help to release chloride ion.

$$\text{Co—N—H---X}^- \rightarrow \text{Co—N}^- \text{---H—X} \rightarrow \text{Co=N---H—X}$$

$$\begin{array}{ccc} | & | & \\ \text{Cl} & \text{Cl} & \text{Cl}^- \end{array} \tag{61}$$

There are some reasons for preferring this mechanism, which may be conveniently called an S_N1IP path (for unimolecular dissociation of an ion pair). One is that the complex *cis*-Co(trien)Cl$_2$$^+$ shows a very large rate of reaction with azide ion in buffered media, Table 20, in comparison with *cis*-Co(en)$_2$Cl$_2$$^+$, although the rates of reaction with neutral ligands are nearly the same. It can be seen from Table 18 that the triethylenetetramine complex also has a rate of reaction with hydroxide ion in water which is about 200 times greater than for the bis(ethylenediamine) complex. However, it is not the methoxide rate which is involved in the azide ion solutions, as is shown by changing the buffer ratio.

Table 20

Rates of Reaction of cis-Co(en)$_2$Cl$_2^+$ and cis-Co(trien)$_2$Cl$_2^+$ with Azide Ion and Radioactive Chloride Ion in Methanol at 25°C

Complex	[N$_3^-$]	[HN$_3$]	k, min^{-1}
cis-Co(en)$_2$Cl$_2^+$	0.0048	0.0024	4.8×10^{-3}
cis-Co(en)$_2$Cl$_2^+$	Rate with *Cl$^-$		2.0×10^{-3}
cis-Co(trien)Cl$_2^+$	0.0048	0.0024	5.3×10^{-1}
cis-Co(trien)Cl$_2^+$	0.0048	0.0048	4.8×10^{-1}
cis-Co(trien)Cl$_2^+$	Rate with *Cl$^-$		1.3×10^{-3}

Another reason for preferring an S_N1IP mechanism is that, if optically active cis-Co(en)$_2$Cl$_2^+$ is used, an inactive product is formed with azide ion and acetate ion and the rate of racemization is the same as the rate of reaction with the two anions. It would seem that a bimolecular displacement process should be more stereospecific. There is no direct evidence, however, excluding an S_N2 reaction in the case of these basic anions in methanol. Also it should be pointed out that, if ion-pair formation occurs, as Fig. 9 strongly suggests, it is kinetically impossible to distinguish between a reaction of an ion pair and a bimolecular reaction of the free ions. This is because the transition state is an ion pair in any event. One other experiment of interest is that of a complex containing no acidic protons, e.g., $trans$-Co(py)$_4$Cl$_2^+$, which reacts quite rapidly with azide ion and acetate ion in methanol, but by decomposition of the entire complex. Pyridine is released as in the reaction with hydroxide ion in water. In these cases it appears that an S_N2 reaction occurs but leads to a fundamental change in the structure of the compound.

In summary, the reactions of cobalt(III) complexes in methanol, when combined with results in water solution, indicate an S_N1CB mechanism for methoxide ion and either an S_N1IP or S_N2 (or S_N2IP) reaction with other basic anions in the case of cis-dichloro but not $trans$-dichloro complexes. The reactions with weakly basic anions, and even acetate ion in the case of the $trans$ isomers, are best considered as S_N1 dissociations. This is because of the fact of steric acceleration found in the rates, and because it seems unlikely that methanol would be a good enough nucleophilic reagent to cause the observed reactions since its complexes are unstable. The factor of ten slower compared to rates in water is accounted for sufficiently in terms of general solvation effects.

ACID CATALYSIS AND A SPECIAL MECHANISM
FOR CHELATES

The rates of most acid hydrolysis reactions are usually independent of hydrogen ion concentrations below a pH of about 4. Above a pH of 4 the contribution due to a very high rate of base hydrolysis may begin to make an appreciable contribution to the total observed rate of hydrolysis. It has also been observed that in some cases the acid hydrolysis reaction is acid catalyzed. The examples of acid-catalyzed acid hydrolysis reactions suggest that the determining factor that need be considered is the nature of the ligand being replaced. In general, acid catalysis is observed for the replacement of two different types of ligands:

(1) Ligands that are strongly basic or have a large tendency to hydrogen bond, e.g., $Co(NH_3)_5CO_3^+$, $Co(NH_3)_5ONO^{2+}$, $Fe(CN)_6^{4-}$, $Cr(CN)_6^{3-}$, $Co(en)_2F_2^+$.

(2) Flexible bi- or multidentate basic ligands, e.g., $Fe(bipy)_3^{2+}$, $Ni(bipy)_3^{2+}$, $Ni(en)_3^{2+}$, $Fe(EDTA)^-$.

Some examples of these types of acid-catalyzed reactions will be be described. The acid-catalyzed acid hydrolysis reaction [66] for the complex $trans$-$Co(en)_2F_2^+$ is shown in Fig. 10. There is an increase in

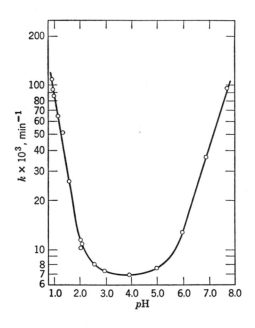

Fig. 10. pH dependence in the hydrolysis of $trans$-$Co(en)_2$-F_2^+ at 59.3°C. (From reference 66.)

acid hydrolysis at the lower pH due to acid catalysis, and another increase at the higher pH due to base hydrolysis. The acid-catalyzed portion of the curve is believed to result from the set of reactions

$$(en)_2FCo\!-\!F^+ + H_2O \xrightarrow[k_1]{\text{slow}} (en)_2FCo\!-\!OH_2{}^+ + F^- \qquad (62)$$

$$(en)_2FCo\!-\!F^+ + H^+ \underset{\xrightarrow{\hspace{1.5cm}}}{\overset{\text{instantaneous}}{\rightleftharpoons}} (en)_2FCo\!-\!FH^{2+} \qquad (63)$$

$$(en)_2FCo\!-\!FH^{2+} + H_2O \xrightarrow[k_2]{\text{fast}} (en)_2FCo\!-\!OH_2 + HF \qquad (64)$$

This means that the observed rate of reaction, k_{obs}, is a function of k_1, k_2, and the equilibrium constant for 63.

$$k_{obs} = k_1[(en)_2FCo\!-\!F^+] + k_2K_{eq}[(en)_2FCo\!-\!F^+][H^+] \qquad (65)$$

The kinetic data are in agreement with such a mechanism. It is to be expected that the Co—F bond will be weakened as a result of hydrogen bonding to form Co—FH. Also in support of this mechanism is the observation that at a fixed acid concentration the rate of reaction is almost twice as fast in D_2O as it is in H_2O.[66] This contrasts with the acid hydrolysis of $Co(NH_3)_5Cl^{2+}$, which is about 60% slower in D_2O than in H_2O.[46] Similar increases in rate for other acid-catalyzed reactions in D_2O are known, and are explained in terms of differences in zero point energies for bonds involving D and H.[67]

This type of acid catalysis for complexes is very closely related to the accelerating effect of $Hg(II)$ aqua ion on the rate of release of halide ion.[68] Also silver ion and $Tl(III)$ ion behave in a similar way. According to the classification of substitution reactions given at the beginning of this chapter, such reactions may be considered as S_E2. The possibility of help from a nucleophilic reagent in carrying the process to completion is not excluded by the observation that an electrophilic reagent is involved. Nevertheless this classification helps to distinguish between the previous examples of acceleration and the next to be discussed, which is special for chelate compounds.

An instance of the acid-catalyzed replacement of a basic bidentate ligand is furnished by studies on the $Fe(bipy)_3{}^{2+}$ complex. Baxendale and George [69a] first observed this acid dependence (Fig. 11), and explained it on the basis of the equilibrium

$$Fe(bipy)_3{}^{2+} + H^+ \rightleftharpoons Fe(bipy)_3H^{3+} \qquad (66)$$

with the assumption that $Fe(bipy)_3{}^{2+}$ reacts more slowly than does $Fe(bipy)_3H^{3+}$. A limiting rate would be reached at high acid con-

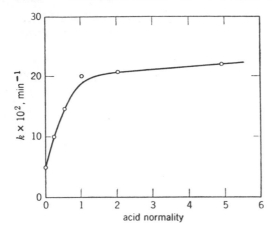

FIG. 11. Effect of acid on the rate of dissociation of $Fe(bipy)_3^{2+}$. (From reference 69.)

centrations where essentially only the latter species is present. In an aqueous solution it is unlikely that there will be much tendency to form large quantities of such a protonated species because of the weak basicity of $Fe(bipy)_3^{2+}$. Furthermore the absorption spectrum of a one molar acid solution of $Fe(bipy)_3^{2+}$ is the same as that of a neutral solution,[15a] so that there cannot be any appreciable quantity of $Fe(bipy)_3H^{3+}$ present.* It seems more likely [15a, 69b] that instead the acid dependence is involved in the mechanism as shown in the scheme in reaction 67. Applying the

$$\text{(bipy)}_2\text{Fe} \underset{k_2}{\overset{k_1}{\rightleftharpoons}} \text{(bipy)}_2\text{Fe} \overset{k_3}{\to} \text{(bipy)}_2\text{Fe} + \quad (67)$$

$$+H^+ \Big\downarrow k_4$$

$$\text{(bipy)}_2\text{Fe} \overset{\text{fast}}{\longrightarrow} \text{(bipy)}_2\text{Fe} +$$

* The formation of protonated species of both $Fe(bipy)_3^{2+}$ and $Fe(phen)_3^{2+}$ in concentrated $HClO_4$ has been reported (E. A. Healy and R. K. Murmann, *J. Am. Chem. Soc.*, **79**, 5827 (1957)). This formation is accompanied by changes in spectra and magnetic susceptibilities and is reversible upon dilution. Thus it still may be possible that the acid dependence of the rates of dissociation of these complexes can be explained without the use of "half-bonded" structures.

steady-state approximation for the concentrations of the partly dissociated species, the observed rate constant, k_{obs}, is given by

$$k_{obs} = k_1 \frac{k_3 + k_4[H^+]}{k_2 + k_3 + k_4[H^+]} \tag{68}$$

The qualitative behavior of the acid dependence is in agreement with formula 68, but a quantitative fit is not possible without considering activity coefficients. It is apparent that a limiting rate is expected at high acidities where the values of k_2 and k_3 are negligible compared to $k_4[H^+]$, and thus $k_{obs} = k_1$. At very low acidity $[H^+]$ is negligible, and then $k_{obs} = k_1 \dfrac{k_3}{k_2 + k_3}$. It was found [15a] that the ratio of the two limiting rates leads to a value of $\dfrac{k_3}{k_2 + k_3} = 0.16$. This means that, in solution of low acidity, for each time a single Fe—N bond breaks the bond will reform approximately 84% of the time, and the second bond will break leading to complete dissociation approximately 16% of the time.

The acid hydrolysis of the closely related $Fe(phen)_3^{2+}$ is not acid dependent, as might be expected on the basis that the non-flexible 1,10-phenanthroline would not easily permit the reaction mechanism shown.[70] It is of interest that the dissociations of $Ni(en)_3^{2+}$ and $Ni(bipy)_3^{2+}$ are also acid catalyzed,[71] the interpretation given above also being applicable here. One other comment is that the iron(II) complexes $Fe(bipy)_3^{2+}$ and $Fe(phen)_3^{2+}$ must dissociate stepwise to the hydrated iron(II), but in both cases the first step is the rate-determining step for this total dissociation. This is undoubtedly related to the change from spin-coupled *tris* complex to labile spin-free *bis* and *mono* complexes,[72a] which would not be strongly crystal field stabilized. Nickel(II) does not show this behavior. It has been found that the complexes $Ni(phen)_3^{2+}$, $Ni(phen)_2^{2+}$, and $Ni(phen)^{2+}$ all dissociate at about the same rate.[72b]

The mechanism shown in equation 67 suggests a very general kind of behavior that is possible for bi- or multidentate ligands. If such a ligand is removed by a dissociation mechanism, it is very likely that it does so by steps. Such a step would usually be easily reversible, because the coordinating atom remains in the vicinity of the vacated spot in the metal atom coordination sphere. It can be prevented from reversing by either an electrophilic group's reacting with the released end of the chelate group, or by a nucleophilic reagent's reacting with the exposed metal atom. The overall dissociation would then be accelerated.

$$
M\!\left(\begin{smallmatrix} A \\ \\ A \end{smallmatrix}\right) \rightleftharpoons M\!\left(\begin{smallmatrix} A \\ \\ A \end{smallmatrix}\right) \xrightarrow{+X} \underset{X}{M-\widehat{AA}} \rightarrow \underset{X}{M} + \widehat{AA}
$$

$$
M-\widehat{AA}-M' \rightarrow M + \widehat{AA}-M'
$$

(69)

In the examples already discussed it was H^+ which took the part of the electrophilic reagent, M'. There is no reason why another metal ion could not serve the same function. Undoubtedly many metal ion exchange reactions involving chelate groups involve such a process (see p. 201).

It is also anticipated that small, well coordinating groups like hydroxide ion can play the role of X, the nucleophilic reagent in equation 69. There is evidence that there is a basic catalysis, or rather a reaction with hydroxide ion, in the case of $Ni(bipy)_3^{2+}$ [73] and $Fe(phen)_3^{2+}$.[74] With the latter the rate of dissociation is greatly increased in alkali over neutral solution. At 0.1 M OH^- the rate is increased by a factor of about ten, but at 4.5 M OH^- the rate is increased by a factor of 400. Empirically terms in hydroxide ion concentration to the first, second, and third powers are needed to express the rate equation, but it is dangerous to identify each of these terms with a reaction process since activity coefficients can change greatly for such a range of concentrations. It may be that more than one 1,10-phenanthroline group is partially dissociated and its place taken by hydroxide ion before the reaction finally goes to completion.

An alternative mechanism [74] is that the rate increase is actually due to an S_N2 displacement process in which the hydroxide ion pushes off one point of attachment of the 1,10-phenanthroline molecule. Again two or more such partial displacements would have to happen if the rate equation has terms in OH^- greater than first power. It is kinetically difficult, but not impossible, to differentiate between the two explanations based on dissociation or displacement. It is of interest that $Ni(phen)_3^{2+}$ does not show base catalysis in its dissociation.[15b] Some evidence that an S_N2 process is involved may be the fact that not only $Co(en)_3^{3+}$ but also $Co(NH_3)_6^{3+}$, in which only unidentate ligands are involved, is decomposed by alkali. In both these cases the reactions are very slow at room temperature but go readily on warming.

An extreme example of the effect of external reagents on the rate of reaction of chelated complexes is shown in the exchange reaction of the system $Fe(EDTA)^- $-$*Fe^{3+}$.[19] The chelating agent ethylenediaminetetraacetic acid can act as a sexadentate ligand when converted into its tetravalent anion. On reducing the pH of the solution one or more of the carboxylate groups can be converted into carboxyl with a reduction in the stability of the complex. A study of the exchange system reveals that the rate is dependent in a complicated way on the concentration of the hydrogen ion. The rate law that seems to give the best fit with the data involves three separate rate terms: in one hydrogen ion concentration enters to the third power, in another to the zero power, and in still another to the inverse first power. The concentration of the exchanging species also appeared in the last two terms. The rate equation, which is not necessarily a unique representation of the data, is given by

$$\text{Rate} = [Fe(EDTA)^-]\left(k_1[H^+]^3 + k_2[*Fe^{3+}] + \frac{k_3[*Fe^{3+}]}{[H^+]}\right) \quad (70)$$

A plausible explanation for each of the terms can be given, the first involving successive dissociations of one, two, and three carboxylate groups which are then captured by H^+ and rendered inactive. The species $Fe(EDTAH_3)^{2+}$ then rapidly dissociates all the way. For the second term it is not hydrogen ion which captures the partly dissociated intermediate but rather $*Fe^{3+}$. The third term, which becomes important in low acidity, would be the result of OH^- reacting with the exposed coordination point of iron(III) in the partly dissociated EDTA complex. Reaction with Fe^{3+} is still needed to complete the dissociation. A similar situation is found in a study of the reaction

$$Cu^{2+} + Cd(EDTA)^{2-} \rightarrow Cu(EDTA)^{2-} + Cd^{2+} \quad (71)$$

in which a complicated pH dependence exists, and in which a competition between Cu^{2+} and Cd^{2+} for some intermediate is clearly evident.[75]

SUBSTITUTION REACTIONS WITHOUT THE CLEAVAGE OF THE METAL-LIGAND BOND

The substitution reactions discussed up till now require a rupture of the metal-ligand bond. However, it has been observed in some systems that reactions occur without the cleavage of this bond. Such is the case for the conversion of amminecarbonato complexes of cobalt(III) to the corresponding aqua complexes and for the formation of amminenitrito complexes of cobalt(III) from the corresponding aqua compounds.

The addition of excess acid to an aqueous solution of $Co(NH_3)_5CO_3^+$ results in the immediate liberation of carbon dioxide and the formation of $Co(NH_3)_5H_2O^{3+}$. Kinetic studies [76] show that the reacting species is the bicarbonato complex, $Co(NH_3)_5CO_3H^{2+}$. Since acid hydrolysis reactions of cobalt(III) complexes such as those mentioned earlier are generally slow, it would appear that this reaction of the bicarbonato complex may proceed by an entirely different process. This has been confirmed by studies using oxygen-18 labeled water as the solvent, which show that the Co—O bond is not severed but rather that the O—C bond is broken:

$$(NH_3)_5Co\text{—}OCO_2^+ + 2H_3{*}O^+ \rightarrow$$

$$(NH_3)_5Co\text{—}OH_2^{3+} + 2H_2{*}O + CO_2 \quad (72)$$

Reaction 72 takes place with little or no uptake of oxygen 18 in either of the two products, $Co(NH_3)_5H_2O^{3+}$ [77] and CO_2.[78] These results suggest a mechanism involving an attachment on the oxygen of Co—O—C by a proton followed by the rupture of the O—C bond (reaction 73).

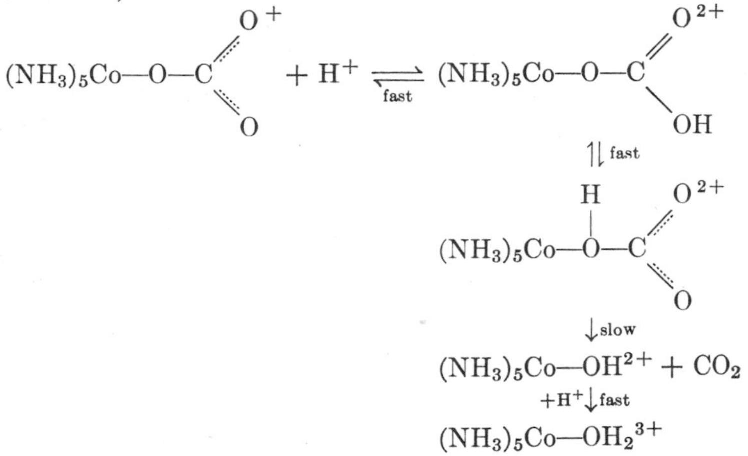

Thus this is a decarboxylation reaction rather than an acid hydrolysis reaction.

Similar studies [79] have been made on the tetrammine complex, $Co(NH_3)_4CO_3^+$. In this system the reaction in oxygen-18 water yields carbon dioxide of normal abundance and a diaqua complex which derives half of its oxygen from the solvent. Such an isotopic distribution must result from the reaction scheme

$$(NH_3)_4Co \begin{array}{c} O \\ \diagup \ \diagdown \\ \diagdown \ \diagup \\ O \end{array} \overset{+}{C}=O \xrightarrow[\text{fast}]{H_3{}^*O^+}$$

$$(NH_3)_4Co \begin{array}{c} {}^*OH_2{}^{2+} \\ \diagup \\ \diagdown \\ OCO_2H \end{array} \xrightarrow[\text{slow}]{H_3{}^*O^+} (NH_3)_4Co \begin{array}{c} {}^*OH_2{}^{3+} \\ \diagup \\ \diagdown \\ OH_2 \end{array} + CO_2 \quad (74)$$

The first step involves a breaking of the Co—O bond, and the second step, like that for $Co(NH_3)_5CO_3H$, requires a cleavage of the O—C bond.

Although the first step of reaction 74 does require the breaking of the Co—O bond, it is extremely rapid. Such an unusual lability of Co—O may be due to a strain in the four-membered chelate ring. Another possible explanation is that conductivity measurements and studies of isotopic effects [80] in these systems indicate that the tetramminecarbonato complexes of cobalt(III) are substantially present in aqueous solution in the aqua form with the carbonate ion functioning as a unidentate, e.g., $Co(NH_3)_4H_2OCO_3{}^+$ and $Co(en)_2H_2OCO_3{}^+$. For example, these complexes, like $Co(NH_3)_5CO_3{}^+$, show no isotopic effects for equilibria of the type

$$Co(NH_3)_5CO_3{}^+ + H^{14}CO_3{}^- \rightleftharpoons Co(NH_3)_5{}^{14}CO_3{}^+ + HCO_3{}^- \quad (75)$$

An isotope effect would be expected for a chelate carbonato.[80]

Other reactions, such as the rapid liberation of sulfur dioxide from a sulfito—O metal complex or the rapid evolution of nitrogen oxide from a nitrito complex upon acidification, have not as yet been studied in detail. However, it would appear by analogy with the reaction of carbonato cobalt(III) ammines that reactions of this type will also occur without M—O bond cleavage. Similarly the reverse of these reactions, that of a hydroxo complex with an acid anhydride, is expected to take place by direct addition to the coordinated oxygen and without M—O bond rupture. Extensive investigations of this reverse reaction have been made in connection with the formation of a nitrito, M—ONO, complex from the corresponding aqua compound. This reaction (76) is quite rapid, which in itself suggests that the Co—O bond is not broken.

$$Co(NH_3)_5H_2O^{3+} + NO_2^- \rightarrow .Co(NH_3)_5ONO^{2+} + H_2O \qquad (76)$$

Kinetic studies [81] of the reaction in HNO_2—NO_2^- buffers show that the general rate expression for the formation of the nitrito complex is given by the equation

$$\text{Rate} = k[\text{aqua complex}][NO_2^-][HNO_2] \qquad (77)$$

However, because of the acid-base equilibrium between the aqua and hydroxo complexes, equation 77 may also be replaced by

$$\text{Rate} = k'[\text{hydroxo complex}][HNO_2]^2 \qquad (78)$$

This expression of the rate law is analogous to the rate equation frequently found [82] for the nitrosation of ammonia and amines,

$$\text{Rate} = k[\text{amine}][HNO_2]^2 \qquad (79)$$

The interpretation given equation 79 is that the nitrosating agent in weakly acid solutions is N_2O_3, which attacks the unshared pair of electrons on the amine nitrogen by splitting into NO^+ and NO_2^-. Thus the observed second-order dependence on HNO_2 results from the equilibrium

$$2HNO_2 \rightleftharpoons N_2O_3 + H_2O \qquad (80)$$

Therefore it may be assumed that the formation of nitrito complexes involves an O-nitrosation type reaction which does not require Co—O bond cleavage. This reaction sequence is further supported by the

$$(NH_3)_5Co—OH_2^{3+} + H_2O \overset{\text{fast}}{\rightleftharpoons} (NH_3)_5Co—OH^{2+} + H_3O^+ \qquad (81)$$

$$(NH_3)_5Co—OH^{2+} + N_2O_3 \overset{\text{slow}}{\longrightarrow} (NH_3)_5Co—O\text{---}H^{2+} \qquad (82)$$

$$O{=}N\text{---}O—N{=}O$$

$$\downarrow \text{fast}$$

$$(NH_3)_5Co—ONO^{2+} + HNO_2$$

observation that the synthesis of a nitro complex from the corresponding chloro complex in a buffered aqueous medium (pH 4–5) takes place in a series of steps, one of which involves the formation of the nitrito complex followed by its subsequent rearrangement to the nitro product (for a discussion of nitrito-nitro isomerization see Chapter 6). However, it is of interest to note that, in the absence of water, a methanolic solution of $Co(en)_2Cl_2^+$ reacts directly with nitrite ion to yield $Co(en)_2(NO_2)Cl^+$ as the first observable product.[63]

The final confirmation that the nitrito complex is formed without the cleavage of Co—O bond was recently provided by studies using oxygen 18.[83] For example, the oxygen-18 enriched aqua complex reacts in ordinary water to yield the enriched nitrito product,

$$(NH_3)_5Co—*OH_2^{3+} + NO_2^- \rightarrow (NH_3)_5Co—*ONO^{2+} + H_2O \quad (83)$$

The percentages of retention of M—O bonds reported for the formation of several nitrito complexes are listed in Table 21.

Table 21

Retention of M—O Bond in the Formation of M—ONO from M—OH$_2$

Complex	% Retention of M—O Bond
$Co(NH_3)_5H_2O^{3+}$	99.4
cis-$Co(NH_3)_4(H_2O)_2^{3+}$	92.3
cis-$Co(en)_2NH_3H_2O^{3+}$	93.0
cis-$Co(en)_2(H_2O)_2^{3+}$	97.5
cis-$Co(en)_2NO_2H_2O^{2+}$	99.5
$Cr(NH_3)_5H_2O^{3+}$	79.5

The reaction scheme proposed for the formation of nitrito complexes, as stated earlier, may also be involved in the reactions of hydroxo complexes with other acid anhydrides. Similarly it has been suggested [83] that, if the M—O bond rupture is a slow process, then a labile oxygen-containing reagent may rapidly replace the acidic hydrogens on a coordinated water molecule to yield the reaction product. This is perhaps the reaction mechanism for the rapid reaction of MoO_4^{2-} or WO_4^{2-} with cis-$Co(en)_2(H_2O)_2^{3+}$. Unlike the nitrite ion both of these oxyions undergo rapid exchange with oxygen-18 water under neutral or slightly alkaline conditions.[84] Furthermore they both react rapidly with aqua complexes in this pH range, whereas the nitrite ion reacts slowly to form the nitro complex without the intermediate formation of the nitrito compound.

Finally the acid and base hydrolysis of pentammineacetatocobalt-(III) ions (Table 13) have been carried out in oxygen-18 water and the isotope enrichment of the acetate ions determined.[78] It was found that the acetic acid resulting from acid hydrolysis contained oxygen of normal abundance which is proof of Co—O bond cleavage,

$$(NH_3)_5Co—O—\overset{\displaystyle O}{\overset{\|}{C}}R + H_2*O \rightarrow (NH_3)_5Co—*OH_2 + RCOOH \quad (84)$$

However, the base hydrolysis reaction showed an enrichment of oxygen 18 in the acetate ion which increased in the series where R $= CH_3 < CH_2$-Cl $< CCl_3 < CF_3$. It was suggested that this is due to a reaction by O—C rather than Co—O cleavage which is like a typical ester hydrolysis by base.

$$H*O^- + \underset{\underset{O}{\|}}{\overset{\overset{CF_3}{|}}{C}}-O-Co(NH_3)_5{}^{2+} \xrightarrow{\text{slow}} H*O^{-}---\underset{\underset{O}{\|}}{\overset{\overset{CF_3}{|}}{C}}---O-Co(NH_3)_5{}^{2+}$$

$$\downarrow \text{fast} \qquad\qquad (85)$$

$$\underset{O}{\overset{*O \quad CF_3}{\underset{\diagdown}{\overset{\diagdown|}{C}}}} + HO-Co(NH_3)_5{}^{2+}$$

Furthermore, it is postulated that such an O—C cleavage becomes of major importance with $(NH_3)_5Co-O\overset{\overset{O}{\|}}{C}-CF_3{}^{2+}$ because of the electronegativity of fluorine and of its small size. This places a maximum positive charge on the carbonyl carbon, making it more susceptible to nucleophilic attack by hydroxide ion while not markedly increasing the hindrance at this carbon. In such a case the trifluoroacetate ion generated would derive half of its oxygen from the solvent, which is what was observed.

However, this same result would also be obtained if the reaction path involves the formation of a carbonyl addition intermediate of finite life followed by Co—O bond cleavage,

$$(NH_3)_5Co-O\overset{\overset{O}{\|}}{C}CF_3{}^{2+} + *OH^- \underset{\text{fast}}{\rightleftharpoons} (NH_3)_5Co-O\underset{\underset{H}{*O}}{\overset{\overset{O^-}{|}}{C}}CF_3{}^{2+}$$

$$\text{fast} \downarrow\uparrow \qquad\qquad (86)$$

$$(NH_3)_5Co^{3+} + \underset{*O}{\overset{O}{\underset{\diagup}{\diagdown C}}}CF_3 \xleftarrow{\text{slow}} (NH_3)_5Co-O-\underset{\underset{*O}{\|}}{C}CF_3{}^{2+} + OH^-$$

$$\text{fast} \downarrow *OH^-$$

$$(NH_3)_5Co*OH^{2+}$$

Exactly such an intermediate leading to oxygen-18 exchange has been demonstrated in ester hydrolysis by base.[85] Unfortunately, therefore, the appearance of oxygen-18 in the trifluoroacetate ion is not diagnostic of bond cleavage. It is apparent that, in order to distinguish between mechanisms 85 and 86, it is necessary to determine the oxygen isotopic enrichment in the complex. Because of the close parallelism between base hydrolysis, acid hydrolysis, and acid strength shown by these compounds (Table 13), it seems unlikely that acyl-oxygen cleavage is a major reaction path.*

SUMMARY

Since so many diverse topics have been dealt with in this chapter, it is necessary to go back and try to sum up the chief conclusions that can be drawn concerning the mechanism of octahedral substitution reactions. We started by making a theoretical prediction, based on electrostatics and crystal field theory, that the best transition state for either an S_N1 or S_N2 process would be the system in which five groups are left unchanged and the incoming and leaving group occupy opposite positions which were front faces of the original octahedron (Fig. 2). The distinction between S_N2 and S_N1 was based on the relative importance of bond making and bond breaking, or on whether the two mobile groups were relatively close in or far away from the central atom.

A list of criteria for the two mechanisms was prepared (Table 2) based on the predicted effects of several variable factors on the rates. An examination of the available data, particularly for cobalt(III), but also for other elements as available, showed that the requirements of the S_N1 mechanism were best fitted. Particularly this was so for the effect of the positive charge of the central ion, for the charges and sizes of the inert ligands, and for the charge, size, and nature of the incoming group. The insensitivity to external reagents is the best evidence that the nature of these reactions is primarily one of dissociation.

Hydroxide ion is in a special category, but, in the case of cobalt(III), it seems that a special dissociation mechanism involving the conjugate base of the complex is responsible for the reactivity. The much slower reactions that can be observed with hydroxide ion in other cases, usually

---

* Other examples of substitution reactions without M—L bond cleavage may include such reactions as the alcoholysis of $Pt(PCl_3)_2Cl_2$ to give $Pt(P(OR)_3)_2Cl_2$. Similarly the fluoridation of $Ni(PCl_3)_4$ yields $Ni(PF_3)_4$ (G. Wilkinson, *J. Am. Chem. Soc.,* **73,** 5501 (1951)).

leading to complete dissociation of the complex, may be displacement processes. In the case of chelates, however, nucleophilic and electrophilic reagents may accelerate the reaction in a non-displacement process.

On theoretical grounds an S_N1 (lim) mechanism is not expected unless rearrangement to a trigonal bipyramid structure occurs. In the case of cobalt(III) such a rearrangement is hindered by a loss of stabilization energy of the d^6 system. However, electron donation, π bonding, by the ligands may help such a rearrangement. By an S_N1 (lim) mechanism is meant one in which the five-coordinated species has a finite lifetime and an independent existence. A search for such an intermediate has been made by Posey and Taube [86] by studying the reaction of $Co(NH_3)_5X^{2+}$ with Ag^+, Hg^{2+}, and Tl^{3+} in oxygen-18 enriched water. The argument is that these metal ions should greatly assist in the formation of the species $Co(NH_3)_5^{3+}$. If this species has an independent existence, it should behave in the same way no matter what its original source (X = Cl, Br, or I) or mode of generation.

The method used to test for $Co(NH_3)_5^{3+}$ was to utilize the expected isotope discrimination in the eventual reaction with water.

$$Co(NH_3)_5^{3+} + H_2O \rightarrow Co(NH_3)_5H_2O^{3+} \tag{87}$$

That is, reaction 87 would have a slightly higher rate for $H_2^{16}O$ than for $H_2^{18}O$. Analysis of the aqua complex will determine the ratio of rates. It was found that all three pentammine-halo complexes did give the same ratio when mercury(II) ion was used, but that different ratios were found for silver(I) and for thallium(III). Hence the same intermediate was not formed in all cases, as would be true if all reactions were S_N1 (lim). Furthermore the results with Tl^{3+} showed that $H_2^{18}O$ reacted more rapidly than $H_2^{16}O$. This can only be rationalized if it is the water coordinated to thallium(III) which reacts, since the heavier isotope would be preferentially found in the coordination sphere of an ion at equilibrium.[87] This is the expected result if the closest available water fills up the coordination sphere of cobalt(III) as the halide ion is removed. In the acid hydrolysis of the chloropentammine there is also evidence that a water molecule from the second coordination sphere is the one which becomes coordinated to cobalt.[46] The results with Hg^{2+}, where the interaction with the halide ion is greatest, indicate that free $Co(NH_3)_5^{3+}$ can persist for a time before reacting with water.

Another experiment which throws a special light on the mechanism of H_2O exchange in $Co(NH_3)_5H_2O^{3+}$ is the study of the effect of pressure on the rate.[88] It is found that increases in hydrostatic pressure up to

7000 atmospheres cause a small but definite decrease in the rate of water exchange. From the general theory of the relationship between rate and pressure, it is possible to calculate the quantity $\Delta V^{\ddagger}$ from the equation [89]

$$\Delta V^{\ddagger} = \frac{RT \ln k_2/k_1}{P_2 - P_1} \qquad (88)$$

where the k's are rate constants at two different pressures. The interpretation of $\Delta V^{\ddagger}$ is that it is the difference in volume between the activated complex and the reactants. The results show $\Delta V^{\ddagger} = 1.2$ ml at both 2080 and 7000 atmospheres, a small increase.

Now the volume of bulk water is 18.05 ml per mole at ordinary pressure and 15.09 ml per mole at 7000 atmospheres. It is estimated that the volume of coordinated water lies in the range of 14.4 to 17.0 ml at atmospheric pressure [90] and, in view of the strong electrostrictive pressure it is under, should not be too much less at very high pressures. Hence neither of the two processes below gives quite the right volume

$$Co(NH_3)_5H_2O^{3+} \rightleftharpoons Co(NH_3)_5{}^{3+} + H_2O \qquad S_N1 \text{ (lim)} \quad (89)$$

$$Co(NH_3)_5H_2O^{3+} + H_2O \rightleftharpoons Co(NH_3)_5(H_2O)_2{}^{+} \qquad S_N2 \qquad (90)$$

change as a function of pressure. The first gives the right direction and magnitude of the volume change for 2080 atmospheres, but should have $\Delta V^{\ddagger} \sim 0$ at high pressure. The second process predicts $\Delta V^{\ddagger}$ to be negative by 1–3.5 ml at low pressure and about zero at high pressure.

The best mechanism is precisely the one which has already been proposed for the exchange reaction of $Co(NH_3)_6{}^{3+}$. This is a stretching of the Co—O bond prior to reaction of another water molecule

$$Co(NH_3)_5H_2O^{3+} \rightleftharpoons Co(NH_3)_5\text{---}H_2O^{3+} \qquad \text{slow}$$
$$(91)$$

$$Co(NH_3)_5\text{---}H_2O^{3+} + H_2O \rightarrow Co(NH_3)_5H_2O^{3+} + H_2O \qquad \text{fast}$$
$$(92)$$

The mechanism is primarily S_N1, but some S_N2 character is obviously present. The increased volume of 1.2 ml is explicable by the stretching of the bond, and this may well be pressure independent. A similar study of the pressure dependence of

$$Co(NH_3)_5Br^{2+} + OH^{-} \rightarrow Co(NH_3)_5OH^{2+} + Br^{-} \qquad (93)$$

has been made.[91]   Here also pressure decreases the rate, and $\Delta V^{\ddagger}$ is calculated to be 8.5 ml up to 1200 atmospheres.   This increasing volume is interpreted as being due to the release of solvent molecule from the reactant ions as the intermediate of lower ionic charge is formed.   Unfortunately it is not possible to tell whether the transition state is $Co(NH_3)_4NH_2Br^+$ or $Co(NH_3)_5BrOH^+$ since the number of solvent molecules released is unknown in either case.   The two possible activated complexes differ by essentially one molecule of water.

It is necessary to guard against making too broad generalizations based on limited observations.   Even if the data point to one mechanism in the case of a certain compound, or group of compounds, there is no assurance that such a mechanism operates for all related systems. In fact, as certain parameters are changed, it is expected that there will be a smooth transition from one mechanism to another.   An example of this is furnished by the halo complexes of cobalt(III).   As seen, the bulk of the evidence and theory points to an essentially S_N1 mechanism in which primary emphasis is on the leaving group, with little or no help from the incoming group.   However, the relative proportions of bond making and bond breaking will certainly change as the complexes

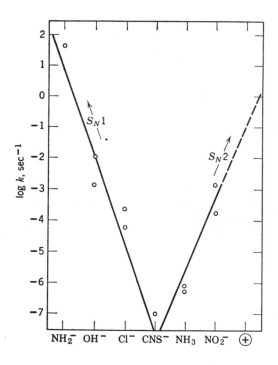

FIG. 12.   Rates of hydrolysis of a series of $Co(en)_2$-XCl^+ complexes as functions of X. The ascending curves indicate increasing S_N1 character (left branch) and increasing S_N2 character (right branch) in the reaction mechanism. (From F. Basolo, *Record Chem. Prog.*, **18**, 1 (1957).)

are varied. Figure 12, patterned after Asperger and Ingold,[92] shows in a qualitative way how various substituents should influence the relative tendencies towards S_N1- and S_N2-type mechanisms. The essential point is that electron-donating ligands will increase the chance of an S_N1 process, whereas electron-attracting substituents will increase the chance of an S_N2 reaction. The position of NCS^- at the bottom of the diagram is an attempt to rationalize the very low rate of reaction of $Co(en)_2(NCS)Cl^+$ in terms of its being neither an electron donor nor acceptor.[92] The ascending portion of the diagram is not an implication that a purely S_N2 mechanism is followed by the complexes with these groups, but rather that there is a greater tendency to bond making in the transition state.

The nitro group is placed above ammonia on the S_N2 branch, in spite of the unfavorable charge difference, because of the special property of withdrawing electrons from the critical d_{xy}-type orbitals. As we have seen, elements with many electrons in these orbitals are definitely stabilized against reaction, more so towards S_N2 reactions than S_N1. The positive charge, which is placed highest of all, refers to an increased positive charge on the nucleus of the central atom. An example of this would be nickel(IV) in its octahedral complexes. It is of the greatest interest that recent kinetic studies on haloammine complexes of Pt(IV) reacting with nucleophilic reagents seem to show the expected second-order behavior, the rate being first order in the nucleophilic reagent.

In the first example,[93] a number of complexes such as $Pt(NH_3)_3Cl_3^+$ and $Pt(en)(NH_3)(NO_2)ClBr^+$ react with pyridine in a second-order process. It is found that, if the complexes are written as PtA_3XYZ^+ with X and Z variable groups *trans* to each other, that *trans*-Br activates X more than *trans*-Cl more than *trans*-NO$_2$. This is a different result from the effect of *trans*-NO$_2$ in the case of cobalt(III) and also platinum(II) (see Chapter 4). Also, if X and Z are Br and Cl, then it is Cl which is displaced more rapidly.

$$Pt(NH_3)_3ClBrCl^+ + py \rightarrow Pt(NH_3)_3ClBrpy^{2+} + Cl^- \qquad (94)$$

However, the reactions of platinum(IV) are very sensitive to light and to the presence of even trace amounts of platinum(II).[94] It has been found that exchange of *trans*-$Pt(en)_2Cl_2^{2+}$ with radiochloride ion does not occur unless platinum(II) is present.[95] The rate of exchange in the dark is given by

$$Rate = k[Pt(II)][Pt(IV)][Cl^-] \qquad (95)$$

which suggests a bridged intermediate and an atom transfer mechanism (see Chapter 7). It is evident that considerable care must be taken to distinguish between a simple displacement mechanism and some catalyzed path. The apparently simple reaction

$$trans\text{-}Pt(en)_2Cl_2^{2+} + NO_2^- \rightarrow Pt(en)_2(NO_2)Cl^{2+} + Cl^- \quad (96)$$

appears to occur only as a result of a platinum(II) catalyzed process.[96]

REFERENCES

1. See C. K. Ingold, *Structure and Mechanism in Organic Chemistry*, Cornell University Press, Ithaca, 1953, Chapters 5 and 7.
2. G. N. Lewis, *Valence and the Structure of Atoms and Molecules*, Chemical Catalog Co., New York, 1923, p. 141; *J. Franklin Inst.*, **226**, 293 (1938).
3. C. G. Swain and C. B. Scott, *J. Am. Chem. Soc.*, **75**, 141 (1953).
4. J. O. Edwards, *ibid.*, **76**, 1540 (1954).
5. See A. A. Frost and R. G. Pearson, *Kinetics and Mechanism*, John Wiley & Sons, New York, 1953, Chapters 1 and 11.
6. F. Basolo, *Chem. Revs.*, **52**, 459 (1953).
7. For a discussion and earlier references see V. Gold, *J. Chem. Soc.*, **1956**, 4633.
8. L. Wilputte-Steinert, P. J. C. Fierens, and H. Hannaert, *Bull. soc. chim. Belges*, **64**, 628 (1955).
9. See reference 5, Chapter 5.
10. A. C. Rutenberg and H. Taube, *J. Chem. Phys.*, **20**, 823 (1952).
11. H. Taube, private communication.
12. H. Taube, *Chem. Revs.*, **50**, 69 (1952).
13. L. E. Orgel, *J. Chem. Soc.*, **1952**, 4756.
14. C. Klixbüll Jørgensen, *Acta Chem. Scand.*, **9**, 605 (1955).
15. (a) F. Basolo, J. C. Hayes, and H. M. Neumann, *J. Am. Chem. Soc.*, **75**, 5102 (1953). (b) R. G. Wilkins and M. J. G. Williams, *J. Chem. Soc.*, **1957**, 1763.
16. D. W. Margerum, R. I. Bystroff, and C. V. Banks, *ibid.*, **78**, 4211 (1956).
17. B. O. West, *J. Chem. Soc.*, **1954**, 578.
18. D. S. Popplewell and R. G. Wilkins, *ibid.*, **1955**, 4098.
19. S. S. Jones and F. A. Long, *J. Phys. Chem.*, **56**, 25 (1952); also *Chem. Abstr.*, **45**, 4166 (1951).
20. J. Bjerrum and K. G. Poulsen, *Nature*, **169**, 463 (1952).
21. R. W. Taft, Jr., and E. H. Cook, private communication.
22. W. R. King, Jr., and C. S. Garner, *J. Am. Chem. Soc.*, **74**, 3709 (1952).
23. (a) A. W. Adamson, J. P. Welker, and W. B. Wright, *ibid.*, **73**, 4789 (1951). (b) A. G. MacDiarmid and N. F. Hall, *ibid.*, **76**, 4222 (1954).
24. M. Kotani, *J. Phys. Soc. Japan*, **4**, 293 (1949); A. H. Cooke and H. J. Duffus, *Proc. Phys. Soc. London*, **A68**, 32 (1955).
25. For a review of earlier work see F. Basolo, *Chem. Revs.*, **52**, 459 (1953).
26. J. P. Mathieu, *Bull. soc. chim. France*, **3**, 2121 (1936).

27. J. E. Prue and G. Schwarzenbach, *Helv. Chim. Acta,* **33,** 974, 985 (1950).
28. (*a*) H. C. Brown and R. S. Fletcher, *J. Am. Chem. Soc.,* **71,** 1845 (1949).
    (*b*) C. K. Ingold, *Structure and Mechanism in Organic Chemistry,* Cornell University Press, Ithaca, 1953, pp. 402 and 415.
29. F. Basolo and R. K. Murmann, *J. Am. Chem. Soc.,* **74,** 5243 (1952); F. Basolo, Y. T. Chen, and R. K. Murmann, *ibid.,* **76,** 956 (1954).
30. A. E. Martell and M. Calvin, *Chemistry of the Metal Chelate Compounds,* Prentice-Hall, New York, 1952, p. 137.
31. F. Basolo, Y. T. Chen, and R. K. Murmann, *J. Am. Chem. Soc.,* **75,** 1478 (1953).
32. K. B. Yatsimirskii, *Doklady Akad. Nauk S.S.S.R.,* **72,** 307 (1950).
33. A. B. Lamb and L. T. Fairhall, *J. Am. Chem. Soc.,* **45,** 378 (1923).
34. G. W. Ettle and C. H. Johnson, *J. Chem. Soc.,* **1940,** 1490.
35. F. J. Garrick, *Trans. Faraday Soc.,* **33,** 486 (1937); **34,** 1088 (1938).
36. F. Basolo, B. D. Stone, J. G. Bergmann, and R. G. Pearson, *J. Am. Chem. Soc.,* **76,** 3079 (1954).
37. A. W. Adamson and R. G. Wilkins, *ibid.,* **76,** 3379 (1954).
38. R. G. Pearson, R. E. Meeker, and F. Basolo, *ibid.,* **78,** 709 (1956).
39. R. E. Meeker, Ph.D. thesis, Northwestern University, 1956.
40. D. D. Brown, C. K. Ingold, and R. S. Nyholm, *J. Chem. Soc.,* **1953,** 2678.
41. F. J. Garrick, *Nature,* **139,** 507 (1937).
42. J. N. Brønsted, *Z. physik. Chem.,* **122,** 383 (1926).
43. N. Bjerrum, *ibid.,* **59,** 336, 581 (1907).
44. See reference 5, p. 204, for a discussion of acid-base catalysis.
45. J. S. Anderson, H. V. A. Briscoe, and N. F. Spoor, *J. Chem. Soc.,* **1943,** 361.
46. A. W. Adamson and F. Basolo, *Acta Chem. Scand.,* **9,** 1261 (1955).
47. A. A. Grinberg and K. I. Gildengershel, *Izvest. Akad. Nauk S.S.S.R. Otdel Khim. Nauk,* **1948,** 479.
48. R. G. Pearson, R. E. Meeker, and F. Basolo, *J. Inorg. Nuclear Chem.,* **1,** 342 (1955).
49. J. LeGros, *Compt. rend.,* **242,** 1605 (1956).
50. M. M. Anderson, private communication.
51. F. H. Westheimer and M. Shookhoff, *J. Am. Chem. Soc.,* **62,** 269 (1940).
52. R. G. Pearson and F. Basolo, *ibid.,* **78,** 4878 (1956).
53. J. C. Bailar and D. F. Peppard, *ibid.,* **62,** 105 (1940).
54. J. Bjerrum and S. E. Rasmussen, *Acta Chem. Scand.,* **6,** 1265 (1952); see also Chapter 9, p. 387.
55. W. K. Wilmarth, H. Graff, and S. T. Gustin, *J. Am. Chem. Soc.,* **78,** 2683 (1956).
56. J. D. Dunitz and L. E. Orgel, *J. Chem. Soc.,* **1953,** 2594.
57. B. Adell, *Z. u. anorg. allgem. Chem.,* **246,** 303 (1941).
58. See reference 5, p. 159.
59. A. B. Lamb, *J. Am. Chem. Soc.,* **61,** 699 (1939).
60. See reference 5, p. 138.
61. H. Taube and F. A. Posey, *J. Am. Chem. Soc.,* **75,** 1463 (1953).
62. C. Postmus and E. L. King, *J. Phys. Chem.,* **59,** 1208, 1217 (1955).
63. D. D. Brown and C. K. Ingold, *J. Chem. Soc.,* **1953,** 2674.

64. R. G. Pearson, P. M. Henry, and F. Basolo, *J. Am. Chem. Soc.*, **79**, 5379, 5382 (1957).

65. (a) A. Unmack, *Z. physik. Chem.*, **133**, 45 (1928). (b) I. M. Kolthoff and L. S. Guss, *J. Am. Chem. Soc.*, **61**, 330 (1939).

66. F. Basolo, W. R. Matoush, and R. G. Pearson, *ibid.*, **78**, 4883 (1956).

67. See, for example, R. P. Bell, *Acid-Base Catalysis*, Oxford University Press, 1941, p. 143ff.

68. J. N. Brønsted and R. Livingston, *J. Am. Chem. Soc.*, **49**, 435 (1927).

69. (a) J. H. Baxendale and P. George, *Trans. Faraday Soc.*, **46**, 736 (1950). (b) P. Krumholz, *J. Phys. Chem.*, **60**, 87 (1956).

70. T. S. Lee, I. M. Kolthoff, and D. L. Leussing, *J. Am. Chem. Soc.*, **70**, 3596 (1948); J. E. Dickens, F. Basolo, and H. M. Neumann, *ibid.*, **79**, 1286 (1957).

71. F. Basolo, J. C. Hayes, and H. M. Neumann, *J. Am. Chem. Soc.*, **75**, 5102 (1953); J. Bjerrum, K. G. Poulsen, and I. Poulsen, *Symposium on Coordination Chemistry*, Copenhagen, August, 1953, p. 51.

72. (a) F. Basolo and F. P. Dwyer, *J. Am. Chem. Soc.*, **76**, 1454 (1954). (b) R. G. Wilkins and M. J. G. Williams, *J. Chem. Soc.*, **1957**, 4514.

73. G. K. Schweitzer and J. M. Lee, *J. Phys. Chem.*, **56**, 195 (1952).

74. D. W. Margerum, *J. Am. Chem. Soc.*, **79**, 2728 (1957).

75. H. Ackerman and G. Schwarzenbach, *Helv. Chim. Acta*, **35**, 485 (1952).

76. A. B. Lamb and K. J. Mysels, *J. Am. Chem. Soc.*, **67**, 468 (1945).

77. J. P. Hunt, A. C. Rutenberg, and H. Taube, *ibid.*, **74**, 268 (1952).

78. C. A. Bunton and D. R. Llewellyn, *J. Chem. Soc.*, **1953**, 1692.

79. F. A. Posey and H. Taube, *J. Am. Chem. Soc.*, **75**, 4099 (1953).

80. D. R. Stranks and R. G. Wilkins, *Chem. Revs.*, **57**, 743 (1957); D. R. Stranks and G. M. Harris, *J. Chem. Phys.*, **19**, 257 (1951); *J. Phys. Chem.*, **56**, 906 (1952); D. R. Stranks, *Trans. Faraday Soc.*, **51**, 492 (1955); P. E. Yankwich and J. E. McNamara, *J. Chem. Phys.*, **20**, 1325 (1952); E. Soito and B. Lazard, *J. Inorg. Nuclear Chem.*, **1**, 218 (1955).

81. R. G. Pearson, P. M. Henry, J. G. Bergmann, and F. Basolo, *J. Am. Chem. Soc.*, **76**, 5920 (1954).

82. (a) For a list of references see A. T. Austin, E. D. Hughes, J. H. Ridd, and C. K. Ingold, *ibid.*, **74**, 55 (1952). (b) L. P. Hammett, *Physical Organic Chemistry*, McGraw-Hill Book Co., New York, 1940, p. 294.

83. R. K. Murmann and H. Taube, *J. Am. Chem. Soc.*, **78**, 4886 (1956).

84. N. F. Hall and O. R. Alexander, *ibid.*, **62**, 3455 (1940); G. A. Mills, *ibid.*, **62**, 2833 (1940).

85. M. L. Bender, *ibid.*, **73**, 1626 (1951).

86. F. A. Posey and H. Taube, *J. Am. Chem. Soc.*, **79**, 255 (1957).

87. H. Feder and H. Taube, *J. Chem. Phys.*, **20**, 1335 (1952); H. Taube, *J. Phys. Chem.*, **58**, 523 (1954).

88. H. R. Hunt, Jr., and H. Taube, private communication.

89. S. Glasstone, K. J. Laidler, and H. Eyring, *The Theory of Rate Processes*, McGraw-Hill Book Co., New York, 1941, p. 470.

90. (a) W. Biltz, *Z. anorg. u. allgem. Chem.*, **124**, 245 (1922). (b) E. Birk, *ibid.*, **158**, 111 (1926).

91. C. T. Burris and K. J. Laidler, *Trans. Faraday Soc.*, **51**, 1497 (1955).

92. S. Asperger and C. K. Ingold, *J. Chem. Soc.*, **1956**, 2862.

93. O. E. Zvyagintsev and E. F. Karandashova, *Doklady Akad. Nauk S.S.S.R.*, **108**, 447 (1956).

94. R. L. Rich and H. Taube, *J. Am. Chem. Soc.*, **76**, 2608 (1954).

95. F. Basolo, P. H. Wilks, R. G. Pearson, and R. G. Wilkins, *J. Inorg. Nuclear Chem.*, **6**, 163 (1958).

96. H. R. Ellison, private communication.

4 | *Substitution reactions of square complexes*

By far the most stable square complexes are those of platinum(II), and as a result the syntheses and reactions of these compounds have been the subject of extensive investigations.[1] Therefore much of the discussion in this chapter has to do specifically with the chemistry of platinum(II) compounds. However, this discussion, with some reservations, can also be expected to apply to other square complexes, e.g., palladium(II), nickel(II), and gold(III). Furthermore it should be pointed out that more careful examination of these "square" complexes shows that they have a marked tendency to coordinate a fifth and/or a sixth group at a slightly longer distance from the central metal ion than are the ligands in the original square.

REACTIONS OF PLATINUM(II) COMPLEXES; THE *trans* EFFECT

The concept of a square configuration, rather than a tetrahedron as is known for carbon compounds, was first introduced by Werner.[2] This was brought about by the fact that the tetrahedral structure could not account for the α and β forms of $Pt(NH_3)_2Cl_2$ prepared more than a century ago by Peyrone (α)[3] and by Reiset (β).[4] The α form was obtained by the reaction of $PtCl_4^{2-}$ with ammonia, and the β form resulted from heating solid $[Pt(NH_3)_4]Cl_2$ to approximately 250°C.

Since the two forms were each found to be monomeric, Werner concluded that they must be *cis-trans* isomers. On the basis of some experimental observations made by Jørgensen,[5] Werner suggested that the α form had the *cis* and the β form the *trans* configuration. Reactions 1 and 2 were the two sets considered. Werner argued that, since only

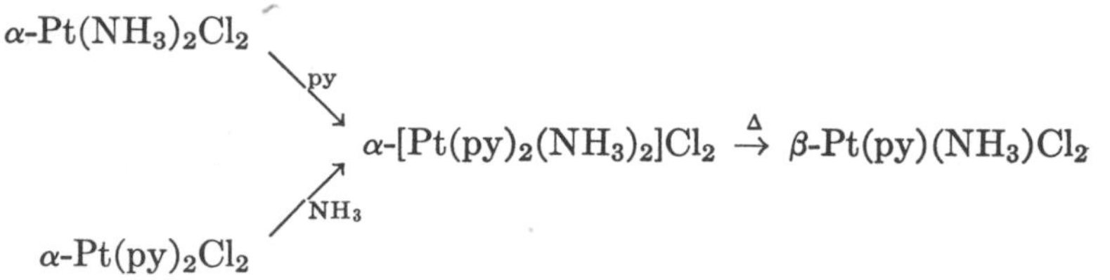
α-Pt(NH3)2Cl2
py
α-[Pt(py)2(NH3)2]Cl2 Δ→ β-Pt(py)(NH3)Cl2
NH3
α-Pt(py)2Cl2

(1)

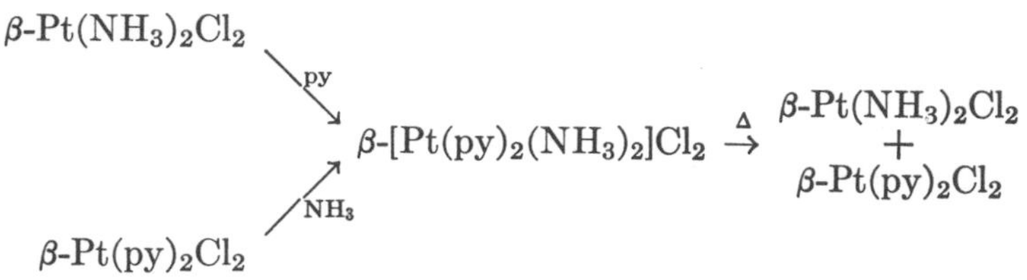
β-Pt(NH3)2Cl2
py
β-[Pt(py)2(NH3)2]Cl2 Δ→
β-Pt(NH3)2Cl2
+
β-Pt(py)2Cl2
NH3
β-Pt(py)2Cl2

(2)

one complex is isolated from reaction 1 and only two complexes are obtained from reaction 2, both the addition and elimination steps must involve stereospecific reactions. Furthermore these results are consistent with the assignment of a *cis* structure to the α form and a *trans* structure for the β form if it is assumed that the addition of ammonia or pyridine in the first steps takes place without isomerization and that *trans* elimination occurs in the final steps. Thus the stereochemical consequence of reactions 1 and 2 may be diagramed as shown in reactions 3 and 4.

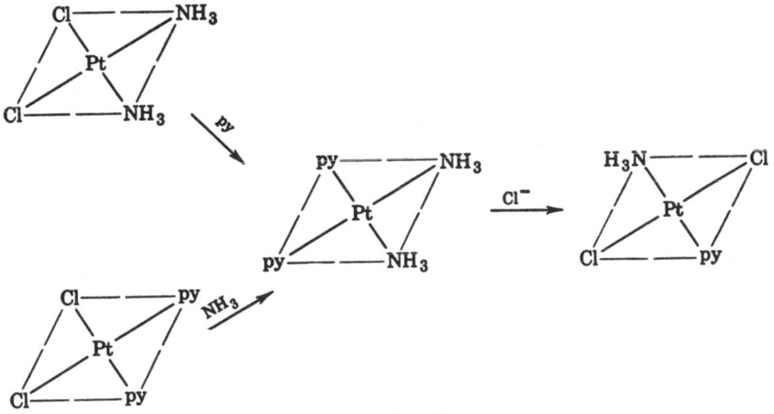
Cl
NH3
Pt
Cl
NH3
py
py
NH3
Pt
py
NH3
Cl⁻
H3N
Cl
Pt
Cl
py
Cl
py
Pt
Cl
py
NH3

cis(α)-PtA_2Cl_2

(3)

The assignment of structure by this method cannot be accepted as proof because of the assumptions which had to be made. However, these assumptions have since been shown to be correct, and the two representations (3 and 4) are valid.[1a] It is of particular interest that the

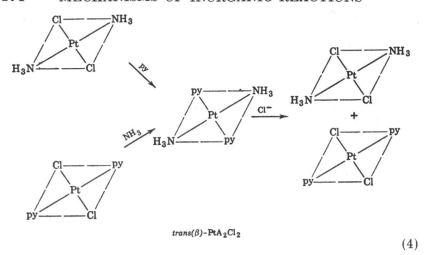

$$trans(\beta)\text{-}PtA_2Cl_2$$

(4)

second steps in these reactions involve solely the replacement of ligands in *trans* positions. This observation was not generally utilized until after 1926, at which time Chernyaev [6] introduced the concept of the *trans effect* to correlate many of the reactions of platinum(II) complexes. Chernyaev called attention to the general phenomenon that a negative ligand, e.g., Cl^-, has a greater labilizing effect on a group *trans* to it than it does on groups in *cis* positions. Furthermore this labilizing effect is usually larger for a negative ligand than it is for a non-π-bonding neutral group, e.g., NH_3.

The utility of an empirical rule such as that of the *trans* effect becomes apparent if we now consider a few reactions of platinum(II) complexes. For example the *trans* elimination step of reaction 3 may be designated as a two-step process (reaction 5). After the first

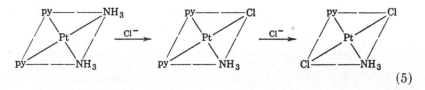

(5)

chloride ion has entered the complex, the second chloride ion will replace the group *trans* to the first since this position is labilized, the chloride ion having a larger *trans* effect than does either pyridine or ammonia. Similarly the methods of synthesis of *cis*- and *trans*-$Pt(NH_3)_2Cl_2$ are in keeping with the concept of the *trans* effect (reactions 6 and 7). Thus in reaction 6 the second ammonia enters a *cis*

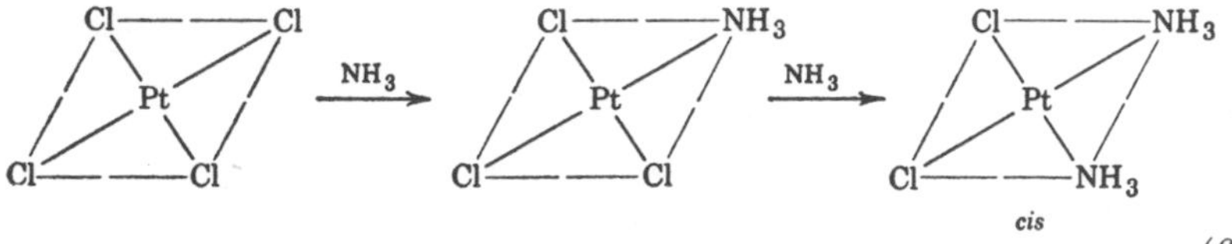

$$(6)$$

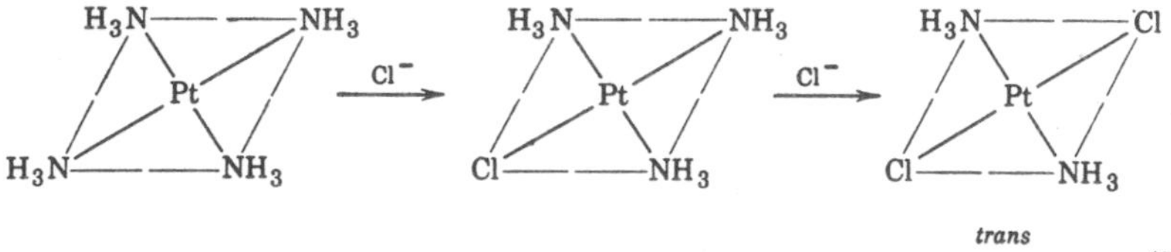

$$(7)$$

position because the *trans*-directing influence of chloride ion is greater than that of ammonia, which means that the least reactive chloro group in $PtNH_3Cl_3^-$ is the one opposite ammonia. In reaction 7 chloride ion replaces the most labile ammonia in $Pt(NH_3)_3Cl^+$, which is the one opposite the chloro group, thus resulting in the formation of *trans*-$Pt(NH_3)_2Cl_2$.

This *trans*-effect rule has often been used, with considerable success, as a guide in the syntheses of desired isomeric platinum(II) complexes. Often, as with the synthesis of *cis*- and *trans*-$Pt(NH_3)(NO_2)$-Cl_2^-,[7] this can be achieved just by reversing the order of introduction of groups into $PtCl_4^{2-}$ (reactions 8 and 9). Reaction 8 is analogous

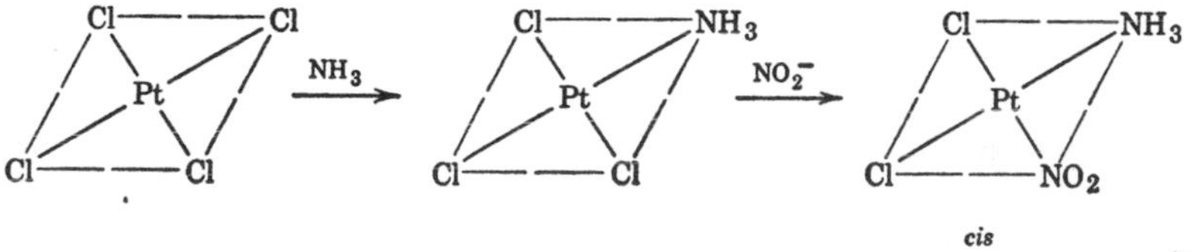

$$(8)$$

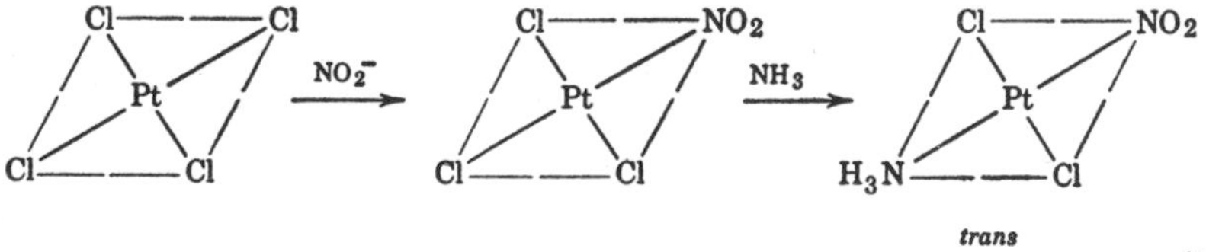

$$(9)$$

to 6, and reaction 9 illustrates that the *trans*-directing ability of the nitrite ion exceeds that of a chloride ion. A similar sequence of reactions can be used to prepare *cis*- and *trans*-$Pt(C_2H_4)(NH_3)Cl_2$;

again the success depends on the *trans* effect of ethylene being greater than that of chloride ion. Chernyaev [8] demonstrated the applicability of his rule by the synthesis of the three isomers of $Pt(NH_2OH)(py)$-$(NH_3)NO_2^+$. More recently [9] the isomers of $Pt(py)(NH_3)BrCl$ were prepared as shown in reactions 10–12. The success of the reactions

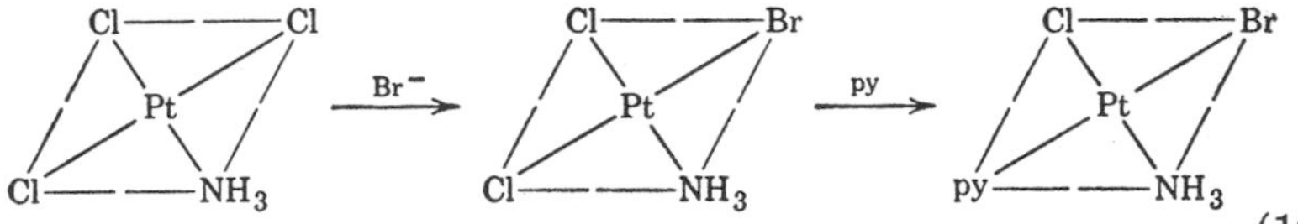

$$\text{Cl}_2(\text{Cl})\text{Pt(Cl)(NH}_3) \xrightarrow{\text{Br}^-} \text{(Cl)(Br)Pt(Cl)(NH}_3) \xrightarrow{\text{py}} \text{(Cl)(Br)Pt(py)(NH}_3) \tag{10}$$

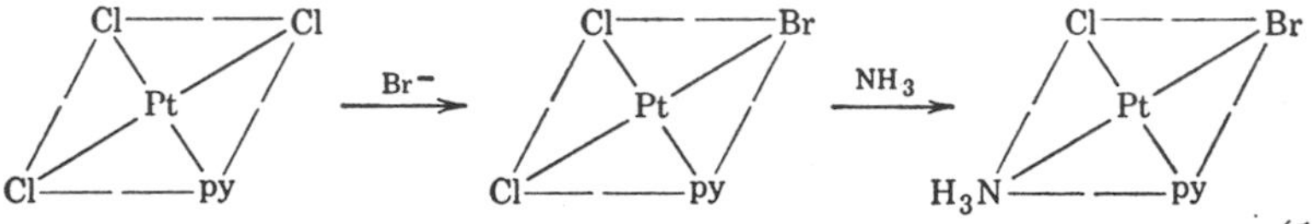

$$\text{(Cl)(Cl)Pt(Cl)(py)} \xrightarrow{\text{Br}^-} \text{(Cl)(Br)Pt(Cl)(py)} \xrightarrow{\text{NH}_3} \text{(Cl)(Br)Pt(H}_3\text{N)(py)} \tag{11}$$

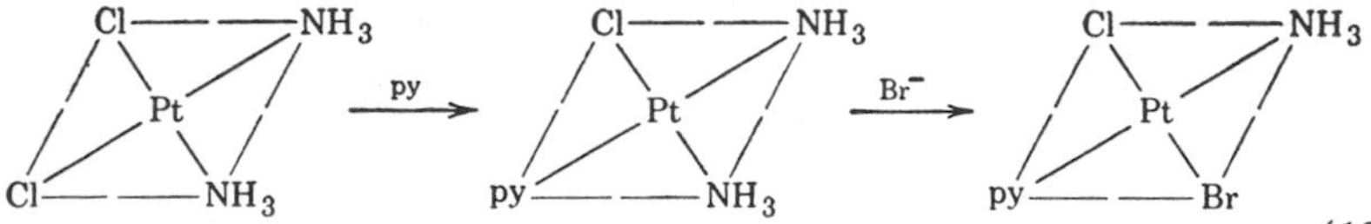

$$\text{(Cl)(NH}_3)\text{Pt(Cl)(NH}_3) \xrightarrow{\text{py}} \text{(Cl)(NH}_3)\text{Pt(py)(NH}_3) \xrightarrow{\text{Br}^-} \text{(Cl)(NH}_3)\text{Pt(py)(Br)} \tag{12}$$

depends upon the greater *trans* effect of the bromo and chloro ligands compared to pyridine and ammonia.

In addition to its utility in the synthesis of desired platinum (II) complexes, the *trans*-effect phenomenon has also been used, principally by Russian chemists, to distinguish between *cis* and *trans* isomers of the type PtA_2X_2. For example, *cis*-$Pt(NH_3)_2Cl_2$ reacts with thiourea (tu) to yield $[Pt(tu)_4]Cl_2$, whereas under the same conditions the *trans* isomer would give $Pt(tu)_2Cl_2$. This *Kurnakow test* [10] works for the dihalodiammineplatinum(II) complexes because the *trans*-directing influence of thiourea exceeds that of the amine and halide ion. Similar results are reported for reactions of thiosulfate ion instead of thiourea, *cis*- and *trans*-$Pt(NH_3)_2Cl_2$ reacting with excess thiosulfate ion to form $Pt(S_2O_3)_4^{6-}$ and $Pt(NH_3)_2(S_2O_3)_2^{2-}$ respectively.[11]

Extensive qualitative observations of the type described above make it possible to place the common ligands in an approximate order of their tendency to direct a second substituent into the *trans* position. Much of this work has been done by chemists of the Russian school. The approximate order of increasing *trans* effect [12] is

$$H_2O \lesssim OH^- < NH_3 \sim RNH_2 < py$$

$$< Cl^- < Br^- < NCS^- \sim I^- \sim NO_2^- \sim SO_3H^- \sim PR_3 \sim R_2S$$

$$\sim SC(NH_2)_2 < NO \sim CO \sim C_2H_4 \sim CN^-$$

The groups at the CN^- end of this series are said to have a high, and those at the water end a low, *trans* effect. The series is based on qualitative observations, and the precise order of ligands in the series is not known with certainty. It is of interest to note that ligands which have a high *trans* effect are usually those which are capable of forming π bonds by accepting electrons from platinum (II). Furthermore the order of increasing *trans* effect of the halide ions is just the reverse of their order of increasing crystal field strength (p. 44), whereas ligands such as CN^-, CO, and NO_2^- which have high *trans* effects also have large crystal field strengths.

trans-EFFECT THEORIES

Several theories have been advanced in attempts to explain this *trans*-effect phenomenon. One of the first theoretical considerations was by Chernyaev,[13] who recognized that a simple coulombic explanation in the Kossel sense is inadequate. Such an explanation would lead to the incorrect conclusion that a negative ligand should exert greater repulsion on a *cis* neighbor than upon a *trans* partner. Thus a simple electrostatic treatment of this type is not consistent with the experimental results.

One method of approach to the problem is based upon interpretations which necessitate a weakening of the metal-ligand bond directly opposite the *trans*-directing group. A second, more recent, approach has been to consider that the metal-ligand bond need not necessarily be weakened but instead that the lability of this group is a consequence of the reaction mechanism. Thus according to this latter interpretation the *trans* effect is a kinetic rather than a thermodynamic effect. A discussion of these different theories of the *trans* effect follows.

The polarization theory. Grinberg [14] has called attention to the parallelism between the decreasing *trans* effect of the halide ions, $I^- > Br^- > Cl^-$, and the decrease in molar refraction of these ions. Thus he suggested that the polarization concept of Fajans [15] may be utilized to explain the weakening of the metal-ligand bond opposite the *trans*-directing group. A pictorial representation of this concept

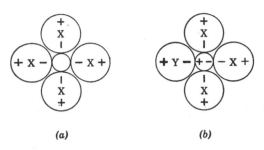

FIG. 1. Grinberg's polarization *trans*-effect theory. (*a*) Symmetrical induced dipoles in square MX_4. (*b*) Unsymmetrical induced dipoles in MX_3Y, where the induced dipole of Y is greater than that of X, and thus bond M—X *trans* to Y is weakened.

is shown in Fig. 1. Mutual polarizability of the central ion and the ligands results in induced dipoles in both. If the four ligands in the complex are identical, then there is a symmetrical distribution of the induced dipoles and the resultant dipole is zero (Fig. 1*a*). If, however, one ligand differs from the other three, then there is no longer a mutual compensation in the induced dipoles, and the result will be a dipole in the central ion as well as in the structure as a whole (Fig. 1*b*). On the basis of such a picture the suggestion is made that, if Y^- is more polarizable than X^-, the central ion is in turn polarized such that it is less positive directly opposite (*trans*) Y^- than it is adjacent (*cis*) to Y^-. It follows, from such an interpretation, that the M—X bond *trans* to Y^- will be weaker than are the M—X bonds *cis* to Y^-.

Although in some cases there appears to be a fairly good correlation between the polarizability of a ligand and its *trans* effect, it would seem that this is not the only factor that needs to be considered. The important thing is not the induced dipole moment of the ligand but instead the total electric potential which the ligand creates in the vicinity of the *trans* group. This electric potential at the *trans* position to the ligand in question is not only a function of the induced dipole moment or polarizability of the ligand, but it is likewise dependent upon its permanent dipole moment, electrical charge, and size. Calculations based entirely upon electrostatic interactions (Chapter 2) show that this potential as well as the bond strengths of metal-halogen bonds should decrease in the order $F^- > Cl^- > Br^- > I^-$. This is also the order of crystal field strengths of the halide ions as determined from the absorption spectra of analogous halometal complexes. Furthermore this is usually the order of thermodynamic stability of the halide complexes of metals in aqueous solution.

However, a small group of metal ions, $Cu(I), Ag(I), Cd(II), Hg(II)$, and $Pt(II)$ form halogen complexes with the opposite sequence of stabilities,[16] viz., $I^- > Br^- > Cl^- > F^-$. It follows that for these latter systems something other than purely electrostatic forces must contribute to the metal-halogen bond strengths. This is further supported by the observation that these metal ions of low charge form relatively strong metal-halogen bonds and that the bond strength increases with decreasing electronegativity of the halide ion. Leden and Chatt [17] point out that for the above metal ions the greater stability of the chloro complexes relative to the fluoro complexes has its analogy in the much greater stability of thio ether complexes relative to ether complexes and also trialkylphosphine complexes relative to trialkylamine complexes. Since the ligand atoms F, O, and N have no vacant orbitals, whereas Cl, S, and P have vacant d orbitals, it is suggested that the greater metal-ligand bond strength (where the ligand atom is Cl, S, or P relative to F, O, or N respectively) is a result of π bonding of the type $dd\text{-}\pi$. That halogens can use vacant d orbitals to form π bonds has been suggested by Mulliken [18] to account for the anomolously low single bond dissociation energy of fluorine, oxygen, and nitrogen compared to the higher elements of the same family. For these higher elements $pd\text{-}\pi$ bonding can contribute to the total bond strength.

Although π bonding should contribute to the total metal-ligand bond strength of the above-mentioned complexes, it is fairly certain that the effect is not great enough to alter the fundamental order M—F > M—Cl > M—Br > M—I. Thus in the gas state the energies of dissociation for the process

$$HgX_2 \text{ (g.)} \rightarrow Hg^{2+} \text{ (g.)} + 2X^- \text{ (g.)} \tag{13}$$

decrease with increasing atomic weight of the halogen. The heats are 638 kcal for the fluoride and 600, 598, and 590 kcal for the chloride, bromide, and iodide respectively.[19] The same order is found for the silver and copper(I) chlorides, bromides, and iodides. Thus, although the contribution due to π bonding cannot easily be evaluated, it would appear that it is small compared to the electrostatic terms in the potential energy.

It is of interest that it is just the d^8 and d^{10} ions which are known to form olefin complexes that show the increased stability of iodide over fluoride complexes in solution. This matter is discussed in Chapter 9. It may also be mentioned that such central atoms have low coordination numbers. This is a factor which will also stabilize iodide relative to fluoride complexes since lower ligand repulsion will increase the importance of ion-induced dipole binding. The larger polarizability of iodide ion makes this term greatest for this ion. It must be remembered that the order of thermodynamic stabilities of metal-halide complexes in aqueous solution does not give a direct measure of the metal-halide bond strength. These measurements give the total heat for the reactions

$$M—X \text{ (aq.)} + H_2O \text{ (aq.)} \rightarrow M(H_2O)^+ \text{ (aq.)} + X^- \text{ (aq.)} \qquad (14)$$

where obviously factors other than metal-halide bond strength are involved. The most important other factor is the heat of hydration of the halide ions, which decreases as follows: $F^- > Cl^- > Br^- > I^-$. Therefore, in some systems where the contributions of ion-induced dipole attraction and π bonding to the total M—X bond strength is large, although the vapor phase order of bond strength remains M—F > M—I, the greater heat of hydration of fluoride ion may now be sufficient to render the metal complexes of fluoride ion in aqueous solution less stable than those of iodide ion.

The position finally reached in the above discussion is that the metal-halide bond strength in the gas phase decreases with increasing atomic number of the halogen. It must also follow, from an electrostatic viewpoint, that the greater the metal-halide bond strength, the greater the repulsive potential at the opposite or *trans* position. However, this is contrary to the *trans*-directing influence of the halide ions, which decreases in the order $I^- > Br^- > Cl^-$. This reversal in order suggests that for these systems the *trans* effect is not controlled by electrostatic phenomena.

One other point which should be made is that negative ligands have a larger *trans* effect than do neutral groups which are incapable of forming π bonds, e.g., $Cl^- > NH_3 > H_2O$. It has been suggested that this is due to the greater polarizability of the negative ligand. It is more correct to say that the negative ligand because of its charge exerts a greater repulsive potential at the *trans* position. Note also that for the non-π-bonding neutral groups the *trans* effect order and the crystal field order is the same: $NH_3 > H_2O$. This seems to be due to the greater induced dipole on NH_3 as postulated by the polarization theory.

The kinetic electrostatic theory. Both the availability of a vacant orbital (p_z) and the general accessibility of the central atom in square platinum(II) complexes make a bimolecular (S_N2) mechanism for substitution reactions in these systems seem very plausible. On the basis of such a mechanism the entering group Y would lead to a transient five-coordinate intermediate with a trigonal bipyramid configura-

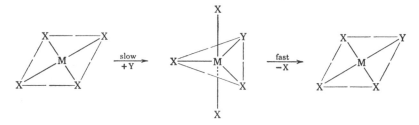

FIG. 2. Bimolecular (S_N2) substitution reaction for square complexes.

tion. Thus, for the reaction of MX_4 with Y (Fig. 2), upon the approach of Y one group is depressed below the original square plane; this group, the group *trans* to it, and the entering group Y form the central trigonal plane of the intermediate. The other two X groups become the apical groups of the trigonal bipyramid intermediate. This is then followed by the rapid loss of one of the two X groups in the trigonal plane, with Y and the remaining X group reverting to *trans* positions in the original plane.

Cardwell [20] suggests that for such a mechanism the most readily formed trigonal bipyramid is that in which the most electron-attracting ligands are apical and the electron-repelling groups are trigonal. In this way one can account for the *trans* effect observed for certain substitution reactions of platinum(II) complexes. For example the last step in the synthesis of *cis*- and *trans*-$Pt(NH_3)_2Cl_2$ can be explained on this basis (Fig. 3). Since the chloride ion is more electron repelling than is ammonia, the approach of the negative end of the ammonia dipole towards $Pt(NH_3)Cl_3^-$ is easier if the *trans*-chloro groups move slightly out of the plane than it is if the *trans* ammonia and chloro combination were to move. Thus the ammonia in the complex is one of the apical groups, so that the entering ammonia must occupy an adjacent position and form *cis*-$Pt(NH_3)_2Cl_2$. Similarly in the reaction of $Pt(NH_3)_3Cl^+$ with Cl^-, the *trans* combination NH_3—Cl offers more resistance to the entry of the chloride ion than does the NH_3—NH_3 pair. Consequently, as represented in Fig. 3, the *trans*-NH_3—Cl becomes part of the trigonal plane and gives rise to the formation of *trans*-$Pt(NH_3)_2Cl_2$.

This theory is based upon the assumption that substitution reactions of platinum(II) complexes are bimolecular. This is a plausible assumption, as already mentioned. However, it must be remembered that the platinum(II) ion also has a filled d_{z^2} orbital and that this

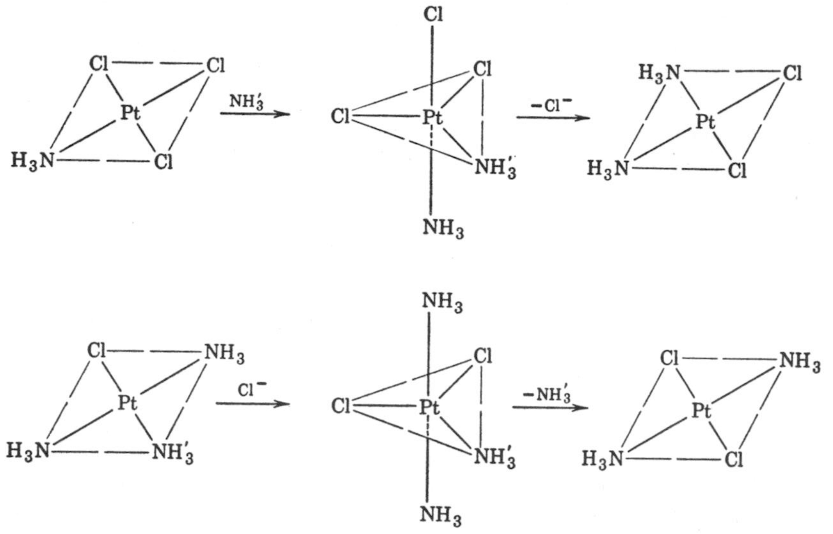

Fig. 3. The kinetic electrostatic theory applied to an S_N2 mechanism.

electron cloud may hinder the approach of an entering group along the z axis. Another way of stating this is to say that there will be a substantial loss of crystal field stabilization energy in forming a trigonal bipyramid structure. Furthermore it is not necessary that the reaction be bimolecular in order to understand the stereospecific substitutions which are characteristic of these systems. For example the reaction of $Pt(NH_3)_3Cl^+$ with chloride ion is also expected to yield *trans*-$Pt(NH_3)_2Cl_2$ by an S_N1 process (Fig. 4). In such a mechanism the assumption is that the entering chloride ion will approach the complex from a position as far removed from the most electron-repelling ligand (chloro group) as possible, which in this case means adjacent to the ammonias and *trans* to the chloro group.

Although this hypothesis affords an adequate explanation of the

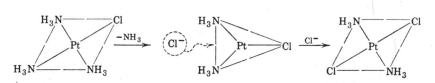

Fig. 4. The kinetic electrostatic theory applied to an S_N1 mechanism.

steric course of either S_N1 or S_N2 substitutions in haloammineplatinum(II) complexes, it has been pointed out that it cannot explain the reactions of certain other types of platinum(II) compounds.[21] For example the reaction of $Pt(NH_3)Cl_3^-$ with ammonia yields *cis*-$Pt(NH_3)_2Cl_2$, as mentioned above, whereas the reaction of $Pt(C_2H_4)$-Cl_3^- with ammonia yields *trans*-$Pt(C_2H_4)(NH_3)Cl_2$. Yet the electron-repelling properties of ethylene and ammonia should not be markedly different. Therefore the very high *trans* effect of ethylene cannot be accounted for on electrostatic grounds, nor is it possible to account for the large *trans* effect of phosphines and thio ethers on this basis. In short, electrostatic arguments are generally not applicable to ligands which show a pronounced tendency to form π bonds.

The π-bonding theory. The concept of π bonding in metal complexes was first introduced by Pauling[22] in order to account for the short Ni—C bond distance in $Ni(CO)_4$ and also to account for the large stability of the cyanide complexes of transition metals as compared to non-transition metals. The existence and significance of such double bonding are now generally recognized. A schematic representation of the double bond in $Pt=PR_3$ is shown in Fig. 5. The σ bond is formed by donation of a lone pair of electrons from the phosphorus atom to platinum(II), or by electrostatic attraction between the central ion and the dipole moment, permanent plus induced, of the ligand molecule. The π-type bond (dative π bond) is formed by the overlap of a filled d orbital of platinum(II) and a vacant d orbital of phosphorus, thus resulting in dd-π hybridization.

According to Chatt, Duncanson, and Venanzi,[12] although ligands in coordination compounds exhibit strong inductive and mesomeric effects, the inductive effect is largely electrostatic in character and should affect all metal-ligand bonds in a similar manner. However, the mesomeric effect should influence almost entirely the *trans* position, just as in benzene chemistry it affects the ortho and para positions preferen-

Fig. 5. Schematic representation of the $R_3P=Pt$ bond. If ligands PR_3 and X are in the xy plane, then the d orbitals shown are either d_{xz} or d_{yz}.

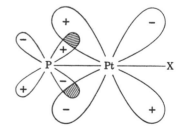

tially. The *trans*-directing influence of a double-bonding ligand L in the reaction

$$trans\text{-}PtA_2LX + Y \rightarrow trans\text{-}PtA_2LY + X \tag{15}$$

is shown in Fig. 6. Because of the π-bonding character of ligand L, the electron density in the filled d_{xz} orbital of platinum (II) is largely shifted towards L and therefore away from X (Fig. 6*b*). Thus the approach of the nucleophilic group Y is both enhanced and directed towards the vicinity of X, the region of lowest electron density. However, should ligand L have little or no tendency to π-bond, then the electron density in the d_{xz} orbital is not markedly disturbed, remaining more or less symmetrically distributed about ligands L and X (Fig. 6*a*). This means that the entry of Y is somewhat opposed by the electron cloud density in the *xz* plane so that the rate of reaction is slow.

Chatt [12] points out that the double-bonding hypothesis does not require that the bond in the activated *trans* position necessarily be weakened. In fact a *trans* bond weakening will only occur if the opposing *trans* groups both have a high *trans* effect (see the discussion of relative bond energies of *cis*- and *trans*-Pt(PR$_3$)$_2$Cl$_2$ on p. 251). Therefore the conclusion reached according to this π-bonding theory is that the fast substitutions found for square complexes containing at least one ligand of high *trans* effect should be bimolecular (S_N2) and furthermore the greater speed of *trans* substitution should result from

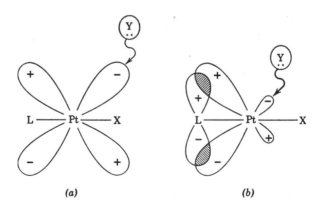

(*a*)   (*b*)

Fig. 6. *trans* effect of L resulting from π bonding which uses d_{xz} electrons and reduces the electron density in the vicinity of X. (*a*) L does not form π bonds; (*b*) L does form π bonds.

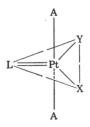

Fig. 7. Transition state proposed for the reaction

$$trans\text{-}PtA_2LX \xrightarrow{Y} trans\text{-}PtA_2LY$$

a lowering of the activation energy of formation of the transition state, rather than from a weakening of the *trans* bond. The slow substitution reactions of systems with weakly activating *trans* ligands may also be S_N2, but an S_N1 mechanism is a possibility.

Orgel [23] independently proposed essentially the same picture to account for the *trans* effect in square complexes. He emphasizes the enhanced stability of the transition state due to π bonding rather than the ease of approach of the incoming group. Since substitution reactions of platinum(II) complexes take place with retention of configuration, a distorted trigonal bipyramid structure (Fig. 7) was proposed in which the entering and leaving groups are in equivalent positions but usually different from the other groups. Furthermore, the distinction between the groups *cis* and *trans* to the reacting group is maintained. The transition state (Fig. 7) results from an approach of Y from one side of the plane with a compensating motion of X into the opposite side of the plane. For the exchange reaction of a symmetrical complex, a regular trigonal bipyramid would be formed.

The crystal field theory (Chapter 2) requires, for the maximum stability of a given geometric configuration, that the d electrons of the metal ion avoid the region of maximum concentration of the ligand electrons. Making use of this criterion, it is apparent that the stability of the transition state increases, and hence the lability of the original complex increases, for any process which reduces the electron density along the Pt—X and Pt—Y directions. If Pt, L, X, and Y in the transition state lie in the xz plane, then it follows that the d_{xz} orbital electrons of platinum(II) are the ones with a maximum concentration along the critical directions. This orbital is also just the one involved in the double bonding of group L, which is *trans* to the reacting group X. Therefore the greater the π-bonding tendency of L, the greater its *trans* effect because of its increased stabilizing influence on the five-coordinated intermediate.

The "dissociation" theory. The above kinetic approaches to the *trans* effect which suggest that the reactions are bimolecular raise the general question of the stability of five- and six-coordinated complexes for these systems. There is certainly ample evidence to support the view that four-coordinated square complexes have a definite tendency to add additional ligands and form five- and/or six-coordinated systems. For example it was reported some years ago that the compound $[Pt(NH_3)_4(CH_3CN)_2]Cl_2$ is isolated from a solution prepared by dissolving $Pt(CH_3CN)_2Cl_2$ in ammonia.[24] Similarly diamagnetic four-coordinated nickel(II) complexes yield paramagnetic solutions which for some systems are known to contain six-coordinated nickel(II).[25] The absorption spectra of hydrochloric acid solutions of palladium(II) indicate the presence of $PdCl_5^{3-}$,[26] and similar studies of nickel(II) in excess cyanide ion give evidence of $Ni(CN)_5^{3-}$.[27] Rhodium(I), which is isoelectronic with palladium(II), has recently been found to form solvated tetraisocyaniderhodium(I) salts of the type $[Rh(CNR)_4X]ClO_4$, where X is either methanol, ethanol, chloroform, or benzene.[28] Furthermore complexes of the type $[M(diarsine)_2X]ClO_4$, where M = Ni(II) or Pd(II), X = Cl^-, Br^-, or I^-, and diarsine = o-phenylenebis(dimethylarsine), have been isolated from acetone solutions.[29a] These metal ions appear to exist as five-coordinated ions, $M(diarsine)_2X^+$, in nitrobenzene solution, where they exhibit the conductivity of a uni-univalent electrolyte. It should of course be pointed out that in all of these solutions the complex may in fact be six-coordinated with the sixth position occupied by a molecule of the solvent. Thus, although in solution the compound $Pd(diarsine)_2I_2$ is a uni-univalent electrolyte, preliminary x-ray analysis of the solid shows that the structure consists of discrete molecules of $Pd(diarsine)_2I_2$. The palladium(II) ion is surrounded by four arsenic atoms in a square at distances of approximately 2.38 A. The two iodide ions complete a distorted octahedral arrangement with elongated metal-iodide bonds of 3.25 A compared to the Pd—I bond distances in PdI_4^{2-} of only 2.65 A. Finally gold(III),[29b] isoelectronic with platinum(II), both of which are generally believed to form square complexes, has also been observed to form five- and six- coordinated complexes of the type $Au(diarsine)_2X^{2+}$ and $Au(diarsine)_2X_2^+$.

These observations strongly suggest that the so-called "square" complexes contain not only four firmly bonded ligands in the xy plane but also two somewhat more weakly held groups along the z axis. This gives rise to a complex with a tetragonal structure, which is in accord with what is expected on the basis of the electrostatic and crystal field theory (Chapter 2).

It is possible to develop a unified theory of substitution reactions of "square" complexes by postulating that all these reactions occur by the dissociation of a tetragonal species in solution.[30] For example the reaction generally represented as

$$MA_2LX + Y \rightarrow MA_2LY + X \tag{16}$$

must instead involve the solvated complex (S = solvent) and might follow the mechanistic paths shown in Fig. 8. Although such a mechanism also involves a five-coordinated intermediate, it differs from the previously mentioned processes in that the intermediate is not formed by the addition of a fifth ligand but instead by a dissociation of the original six-coordinated system. It is immediately apparent that such a reaction process for the distorted octahedron is essentially the same as that assumed for substitutions in the regular octahedron of cobalt (III) complexes (Chapter 3). The five-coordinated intermediates in Fig. 8 are designated as having a tetragonal pyramid structure. This mechanism is consistent with the stereospecific reactions of platinum (II) complexes and also with the observations, to be discussed later, that these reactions follow either first- or second-order kinetics. If the reaction proceeds via path I it will usually show a zero-order dependence on the concentration of Y, whereas if it involves path II there will usually be a first-order dependence on the concentration of Y. Which of the two paths predominates will depend not only upon the complex but also upon the nature of Y and of the solvent. Naturally, if in a given reaction both paths I and II are involved, the rate will be made up of two terms, one zero order in Y and the other first order in Y.

For systems which contain one or more π-bonding ligands, either originally present in the complex or introduced by group Y, the trigonal bipyramid structure for the five-coordinated intermediate is stabilized as described earlier. Thus the theories of Chatt [12] and of Orgel [23] can be slightly modified as shown in Fig. 9. According to the theory, the presence of the π-bonding ligand L will stabilize the trigonal bipyramid structure for the five-coordinated intermediate. Since it is assumed that the trigonal plane contains the π-bonding *trans* ligand L and also the entering group Y, it follows that the substitution will be stereospecific in accord with the experimental observations for reactions of platinum (II) complexes. Furthermore the rate of reaction will generally be first order in Y. However, in some cases the solvent S may take the place

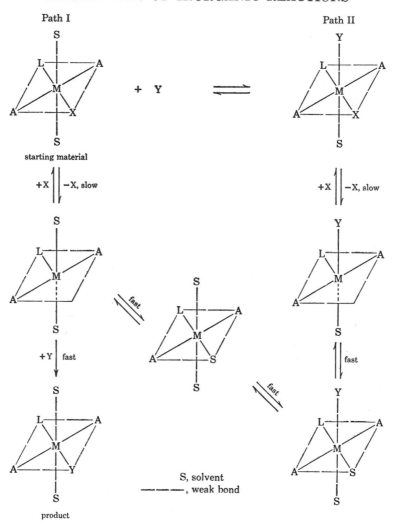

FIG. 8. The "dissociation" mechanism of substitution in tetragonal ("square") complexes through a square pyramid intermediate.

of Y as a reagent and the overall rate may be independent of the concentration of the reagent which eventually replaces the solvent. Figure 9 also considers the possibility that X may be lost initially in forming the trigonal bipyramid.

A similar trigonal bipyramid intermediate has been proposed for the base hydrolysis of cobalt(III) complexes proceeding by an S_N1CB mechanism, and for certain other dissociation reactions of octahedral complexes (see pp. 132–138). In fact it is identical except that a d^8 central atom is involved in the case of platinum(II) and a d^6 atom for cobalt(III) (d^3 for chromium(III)). The extra pair of electrons in the case of platinum is in one of the d orbitals lying in the trigonal plane. That is, both d orbitals in this plane are filled, whereas for cobalt(III) and chromium(III) only one is filled, or half-filled, and one is empty.

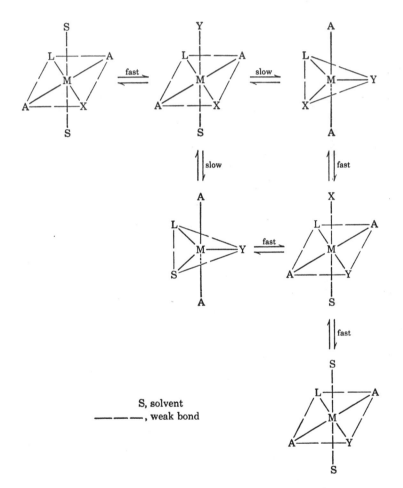

S, solvent

—————, weak bond

Fɪɢ. 9. The "dissociation mechanism" of substitution in tetragonal ("square") complexes through a trigonal bipyramid intermediate.

This leads to a fundamental difference in the kind of group that can stabilize the trigonal bipyramid by π bonding. For platinum(II) the groups must be unsaturated or have vacant d or p orbitals to take electrons from the filled d orbitals. For cobalt(III) and chromium(III), the groups must have unshared pairs of electrons (OH^-, NH_2^-, Cl^-) to donate to the vacant d orbital. Another difference, of course, is that the incoming group, Y, may be a part of the coordination sphere in the case of platinum(II) but not in the case of cobalt(III) or chromium(III). Hence the rate may be affected by the presence of an external reagent in the case of platinum but not in the case of cobalt or chromium.

A third difference is stereochemical in that the two groups labeled A in Fig. 9 are kept in the *trans* position with respect to each other. This suffices to maintain the overall stereochemistry of the tetragonal system. In an octahedral system, the fixing of two groups does not fix the total geometry of the complex and rearrangement is possible. A group, even if a good activator, such as $(C_2H_5)_3P$, cannot activate the positions *cis* to it in a square complex. Such a restriction does not hold for the cobalt and chromium cases, and in fact an electron-donating *cis* group is more effective than the *trans*.

Summary of the theories on the *trans* effect. The above discussion shows that there are two approaches to the *trans* effect, one emphasizing electrostatic factors and one mesomeric, or π-bonding, phenomena. The first can apply to both thermodynamic and kinetic examples, and the second usually only to kinetic examples.

For compounds with ligands that have little or no tendency to double-bond, the electrostatic factors must be of major importance. One of the theories based upon electrostatic effects requires that the lability of the *trans* ligand results from a weakening of the metal-ligand bond. There is at present no direct information on whether or not this does occur. However, some indirect evidence on the Pt—N bond strength in a series of compounds of the type $PtLACl_2$, where A is ammonia or an amine *trans* to L, has been obtained from infrared studies of N—H [31] and of Pt—N [32] stretching frequencies. These results show that in general there is an inverse correlation between the Pt—N bond strength and the *trans* effect of ligand L. The only apparent anomaly is the case of L = C_2H_4, where the assignment of Pt—N bond strength was done on the basis of the N—H stretching frequency, a procedure which is open to some question. Additional information in support of the bond-weakening hypothesis is offered by the acid strengths of *cis-* and *trans-*

$Pt(NH_3)_2(H_2O)_2$: cis, $pK_1 = 5.56$ and $pK_2 = 7.32$; $trans$, $pK_1 = 4.32$ and $pK_2 = 7.38$.[33] These are the relative values expected on the basis of the $trans$-effect order $NH_3 \sim OH^- > H_2O$. It may be argued that the greater the Pt—O bond strength the stronger the acid, whence it follows that the pK_2 values of the two isomers should be approximately the same because the $trans$ effects of NH_3 and OH^- are about the same. However, the Pt—O bond strength of cis-$Pt(NH_3)_2(H_2O)_2^{2+}$ is less than that of the $trans$ isomer because the $trans$ effect of ammonia is larger than that of water and therefore the cis complex is expected to be the weaker acid (see p. 393 for an alternative interpretation of the acid strengths of these ions). Finally, the observation that the bond strength of cis-$Pt(P(C_2H_5)_3)_2Cl_2$ is greater than that of the $trans$ isomer,[34] the difference in total bond energy being estimated as about 10 kcal, is also consistent with the electrostatic concept. The two chloride ions in $trans$ positions, because of their negative charge, should have a mutual bond-weakening effect on each other and therefore should prefer to be opposite ($trans$) to neutral groups. This gives rise to a more stable cis isomer. However, it is also possible to explain the relative stabilities of such isomers on the basis of π bonding [34] (see p. 251).

There is need for more information on the bond strengths of platinum(II) complexes before the role played by electrostatic forces in the $trans$ effect can be reliably assessed. For example the infrared studies mentioned above indicate that the $trans$-directing influence of ethylene is not entirely a result of the Pt—X bond weakening. Likewise equilibrium studies [30] in aqueous solutions show that cis-$Pt(NH_3)_2(H_2O)Cl^+$ is more stable than cis-$Pt(NH_3)_2Cl_2$, whereas the order of stability is just the reverse for the corresponding $trans$ isomers. According to the electrostatic theory the opposing $trans$ chloride ions, because of their negative charge, would be expected to be more weakly bound than in the cis system.

Although electrostatic forces must be considered in any attempt to understand the $trans$ effect, there is also a considerable amount of evidence to show that it is of less significance in systems which contain one or more π-bonding ligands. In such complexes the double-bonding character of these groups seems to make the largest contribution to the $trans$ effect. Perhaps the best illustration of this at present is afforded by the ligand ethylene, which has one of the largest $trans$ effects but for which an electrostatic explanation would be difficult to devise. Therefore the π-bonding hypothesis assumes that the $trans$ effect is kinetically controlled, with or without any assistance from the thermodynamic bond strength. It must be concluded on the basis of what is now known that the *trans* effect of a non-π-bonding ligand (H_2O, NH_3) is due to electrostatic forces, whereas that of a strong π-bonding ligand (PR_3, C_2H_4) is due largely to mesomeric effects.

The *trans* effect of platinum(II) complexes is concerned directly with the ligands present in the complex. Consequently most of the attention has been devoted to these ligands and little or no emphasis placed on the nature of the entering groups. The effect of this group will be considered in connection with the kinetic studies to be discussed next.

KINETICS OF REACTIONS OF SQUARE COMPLEXES

Although there is a wealth of qualitative information on the reactions of square complexes, particularly of platinum(II) compounds,[1] only a limited amount of quantitative data is available. Such data are necessary to test the proposed theories on the *trans* effect and to afford an understanding of the mechanisms of reactions of square complexes. This section will describe the kinetic investigations reported for reactions of "square" complexes, keeping in mind again that these probably all have a tetragonal structure.

Exchange reactions of platinum(II) complexes. The rates of ligand exchange in the system PtX_4^{2-}-$*X^-$, where X^- is CN^-, I^-, Br^-, or Cl^- have been reported[35] (Table 1). It is apparent from

Table 1

Rates of Ligand Exchange in PtX_4^{2-}-$*X^-$

X^-	Complex, M	$t_{1/2}$, min	Instability Constant
CN^-	0.037	1	10^{-35}
I^-	0.103	5	10^{-25}
Br^-	0.05	8	10^{-21}
Cl^-	0.072	280	10^{-16}

these data that the order of increasing exchange rate is opposite to the order of increasing thermodynamic stability of the complex ions. Such a result could be explained provided that the effectiveness of X^- as a reactant decreased from CN^- to Cl^-, and/or that the labilizing effect of the ligands originally in the complex decreased from CN^- to Cl^-. It is of interest to note that this is also the order of decreasing *trans* effect for these ions.

More detailed kinetic studies have been made on the systems $PtBr_4^{2-}$-*Br^- and $PtCl_4^{2-}$-*Cl^-. The rate of exchange in the former [36] is first order in complex concentration and zero order in bromide ion concentration. Therefore the reaction may proceed via interaction with the solvent. Evidence in support of the solvent intervention mechanism is offered by the observation that "aged" solutions (containing greater concentrations of $Pt(H_2O)Br_3^-$) exchange at a much more rapid rate than do freshly prepared solutions of the complex.

Kinetic studies on the chloride ion exchange in aqueous solutions of potassium tetrachloroplatinate(II) and potassium radiochloride [37] reveal that exchange involves the species $PtCl_4^{2-}$ and $Pt(H_2O)Cl_3^-$. The exchange with $PtCl_4^{2-}$ definitely occurs by means of the reversible acid hydrolysis,

$$PtCl_4^{2-} + H_2O \underset{k_2}{\overset{k_1}{\rightleftharpoons}} Pt(H_2O)Cl_3^- + Cl^- \tag{17}$$

The rate of acid hydrolysis (k_1) was followed by titration with standard alkali of the acid ($pK_a = 7$) $Pt(H_2O)Cl_3^-$ which is formed. The equilibrium constant for reaction 17 was also measured and set equal to k_1/k_2. A combination of the forward and reverse reactions accounts (to within 10%) for the rate of chloride exchange in freshly prepared solutions of potassium tetrachloroplatinate(II). The rate laws for the forward and reverse reactions 17 are $k_1[PtCl_4^{2-}]$ and $k_2[Pt(H_2O)Cl_3^-]$ $[Cl^-]$ respectively. Because of the interaction with the solvent these observations give no information as to the molecularity of the reactions.

Although there is good agreement between the rate of exchange observed and that calculated on the basis of equilibrium 17 for fresh solutions, the observed rate is much faster than the calculated rate for aged solutions which contain appreciable concentrations of $Pt(H_2O)Cl_3^-$. It therefore follows that chloride ion exchange must also take place with $Pt(H_2O)Cl_3^-$. Since there was some indication that the rate of acid hydrolysis of $Pt(H_2O)Cl_3^-$ is too slow to provide the observed exchange rate, it was suggested that this proceeds by a direct exchange,

$$Pt(H_2O)Cl_3^- + *Cl^- \overset{k'}{\rightleftharpoons} Pt(H_2O)*Cl_3^- + Cl^- \tag{18}$$

The rate of chloride exchange with $Pt(H_2O)Cl_3^-$ is approximately equal to the rate of hydrolysis of $PtCl_4^{2-}$, and the rate law for the exchange is $k'[Pt(H_2O)Cl_3^-]$. Because of this it has been proposed that an S_N1 mechanism is required, and furthermore that reactions 17 also proceed by the same mechanism. These results might therefore be explained by the dissociation process of path I in Fig. 8.

Recently exchange studies have been carried out on other platinum(II) complexes so that now data are available on the entire series from $PtCl_4{}^{2-}$ through $Pt(NH_3)_3Cl^+$ (Table 2). The rate of chloride ion exchange in all of these systems is independent of the concentration of

Table 2

Rates of Chloride Exchange and of Hydrolysis for the Complete Series of Chloroammineplatinum(II) Complexes at 25°C

Complex	k_{*Cl^-}, min^{-1}	k_{H_2O}, min^{-1} [a]	Reference
$PtCl_4{}^{2-}$	2.3×10^{-3}	2.3×10^{-3}	37
$PtNH_3Cl_3{}^-$	1.6×10^{-3}	2.2×10^{-3}	38
$trans$-$Pt(NH_3)_2Cl_2$	2.1×10^{-3}	5.0×10^{-3} [b]	30
cis-$Pt(NH_3)_2Cl_2$		2.3×10^{-3}	30
$Pt(NH_3)_3Cl^+$	0.9×10^{-3}	1.0×10^{-3} [b]	30
$Pt(en)Cl_2$		3.2×10^{-3}	30
cis-$Pt(NH_3)_2pyCl^+$		1.5×10^{-3} [b]	30

[a] The rates of hydrolysis are for the replacement of one chloro group by water.

[b] These are from the rates with pyridine which are believed to involve first the water reaction (see next section). At equilibrium $trans$-$Pt(NH_3)_2Cl_2$ and $Pt(NH_3)_3Cl^+$ are present as such in aqueous solution, and no perceptible hydrolysis occurs in acidic media.

chloride ion so that the mechanism of exchange appears to be the same in all cases. Also the rate of hydrolysis is independent of pH in all cases where the pH has been varied. The other point of interest is that the rates of exchange and/or hydrolysis are approximately the same for all of the members of the series. This is certainly unexpected in view of the fact that the charges on the complex vary from -2 to $+1$. For example, the rate constants (k, min^{-1}) at 25°C for the acid hydrolysis of $Co(NH_3)_5Cl^{2+}$ and $trans$-$Co(NH_3)_4Cl_2{}^+$ are respectively 1.3×10^{-4} and 1.1×10^{-1}.

The immediate conclusion that can be drawn from such a comparison is that, in the reactions of the platinum(II) complexes, bond making in the transition state is at least as important as bond breaking. Thus the data for cobalt(III) show that the effect of changing the total charge on the complex is well over in the direction that would be predicted if only bond breaking were important in the transition state (increased coulombic attraction of chloride ion for the rest of the complex slows down the rate). Since the effect of charge is small in the complexes of platinum (II), it must be argued that, although the release of halide ion is hindered by increasing positive charge, this is counterbalanced by a greater attraction between the incoming ligand Y and the platinum ion.

The importance of this latter attraction is also attested by the observation [39] that chloride ion exchange in $AuCl_4^-$ (via the hydrolysis path) is some two hundred times faster than in $PtCl_4^{2-}$. The two ions are isoelectronic and differ only in charge and slightly in size, gold (III) being the smaller. It would be expected on electrostatic, or covalent grounds, that the Au—Cl bond would be stronger than the Pt—Cl bond. The inversion in the expected rates can only be attributed to an important contribution to the overall energetics from the incoming group. This is true even when the group is the solvent as in these cases. It does not appear possible to invoke an S_N1 mechanism in which only bond breaking is involved.

If the incoming group is a better coordinating agent, it may be anticipated that still greater importance will be attached to the M—Y bond. Thus the rate-determining step of the whole reaction may become the formation of this bond even in the relatively weak positions above and below the square plane of the complex. In this case the reactions would be classified as being of the S_N2 (lim) type (see p. 96). In such cases it will be noted that the rate becomes independent of the M—X bond strength, and X exerts its influence only as it aids or hinders the addition of Y to the complex. These considerations help explain why radioisotope exchange can be faster with a stable complex such as $Pt(CN)_4^{2-}$ than with a less stable one such as $PtCl_4^{2-}$.

Exchange studies [40] on the system $cis\text{-}Pt(P(C_2H_5)_3)_2Cl_2\text{-}*Cl^-$ in acetone solution show the rate to be zero order in Cl^-. Therefore in this case of a complex containing strong π-bonding ligands, $P(C_2H_5)_3$, first-order kinetics are observed just as in the non-π-bonding systems of the chloroammineplatinum(II) complexes mentioned above. This may mean that acetone, although a poor coordinating solvent compared to water, is involved in the exchange reaction. It is of further interest that, although the exchange rate of chloride ion in $cis\text{-}Pt(P(C_2H_5)_3)_2Cl_2\text{-}*Cl^-$ is rapid even at 0°C, the *trans* isomer does not exchange.* Similarly the rate of exchange [41] in $cis\text{-}Pt(NO_2)_2^\bullet Cl_2^{2-}\text{-}*Cl^-$ is faster than that in $PtCl_4^{2-}\text{-}*Cl^-$. These results agree with the decreasing *trans*-directing influence of the ligands, $P(C_2H_5)_3 > NO_2^- > Cl^-$.

* Additional evidence in support of a "dissociative" process is provided by the observation that there is chloride ion exchange in an acetone solution of the system $cis\text{-}Pt(P(C_2H_5)_3)_2Cl_2\text{-}cis\text{-}Pt(P(C_4H_9)_3)_2*Cl_2.$ [40]

Substitution reactions of platinum (II) complexes. Quantitative kinetic studies on substitution reactions of platinum (II) complexes were not reported prior to 1952. The first such report [42] was made for reaction 19, where L = Cl⁻, Br⁻, or NO_2^-. The rates of reaction

were followed by potentiometric titration with standard acid to determine the amount of unreacted pyridine. It was found that the reactions are of the second order, there being a first-order dependence on the concentration of the complex and that of pyridine. The rates of reaction increase with changes in X^- in the order $Cl^- < Br^- < NO_2^-$, and this is a result of a decrease in energy of activation. This order of reactivity is in agreement with qualitative observations on the relative *trans* effect of these three ligands. It is further of interest that the activation energy for the reaction of *trans*-$Pt(NH_3)Br_2Cl^-$ is less and the rate is greater than for the reaction of $Pt(NH_3)BrCl_2^-$. Nevertheless the product of the reaction between $Pt(NH_3)BrCl_2^-$ and pyridine is $Pt(NH_3)(py)BrCl$ instead of $Pt(NH_3)(py)Cl_2$. The reason is that the greater *trans*-directing influence of Br^- compared to Cl^- leads to a more rapid replacement of the chloro group so that the product obtained is the kinetic product and not necessarily the thermodynamically more stable product. Since these non-ionic complexes are only very sparingly soluble in water, it follows that in the synthesis of these materials the more rapidly produced complex will separate from solution and be the one which is isolated.

Kinetic studies are now available for substitution reactions in aqueous solution of several platinum (II) complexes with a variety of nucleophilic reagents.[30] Some of these data on the rate of chloride ion release are collected in Table 3. It is apparent from these data that the reactions investigated fall into two different categories: (1) those that are first order in complex but zero order in reactant and all of approximately the same rate; (2) those that are first order in both the complex and the reactant and faster than those of the first category. In general the reactants of category 1 are low in the *trans*-effect series, e.g., C_5H_5N, OH^-, Cl^-. Such reactions are believed to involve the solvent and to proceed by path I, Fig. 8. The reactants of category 2 are usually high in the *trans*-effect series, e.g., NO_2^-, $SC(NH_2)_2$,

Table 3

Rates of Reaction in Aqueous Solution of some Platinum(II) Complexes with Different Reagents at 25°C

First-Order Rate Constants for Different Reagents, k min^{-1}

Complex	H$_2$O	OH$^-$	*Cl$^-$	NH$_3$	C$_5$H$_5$N	NO$_2^-$	(NH$_2$)$_2$CS	CH$_2$=CHCH$_2$OH	C$_2$O$_4^{2-}$
Pt(NH$_3$)$_3$Cl$^+$			9.0×10^{-4}	1.5×10^{-3}	1.0×10^{-3}	5.8×10^{-3} [a]	4.7×10^{-2} [b]		
trans-Pt(NH$_3$)$_2$Cl$_2$		6.1×10^{-3}	2.1×10^{-3}	1.1×10^{-2} [c]	5.1×10^{-3}	fast	fast	7.5×10^{-3} [d]	4.8×10^{-3} [e]
cis-Pt(NH$_3$)$_2$Cl$_2$	2.3×10^{-3}	2.3×10^{-3}							
cis-Pt(en)Cl$_2$	3.2×10^{-3}	3.2×10^{-3}							
PtCl$_4^{2-}$	2.3×10^{-3} [f]	1.8×10^{-3}					8.5×10^{-3} [g]		

[a,b,c,d,e,g] Substitution rates are first-order in the concentration of the reagent. The pseudo first-order constants given are for reaction mixtures containing 0.0005 M complex and the following concentrations of reagents (a) 0.01 M, (b) 0.01 M, (c) 0.009 M, (d) 0.01 M, (e) 0.01 M, (g) complex = 0.002 M and C$_3$H$_6$O = 0.3 M.
[f] Reference 37.

CH_2=$CHCH_2OH$, and the second-order kinetics can be explained on the basis of Fig. 9. It is further of interest that in these systems ammonia seems to be a borderline reagent, since in its reaction with trans-$Pt(NH_3)_2Cl_2$ there is no dependence upon the concentration of ammonia whereas there is a dependence in its reaction with $Pt(NH_3)_3$-Cl^+. Ammonia and the oxalate ion, which also cannot form π bonds, are believed to react according to path II of Fig. 8.

The poor correlation between the basicity and general nucleophilic character of the reagents and their rates of substitution in platinum(II) complexes is surprising. For example, it is remarkable to find that hydroxide ion, which is such a powerful reagent for organic halides and for cobalt(III) ammines, is so ineffective towards platinum(II) complexes. Furthermore one finds that allyl alcohol, which is neither a strong base nor strongly nucleophilic, turns out to be an effective reagent for certain platinum(II) complexes. This rather striking difference between hydroxide ion and allyl alcohol clearly suggests the importance of π bonding in the stabilization of the five-coordinated transition state. The hydroxide ion cannot accommodate d-orbital electrons from the platinum whereas the olefinic linkage of allyl alcohol is known to form pd-π bonds with platinum(II). In fact the interaction of the filled p orbitals of the hydroxide ion and the filled d orbitals of the metal is expected to be one of repulsion (quantum mechanical filled shell interaction as opposed to purely electrostatic repulsion). This may account for the low reactivity of OH^-. Although the trans-effect theory of Orgel (p. 185) is concerned only with π-bonding ligands present in the original complex, it is apparent that the same stabilization of the trigonal bipyramid intermediate is achieved if the entering group is capable of π bonding. In accord with this view are the observations that the more effective reagents for reactions with platinum(II) complexes are usually among the good π bonders, e.g., NO_2^-, $SC(NH_2)_2$, CH_2=$CHCH_2OH$, R_3P. This is another factor which helps account for the high reactivity of $Pt(CN)_4^{2-}$ with *CN^- as compared to the lower reactivity of $PtCl_4^{2-}$ with *Cl^-.

Exchange reaction of $AuCl_4^-$-*Cl^-. Kinetic studies on radio-chloride ion exchange in the system $AuCl_4^-$-*Cl^- have been reported.[39] It should be noted that the square complex $AuCl_4^-$ is isoelectronic with $PtCl_4^{2-}$, the chief difference between the two being that of anionic charge. The observed rates of exchange over a fairly wide range of experimental conditions for the equilibrium

$$AuCl_4^- + *Cl^- \rightleftharpoons Au*Cl_4^- + Cl^- \tag{20}$$

can be correlated by the rate equation

$$R = k_1[AuCl_4^-] + k_2[AuCl_4^-][Cl^-] \tag{21}$$

For the first term in the rate expression k_1 (min^{-1} at 10°C) = 0.27, E_a = 4.5 kcal, and log pZ = 2.9, whereas for the second term k_2 (M^{-1} min^{-1} at 10°C) = 32.4, E_a = 16.5 kcal, and log pZ = 14.3. Furthermore the exchange rate increases with increasing ionic strength as is expected if the transition state for the second term of the rate expression 21 involves the coming together of two negative ions. On the assumption that alterations in ionic strength only affect k_2, it was found that the observed change in this constant is consistent with the Debye-Hückel limiting law.

On the basis of these results it would appear that both paths I and II (Fig. 8) contribute to the observed rate of chloride ion exchange. The chloride ion independent process (k_1) involves path I, whereas the chloride ion dependent route (k_2) takes place by path II. It has already been mentioned that the faster ($\sim$200 times) rate of chloride ion exchange in $AuCl_4$-*Cl$^-$ compared to $PtCl_4^{2-}$-*Cl$^-$ is indicative of an S_N2- or even S_N2-(lim)-type mechanism. One other point to consider is that a large fraction of the total exchange in the gold(III) system takes place by path II, whereas such a path must contribute less than 10% of the total exchange in the platinum(II) system. It may appear that this difference should be attributed to the additional coulombic barrier of the doubly negative charged platinum anion. However, recalling that, even with the cationic complex, $Pt(NH_3)_3Cl^+$, the rate of chloride ion exchange does not depend upon the concentration of chloride ion (Table 2), it can be said that for these systems the net charge on the complex must play a minor role. It must therefore be concluded that the important thing is the charge and size of the central metal ion. Since gold(III) has both a larger positive charge and a smaller size than platinum(II), it follows that gold(III) would exhibit the greater electrostatic attraction for the entering chloride ion.

Exchange of the central metal ion in some "square" metal chelates. Kinetic studies have been reported for the exchange of metal ions with certain metal chelates of copper(II), nickel(II), and cobalt(II). The group of compounds most extensively investigated involve either bidentate or quadridentate ligands of the Schiff-base type, generally derivatives of salicylaldehyde. Largely on the basis of magnetic data and some x-ray data these solid compounds are believed to have a planar configuration, so that it would seem appropriate to describe their exchanges in this chapter on "square" complexes. However, in solution, particularly pyridine solutions where most of the studies have been made, these materials are highly solvated, possessing a coordination number of six with a tetragonal structure.[25] Therefore again it is not entirely correct to think of the exchanges in these systems as taking place strictly between square complexes.

The earliest study reported is that on the exchange of a series of copper(II) chelates with copper(II) acetate in pyridine solution.[43] It was observed that, for a series of copper complexes derived from very similar chelating agents, the orders of decreasing rates of exchange parallel the increasing thermodynamic stabilities of the complexes. Thus, although disalicylatocopper(II) undergoes complete exchange in the time of separation, N,N'-ethylenebis(salicylaldimine)copper(II) exchanges with a half-time of several hours at room temperature. When both reactants are of equal concentration, then the half-time of exchange is proportional to the reciprocal of the reactant concentration and the exchange rate can be described by a second-order rate law, k[complex][Cu^{+2}].

This second-order kinetics certainly does not mean that the mechanism of exchange is one of direct bimolecular collision where copper in the chelate is directly replaced by the non-chelated radiocopper ion. The energy of activation to effect simultaneous rupture of four metal-ligand bonds in the chelate is expected to be extremely high and thus to render such a process very unlikely. Furthermore it is known that these exchange reactions do not involve unusually high activation energies, e.g., E_a for N,N'-o-phenylenebis(salicylaldimine)copper(II) is 23 kcal,[43] and that for the corresponding cobalt(II) complex is 17 kcal.[44] Certainly a more plausible reaction path is one where there is a stepwise dissociation or uncoiling of the metal chelate and simultaneous chelation of the ligand with the exchanging metal ion (Fig. 10). Such a reaction scheme does not require an unusually high activation energy and is also consistent with the observed second-order kinetics, regardless of which of the reaction steps in the sequence after the first are rate determining. The necessity for breaking several points of attachment to the original metal atom before transfer of the chelating group can be assured adequately explains why the rate of exchange is slower the greater the total number of points of

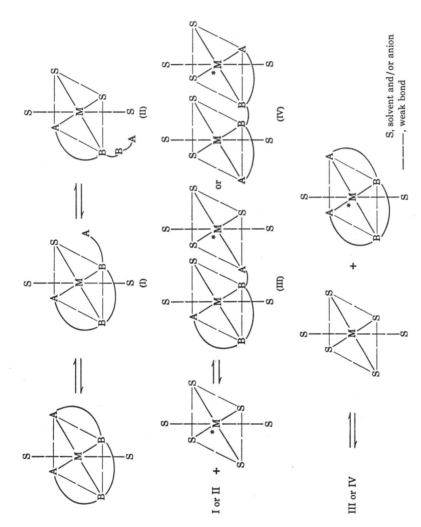

FIG. 10. Proposed mechanism for second-order metal ion-metal chelate exchange.

attachment of the chelate. The hydrogen ion dependence of exchange in the system $FeEDTA^- - *Fe^{3+}$ has been attributed to a similar type of chelate uncoiling mechanism (p. 157).

These studies have been extended to include analogous systems for metal complexes of nickel(II), cobalt(II), and zinc(II). Some of the available data for the metal ion exchange rates in these systems are shown in Table 4. It is apparent that the ease of metal ion exchange

Table 4

The Exchange of Metal Ions with Metal-Chelate Complexes of N,N′-Ethylenebis(salicylaldimine) and N,N′-o-Phenylenebis(salicylaldimine)

Metal Ion	Ni(II) [45]	Cu(II) [43]	Co(II) [44]	Zn(II) [46]
Concentration, M	0.01	0.015	0.017	0.01
Temperature, °C	room	25	25	25
	N,N′-Ethylenebis(salicylaldimine)			
$t_{1/2}$	no exchange after 48 hr	2.1 hr	complete in 6 min (30°C)	complete in 0.5 min
	N,N′-o-phenylenebis(salicylaldimine)			
$t_{1/2}$	no exchange after 48 hr	4 hr	30 min	99% in 0.5 min

increases in the order Ni(II) < Cu(II) < Co(II) < Zn(II). Except for the nickel(II) complexes, which show no exchange upon standing 48 hr, the rates of exchange parallel the natural order of stabilities, Co(II) < Ni(II) < Cu(II) > Zn(II).

To account for the variation in rates of reaction of tetragonal complexes with the nature of the central atom, the changes in crystal field stabilization energy have been calculated for two reaction paths. The first is with the formation of a trigonal bipyramid transition state, and the second is with a square pyramid structure for the transition state. The latter corresponds to the paths shown in Fig. 8, in which it is assumed that the two more distant groups move in and help to displace the replaceable ligand. Use has been made of the theoretical energy levels for the d electrons given in Table 5, Chapter 2. It may be noted that there is assumed to be a transfer of electrons from the less stable orbits to the more stable orbits in the process of forming the new configuration.

The calculated changes in C.F.S.E. are shown in Table 5. Two points of interest are that the losses in energy are greater for a trigonal

Table 5

Activation Energies for Reactions of Square Complexes Due to Crystal Field Energy Changes

	Square Planar	Trigonal Bipyramid	ΔE_a	Square Pyramid	ΔE_a
d^7	$26.84Dq$	$13.32Dq$	$13.52Dq$	$19.14Dq$	$7.70Dq$
d^8	24.56	14.14	10.42	18.28	6.28
d^9	12.28	7.07	5.21	9.14	3.14
d^{10}	0	0	0	0	0

Strong crystal field energies for regular complexes.

bipyramid intermediate than for a square pyramid. For platinum(II) the magnitude of Dq is 4.5 kcal from spectral data,[47] so the contribution to the activation energy is large (about 47 kcal). Nevertheless it seems very likely that a trigonal arrangement of the activated complex will occur if it is stabilized by π bonding. For the tetragonal pyramid structure with C.N. five, the losses in C.F.S.E. are smaller and would be smaller still if the groups above and below the original square plane did not move in as postulated. Opposed to this is the better total energy of having five groups rather than three close in to the central atom. To obtain the energies shown in Table 5, it is necessary that electrons transfer from the less stable orbitals to the more stable orbitals during the process of formation of the activated complex. Presumably this could happen at some intermediate stage when, say, the energies of the $d_{x^2-y^2}$ and the d_{z^2} orbital became equal. Although one electron might transfer in this way, it is possible that transfer of more than one electron would be slow. The d^7 and d^9 systems can attain fairly stable arrangements by transferring one electron only, but a d^8 system would need to transfer two.

The second point is that by either mechanism (trigonal or non-trigonal), the predicted order of rates is Zn > Cu > Ni as found. However, it also predicted that Co will be slower than any of these in direct contradiction to what is observed. A very probable explanation is that the calculated stabilization energy of cobalt(II) in the square planar state is too large. From the great tendency of this ion to be five-coordinated with ions of large crystal field strength (see Table 2, Chapter 1), it is probable that one or two solvent molecules are drawn in close enough to the square plane to give effectively the crystal field of a square pyramid. Particularly if the relative energies of the d_{xy} and d_{z^2} orbitals become interchanged so that the former is more stable than the latter, the losses in C.F.S.E. on forming either a trigonal bipyramid or square pyramid transition state will be greatly reduced. In fact, even for d^8 and d^9 systems it is not certain that the compromise structure will be sufficiently "square planar" to have d_{xy} be less stable than d_{z^2}. Hence the energy levels of Table 5, Chapter 2, must be used with caution.*

Although the nickel(II) and copper(II) Schiff-base complexes mentioned above are fairly inert, the ethylenediamine complexes of these metal ions are labile. In spite of this, kinetic studies have been made on these systems at low temperatures in methanol solutions.[48] Some of the data reported are collected in Table 6. These results again show

Table 6

Kinetic Data on the Formation and Dissociation of Nickel(II) and Copper(II) Complexes of Ethylenediamine in Methanol at 0°C

	Formation		Dissociation	
Complex	$k, M^{-1} \sec^{-1}$	E_a, kcal/mole	$k, \sec^{-1}$	E_a, kcal/mole
Ni(en)$^{2+}$	2.5×10^4	. . .	1×10^{-1}	22.3
Ni(en)$_2{}^{2+}$	2.5×10^4	13.0	6.3×10^{-1}	19.9
Ni(en)$_3{}^{2+}$	6.3×10^4	12.7	7.9	20.2
Cu(en)$^{2+}$	5×10^{11}	4	2.5	17
Cu(en)$_2{}^{2+}$	. . .	2	. . .	14

that copper(II) complexes are more labile than the corresponding nickel(II) compounds. It is also of interest to note that some reactions of labile complexes are instantaneous at room temperature not because of a low activation energy but rather because of a high entropy of activation. It was likewise observed that the rates of dissociation are dependent upon the acid concentration at low acid concentration but reach a limiting rate at high acid concentrations. Such a behavior

---

* Thus the spectrum of square planar bis(acetylacetonato)copper(II), even in a poor coordinating solvent such as chloroform, has only two bands in the visible and near-infrared regions (R. L. Belford, M. Calvin, and G. Belford, *J. Chem. Phys.*, 26, 1165 (1957)). This can be interpreted to mean that d_{xy} and d_{z^2} are about equal in energy. In a solvent such as piperidine, three bands appear, suggesting that the d_{xy} orbital is now more stable than the d_{z^2}. In the case of platinum(II) complexes, the spectra are less sensitive to the solvent, indicating a smaller interaction of the groups above and below the plane (J. Chatt, G. A. Gamlen, and L. E. Orgel, *J. Chem. Soc.*, **1958**, 486).

is the same as that discussed earlier (p. 154) for the dissociations of $Ni(bipy)_3^{2+}$ and $Fe(bipy)_3^{2+}$, and it is believed that essentially the same mechanism must be operative with these ethylenediamine complexes.

Substituted ethylenediamine complexes of nickel(II) and copper(II) dissociate much more slowly than do the corresponding ethylenediamine complexes. The first observation [49] of this steric retardation was reported for the yellow diamagnetic complex $Ni(NH_2C(CH_3)_2C(CH_3)_2-NH_2)_2^{2+}$, which in excess of acid dissociates with $t_{1/2} = 142$ sec at 25°C. It was observed [50] recently in the system $Ni(NH_2C(CH_3)_2C(CH_3)_2-NH_2)_2^{2+}$-*$Ni^{2+}$ at pH 6.8, where [complex] = 0.006 and $[Ni^{2+}] = 0.014$ at 25°C, that the half-life for nickel ion exchange is $t_{1/2} = 67$ min, and $E_a = 21$ kcal. This again illustrates the very pronounced acid catalysis, because the half-life for dissociation in excess acid, as stated above, is only $t_{1/2} = 2.3$ min. Furthermore the use of ^{14}C-labeled 1,1,2,2-tetramethyl-1,2-ethanediamine in exchange studies of the diamine with $Cu(NH_2C(CH_3)_2C(CH_3)_2NH_2)_2^{2+}$ at pH 6.8 and 0.7°C, where [complex] and [amine] = 0.01, shows $t_{1/2} = 3$ min and $E_a = 17$ kcal.[50] Finally the acid dissociation of the more sterically hindered complex

$$Ni\left(NH_2-\underset{\overset{|}{C_2H_5}}{\overset{\overset{CH_3}{|}}{C}}-\underset{\overset{|}{C_2H_5}}{\overset{\overset{CH_3}{|}}{C}}-NH_2\right)_2^{2+}$$

at 22°C has a half-life of 50 min.[50]

At 0°C and pH 11 in water $Zn(en)_3^{2+}$, $Cu(en)_2^{2+}$, and $Hg(en)_2^{2+}$ undergo exchange with *en within 5 sec. At pH 1 and temperature 25°C $Au(en)_2^{3+}$ undergoes slow exchange, the half-life being 2 hr.[51] That the rate should be slower for gold(III) as compared to nickel(II) is understandable chiefly in terms of the greater charge of the former ion which would increase the bond strength considerably. Both ions are d^8, but, since the gold complex is diamagnetic whereas $Ni(en)_3^{2+}$ is paramagnetic, there will also be different crystal field effects, in this case acting to stabilize gold(III) preferentially.

Catalysis of exchange reactions. During their investigations on chloride ion exchange in the system $AuCl_4^-$-*Cl^-, Rich and Taube [52] observed an exchange induced by some impurity in ordinary distilled water. This led to a study of the exchange induced by various reducing agents, and it was found that the system is particularly sensitive to one-electron reducing agents, e.g., Fe^{2+}. Thus the storage of solutions in green glass containers will generate enough iron(II) ion to cause a significant amount of induced exchange. For every Fe^{2+} oxidized by $AuCl_4^-$, it is estimated that approximately 10^4 chloride ion substitutions are effected. Similarly vanadium(IV) ion is a good catalyst, but its efficiency is diminished by the accumulation of vanadium(V). However, two-electron reducing agents such as tin(II) and antimony(III) ions have little or no catalytic effect on the rate of chloride ion exchange. Similarly gold(I) induces, at most, only a slow exchange.

Therefore the exchange induced by one-electron reducing agents is believed to be due to the formation of a labile gold(II) species which is not generated by the two-electron reagents. The kinetics of the reaction catalyzed by Fe^{2+} are consistent with a mechanism whereby Au(II) is produced by a second-order reaction (22) between $AuCl_4^-$ and Fe^{2+}; the Au(II) chloro complex then undergoes rapid exchange (23); it may also undergo a rate-determining exchange (24) with $AuCl_4^-$, and is finally disproportionated (25) to terminate the sequence of reactions

Rate

$$AuCl_4^- + Fe^{2+} \xrightarrow{k_1} Fe^{3+} + AuCl_4^{2-} \qquad k_1[AuCl_4^-][Fe^{2+}] \qquad (22)$$

$$AuCl_4^{2-} + {}^*Cl^- \rightleftharpoons Au^*Cl_4^{2-} + Cl^- \qquad \text{very rapid} \qquad (23)$$

$$Au^*Cl_4^{2-} + AuCl_4^- \xrightarrow{k_2} AuCl_4^{2-} + Au^*Cl_4^- \qquad k_2[AuCl_4^-][Au^*Cl_4^{2-}] \quad (24)$$

$$2Au(II) \xrightarrow{k_3} Au(I) + Au(III) \qquad k_3[Au(II)]^2 \qquad (25)$$

The exact nature of the Au(II) chloro species (written as $AuCl_4^{2-}$) is not known, but its lability may be attributed to its being a d^9 system like copper(II). The latter system is very labile in all of its simple unidentate complexes.

Similar studies on the catalysis of exchange reactions of platinum complexes reveal that the catalyzed exchange must involve a Pt(III) complex.[53] For example the exchange of chloride ion in $PtCl_4^{2-}$-$^*Cl^-$ is induced by cerium(IV), a one-electron oxidizing agent, but not by chlorine, a two-electron oxidizing agent. Rate laws have not been established, but it appears that the induced exchange proceeds by a chain mechanism corresponding to reactions 22–25, where the active intermediate is a platinum(III) species, e.g., $PtCl_5^{2-}$.

Furthermore the chloride ion exchange in $PtCl_6^{2-}$-$^*Cl^-$ by a chain mechanism is initiated by light, catalyzed by $PtCl_4^{2-}$ but inhibited by $Fe(CN)_6^{3-}$, $IrCl_6^{2-}$, Cl_2, and some reducing agents. The photo-catalytic effect is attributed to the formation of labile $PtCl_5^{2-}$

$$PtCl_6^{2-} \overset{h\nu}{\rightarrow} PtCl_5^{2-} + Cl \tag{26}$$

For a discussion of other photosensitive reactions of complex ions see p. 374. Tetrachloroplatinate(II) can generate the catalyst by the reaction

$$PtCl_4^{2-} + PtCl_6^{2-} \rightleftharpoons 2PtCl_5^{2-} \tag{27}$$

For another mechanism for platinum(II) catalysis of reactions of platinum(IV), see p. 167. Finally certain oxidizing and reducing agents inhibit reaction by this path, presumably by preventing the formation of $PtCl_5^{2-}$. The exceptional exchange lability of the Pt(III) chloro intermediate, like that of the chloro Au(II) species, is of considerable interest. It should be noted that Pt(III) is a d^7 system which, like cobalt(II), is expected to be labile.

Recently it was observed [54] that l-Pt(i-bn) (m-stien)$^{2+}$, where i-bn = 2-methyl-1,2-propanediamine, and m-stien = $meso$-1,2-diphenyl-1,2-ethanediamine, can be oxidized by either a one- or two-electron oxidizing agent and then in turn reduced by either a one- or a two-electron reducing agent with little or no racemization. These results suggest that, if in the one-electron processes a Pt(III) species is involved, it is not labile, and furthermore that it has a tetragonal pyramid structure with essentially no disturbance of the coplanarity of the two chelate rings. Apparently the marked stability of this Pt(III) species can be attributed to its being a chelate complex.

Substitution reactions of palladium(II) complexes. Square complexes of palladium(II) are generally less stable and more labile than are the corresponding platinum(II) compounds. For example, both $Pd(CN)_4^{2-}$ and $Ni(CN)_4^{2-}$ undergo instantaneous exchange with radioactive CN^-, and $PdCl_4^{2-}$ exchanges very rapidly with *Cl$^-$ (Table 5, Chapter 9). Consequently there are fewer known geometric isomers of palladium(II) complexes, and these often isomerize with considerable ease. One other point of difference is that, although the *trans* effect is operative, it does not appear to play as important a role as it does in the reactions of platinum(II) compounds. For example, the rate of hydrolysis of cis-Pd(NH$_3$)$_2$X$_2$ (X$^-$ = Cl$^-$ or Br$^-$) is greater than that of the corresponding *trans* isomer,[55] although the halide ions are expected to be better *trans*-directing ligands than is ammonia. It is probable that phenomena dependent on π bonding will be less important for palladium and nickel complexes than for platinum.

Because of the lability of palladium(II) compounds it is not possible to be certain that a given reaction product is a direct result of a one-step replacement in the complex. It therefore follows that the stereochemistry of a final reaction product in these systems cannot be used as a criterion of reaction mechanism. This can be illustrated by the reaction of $K_2[Pd(NO_2)_4]$ with ammonia.[56] This reaction at room temperature, contrary to what is expected in view of the large *trans*-directing influence of the nitro group, yields *trans*-$Pd(NH_3)_2$-$(NO_2)_2$. However, it has been shown that at a lower temperature the reaction product contains appreciable quantities of *cis*-$Pd(NH_3)_2$-$(NO_2)_2$. Thus it was concluded [57] that the *trans* effect of the nitro ligand is operative but that the equilibria shown in reactions 28 are

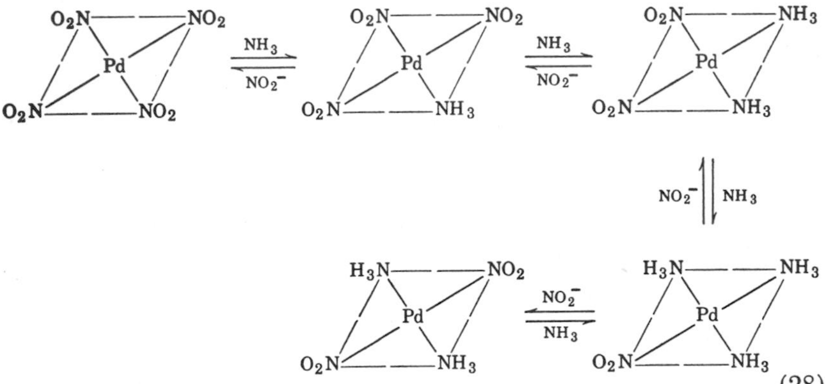

$$
\begin{array}{ccccc}
\text{O}_2\text{N} \quad \text{NO}_2 & & \text{O}_2\text{N} \quad \text{NO}_2 & & \text{O}_2\text{N} \quad \text{NH}_3 \\
\underset{\text{O}_2\text{N} \quad \text{NO}_2}{\text{Pd}} & \underset{\text{NO}_2^-}{\overset{\text{NH}_3}{\rightleftharpoons}} & \underset{\text{O}_2\text{N} \quad \text{NH}_3}{\text{Pd}} & \underset{\text{NO}_2^-}{\overset{\text{NH}_3}{\rightleftharpoons}} & \underset{\text{O}_2\text{N} \quad \text{NH}_3}{\text{Pd}}
\end{array}
$$

$$ \text{NO}_2^- \updownarrow \text{NH}_3 $$

$$
\begin{array}{ccc}
\text{H}_3\text{N} \quad \text{NO}_2 & & \text{H}_3\text{N} \quad \text{NH}_3 \\
\underset{\text{O}_2\text{N} \quad \text{NH}_3}{\text{Pd}} & \underset{\text{NH}_3}{\overset{\text{NO}_2^-}{\rightleftharpoons}} & \underset{\text{O}_2\text{N} \quad \text{NH}_3}{\text{Pd}}
\end{array}
$$

$$(28)$$

involved. Since *trans*-$Pd(NH_3)_2(NO_2)_2$ is less soluble than the *cis* isomer, the *cis* product which is formed initially will react further to generate the less soluble *trans* isomer. That such a reaction sequence is responsible for a *trans* product is also supported by the observation that a warm ammoniacal solution of *cis*-$Pd(NH_3)_2(NO_2)_2$ gives exclusively crystals of the *trans* isomer.

SUBSTITUTION REACTIONS OF TETRAHEDRAL COMPLEXES

The mechanism of substitution reactions of tetrahedral complexes has been little studied. One reason for this is that such structures are usually found only for systems which are not stabilized by crystal field effects. This means in turn that their reactions are generally quite rapid and not easy to study kinetically or stereochemically. This is true even in the case of $Ni(CO)_4$, which is reported to rapidly exchange with radioactive carbon monoxide in benzene solution.[58]

The well-studied prototype of tetrahedral systems would be the organic compounds containing four groups bound to carbon. It is well established that both S_N1- and S_N2-type reactions occur for such carbon compounds, but not S_N2 (lim), which is restricted to unsaturated carbon compounds. The bond strengths of ligands attached to carbon(IV) are usually much stronger than for other central elements of interest in coordination chemistry. This may be considered as a factor which would promote dissociation-type mechanisms in tetrahedral complexes compared to organic compounds.

As opposed to this, the larger size of other central elements than carbon will greatly favor a displacement-type mechanism in that a fifth group can be held without steric crowding. Such an intermediate may often be one of some stability so that, in effect, an S_N2 (lim) mechanism is operating. The presence of either empty or filled d orbitals on the central atom may help stabilize such a five-coordinated species. By analogy with the case of carbon where the fact of inversion on bimolecular substitution has been often demonstrated, one would expect this intermediate to be a trigonal bipyramid, with the entering group and the leaving group lying on the digonal axis.

There is no proof for this reasonable assumption in the case of tetrahedral coordination compounds. What has been demonstrated in a number of cases is that a bimolecular displacement on the central atom has occurred. For example, the neutral methanolysis of an ester of chromic acid with optically active tertiary alkoxy radicals attached to chromium(VI) gives an optically active alcohol[59] (reaction 29).

$$\begin{array}{ccc} & O & & O \\ & \| & & \| \\ R^*\!-\!O\!-\!\overset{}{\underset{\|}{Cr}}\!-\!OR^* & \xrightarrow{\ CH_3OH\ } & R^*OH + CH_3O\!-\!\overset{}{\underset{\|}{Cr}}\!-\!OR^* \\ & O & & O \end{array} \qquad (29)$$

(Oxidation-reduction of the methyl chromate then follows.) This can only mean an attack of methanol on chromium, displacing the optically active alcohol without breaking the C—O bond, a conclusion substantiated by hydrolysis experiments of chromate esters in water labeled with oxygen-18.[60] Furthermore since a much more rapid methanolysis occurs when methoxide ion is present, we have all the earmarks of an S_N2 attack on the metal atom,

$$\left[\begin{array}{c} \overset{\displaystyle O \quad\; O}{\underset{\displaystyle \underset{\displaystyle OR^*}{|}}{CH_3O\text{-}\text{-}\text{-}Cr\text{-}\text{-}\text{-}OR^*}} \end{array} \right]^-$$

This is similar to the results found in a kinetic study of the reaction of hydroxide ion and dichromate ion, a binuclear complex of chromium(VI).[61]

$$Cr_2O_7{}^{2-} + 2OH^- \rightarrow 2CrO_4{}^{2-} + H_2O \tag{30}$$

The reaction is first order in hydroxide ion and first order in dichromate ion, which is only reasonable in terms of a bimolecular displacement of $CrO_4{}^{2-}$ by OH^- acting on chromium

$$\left[\begin{array}{c} \overset{\displaystyle O \quad\; O \quad\;\; O}{HO\text{-}\text{-}\text{-}Cr\text{-}\text{-}\text{-}O\text{-}Cr\text{-}O} \\ \underset{\displaystyle O \qquad\quad O}{|\qquad\qquad\; |} \end{array} \right]^{3-}$$

followed by a rapid neutralization of $HCrO_4{}^-$ with OH^-.

Some similar data exists which indicates that S_N2 displacement processes also occur on sulfur(VI) in organic sulfates [62] and on phosphorus(V) in organic and inorganic phosphates.[63] A number of kinetic studies of reactions of compounds of silicon(IV) have been made which are always interpreted as proceeding by an S_N2 or S_N2 (lim) mechanism.[64] It is of interest that systems such as triphenylsilyl chloride, which would presumably be prone to react by an S_N1 mechanism, as in the case of the carbon analog, seem to react bimolecularly.[65] The difference may be attributed to the presence of empty d orbitals on silicon.[66] This permits covalent binding of the fifth group by sp^3d hybridization, which is not possible for carbon. It may also be possible that the trigonal bipyramid intermediate is moderately long-lived for this reason, though no evidence for such an intermediate has been presented. Silicon(IV) is known to have a coordination number as high as six in $SiF_6{}^{2-}$.

REFERENCES

1. (a) D. P. Mellor, *Chem. Revs.*, **33**, 137 (1943). (b) J. V. Quagliano and L. Schubert, *ibid.*, **50**, 201 (1952). (c) A. A. Grinberg. *Einführung in die Chemie der Komplexverbindungen*, Veb Verlag Technik, Berlin, 1955, Chapter 5.
2. A. Werner, *Z. anorg. Chem.*, **3**, 267 (1893).
3. M. Peyrone, *Ann.*, **51**, 15 (1845).
4. J. Reiset, *Compt. rend.*, **18**, 1103 (1844).

5. S. M. Jørgensen, *J. prakt. Chem.*, **33**, 489 (1886).
6. I. I. Chernyaev, *Ann. inst. platine U.S.S.R.*, **4**, 261 (1926).
7. I. I. Chernyaev, *ibid.*, **4**, 243 (1926); **5**, 102, 118 (1927).
8. I. I. Chernyaev, *ibid.*, **6**, 55 (1928).
9. A. D. Hel'man, E. F. Karandashova, and L. N. Essen, *Doklady Akad. Nauk S.S.S.R.*, **63**, 37 (1948).
10. N. S. Kurnakow, *J. prakt. Chem.*, **50**, 483 (1894).
11. D. I. Ryabchikov, *Compt. rend. acad. sci. U.R.S.S.*, **32**, 344 (1941).
12. J. Chatt, L. A. Duncanson, and L. M. Venanzi, *J. Chem. Soc.*, **1955**, 4456.
13. I. I. Chernyaev, *Ann. inst. platine U.S.S.R.*, **5**, 109 (1927).
14. A. A. Grinberg, *ibid.*, **10**, 58 (1932); *Acta Physicochim. U.R.S.S.*, **3**, 573 (1935).
15. K. Fajans, *Z. Elektrochem.*, **34**, 502 (1928).
16. J. Bjerrum, *Chem. Revs.*, **46**, 381 (1950); B. G. F. Carleson and H. Irving, *J. Chem. Soc.*, **1954**, 4390; S. Ahrland and R. Larsson, *Acta Chem. Scand.*, **8**, 354 (1954).
17. I. Leden and J. Chatt, *J. Chem. Soc.*, **1955**, 2936.
18. R. S. Mulliken, *J. Am. Chem. Soc.*, **77**, 884 (1955).
19. T. L. Cottrell, *The Strengths of Chemical Bonds,* Academic Press, New York, 1954, Chapter 9.
20. H. M. E. Cardwell, *Chemistry & Industry,* **1955**, 422.
21. J. Chatt, L. A. Duncanson, and L. M. Venanzi, *Chemistry & Industry,* **1955**, 749.
22. L. Pauling, *The Nature of the Chemical Bond,* 2nd ed., Cornell University Press, Ithaca, N. Y., 1940, p. 252.
23. L. E. Orgel, *J. Inorg. Nuclear Chem.*, **2**, 137 (1956).
24. L. Tschugaeff, *Compt. rend.*, **161**, 563 (1915); C. M. Harris and N. C. Stephenson, *Chemistry & Industry,* **14**, 426 (1957).
25. J. B. Willis and D. P. Mellor, *J. Am. Chem. Soc.*, **69**, 1237 (1947); F. Basolo and W. R. Matoush, *ibid.*, **75**, 5663 (1953); H. C. Clark and A. L. Odell, *J. Chem. Soc.*, **1955**, 3431, 3435; L. Sacconi, P. Paoletti and G. Del Re, *J. Am. Chem. Soc.*, **79**, 4062 (1957).
26. A. K. Sundaram and E. B. Sandell, *J. Am. Chem. Soc.*, **77**, 855 (1955).
27. C. M. Harris, thesis, New South Wales, 1955.
28. L. Malatesta and L. Vallarino, *J. Chem. Soc.*, **1956**, 1867.
29. (a) C. M. Harris, R. S. Nyholm, and N. C. Stephenson, *Nature,* **177**, 1127 (1956); *J. Chem. Soc.*, **1956**, 4375; (b) *Rec. trav. chim.*, **75**, 687 (1956).
30. D. Banerjea, F. Basolo, and R. G. Pearson, *J. Am. Chem. Soc.*, **79**, 4055 (1957).
31. J. Chatt, L. A. Duncanson, and L. M. Venanzi, *J. Chem. Soc.*, **1955**, 4461; **1956**, 2712.
32. D. B. Powell, *ibid.*, **1956**, 4495.
33. K. A. Jensen, *Z. anorg. u. allgem. Chem.*, **242**, 87 (1939).
34. J. Chatt and R. G. Wilkins, *J. Chem. Soc.*, **1952**, 4300; **1956**, 525.
35. A. A. Grinberg and L. E. Nikol'skoya, *Zhur. Priklad. Khim.*, **22**, 542 (1949); **24**, 893 (1951).
36. A. A. Grinberg, L. E. Nikol'skoya, and G. A. Shagisultanova, *Doklady Akad. Nauk S.S.S.R.*, **101**, 1059 (1955).
37. L. F. Grantham, T. S. Elleman, and D. S. Martin, Jr., *J. Am. Chem. Soc.*, **77**, 2965 (1955).
38. T. S. Elleman, J. W. Reishus, and D. S. Martin, Jr., *ibid.*, **80**, 536 (1958).

39. R. L. Rich and H. Taube, *J. Phys. Chem.*, **58**, 1 (1954).
40. R. G. Wilkins and J. Lewis, private communication.
41. A. A. Grinberg, L. I. Kozlova, L. E. Nikol'skoya, and G. A. Shagisultanova, *J. Appl. Chem. U.S.S.R.*, **28**, 5 (1955).
42. A. D. Hel'man and E. F. Karandashova, *Doklady Akad. Nauk S.S.S.R.*, **87**, 597 (1952); O. E. Zvyaginsev and E. F. Karandashova, *ibid.*, **101**, 93 (1955).
43. R. B. Duffield and M. Calvin, *J. Am. Chem. Soc.*, **68**, 557 (1946).
44. B. O. West, *J. Chem. Soc.*, **1952**, 3115; **1954**, 395, 578.
45. N. F. Hall and B. R. Willeford, Jr., *J. Am. Chem. Soc.*, **73**, 5419 (1951).
46. D. C. Atkins and C. S. Garner, *ibid.*, **74**, 3527 (1952).
47. C. Klixbüll Jørgensen, *Acta Chem. Scand.*, **10**, 517 (1956).
48. J. Bjerrum·and K. G. Poulsen, *Nature*, **169**, 463 (1952); *Symposium on Coordination Chemistry*, Danish Chemical Society, **1955**, 51.
49. F. Basolo, Y. T. Chen, and R. K. Murmann, *J. Am. Chem. Soc.*, **76**, 956 (1954).
50. R. G. Wilkins, *J. Chem. Soc.*, **1957**, 4521.
51. D. S. Popplewell and R. G. Wilkins, *J. Chem. Soc.*, **1955**, 4098; *Rec. trav. chim.*, **75**, 815 (1956).
52. R. L. Rich and H. Taube, *J. Phys. Chem.*, **58**, 6 (1954).
53. R. L. Rich and H. Taube, *J. Am. Chem. Soc.*, **76**, 2608 (1954).
54. A. F. Messing and F. Basolo, *ibid.*, **78**, 4511 (1956).
55. A. A. Grinberg, W. M. Schul'man, and S. I. Khorunzhenkov, *Ann. inst. platine U.S.S.R.*, **12**, 119 (1935).
56. F. G. Mann, D. Crowfoot, D. Gattiker, and W. Wooster, *J. Chem. Soc.*, **1955**, 1642.
57. H. B. Jonassen and N. L. Cull, *J. Am. Chem. Soc.*, **73**, 274 (1951).
58. D. F. Keeley and R. E. Johnson, Meeting of the American Chemical Society, Miami, Florida, April, 1957.
59. H. H. Zeiss and C. N. Matthews, *J. Am. Chem. Soc.*, **78**, 1694 (1956).
60. M. Anbar, I. Dostrovsky, D. Samuel, and A. D. Yoffe, *J. Chem. Soc.*, **1954**, 3603 (1954).
61. V. K. Lamer and C. L. Read, *J. Am. Chem. Soc.*, **52**, 3098 (1930).
62. R. L. Burwell, Jr., *ibid.*, **74**, 1462 (1952); O. Foss, *Acta Chem. Scand.*, **3**, 1385 (1949); **4**, 866 (1950).
63. M. Kilpatrick and M. Kilpatrick, *J. Phys. Chem.*, **53**, 1371 (1949); D. F. Heath, *J. Chem. Soc.*, **1956**, 3796.
64. See L. Kaplan and K. E. Wilzbach, *J. Am. Chem. Soc.*, **77**, 1298 (1955), for references.
65. C. G. Swain, R. M. Esteve, Jr., and R. H. Jones, *ibid.*, **71**, 965 (1949).
66. N. V. Sidgwick, *The Electronic Theory of Valency*, Oxford University Press, London, 1927, pp. 159–160.

5 The stereochemistry of substitution reactions of octahedral complexes

Investigations of reactions of geometrical and optical isomers of octahedral complexes furnish information on the stereochemical changes that accompany the replacement of one ligand by another. Much of this work has been done with the more well-defined complexes of cobalt(III), and attempts have been made to account for the observed stereo changes on the basis of molecular rearrangements which appear to be possible. The discussion in this chapter deals, first, with the rearrangement processes that have been suggested and, second, with some of the experimental observations.

MOLECULAR REARRANGEMENT PROCESSES

Outer sphere orientation. Werner[1] suggested that the stereochemical changes observed for the reactions of cobalt(III) complexes are due to the specific orientation of the entering group outside the complex. He assumed that, in addition to the first coordination sphere, a second sphere of molecules or ions surrounds the complex. Further, he assumed that there might exist a preferred orientation of the groups in the second coordination sphere with respect to the complex. Therefore, should the incoming group Y be located in a position opposite to that of the outgoing ligand X, then a *trans* isomer would yield a *cis* product (Fig. 1). Since the group Y is separated from X by the four ligands A, the net result is that as X leaves one of the A groups moves down to make room for Y adjacent to B. If, on the other hand, Y

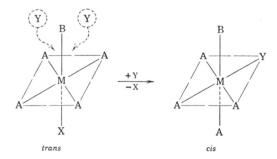

FIG. 1. Substitution where the entering group Y in the second coordination sphere is opposite the departing group X.

groups are located near X, then there would be no change in structure and a *trans* product would result (Fig. 2). Similarly a *cis* isomer is expected to yield a *cis* product if the entering group in the second sphere is near the departing ligand. However, if it is opposite to the group leaving, then a mixture of isomers is predicted for the product (statistically three parts *cis* and one part *trans*).

This explanation was given for reactions that yielded primarily only one isomer. It was suggested that a mixture of isomers is obtained whenever there is no preferred orientation of the groups in the second sphere. Werner was forced to conclude that, as there is no way to predict the orientation of the entering group in the second sphere, it is not possible to anticipate the stereochemical change that will take place during substitution. It is of interest to note that spectrophotometric

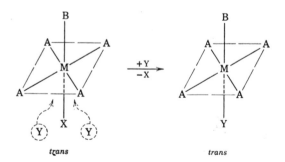

FIG. 2. Substitution where the entering group Y in the second coordination sphere is adjacent to the departing group X.

evidence is now available [2] for the existence of part of the second coordination sphere assumed by Werner.* This is generally referred to as an ion pair or an outer sphere complex (Chapter 9).

Dissociation (S_N1) and displacement (S_N2) processes. A dissociation (S_N1) process for a six-coordinated complex requires the formation of a five-coordinated intermediate. The stereochemical consequence of the formation of either a tetragonal pyramid or trigonal bipyramid for the intermediate have been discussed.[3] These two structures appear to be the most plausible ones because (1) stable compounds of such structures are known, (2) these structures can be derived from the octahedron with little atomic motion, and (3) such structures are in keeping with current theories of bonding in metal complexes. It is apparent that the reaction of either cis- or trans-MA_4BX through a tetragonal pyramid intermediate can take place without rearrangement (Fig. 3). The assumption is made that group Y enters the position vacated by X. This seems to be a valid assumption because the central atom is most accessible at this position and because the formation of the new octahedron requires no additional atomic motion. Furthermore, in terms of the valence bond theory, the vacant d^2sp^3 hybrid orbital is projected outward in this direction, suitable for maximum overlap with the orbital electrons of the entering group. Alternatively, according to the crystal field theory, nucleophilic attack at this position is favored because of the low electron density.

Reactions of cis- and trans-MA_4BX by way of a trigonal bipyramid intermediate may lead to rearrangement (Fig. 3). Only trigonal bipyramid I is believed possible for the trans isomer, because structure II in which B is normal to the trigonal plane would necessitate excessive rearrangement. However, both of these are equally possible for the cis isomer. Subsequent addition of Y to the intermediate is assumed to take place in the trigonal plane. This is believed to be correct be-

---

* Brintziner (*Z. anorg. u. allgem. Chem.*, **220**, 172 (1934); **256**, 98 (1948)) reports the formation of "two-shelled" complexes such as $\{[Co(NH_3)_6](SO_4)_4\}^{5-}$ in solution based on detailed dialysis studies. Polarographic studies on these systems have also been cited in support of the existence of ionic association in these solutions (see H. A. Laitinen, J. C. Bailar, Jr., H. F. Holtzclaw, Jr., and J. V. Quagliano, *J. Am. Chem. Soc.*, **70**, 2999 (1948)). In addition there is a considerable amount of kinetic data on the reaction of metal complexes which indicate the presence of different species in solutions containing different "inert" salts (Chapter 9).

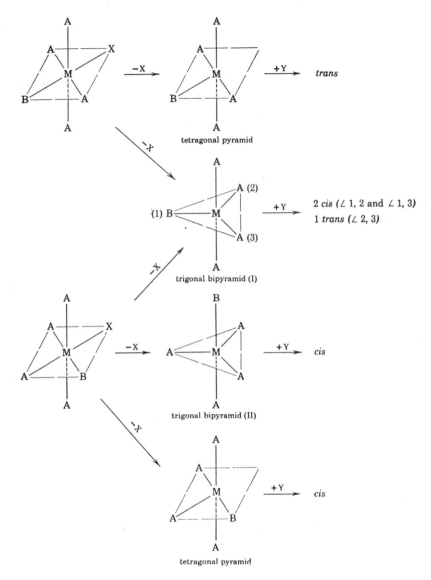

Fig. 3. Stereochemical changes accompanying reactions of *cis*- and *trans*-MA₄BX with Y by a dissociation $(S_N 1)$ mechanism through either a tetragonal pyramid or trigonal bipyramid intermediate.

cause the central atom is more accessible at these angles of 120° and because a minimum amount of atomic motion is required to regenerate the octahedron. Since the trigonal xy plane contains a vacant $d_{x^2-y^2}$ orbital, nucleophilic attack in this plane is also in keeping with current bond theories. Thus the addition of Y to trigonal bipyramid II yields a *cis* product but addition to I gives a mixture of *cis* and *trans* isomers. If the group enters between either positions 1,2 or 1,3 the product will have a *cis* structure, but if it comes in between 2,3 it will give a *trans* product. In the idealized situation where the statistical factor is all that need be considered, the *trans* isomer is expected to yield a mixture of 66.6% *cis* and 33.3% *trans* whereas the *cis* isomer gives 83.3% *cis* and 16.6% *trans*. However, both steric and electrostatic factors must play an important role in the position of entry of Y as well as in the formation of the trigonal bipyramid so that the relative amount of isomers calculated on a statistical basis is probably of very little meaning. The only conclusion that can be reached is that a trigonal bipyramid intermediate does permit rearrangement, whereas the tetragonal pyramid does not. Furthermore, a reaction through a trigonal bipyramid will yield more *cis* product starting with a *cis* reactant than with the corresponding *trans* isomer. It should also be mentioned that, although the five-coordinated intermediates in Fig. 3 represent a complete removal of the group being replaced, this need not be the case. Instead a transient intermediate with one group further removed from the central metal ion than the remaining five ligands is perhaps possible. However, such a structure would lead to the same stereochemical changes described above.

The above discussion was limited to stereo changes for reactions of geometrical isomers, but naturally the same treatment applies to optical isomers. Most of the studies reported for substitution reactions in optically active complexes was done with cobalt(III) cations of the type *cis*-Co(en)$_2$AX. For an S_N1 process it is of interest to note that inversion cannot take place; there can be only retention of configuration and/or loss of optical activity (Fig. 4). If the reaction goes through a tetragonal pyramid, the retention of configuration is obvious. However, if a trigonal bipyramid is involved, then a mixture of isomers is expected. Any optical activity observed in the product must, however, have come from the optically active trigonal bipyramid A and must have the same generic configuration as that of the starting material. The loss of optical activity is due to the formation of a *trans* product via trigonal bipyramid A and/or a racemic mixture of the *cis*

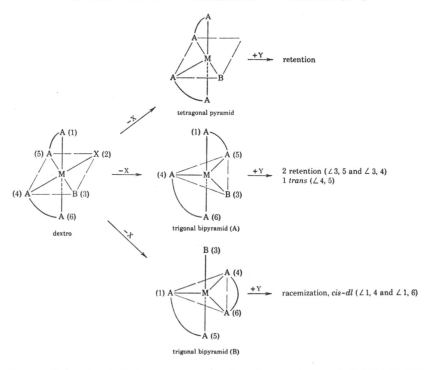

FIG. 4. Stereochemical changes accompanying the reaction of d-cis-$M(AA)_2BX$ with Y by a dissociation (S_N1) mechanism through either a tetragonal pyramid or trigonal bipyramid intermediate.

isomer via the symmetrical trigonal bipyramid B. With but two known exceptions, to be discussed later, the reactions of optical isomers that have been investigated and found to yield some optically active product do appear to give the enantiomorph of the same generic configuration as that of the starting material.

Substitution by means of a displacement (S_N2) mechanism requires the intermediate formation of a seven-coordinated complex. Stable compounds in which the central ion has a coordination number of seven are not numerous. X-ray and electron diffraction data demonstrate the existence of two different structures for these compounds (Fig. 5). Iodine heptafluoride [4] and ZrF_7^{3-} [5] both have a pentagonal bipyramid structure. The complex NbF_7^{2-} has been assigned a trigonal biprism structure with a fluoride ion protruding from one of the tetragonal faces.[6] The structure in Fig. 5a is readily generated from an octa-

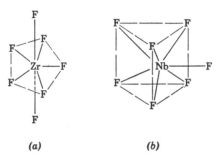

Fig. 5. Structures of seven-coordinated systems: (a) $(NH_4)_3$-$[ZrF_7]$;[5] (b) $K_2[NbF_7]$.[6]

(a)   *(b)*

hedron in an S_N2 process, and stereochemical changes are discussed on the basis of this structure.[3] *

The seven-coordinated intermediate may be formed either by an approach of the entering group towards a position adjacent to that of the departing ligand (*cis* attack) or towards a position opposite from that of the departing ligand (*trans* attack). This definition of *cis* and *trans* attack is applicable to all geometric structures and is preferred to frontside and backside attack (see footnote, p. 116). Stereochemical changes accompanying substitution reactions of *cis*- and *trans*-MA₄BX by an S_N2 mechanism are summarized in Fig. 6. Replacement by means of a *cis* attack results in no net rearrangement; thus a *cis* isomer yields a *cis* product and *trans* yields *trans*. However, for a *trans* attack, the *cis* isomer gives a mixture of *cis* and *trans* products whereas the *trans* isomer yields only a *cis* product. This prediction that a *trans* displacement in a *trans* isomer yields exclusively a *cis* product uniquely distinguishes this process from all the other mechanisms being considered.

The same treatment can be applied to S_N2 reactions of optical isomers (Fig. 7). Substitution by a *cis* attack, as usual, leads to a retention of configuration. However, for a *trans* approach, unlike an S_N1 process, the S_N2 mechanism does permit inversion of configuration. Furthermore none of the seven-coordinated intermediates are symmetrical, so that loss of optical rotation is due to the formation of a *trans* product and/or to the same extent of reaction through the two intermediates that lead to the *cis* enantiomorphs.

* It is important to remember that the pentagonal bipyramid structure is discussed primarily because it is then easy to visualize the stereochemical changes that take place. A more probable position of attack for the entering group, as is discussed later, is at the octahedral face. However, the net stereochemical consequences are the same for the two processes. The important consideration in both cases, as shown in Figs. 6 and 7, is whether *cis* or *trans* attack occurs.

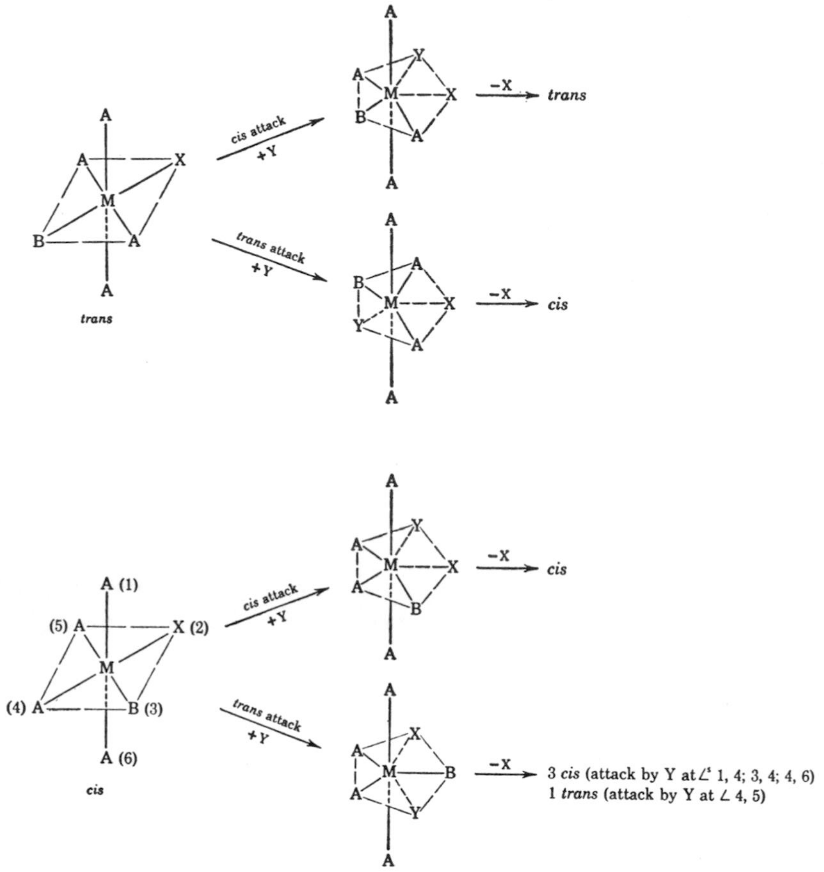

FIG. 6. Stereochemical changes accompanying reactions of *cis*- and *trans*-MA₄BX with Y by a displacement (S_N2) mechanism through a pentagonal bipyramid intermediate.

If it is assumed that the stereochemical changes just described for S_N1 and S_N2 reaction processes occur with equal probability, then the data collected in Table 1 are expected. This assumes that for any mechanism all possible intermediates form with equal ease and a statistical distribution of structures is obtained. It is apparent from the data in Table 1 that the stereochemistry of the reaction product is often not in itself diagnostic of the mechanism involved. For example a *trans* isomer may yield exclusively a *trans* product either by an S_N1 process involving a tetragonal pyramid intermediate or an

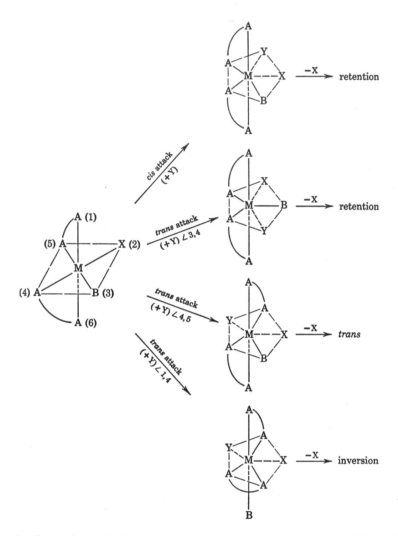

FIG. 7. Stereochemical changes accompanying the reaction of d-cis-M(AA)$_2$BX with Y by a displacement (S_N2) mechanism through a pentagonal bipyramid intermediate.

Table 1

Statistical Amounts (%) of Isomeric Products Predicted for Different Mechanisms of Substitution in Octahedral Complexes

Reactant	Dissociation (S_N1)				Displacement (S_N2)			
	Tetragonal Pyramid		Trigonal Bipyramid		cis Attack		trans Attack	
	cis	trans	cis	trans	cis	trans	cis	trans
trans-MA₄BX	0	100	66.6	33.3	0	100	100	0
cis-MA₄BX	100	0	83.3	16.6	100	0	75	25
D-M(AA)₂BX *	D-100	0	D-33.3	16.6	D-100	0	D-33.3	33.3
			DL-50				L-33.3	

* *D* and *L* refer to generic configuration: $D \rightarrow D$ (retention); $D \rightarrow L$ (inversion); and $D \rightarrow DL$ (racemization).

S_N2 reaction with a *cis* attack. A distinction can be made between these two paths only whenever the molecularity of the reaction is known. However, if a *trans* isomer yields exclusively a *cis* product or if an optical isomer gives an optically active product of inverted configuration, this furnishes good evidence in support of a *trans*-displacement (S_N2) mechanism.

Edge-displacement hypothesis. Brown, Ingold, and Nyholm [7] suggest that *d-l* conversions and *cis-trans* changes are essentially of the same type and that either can arise in an octahedral system as a result of what they call *edge displacement* (Fig. 8). For example the stereo change accompanying the replacement of X by Y does not depend on groups A, X, and Y, but on the position of some unaffected group B, whose relation to the replaced and replacing groups X and Y is designated by the prefixes *d* and *l*, or *cis* and *trans*. If B is at 3, then *cis* →

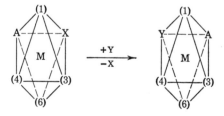

Fig. 8. Edge displacement of X by Y. The stereochemical consequence of edge displacement depends upon the unaffected groups at positions 1, 3, 4, and 6 as described in the text.

trans; if at 4, *trans* → *cis*; and if at 1 or 6, then either $d \to l$ or $l \to d$. Although any observed stereo change can be understood as an edge displacement, an observed absence of a stereo change in octahedral substitution does not imply the absence of an edge displacement. The authors point out that, if the groups in positions 1 and 6, and likewise those in positions 3 and 4 can be superposed either on the other by a rotation of the molecule, then a *cis* factor will give a *cis* product, identical with that which would be given by substitution without edge displacement. Similarly, if the positions 1 and 3 and the positions 4 and 6 are identically coupled, as by ethylenediamine molecules, then there is retention of configuration ($D \to D$ or $L \to L$) during substitution just as there is without edge displacement. The two processes do yield different results for reactions of *trans*-MA₄BX. In this case substitution with edge displacement must yield a *cis* product, MA₄BY, whereas substitution without edge displacement gives the corresponding *trans* isomer.

The relation of stereo change to edge- and non-edge-displacement processes for a complex of the type MA₄BX is schematically represented in Table 2. A comparison of these results with those in Table 1

Table 2 *

Relation of Stereo Change to Edge Displacement in Nucleophilic Substitutions in Octahedral Complexes MA₄BX

	Substitution without Edge Displacement			
Stereo Change		No Stereo Change		
cis ↔ *trans*	$D \leftrightarrow L$	$D \leftrightarrow D$ $L \leftrightarrow L$	*cis* ↔ *cis*	*trans* ↔ *trans*
Substitution with edge displacement				

* From reference 7.

shows that they are identical with the S_N2 mechanism described in the previous section. It should be pointed out that the edge-displacement hypothesis is concerned only with bimolecular reactions. The term edge displacement does not imply an attack along the octahedral edge. For systems such as cobalt(III) complexes this position of attack is most unlikely, since it is the region of maximum electron density due to electrons in the d_{xy}, d_{xz}, and d_{yz} orbitals.*

REACTIONS OF GEOMETRICAL ISOMERS

Rather extensive studies have been conducted on the reactions of geometric isomers of cobalt(III) complexes. Werner [1] and his students made numerous qualitative observations on the relative amounts of *cis* and *trans* product obtained from various different reactions. The technique they employed was to carry out the reaction, and then to isolate the product and separate the geometric isomers. These results can be given only qualitative significance because under these conditions both reactants and products may undergo rearrangement without net chemical change (Chapter 6). Furthermore the reactions are often complicated due to participation of the solvent water, that is, the direct replacement of one ligand by another need not take place but rather may first involve the formation of the aqua complex.[8] However, it must be concluded that, even by this procedure, whenever the *cis* and the *trans* isomers of the same compound each react under the same experimental conditions to yield different ratios of isomers of the same product, then the stereochemistry of the products is at least to some extent kinetically controlled. If such reactions were entirely thermodynamically controlled, then the two isomeric reactants would each yield the same equilibrium mixture of isomeric products. Therefore, in many cases, results obtained by the preparative method are indicative of the stereo change during reaction.

The reaction products of some reactions of cobalt(III) complexes have also been examined spectrophotometrically.[3] The advantage of this over the preparative method is that it minimizes the chances of rearrangement prior and subsequent to reaction. However, even this procedure is not entirely free of complications. In order to be certain that the products observed are a direct result of the rearrangement accompanying the substitution reaction in question, it is necessary to show that the ratio of isomeric products does not change throughout

---

* That the authors did not mean "edge attack" was clarified in subsequent publications (see reference 9e and R. S. Nyholm, *Progress in Stereochemistry,* edited by W. Klyne, Academic Press, New York, Vol. I, 1954, p. 355). In order to avoid any confusion it has been suggested (C. K. Ingold, private communication) that the term *edge shift* be used instead.

their formation. Recent studies [9] of this type have been made for the base hydrolysis reaction of several cobalt(III) complexes as designated by footnote *b* in Table 3.

Stereochemical studies of substitution reactions of octahedral complexes other than cobalt(III) are few in number, and the information is limited to some rather incomplete qualitative observations. In spite of this, it is of interest to bring together some of the available data for these reactions (Table 3, *E*). It should be kept in mind that in general these data can be given only qualitative significance.

On the basis of information now available (Table 3, *A* and *C*), it would appear that for reactions of geometric isomers of the type,

$$Co(AA)_2BX + H_2O \rightleftharpoons Co(AA)_2B(H_2O) + X^- \qquad (1)$$

both the forward and reverse reactions proceed largely without stereo change. The only exception to this known at present is a report [9c] that, on the basis of a kinetic analysis of reaction products, the acid hydrolysis of *trans*-$Co(en)_2(NCS)Br^+$ yields 45% *cis*- and 55% *trans*-$Co(en)_2(H_2O)NCS^{2+}$. Thus these observations of extensive retention of configuration tentatively suggest that substitution proceeds either by an S_N1 process through a tetragonal pyramid intermediate (Fig. 4) or by an S_N2 mechanism with a *cis* attack (Fig. 7). In terms of the edge-displacement theory, the results suggest that the reactions occur primarily without edge displacement. The weight of kinetic evidence is in support of an S_N1 reaction for acid hydrolysis of cobalt(III) complexes (Chapter 3). Therefore as these reactions generally proceed with retention of configuration it follows that for the most part the five-coordinated intermediate must have a tetragonal pyramid structure. Such a mechanism can also account for the reverse reaction, the replacement of coordinated water by some other ligand, assuming these reactions are likewise unimolecular. Reactions of platinum(IV) complexes in general take place with retention of configuration (Table 3, *E*). These reactions may be complicated owing to platinum(II) catalysis. However, if they are S_N2, as has been claimed (p. 167), then substitution occurs largely by *cis* attack.

The one category of substitution reactions in cobalt(III) complexes which appears to be accompanied by extensive rearrangement is that of base hydrolysis (Table 3, *B*). Although *cis* isomers yield chiefly *cis* products, this would be true regardless of mechanism (Table 1) and does not exclude the possibility of rearrangement during these reactions. The stereochemical observation most diagnostic of the reaction process

Table 3

Substitution Reactions of Geometrical Isomers [a]

Reactant	Reagent	Product	% cis	% trans	Reference
		A. Acid Hydrolysis			
$cis\text{-}Co(en)_2(NH_3)Cl^{2+}$	H_2O, $HClO_4$, $AgClO_4$	$Co(en)_2(NH_3)H_2O^{3+}$	75	25	3
$trans\text{-}Co(en)_2(NH_3)Cl^{2+}$	H_2O, $HClO_4$, $AgClO_4$	$Co(en)_2(NH_3)H_2O^{3+}$	20	80	3
$cis\text{-}Co(en)_2Cl_2^+$	H_2O	$Co(en)_2(H_2O)Cl^{2+}$	+	−	1
$trans\text{-}Co(en)_2Cl_2^+$	H_2O	$Co(en)_2(H_2O)Cl^{2+}$	−	+	1
$cis\text{-}Co(en)_2(NO_2)Cl^{+\ b}$	H_2O, $HClO_4$	$Co(en)_2(H_2O)NO_2^{2+}$	100	−	3, 9e
$trans\text{-}Co(en)_2(NO_2)Cl^{+\ b}$	H_2O, $HClO_4$	$Co(en)_2(H_2O)NO_2^{2+}$	−	100	3, 9e
$cis\text{-}Co(en)_2(NO_2)Cl^+$	H_2O, $HClO_4$, $AgClO_4$	$Co(en)_2(H_2O)NO_2^{2+}$	100	−	3
$trans\text{-}Co(en)_2(NO_2)Cl^+$	H_2O, $HClO_4$, $AgClO_4$	$Co(en)_2(H_2O)NO_2^{2+}$	−	100	3
$cis\text{-}Co(en)_2(NCS)Cl^+$	H_2O	$Co(en)_2(H_2O)NCS^{2+}$	+	−	1
$trans\text{-}Co(en)_2(NCS)Br^{+\ b}$	H_2O	$Co(en)_2(H_2O)NCS^{2+}$	45	55	9c
		B. Base Hydrolysis			
$cis\text{-}Co(en)_2(NH_3)Cl^{2+\ b}$	OH^-	$Co(en)_2(NH_3)OH^{2+}$	84	16	9d
$trans\text{-}Co(en)_2(NH_3)Cl^{2+\ b}$	OH^-	$Co(en)_2(NH_3)OH^{2+}$	76	24	9d
$cis\text{-}Co(en)_2(NH_3)Br^{2+\ b}$	OH^-	$Co(en)_2(NH_3)OH^{2+}$	85	15	9d
$cis\text{-}Co(en)_2(NH_3)NO_3^{2+\ b}$	OH^-	$Co(en)_2(NH_3)OH^{2+}$	86	14	9d
$cis\text{-}Co(en)_2Cl_2^c$	OH^-	$Co(en)_2(OH)Cl^+$	9	50	10
$trans\text{-}Co(en)_2Cl_2$	OH^-	$Co(en)_2(OH)Cl^+$	18	55	10
$cis\text{-}Co(en)_2(NO_2)Cl^{+\ b}$	OH^-	$Co(en)_2(OH)NO_2^+$	66	34	9e
$trans\text{-}Co(en)_2(NO_2)Cl^{+\ b}$	OH^-	$Co(en)_2(OH)NO_2^+$	6	94	9e
$cis\text{-}Co(en)_2(NCS)Cl^{+\ b}$	OH^-	$Co(en)_2(OH)NCS^+$	82	18	9c
$trans\text{-}Co(en)_2(NCS)Cl^{+\ b}$	OH^-	$Co(en)_2(OH)NCS^+$	76	24	9c
$trans\text{-}Co(en)_2(NCS)Br^{+\ b}$	OH^-	$Co(en)_2(OH)NCS^+$	81	19	9c
		C. Replacement of Water			
$cis\text{-}Co(en)_2(NH_3)H_2O^{3+}$	$NaNO_2$	$Co(en)_2(NH_3)NO_2^{2+}$	80	20	3
$trans\text{-}Co(en)_2(NH_3)H_2O^{3+}$	$NaNO_2$	$Co(en)_2(NH_3)NO_2^{2+}$	35	65	3
$trans\text{-}Co(en)_2(NH_3)H_2O^{3+}$	HNO_3	$Co(en)_2(NH_3)NO_3^{2+}$	−	+	1
$cis\text{-}Co(en)_2(H_2O)Cl$	HBr	$Co(en)_2ClBr^+$	+	−	1
$cis\text{-}Co(en)_2(H_2O)Br$	HCl	$Co(en)_2ClBr^+$	+	−	1
$cis\text{-}Co(en)_2(H_2O)Br$	HBr	$Co(en)_2Br_2^+$	+	−	1
$cis\text{-}Co(en)_2(H_2O)NO_2^{2+}$	$NaNO_2$	$Co(en)_2(NO_2)_2^+$	100	−	3
$trans\text{-}Co(en)_2(H_2O)NO_2^{2+}$	$NaNO_2$	$Co(en)_2(NO_2)_2^+$	−	100	3
$cis\text{-}Co(en)_2(H_2O)NO_2^{2+}$	$KNCS$	$Co(en)_2(NO_2)NCS^+$	100	−	3
$trans\text{-}Co(en)_2(H_2O)NO_2^{2+}$	$KNCS$	$Co(en)_2(NO_2)NCS^+$	−	100	3
		D. Substitutions in Non-Aqueous Media			
$cis\text{-}Co(en)_2Cl_2^{+\ b, d}$	$*Cl^-$	$Co(en)_2Cl*Cl^+$	18	82	9b
$cis\text{-}Co(en)_2Cl_2^{+\ b, d}$	NCS^-	$Co(en)_2(NCS)Cl^+$	64	36	9b
$trans\text{-}Co(AA)_2Cl_2^{+\ d, e}$	$*Cl^-$	$Co(AA)_2Cl*Cl^+$	−	+	10b
$trans\text{-}Co(en)_2Cl_2^{+\ f}$	$Cl^-(?)$	$Co(en)_2Cl_2^+$	+	−	10b
$l\text{-}cis\text{-}Cr(en)_2Cl_2^{+\ g}$	$Cl^-(?)$	$dl\text{-}cis\text{-}Cr(en)_2Cl_2^+$	+	−	10c
		E. Reactions of Complexes Other than Cobalt(III)			
$cis\text{-}Cr(en)_2Cl_2^+$	H_2O	$Cr(en)_2(H_2O)_2^{3+}$	+	−	11
$trans\text{-}Cr(en)_2Cl_2^+$	H_2O	$Cr(en)_2(H_2O)_2^{3+}$	−	+	11
$cis\text{-}Cr(en)_2(H_2O)_2^{3+}$	HBr	$Cr(en)_2Br_2^+$	+	−	11
$trans\text{-}Cr(en)_2(H_2O)_2^{3+}$	HBr	$Cr(en)_2Br_2^+$	−	+	11
$trans\text{-}Pt(en)_2(H_2O)_2^{4+}$	HCl	$Pt(en)_2Cl_2^{2+}$	−	+	12a
$trans\text{-}Pt(en)_2BrCl^{2+}$	HBr	$Pt(en)_2Br_2^{2+}$	−	+	12b
$trans\text{-}Pt(en)_2Br_2^{2+}$	HCl	$Pt(en)_2BrCl^{2+}$	−	+	12b
$trans\text{-}Pt(NH_3)_2(NO_2)_2Cl_2^h$	$NaBr$	$Pt(NH_3)_2(NO_2)_2ClBr$	−	+	13
$trans\text{-}Pt(NH_3)_2(NO_2)_2Cl_2^h$	$NaNO_2$	$Pt(NH_3)_2(NO_2)_3Cl$	−	+	13
$trans\text{-}Pt(en)(NH_3)(NO_2)BrCl^{+\ h}$	$NaBr$	$Pt(en)(NH_3)(NO_2)Br_2^+$	−	+	13
$trans\text{-}Pt(en)(NH_3)(NO_2)BrCl^{+\ h}$	$NaNO_2^-$	$Pt(en)NH_3(NO_2)_2Br^+$	−	+	13
$trans\text{-}Pt(en)(NH_3)(NO_2)BrCl^{+\ h}$	NH_3	$Pt(en)(NH_3)_2(NO_2)Br^{2+}$	−	+	13
$cis\text{-}Rh(py)_2Cl_4^-$	H_2O	$Rh(py)_2(H_2O)Cl_3$	+	−	14
$trans\text{-}Rh(py)_2Cl_4^-$	H_2O	$Rh(py)_2(H_2O)Cl_3$	−	+	14
$cis\text{-}Ir(py)_2Cl_4^-$	H_2O	$Ir(py)_2(H_2O)Cl_3$	+	−	15
$trans\text{-}Ir(py)_2Cl_4^-$	H_2O	$Ir(py)_2(H_2O)Cl_3$	−	+	15
$trans\text{-}Ir(C_2O_4)_2Cl_2^{3-}$	py	$Ir(C_2O_4)_2(py)_2$	−	+	16

[a] Notation of + signifies chief isomeric product.

[b] Ratio of isomeric products do not change during the course of the reaction; thus the ratio observed is a direct consequence of the substitution reaction in question and is not complicated by subsequent isomerization.

[c] From the reaction of one mole complex with one mole NaOH which gives in addition 21% and 14% of the dihydroxo complexes for the cis and $trans$ starting materials respectively.

[d] Solvent is methanol.

[e] Symbol AA is used for ethylenediamine and its C-substituted analogs.

[f] Solvent is dimethylformamide or dimethylsulfoxide.

[g] Solvent is 2-methoxyethanol.

[h] $trans$ refers to either Cl—Cl or Br—Cl in the reactant, and the designation of a $trans$ product means that the entering group takes the place of the departed chloride so that there is no change in configuration. These are only a few representative examples; the Russian chemists have studied many other similar systems and report that in all cases the reactions take place largely without rearrangement. It should also be noted that many of these reactions of Pt(IV) complexes are perhaps not simple substitution reactions but instead occur as a result of Pt(II) catalysis [12b] (p. 167).

is that which occurs during the reaction of the *trans* isomer. In such a case, as discussed earlier (Table 1), a *trans* factor yields a *trans* product unless the reaction takes place either through a trigonal bipyramid intermediate which gives largely a *cis* product or a *trans* displacement giving entirely a *cis* product. It is therefore significant that base hydrolysis reactions of *trans*-Co(en)$_2$BX in general yield large quantities of *cis*-Co(en)$_2$B(OH). These results indicate a different mechanism from that of acid hydrolysis and replacement of coordinated water, for which *trans* reactants yield largely *trans* products.

Ingold [9] assumes that the base hydrolysis reactions are bimolecular, S_N2, and accounts for the large amount of *cis* product obtained from a *trans* reactant on the basis of an edge-displacement mechanism. If this were completely an edge displacement, then the product would be 100% *cis*. Since some *trans* product is obtained, it is suggested that, unlike bimolecular substitutions on tetrahedral carbon, which are known to produce practically exclusive inversion, these substitutions on octahedral cobalt lead predominately, but not exclusively, to edge displacement. The different behavior of these two structures might be due to the different forms of tetrahedral and octahedral orbitals (Fig. 9). The part of a bonded tetrahedral orbital most accessible to a substituting agent is assumed to be the lower lobe, which has a considerable magnitude in angle, 1.00, in the best possible direction for inversion. The part of a bonded octahedral orbital least inaccessible to a reagent is presumably the cap-like member, whose greatest magnitude in angle is only 0.43 and is directed only 18° below the equatorial plane. Thus, whereas the bias towards inversion in bimolecular tetrahedral substitution might be very large, the bias towards edge displacement in bimolecular octahedral substitution might well be much smaller. One immediate objection to this interpretation is the assumption that these reactions are bimolecular, whereas kinetic studies suggest that the reactions are of the S_N1CB type (Chapter 3).

For the base hydrolysis of a *trans* isomer to yield largely a *cis* product by the dissociation of the reactant's conjugate base (S_N1CB), it is necessary that the five-coordinated intermediate have a trigonal bipyramid structure. It has been suggested [17] that this structure is favored for the intermediate containing ligands capable of strong π bonding because there is more orbital overlap with the trigonal bipyramid (Fig. 5, Chapter 3) than the tetragonal pyramid structure. Therefore, since the conjugate base of the reacting species contains an amido group which has a tendency to form π bonds, it follows that the trigonal bipyramid structure will be greatly stabilized. Much the same

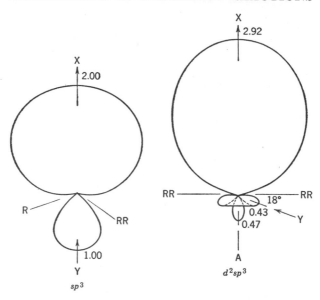

Fɪɢ. 9. Graphic representations of the approach of Y and departure of X from sp^3 and d^2sp^3 orbital hybrids, where compounds involved are CR_3X and MR_4AX respectively. (From reference 9a.)

conclusion has been reached for the structure of the five-coordinated intermediate in substitution reactions of square complexes which contain π-bonding ligands (Chapter 4). This suggests that rearrangement may accompany the reaction of octahedral ammine complexes containing N—H bonds with alkali. This explanation of the observed stereo change for the base hydrolysis of *trans*-Co(en)$_2$BX is in agreement with both the S_N1CB mechanism indicated by kinetic studies and the formation of small amounts of *trans* product along with the *cis* isomer. Furthermore it is also in agreement with the observation that a *cis* isomer yields a larger amount of *cis* product than does the same *trans* starting material. It remains necessary, however, to account for the observation that the base hydrolysis of *trans*-Co(en)$_2$NO$_2$Cl yields 96% of the *trans*-hydroxo isomer. This result can be explained if there is an inhibition of nucleophilic attack adjacent to the nitro group ($\angle$s 1,2 and 1,3 in trigonal bipyramid I of Fig. 3, where B = NO$_2^-$) and hence an orientation of attack in an opposite position ($\angle$ 2,3). Such a stereospecific approach may result from steric and/or polarization effects of the nitro ligand. Since this group is expected to π-bond with a pair of the d electrons on cobalt(III) it follows that the electron density near the nitro group will be large and thus nucleophilic attack adjacent to it very slow. Alternatively, as was discussed earlier (p. 166), contributions of an S_N2 process may become important in this nitro complex.

REACTIONS OF OPTICAL ISOMERS

Retention of configuration. Werner [18] also investigated substitution reactions of optical isomers and found that in many cases optically active products could be isolated. It was concluded that these optically active products had the same generic configuration as the starting material so that this portion of the reaction had proceeded with retention of configuration. Werner's assignment of relative generic configuration was based upon his assumption that, for analogous complex ions, the antipodes which form the least soluble salts with the same resolving agent have the same generic configuration. For example, the reaction

$$l\text{-Co(en)}_2(\text{NCS})\text{Cl}^+ + \text{NaNO}_2 \rightarrow d\text{-Co(en)}_2(\text{NCS})\text{NO}_2^+ + \text{NaCl} \quad (2)$$

is said to proceed with retention of configuration because, in the resolution of these racemic complexes by fractional crystallization of their dextro-α-bromocamphor-π-sulfonate salts, the least soluble fractions are formed with l-Co(en)$_2$(NCS)Cl$^+$ and d-Co(en)$_2$(NCS)NO$_2^+$ respectively. This view was criticized by Jaeger,[19] who, however, later became convinced that Werner's empirical rule was correct and actually employed it in some of his studies. Mathieu [20] repeated some of Werner's work and, by correlating the absorption spectra and rotatory dispersion curves of the complexes, agreed that these reactions take place with retention of configuration. Although the method of Mathieu does have some theoretical support, neither method can be taken as absolute proof of relative generic configuration.

The term *rotatory dispersion* applies to the change of optical rotation of a compound with respect to the wavelength of the light source. The optical activity of a compound is known to change markedly in the wavelength regions of its absorption bands. Therefore colorless compounds show little or no dependence of optical activity on wavelength in the visible region, whereas colored complexes show a large anomalous effect (Fig. 10). Thus the optical rotation of d-K$_3$Co(C$_2$O$_4$)$_3$ shows a large change in the vicinity of its absorption band, and, of course, the same but mirror image effect is observed for the levo antipode. If two similar complexes, such as Co(en)$_2$AX and Co(en)$_2$AY, have essentially the same rotatory dispersion they are believed to have the same con-

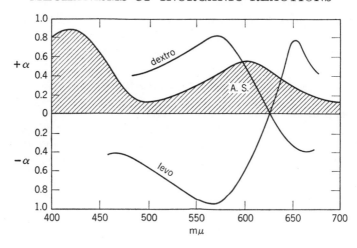

FIG. 10.   Absorption spectrum (A. S.) and rotatory dispersion of *d*- and *l*-trioxalatocobaltate(III) ion.

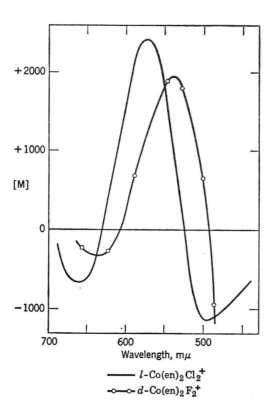

FIG. 11.   Rotatory dispersion of l-Co(en)$_2$Cl$_2$$^+$ and d-Co(en)$_2$F$_2$, which are believed to have the same generic configuration. (From reference 21.)

figuration, whereas if the rotatory dispersions are approximate mirror images they have opposite generic configurations. On the basis of this method, l-Co(en)$_2$Cl$_2^+$ and d-Co(en)$_2$F$_2^+$ are assigned [21] the same configuration (Fig. 11). Although results obtained by such a method are believed to be correct, it would be of interest to check some of this work by x-ray analysis, a method which has been used to establish the absolute configuration of certain optical isomers.[22]

Substitution reactions of some optically active complexes, believed to take place with retention of configuration, are summarized in Table 4. The generic configurations of reactants and products were related

Table 4

Substitution Reactions in Optically Active Complexes with Retention of Configuration

Reactant	Reagent	Product	Reference
l-Co(en)$_2$Cl$_2^+$	H$_2$O	d-Co(en)$_2$(H$_2$O)Cl^{2+}	24
l-Co(en)$_2$Cl$_2^+$	K$_2$CO$_3$(H$_2$O)	d-Co(en)$_2$CO$_3^+$	18
l-Co(en)$_2$Cl$_2^+$	(NH$_4$)$_2$C$_2$O$_4$	d-Co(en)$_2$C$_2$O$_4^+$	18
l-Co(en)$_2$Cl$_2^+$	HF(AgF)	d-Co(en)$_2$F$_2^+$	21
l-Co(en)$_2$(NO$_2$)Cl$^+$	H$_2$O	d-Co(en)$_2$(H$_2$O)NO$_2^{2+}$	24
l-Co(en)$_2$(NO$_2$)Cl$^+$	NaNO$_2$	d-Co(en)$_2$(NO$_2$)$_2^+$	18
l-Co(en)$_2$(NO$_2$)Cl$^+$	KNCS	l-Co(en)$_2$(NO$_2$)NCS$^+$	18
l-Co(en)$_2$(NO$_2$)Cl$^+$	HF(AgF)	d-Co(en)$_2$(NO$_2$)F$^+$	21
l-Co(en)$_2$(NO$_2$)Cl^{+} ^{a}	NaOH	l-Co(en)$_2$(NO$_2$)OH$^+$	23
l-Co(en)$_2$(NCS)Cl$^+$	H$_2$O	l-Co(en)$_2$(H$_2$O)NCS^{2+}	24
l-Co(en)$_2$(NCS)Cl$^+$	NH$_3$	d-Co(en)$_2$(NH$_3$)NCS^{2+}	18
l-Co(en)$_2$(NCS)Cl$^+$	NaNO$_2$	d-Co(en)$_2$(NCS)NO$_2^+$	18
d-Co(en)$_2$(NH$_3$)Cl^{2+}	H$_2$O	d-Co(en)$_2$(NH$_3$)H$_2$O^{3+}	24
d-Co(en)$_2$(NH$_3$)Cl^{2+}	HF(AgF)	d-Co(en)$_2$(NH$_3$)F^{2+}	21
d-Co(en)$_2$(NH$_3$)Cl^{2+} ^{b}	OH$^-$	d-Co(en)$_2$(NH$_3$)OH^{2+}	9d
d-Co(en)$_2$(NH$_3$)Br^{2+} ^{b}	OH$^-$	d-Co(en)$_2$(NH$_3$)OH^{2+}	9d
l-Co(en)$_2$(NH$_3$)Br^{2+} ^{b}	OH$^-$	l-Co(en)$_2$(NH$_3$)OH^{2+}	9d
d-Co(en)$_2$F$_2^+$	CO$_3^{-2}$	d-Co(en)$_2$CO$_3^+$	21
l-Cr(en)$_2$Cl$_2^+$	(NH$_4$)$_2$C$_2$O$_4$	d-Cr(en)$_2$C$_2$O$_4^+$	18

^{a} Kinetic reaction products show approximately 25% retention, 40% racemization, and 35% isomerization.

^{b} Kinetic products of these reactions show approximately 35% retention, 50% racemization, and 15% isomerization.

either by Werner's solubility method or by a comparison of rotatory dispersion curves, or in some cases by both. Unfortunately these studies were not quantitative, and in general the extent of racemization and isomerization is not known. Furthermore for cobalt(III) complexes the replacement of one negative ligand by another in aqueous solution often does not proceed directly but rather goes by a two-step process [8]

$$Co(en)_2AX + H_2O \rightarrow Co(en)_2AH_2O + X^- \qquad (3)$$

$$Co(en)_2AH_2O + Y^- \rightarrow Co(en)_2AY + H_2O \qquad (4)$$

The observed net retention of configuration might be due either to reaction with retention for both steps or inversion for both steps. However, since the acid hydrolysis reaction 3 generally proceeds with retention of configuration, step 4 must also take place without inversion. The best evidence that acid hydrolysis of complexes of the type Co(en)$_2$ACl takes place largely with retention of configuration is furnished by Mathieu.[24] He observed that the rate of mutarotation of optically active Co(en)$_2$ACl is equal to the rate of formation of Co(en)$_2$A(H$_2$O). He also observed that within experimental error the optical rotation and rotatory dispersion of the mutarotated product is that expected for the aqua complex of the same generic configuration. Thus the change in optical activity is a direct result of the replacement of the chloride ion by water, and the amount of racemization and isomerization is not extensive. That isomerization does occur was recently demonstrated [10a] for the reaction of cis-Co(en)$_2$Cl$_2^+$, which yields 80% cis and 20% trans-Co(en)$_2$(H$_2$O)Cl^{2+}.

One other point of interest is that, although some of the reactions in Table 4 were carried out under a variety of different experimental conditions, always the same optically active antipode was obtained. One exception to this is the conversion of Co(en)$_2$Cl$_2^+$ into Co(en)$_2$-CO$_3^+$, which is discussed in the next section. However, similar studies [21] with d-Co(en)$_2$F$_2^+$ show that in this case, regardless of experimental conditions, the product is always d-Co(en)$_2$CO$_3^+$.

It should perhaps not be too surprising that the optically active portion of the product of these reactions has the same generic structure as the reactant. It has already been pointed out (Table 1, Fig. 7) that the only way in which inversion of M(AA)$_2$BX can take place is by an S_N2 trans attack mechanism, and even this might lead to racemization and isomerization. The fact that there is retention of configuration can be accounted for by any of the other three reaction paths discussed (Figs. 4 and 7). For acid hydrolysis reactions, believed to proceed by dissociation, the retention of configuration observed is consistent with a process involving largely a tetragonal pyramid intermediate. How-

ever, because of the qualitative nature of these results, the possibility
of a trigonal bipyramid intermediate cannot be excluded. For other
reactions where the molecularity of the reaction is not known, there
exists the added possibility of a *cis* displacement process.

Quantitative data on the base hydrolysis of optically active co-
balt(III) complexes are extremely interesting. These results can be
used to test the assumption that such reactions proceed by way of a
trigonal bipyramid intermediate. For example it was mentioned
earlier (Fig. 3) that *cis*-MA$_4$BX may readily yield two such intermediates, one of which is identical with the only one formed by the
trans isomer. Furthermore it was pointed out (Fig. 4) that for *d-cis*-
M(AA)$_2$BX one trigonal bipyramid is symmetrical and thus optically
inactive, whereas the other is asymmetric. Therefore in the base
hydrolysis of *d-cis*-Co(en)$_2$(NH$_3$)Cl^{2+} (Fig. 12) it follows that the
racemic-*cis* product must come from A and the retention of optical
activity and isomerization via intermediate B. Since this reaction is
found to take place with 48% racemization,[9d] then it can be said that
48% of the reaction proceeds through intermediate A and 52% through
intermediate B. It is also apparent from this schematic diagram
that the optically active intermediate B generated by the dextro-*cis*
isomer is the same as the racemic intermediate produced by the *trans*
form. Since the base hydrolysis of the *trans* isomer yields 76% *cis*-
and 24% *trans*-hydroxo complex, this same isomeric ratio is expected
for that portion (52%) of the reaction of the dextro-*cis* form which
proceeds through this intermediate (B). It is then possible to estimate
that the base hydrolysis of *d-cis*-Co(en)$_2$(NH$_3$)Cl^{2+} should yield 39%
d-cis- and 13% *trans*-Co(en)$_2$(NH$_3$)OH^{2+}, which is seen to be in good
agreement with the experimental values of 36% and 16% respectively.

These same calculations cannot be made for the analogous bromo
complex because quantitative data are not available on the isomeric
mixture resulting from the base hydrolysis of the *trans* isomer. However, the base hydrolysis of *d-cis*-Co(en)$_2$(NH$_3$)Br^{2+} proceeds with
52% racemization, 32% retention, and 15% isomerization,[9d] which is
almost the same distribution obtained for the chloro compound. Since
the group being replaced does not have any effect on the isomeric ratio
of products, it would seem as if the five-coordinated intermediates are
the same in both cases. This supports the view that in these reactions
the halide ion is completely removed from the coordination sphere before a new ligand is added. One final point is that the above treatment
does not explain the base hydrolysis of *d-cis*-Co(en)$_2$(NO$_2$)Cl$^+$, which
is found to take place with approximately 25% retention of configura-

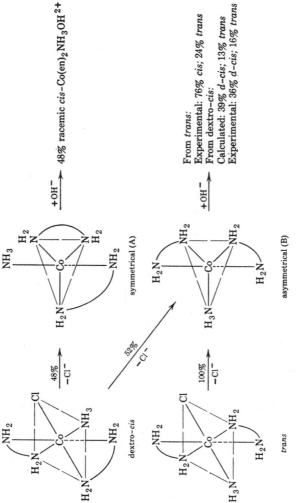

Fig. 12. A comparison of the experimental and calculated isomerization and racemization during the base hydrolysis of d-Co(en)$_2$NH$_3$Cl^{2+} through a symmetrical (A) and asymmetrical (B) five-coordinated intermediate. See the text for further discussion.

tion.[23] If this reaction were to proceed by way of trigonal bipyramids A and B (Fig. 12, where NO_2^- is substituted for NH_3), then almost complete loss of optical rotation is expected, since the base hydrolysis of the *trans*-chloronitro isomer gives 94% *trans* product. This may again suggest a contribution of an S_N2 process (Fig. 12, Chapter 3) for the reaction of this chloronitro complex.

Inversion of configuration. Only two examples have been reported where substitution in an optically active complex yields an optically active product with inversion of configuration. The first of these was discovered by Bailar and Auten [25] for the conversion of $Co(en)_2Cl_2^+$ into $Co(en)_2CO_3^+$ by the reaction with aqueous potassium carbonate and with dry silver carbonate. This system was studied in some detail,[26] and it was found that the solvent plays an important role in these reactions. It was observed that mercury(I) carbonate gave the same results as did potassium carbonate. Furthermore if an excess of silver carbonate is used the levo salt is formed, whereas with equivalent concentrations or less the dextro complex is obtained. When an aqueous solution of l-$[Co(en)_2Cl_2]Cl$ is permitted to stand for various periods of time before allowing it to react with silver carbonate it was found that the freshly prepared solution gives the levo antipode, whereas the aged solutions give the dextro form. However, when the dry levo dichloro complex was intimately mixed with either dry potassium or silver carbonate and then water was added, the solution showed levo rotation. It was concluded on the basis of these studies that the conversion of l-$Co(en)_2Cl_2^+$ to d-$Co(en)_2CO_3^+$ proceeds by way of an aqua intermediate and that a direct replacement yields l-$Co(en)_2CO_3^+$. Investigations of Werner [18] and Mathieu [20] indicate that the reaction with aqueous potassium carbonate proceeds with retention of configuration. Furthermore this dextro carbonato product when treated with alcoholic hydrochloric acid yields the original levo dichloro, whereas the levo carbonato obtained from the dry reaction gives the dextro dichloro complex. On the basis of this information the relative configurations of the complexes in these reactions were assigned as represented in Fig. 13.

Reactions that lead to retention of configuration, such as that with aqueous potassium carbonate, were discussed in the previous section. The unique substitution here is the one that gives inversion, believed to be the reaction which occurs in absence of water. Such an inversion of L-$Co(en)_2Cl_2^+$ into D-$Co(en)_2CO_3^+$, where L and D refer to generic configurations, based on the previous discussion, can only occur

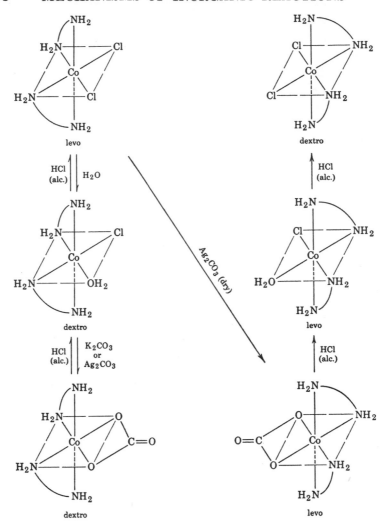

FIG. 13. Walden inversion-type reaction in cobalt(III) complexes.

by a *trans* displacement (S_N2) process (Fig. 7). It is tempting to suggest that the difference observed is due to the reaction in solution proceeding by a dissociation mechanism, whereas the "dry" reaction must be bimolecular. In support of this it can be suggested that the electrophilic "pull" on the chloro group by hydrogen bonding to the solvent water would enhance its dissociation from the complex, whereas in absence of such a pull by water the chloro group must be helped off by a "push" or attack from the carbonate ion. An immediate argument against this interpretation is the observation that freshly prepared solutions of l-Co(en)$_2$Cl$_2^+$ react with silver carbonate with inversion of configuration. However, it may be that the reaction under these conditions is still largely a "solid-state" reaction, a reaction between the insoluble silver carbonate and the dichloro complex absorbed on its surface.

The second example of inversion of optically active compounds was reported [27] for the reaction of l-Co(en)$_2$Cl$_2^+$ with ammonia. In this case the optical rotation of the reaction product, Co(en)$_2$(NH$_3$)$_2^{3+}$, depends upon the reaction temperature. For example the reaction in liquid ammonia at $-33°$ and $-70°$C gives a levorotatory product, but at $25°$C the rotation of the product obtained is dextro. Similarly the reaction with either gaseous ammonia or ammoniacal alcohol at room temperature or above gives the dextro antipode. Since this reaction must proceed stepwise,

$$\text{Co(en)}_2\text{Cl}_2{}^+ \xrightarrow{\text{NH}_3} \text{Co(en)}_2(\text{NH}_3)\text{Cl}^{2+} \xrightarrow{\text{NH}_3} \text{Co(en)}_2(\text{NH}_3)_2{}^{3+} \quad (5)$$

inversion of configuration is possible only if the steps proceed by different mechanisms, e.g., for overall inversion, one step must go with retention and the other with inversion of configuration. The relative configurations of reactant and products were not determined so that it is not known whether it is the high or the low temperature that leads to inversion. However, the temperature dependence suggests that a reaction of lower activation energy predominates at the lower temperature, and it would be of interest to know the stereo change for this reaction path.

SUMMARY

For the sake of clarity the stereochemistry of octahedral substitution on the basis of our present knowledge is summarized here. This can be done according to the two subdivisions used in Chapter 3 of unimolecular [S_N1 and S_N1 (lim)] and bimolecular [S_N2 and S_N2 (lim)] substitutions. In the first place the unimolecular reactions of cobalt(III) complexes seem to take place largely with retention of configuration providing that none of the five ligands in the transition state have any marked tendency to donate π electrons to the cobalt(III) ion. This suggests that the five-coordinated intermediate has a tetragonal pyramid structure which according to crystal field considerations

(Chapter 2) should be more stable than a trigonal bipyramid structure. However, the latter structure is stabilized by the presence of π-bonding ligands of the type that donates electrons to the cobalt(III) ion, e.g., NH_2^- and OH^-. Thus, substitution reactions of cobalt(III) complexes with π-bonding ligands are accompanied by extensive rearrangement. In general, then, it is considered that the acid hydrolysis of chloroamminecobalt(III) complexes takes place largely with retention of configuration through a tetragonal pyramid, and that the base hydrolysis takes place primarily with rearrangement through a trigonal bipyramid intermediate.

That a trigonal bipyramid intermediate is a plausible route for rearrangement and that π bonding of the type mentioned above is important are further supported by the observation that the rates of racemization of $Co(en)_2(H_2O)X$ decrease with changes of X in the order $Cl^- > F^-$ [28] $> NO_2^- \sim NCS^- > NH_3$.[24] If the assumption is made that these complexes racemize by the exchange of coordinated water with solvent, then it can be argued that this must occur by a trigonal bipyramid intermediate. This is true because a tetragonal pyramid gives retention of configuration as does also *cis* displacement, which is discussed below. It is therefore of interest that the aquahalo complexes racemize most rapidly since they are just the ones with the greatest tendency to donate electrons to the central metal ion in π bonding. However, this cannot be the sole factor that need be considered because the acid hydrolysis of *trans*-$Co(en)_2(NCS)Cl^+$ does take place with rearrangement (Table 3).

Bimolecular reactions, on the other hand, take place largely with retention of configuration. This is perhaps best illustrated by the reactions of platinum(IV) complexes but may also be true of certain cobalt(III) complexes such as, for example, the chloronitroammines. It follows from these observations that the displacement must take place primarily by *cis* attack. It is now of interest therefore to consider why there is little or no *trans* displacement in such systems. First it is necessary to point out that, because of the high electron density along the octahedral edges resulting from filled d_{xy}, d_{xz}, and d_{yz} orbitals, the most likely positions of attack are at the octahedral faces. Besides being the most positive regions, the centers of these triangular faces are also the least sterically hindered positions for approach to the central metal ion. It can easily be seen that *cis* attack at the octahedral face readily generates the reaction product with retention of configuration (Fig. 14). It is also apparent that a corresponding *trans* attack would necessitate extensive atomic re-

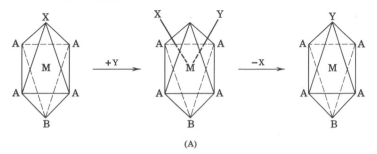

(A)

FIG. 14. *cis* attack (S_N2) at the octahedral face, which takes place with retention of configuration.

arrangement and therefore that the energy of activation for this process will be much higher than that for *cis* attack. It must further be kept in mind that the principle of microscopic reversibility requires that in the transition state the incoming and outgoing groups have a like geometrical relation to the rest of the structure. This is readily possible for *cis* attack by the simultaneous motion of X into the octahedral face opposite that of Y (Fig. 14). However, this same type of symmetry is not achieved by the mere motion of X with the approach of Y by *trans* attack. Thus in general it is believed that bimolecular octahedral substitutions will take place with retention of configuration through a seven-coordinated intermediate of structure A in Fig. 14. This conclusion is of course not necessarily valid for systems with one or more of the d_{xy}-type orbitals vacant.

Finally, as mentioned earlier, the Walden inversion-type reactions observed for two cobalt(III) systems are difficult to rationalize. In terms of our present treatment such inversion requires a *trans* displacement, which is considered above to be very unlikely. However, the reactions found to give inversion were carried out under rather unusual experimental conditions.[25, 27] Perhaps another good place to look for such inversions would be in the bimolecular reactions of platinum(IV) complexes constructed such that *cis* attack is retarded by steric hindrance at the front of the complex.

REFERENCES

1. A. Werner, *Ann.*, **386**, 1 (1912).
2. M. Linhard, *Z. Elektrochem.*, **50**, 224 (1944).

3. F. Basolo, B. D. Stone, and R. G. Pearson, *J. Am. Chem. Soc.*, **75**, 819 (1953); H. M. Cardwell, *Chemistry & Industry*, **1955**, 422.
4. K. C. Lord, M. A. Lynch, Jr., W. C. Schumb, and E. J. Slowinski, Jr., *J. Am. Chem. Soc.*, **72**, 522 (1950).
5. G. C. Hampson and L. Pauling, *ibid.*, **60**, 2702 (1938); W. H. Zachariasen, *Acta Cryst.*, **7**, 792 (1954).
6. J. L. Hoard, *J. Am. Chem. Soc.*, **61**, 1252 (1939).
7. D. D. Brown, C. K. Ingold, and R. S. Nyholm, *J. Chem. Soc.*, **1953**, 2673.
8. F. Basolo, *Chem. Revs.*, **52**, 459 (1953).
9. (a) C. K. Ingold, The Chemical Society, *Special Publ. No.* 1, London, 1954, p. 10. (b) D. D. Brown and R. S. Nyholm, *J. Chem. Soc.*, **1953**, 2696. (c) C. K. Ingold, R. S. Nyholm, and M. L. Tobe, *ibid.*, **1956**, 1691. (d) R. S. Nyholm and M. L. Tobe, *ibid.*, **1956**, 1707. (e) S. Asperger and C. K. Ingold, *ibid.*, **1956**, 2862.
10. (a) R. G. Pearson, K. E. Meeker, F. Basolo, *J. Am. Chem. Soc.*, **78**, 709 (1956). (b) P. M. Henry, thesis, Northwestern University, Evanston, Ill., 1956. (c) R. F. Trimble, Jr., *J. Am. Chem. Soc.*, **76**, 6321 (1954).
11. P. Pfeiffer, *Z. anorg. Chem.*, **56**, 285 (1907); *Ber.*, **40**, 3126 (1907).
12. (a) F. Basolo, J. C. Bailar, Jr., and B. R. Tarr, *J. Am. Chem. Soc.*, **72**, 2433 (1950). (b) A. F. Messing, thesis, Northwestern University, Evanston, Ill., 1957.
13. A. A. Grinberg, *Introduction to the Chemistry of Complex Compounds,* State Scientific-Technical Publications of Chemical Literature, Moscow, 1951, p. 155 (in Russian). I. I. Chernyaev, *Izvest. Akad. Nauk S.S.S.R. Otdel. Khim. Nauk,* **1945**, 203.
14. M. Delepine, *Bull. soc. chim. France,* [4]**45**, 245 (1929).
15. M. Delepine, *Ann. chim.* (Paris), [11]**4**, 292 (1935).
16. M. Delepine, *Compt. rend.,* **176**, 445 (1923).
17. R. G. Pearson and F. Basolo, *J. Am. Chem. Soc.*, **78**, 4878 (1956).
18. A. Werner, *Bull. soc. chim. France,* [4]**11**, 19 (1912); *Ber.*, **45**, 1228 (1912).
19. F. M. Jaeger, *Optical Activity and High Temperature Measurements,* McGraw-Hill Book Co., New York, 1930, pp. 93 and 139.
20. J. P. Mathieu, *Compt. rend.,* **199**, 278 (1934); **201**, 1183 (1935); *Bull. soc. chim. France,* [5]**3**, 476 (1936).
21. W. R. Matoush and F. Basolo, *J. Am. Chem. Soc.*, **78**, 3972 (1956).
22. J. M. Bijvoet, A. F. Purdeman, and A. J. VanBommel, *Koninkl. Ned. Akad. Wetenschap., Proc.,* **B54**, 3 (1951); *Nature*, **168**, 271 (1951); Y. Saito, K. Nakatsu, M. Shiro, and H. Kuroya, *Acta Cryst.*, **7**, 636 (1954).
23. A. Jensen, F. Basolo, and R. G. Pearson, unpublished results.
24. J. P. Mathieu, *Bull. soc. chim. France,* [5]**4**, 687 (1937).
25. J. C. Bailar, Jr., and W. Auten, *J. Am. Chem. Soc.*, **56**, 774 (1934).
26. J. C. Bailar, Jr., F. G. Jonelis, and E. H. Huffman, *ibid.*, **58**, 2224 (1936); J. C. Bailar, Jr., and D. F. Peppard, *ibid.*, **62**, 820 (1940).
27. J. C. Bailar, Jr., J. H. Haslam, and E. M. Jones, *ibid.*, **58**, 2226 (1936).
28. F. Basolo, W. R. Matoush, and R. G. Pearson, *ibid.*, **78**, 4883 (1956).

6 Isomerization and racemization reactions

ISOMERIZATION OF OCTAHEDRAL COMPLEXES

That isomerization of geometrical isomers of complex compounds can occur was recognized by Jørgensen [1] as early as 1889 for the system $cis\text{-}Co(en)_2Cl_2^+ \rightleftharpoons trans\text{-}Co(en)_2Cl_2^+$. Rearrangements of this type complicate stereochemical studies of substitution reactions of the type described in the previous chapter. Also because of this interconversion it is generally not possible to make a structural assignment of a complex on the basis of its method of synthesis alone. Although these rearrangements are not common among square complexes, they have often been observed with octahedral complexes. For example, prolonged boiling or evaporation to dryness of the *cis* salts, $[Co(en)_2NO_2Cl]Cl$,[2] $[Co(en)_2(NO_2)_2]NO_3$,[3] $K_3[Ir(C_2O_4)_2Cl_2]$,[4] and $K_3[Rh(C_2O_4)_2Cl_2]$,[5] is known to yield the corresponding *trans* isomers. Detailed studies of isomerization are reported for only a few systems; several of these will be discussed.

Bis(ethylenediamine)dichlorocobalt(III) ion. The *cis-trans* isomerization most extensively studied is that between the *praseo, trans*-$Co(en)_2Cl_2^+$, and *violeo, cis*-$Co(en)_2Cl_2^+$, ions. If an aqueous solution of green *trans*-$[Co(en)_2Cl_2]Cl$ is concentrated on a steam bath, the crystals that separate from solution are violet and consist largely of *cis*-$[Co(en)_2Cl_2]Cl$. This violet salt can in turn be transformed into the green isomer by the evaporation of a hydrochloric acid solution of the *cis* salt to yield *trans*-$[Co(en)_2Cl_2]Cl \cdot HCl$.

It was suggested [6] that these transformations take place by the opening up of an ethylenediamine ring and the entry of either chloride or hydroxide ion into the vacant position, followed by closing of the ring in such a way as to permit rearrangement. This suggestion was made primarily on the supposition that the structure of the green hydrochloride generally designated as trans-[Co(en)$_2$Cl$_2$]Cl·HCl is instead [Co(en)(enH)Cl$_3$]Cl because structures of this type are known for platinum(II) compounds.[7] However, the green color of the hydrochloride does not change with loss of hydrogen chloride to yield trans-[Co(en)$_2$Cl$_2$]Cl. This lack of change would not be expected if the trichloro structure were correct for the hydrochloride salt.

Ettle and Johnson [8] made a detailed study of this system, using radiochlorine, and were able to demonstrate that the reaction mechanism need not involve the opening of a chelate ring. They found that isomerization in the presence of radiochlorine is accompanied by a completely random distribution of chloride ion with coordinated chloro groups; thus isomerization may occur as a result of an intermolecular process. It was also observed that there is no direct replacement of coordinated chloride by chloride ion. Therefore in absence of direct replacement of chloride, it appears that isomerization is associated with the known equilibria:

$$Co(en)_2Cl_2{}^+ + H_2O \underset{b}{\overset{a}{\rightleftharpoons}} Co(en)_2(H_2O)Cl^{2+} + Cl^- \qquad (1)$$

$$Co(en)_2(H_2O)Cl^{2+} + H_2O \underset{d}{\overset{c}{\rightleftharpoons}} Co(en)_2(H_2O)_2{}^{3+} + Cl^- \qquad (2)$$

Reactions a and c take place during the initial stages of the concentration at steam bath temperatures. The reverse reactions, b and d, become important in the final stages when the chloride ion concentration reaches a maximum. The slowness of reactions b and d is responsible for failure to achieve more than partial isomerization by evaporation at room temperature. Under such conditions the product still contains appreciable quantities of the aqua complex ions.

The particular isomer that separates from solution is largely determined by the relative solubilities of the isomeric salts. The less soluble isomer, cis-[Co(en)$_2$Cl$_2$]Cl, is obtained from aqueous solution, whereas the still less soluble trans-[Co(en)$_2$Cl$_2$]Cl·HCl is isolated from a hydrochloric acid solution. On the other hand an aqueous solution of either cis- or trans-[Co(en)$_2$Cl$_2$]NO$_3$ yields the less soluble trans isomer upon concentration. That the role played by hydrochloric acid is that of a precipitant and not that of opening up the chelate ring was shown by the use of trans-[Co(en)$_2$*Cl$_2$]Cl. This salt was dissolved in cold water and precipitated from solution by the addition of hydrochloric acid. Hydrogen chloride liberated at 110°C by this hydrochloride salt was not radioactive.

It was pointed out [8] that the following mechanism is consistent with these observations:

$$cis\text{-Co(en)}_2\text{Cl}_2{}^+ + \text{H}_2\text{O} \rightleftharpoons cis\text{-Co(en)}_2(\text{H}_2\text{O})\text{Cl}^{2+} + \text{Cl}^- \qquad (3)$$

$$\text{⇅}$$

$$trans\text{-Co(en)}_2\text{Cl}_2{}^+ + \text{H}_2\text{O} \rightleftharpoons trans\text{-Co(en)}_2(\text{H}_2\text{O})\text{Cl}^{2+} + \text{Cl}^- \qquad (4)$$

No mention was made of how the rearrangement may occur between the aquachloro species. It is in fact now known that some rearrangement does take place during acid hydrolysis (steps 3 and 4). Although it has been stated [9] that l-Co(en)$_2$Cl$_2{}^+$ reacts with complete retention of configuration, recent studies show [10] that acid hydrolysis of the *cis* isomer does yield a mixture of *cis*- and *trans*-Co(en)$_2$(H$_2$O)Cl^{2+} (p. 265); the latter is formed by rearrangement of the former. Furthermore the isomerization at experimental conditions of steam bath temperatures (approximately 80°C) must certainly involve the diaqua complexes, so that equilibrium 2 cannot be ignored. This means that the system is sufficiently complicated to permit the observed rearrangements. On the basis of a dissociation mechanism, it is apparent (Fig. 1) that the *cis* and *trans* isomers may have a common trigonal bipyramid intermediate which readily provides a path for isomerization. Rearrangement of the system under discussion is not limited to any one set of *cis-trans* isomers but instead X can be either chloride ion or water.

This same isomerization has also been studied [11] in methanol solution. Here there are no complications due to the formation of stable methanol complexes nor due to solubilities. It was observed that the violet color

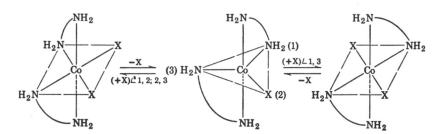

Fıg. 1. Isomerization of *cis-trans* isomers of the type M(AA)$_2$X$_2$ by a dissociation mechanism.

of an alcoholic solution of $cis\text{-}Co(en)_2Cl_2{}^+$ becomes green upon standing ($t_{1/2} = 130$ min; $35.8°C$). At equilibrium the *cis* isomer is almost quantitatively transformed into the thermodynamically more stable *trans* form. However, the rate of formation of $trans\text{-}Co(en)_2Cl_2{}^+$ is not as great as the rate of loss of optical activity of $l\text{-}Co(en)_2Cl_2{}^+$, which is the same as the rate of radiochlorine exchange. At a temperature of $35.8°C$ isomerization accounts for approximately 80% of the rate of loss of optical activity. The activation energy for the rate of formation of the *trans* cation (23.7 kcal/mole) is a little larger than that for the rate of loss of optical rotation (22.6 kcal/mole), so that at higher temperatures the former rate becomes a larger fraction of the latter. Radiochloride ion was found to exchange with coordinated chloride ion by dissociation to a symmetrical intermediate, so that the reaction scheme has been represented as in reaction 5. The difference

$$l\text{-}cis\text{-}Co(en)_2Cl_2{}^+ \xrightarrow{\text{slow}} Co(en)_2Cl^{2+} \underset{\underset{dl\text{-}cis\text{-}Co(en)_2Cl_2{}^+}{\xrightleftharpoons[\text{slow}]{\text{fast (2)}}}}{\overset{trans\text{-}Co(en)_2Cl_2{}^+}{\xrightarrow{\text{fast (1)}}}} \tag{5}$$

between the activation energies of the alternative final fast steps 1 and 2 was estimated to be approximately 5 kcal/mole. On the basis of this the authors suggested that the five-coordinated intermediate has a trigonal bipyramid structure (Fig. 2). Such an intermediate would require less reorganization or, in other words, a lower activation energy to form a *cis* product than it would to generate the *trans* isomer. The reverse is true for a tetragonal pyramid (B) intermediate, which more easily gives the *trans* than the *cis* cation. Since the lower activation energy is observed for the formation of the *cis* isomer, this argues in favor of the trigonal bipyramid (A) intermediate. While it is true that a symmetrical configuration must be involved somewhere in the reaction process, it need not be the five-coordinated intermediate (see p. 265).

It is of interest to note that, whereas isomerization accounts for 80% of the loss of optical activity of alcoholic $l\text{-}Co(en)_2Cl_2{}^+$, under the same conditions but in presence of thiocyanate ion, the formation of $trans\text{-}Co(en)_2(NCS)Cl^+$ accounts for only 36%. In spite of this the thiocyanate reaction is believed to take place through the same intermediate. This difference must therefore result from the fact that the characteristic modes of addition of chloride ion and of thiocyanate ion are not the same. One final point is that, although $cis\text{-}Co(en)_2Cl_2{}^+$ rearranges quantitatively to the *trans* cation in methanol and Methyl Cellosolve, $cis\text{-}l\text{-}Cr(en)_2Cl_2{}^+$ does not change to the *trans* isomer in

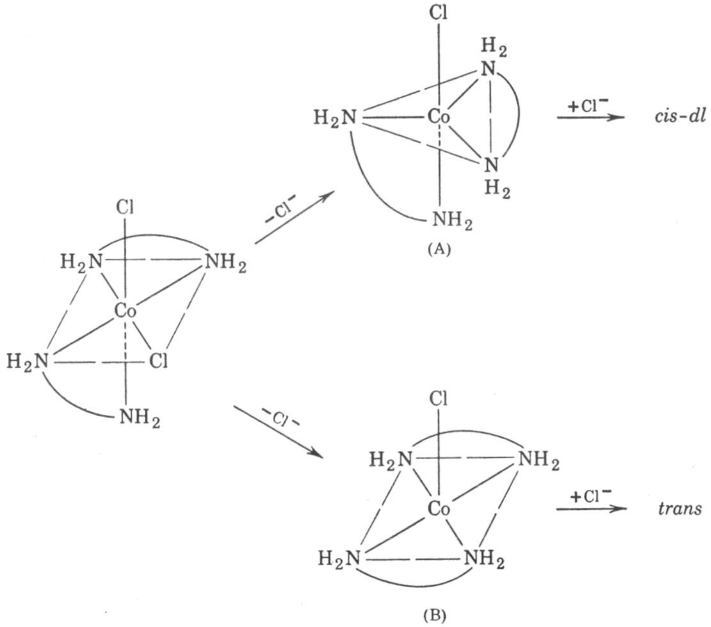

Fig. 2. cis-trans isomerization of $Co(en)_2Cl_2{}^+$ by dissociation to symmetrical intermediates: A, trigonal bipyramid; B, tetragonal pyramid. (From reference 11.)

Cellosolve but it does racemize.[12] It would be desirable to know the rate of radiochloride exchange compared to the rate of racemization of the chromium(III) complex and also whether or not the *trans* isomer will isomerize to the *cis* form in this solvent.

Bis(ethylenediamine)diaquacobalt(III) ion. It was observed [13] that the absorption spectra of *cis*- and of *trans*-$Co(en)_2(H_2O)_2{}^{3+}$ change rapidly to the same spectrum in aqueous solution forming an equilibrium mixture of *cis-trans* isomers. It was later found [14] that this change is much slower in acid solution than it is in water, which means that the aquahydroxo species, $Co(en)_2(H_2O)OH^{2+}$, isomerize more readily than do the diaqua complexes. For example, *cis*- and *trans*-$[Co(en)_2(H_2O)OH]Br_2$ dissolved in water give identical spectra (30 min at room temperature), whereas if dissolved in hydrobromic acid ($pH = 1$) the spectra are different. Bjerrum and Rasmussen [15] have investigated this rather complicated system of acid-base and *cis-trans* equilibria:

$$cis\text{-Co(en)}_2(H_2O)_2{}^{3+} \;\rightleftharpoons\; cis\text{-Co(en)}_2(H_2O)OH^{2+} \;\rightleftharpoons\; cis\text{-Co(en)}_2(OH)_2{}^{+}$$
$$\uparrow\downarrow \qquad\qquad\qquad \uparrow\downarrow \qquad\qquad\qquad \uparrow\downarrow \qquad (6)$$
$$trans\text{-Co(en)}_2(H_2O)_2{}^{3+} \;\rightleftharpoons\; trans\text{-Co(en)}_2(H_2O)OH^{2+} \;\rightleftharpoons\; trans\text{-Co(en)}_2(OH)_2{}^{+}$$

The rates of isomerization of the diaqua ions in acid solution and the dihydroxo ions in basic solution are slow; equilibrium is reached in approximately one week at room temperature. The aquahydroxo complexes isomerize much more rapidly reaching equilibrium within one hour. The equilibrium *cis/trans* ratios and the rates of isomerization are summarized in Table 1. The rates of isomerization follow first-

Table 1 * †

cis-trans Isomerization of Co(en)₂X₂ where X = H₂O, OH⁻

(Concentrations: complex $\sim 0.01\ M$, $NaNO_3 = 1.0\ M$; temperature 25°C)

	$(H_2O)_2$	$(H_2O)(OH)$	$(OH)_2$
cis/trans ratio at equilibrium	58	1.42	0.80
Isomerization rate, $t_{1/2}$ min	637	Fast	1500

* From reference 15.

† Yalman and Kuwana [16] report the following data for the *cis-trans* isomerization of $Co(NH_3)_4(H_2O)_2{}^{3+}$: *cis/trans* ratio at equilibrium = 0.17; $t_{1/2} = 21$ min at 30°; $E_a = 25.0$ kcal/mole.

order kinetics, but as the solvent is the reactant this gives no information as to the molecularity of these reactions. One very likely possibility is that rearrangements occur as a result of water exchange. This could of course be checked by the use of oxygen-18 experiments. However, on the assumption that this is correct, it is apparent that isomerization can take place as was described above for $Co(en)_2Cl_2{}^+$. Furthermore, if the isomerization does involve water exchange, then the rapid rate for the aquahydroxo ions compared to the diaqua and dihydroxo is understood. In acid solution the diaqua complex undergoes water exchange by a relatively slow acid-hydrolysis-type reaction, whereas the extremely rapid ($\sim 10^6$ faster than acid hydrolysis) base hydrolysis reaction makes an appreciable contribution to the total hydrolysis rate responsible for water exchange (isomerization) of an aqueous solution (pH 7–8) of the aquahydroxo ions. Furthermore the hydroxo group probably labilizes the water ligand by π bonding.[10b] The slow rate of isomerization of the dihydroxo complex in alkali may be due to the relatively strong Co—O bond in Co—OH compared to Co—OH₂ which prevents rapid exchange with the solvent. One final point of interest is that the rate of isomerization of the diaqua complex is approximately ten times faster in the presence of charcoal (p. 355).

Diaquadiaxolatochromate(III) ion. A solution of $K[Cr(H_2O)_2-(C_2O_4)_2]$ at equilibrium consists almost entirely of the *cis* isomer, but if such a solution is allowed to evaporate slowly the less soluble *trans* isomer separates first.[17] The kinetics of isomerization of the *trans* isomer into the *cis* form in aqueous solution have been investigated.[18] Spectrophotometric measurements were made at 415 mμ, since the *cis* ion absorbs considerably more and its absorption bands are slightly shifted toward the red as compared to the *trans* form. The rate of isomerization is first order with respect to the complex and independent of hydrogen ion concentration over the pH range 1.85 to 4.28. There is a slight increase in rate with increase in ionic strength.

It was suggested that isomerization can occur upon collision of the *trans* complex ion with a properly oriented water molecule. The water then occupies the position vacated by one end of the oxalate ligand, which in turn is kept in the vicinity of the chromium(III) by hydrogen bonding with two adjacent water molecules. This oxalate end can re-attach itself to the same position, in which case there is no net change, or it can replace one of the *trans* aqua groups to yield the *cis* isomer. An alternative mechanism, which appears somewhat more plausible, is one that does not necessitate the opening up of the stable oxalato chelate rings. In such a case the isomerization takes place by the exchange of coordinated water with the solvent accompanied by re-arrangements of the type described earlier. Whether or not either of these mechanisms is involved must await oxygen-18 experiments in order to compare the rate of water exchange with the rate of isomerization. It would also be helpful to know the extent and rate of exchange of oxalate oxygen with oxygen of the solvent (p. 272).

1,10-Bis(salicylideneamino)-4,7-dithiodecanecobalt(III) ion. The examples of *cis-trans* isomerization described above involve an intermolecular mechanism, whereas in the discussion to follow a unique example of isomerization by an intramolecular process is related. This example was found for a particular type of sexadentate complex of cobalt(III). Dwyer and Lions [19] have prepared many coordination compounds using sexadentate ligands of the type

$$CH{=}N(CH_2)_xS(CH_2)_yS(CH_2)_zN{=}CH$$
$$OH \qquad\qquad HO$$

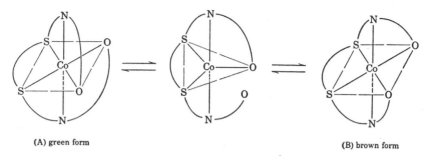

(A) green form   (B) brown form

Fig. 3. Intramolecular isomerization of 1,10-bis(salicylindeneamino)-4,7-dithio-decanecobalt(III) ion by a dissociation mechanism.

where x, y, and z may be either two or three. Whenever $x = y = z = 2$, a green cobalt(III) compound is isolated, whereas, if $x = y = z = 3$, a brown-colored product is obtained. Since the $C{=}N{-}C$ grouping must be linear, this is possible in the green compound, with rigid five-membered chelate rings, only if the two chelate rings formed by $S{-}N{-}O$ lie in the same plane (Fig. 3, A). However, the greater flexibility of the six-membered chelate rings permits the existence of structure B which is assigned to the brown form. Both the green and the brown forms were isolated for complexes in which either $x = z = 3$, $y = 2$, or $x = y = 3$, $z = 2$. The green isomer is the stable form in solution so that gentle warming of a solution of the brown cation results in its rearrangement to the green isomer. However, as the brown iodide is less soluble than the green, if a solution of the green iodide is heated it will slowly yield crystals of the brown iodide. Excellent proof that this isomerization takes place by an intramolecular process is offered by the observation that these optically active complexes isomerize without any loss of optical rotation. Thus, because of the extremely limited freedom of movement of the sexadentate ligand, the oxygen atoms must interchange position by way of a trigonal bipyramid intermediate (Fig. 3). The only difference between this intramolecular process and the intermolecular mechanisms described earlier is that in this complex the ligand atom that becomes unattached is not liberated into the solution but rather is held in the coordination sphere as part of the chelate molecule. It would appear that an aqua intermediate may form when the chelating group behaves as a quinquidentate. Therefore reference to this as an intramolecular process is not strictly correct.

cis-trans ISOMERIZATION OF SQUARE COMPLEXES

Geometrical isomers of square complexes of Ni(II), Pd(II), and Pt(II) have been isolated.[20] Square complexes of Ni(II) and Pd(II), unlike those of Pt(II), are generally sufficiently labile so that any given reaction may yield only one isomer: that which is the more stable or the least soluble under the conditions of the experiment. However, in a few cases it has been possible to isolate both isomers,[21] and some of these were observed to undergo isomerization. For example, two interconvertible forms of the complex bis-benzylmethylglyoximato)-nickel(II) (Fig. 4) have been observed.[22] A β form, much more soluble in cold acetone, can be separated from a less soluble α form. If the β form is quickly heated it melts at 76°C (mp of α form is 168°C), but if heated gradually it melts at 152°C. Above 120°C the solid isomerizes to an equilibrium mixture of α and β forms which melts at 152°C. This mixture may be extracted with acetone to give the β form in solution and leave behind the insoluble α form. Similar interconvertible forms are reported for analogous nickel(II) complexes where the benzyl group in the glyoxime is replaced by n-propyl and by n-butyl.[23] Essentially the same observation was also made [24] on the compound bis(benzylmethylglyoximato)palladium(II). The structures of these α and β glyoximato complexes are not known, and although it appears logical that they are cis-trans isomers there is as yet no definite proof that this is correct. In some instances the isolation of two different forms of a complex has been erroneously attributed to cis-trans isomerism. A good example of this is the case of $Te(CH_3)_2I_2$, where one of the two forms was later shown to be $[Te(CH_3)_3I][Te(CH_3)I_3]$.[25] The isomerization of dipicolinatocop-

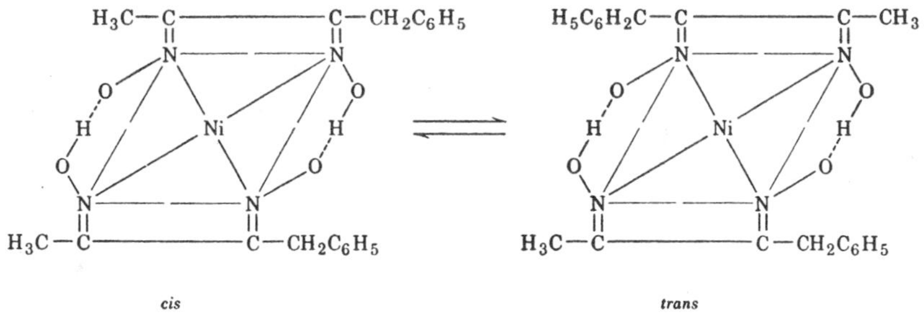

FIG. 4.   cis-trans isomerization of bis(benzylmethylglyoximato)nickel(II).

per (II) [26] and of diglycinatopalladium (II) [27] have also been reported.

Some platinum (II) complexes are known to isomerize in solution, but more often these resist isomerization. This is partly due to the inertness of these compounds. However, even when reactions of platinum (II) complexes do occur these do not generally lead to a stereo change (Chapter 4). Therefore, although in solution an equilibrium of the type

$$PtA_2X_2 + solvent \rightleftharpoons PtA_2X(solvent)^+ + X^- \qquad (7)$$

might exist, it does not give rise to isomerization.

Neither kinetic nor exchange studies have as yet been reported on square complexes that undergo cis-trans isomerization, and at present the mechanism of these rearrangements is not known. Chatt and Wilkins [28] have, however, collected an appreciable amount of thermodynamic data on cis-trans equilibria in benzene solutions of $Pt(MR_3)_2X_2$, where M = P, As, and Sb; R = methyl to n-pentyl; X = Cl^- and I^-. Both cis- and trans-$Pt(PEt_3)_2Cl_2$ are stable in benzene solution at room temperature, but, if a trace of triethylphosphine is added, then isomerization to an equilibrium mixture is complete within a half hour. This equilibration can be quenched by the addition of $(Pt(PEt_3)_2Cl_2)_2$, which removes the catalyst as shown in reaction 8.

$$(8)$$

Since the cis isomer has a dipole moment of 10.7 debyes, whereas the trans isomer has a zero moment, it is possible to determine the amount of these two isomers at equilibrium by measuring the dielectric constant of their benzene solutions. Measurements were made at different temperatures, and the thermodynamic data summarized in Table 2 was calculated. These data are of interest on several accounts. In the first place it has generally been assumed that the trans isomer of square complexes is the more stable and that heat is evolved in the transformation of a cis isomer into the trans form. The data in Table 2 clearly show that this is not correct, that heat is in fact absorbed in this process, and that the greater stability of the trans isomer is a result of an increase in entropy. This increase in entropy is attributable to the greater solvation of the highly dipolar cis isomer such that isomer-

Table 2 *

Thermodynamic Data for the Isomerizations
cis-PtA₂X₂ ⇌ trans-PtA₂X₂ in Benzene at 25°C

Complex	% cis Isomer at Equilibrium	K	$-\Delta F$, cal	ΔH, cal	ΔS, cals/ mole/degree
Pt(PEt₃)₂Cl₂	7.5	12.2	1480	2470	13.3
Pt(PPr₃)₂Cl₂	3.3	29.5	2000	1980	13.3
Pt(PPr₃)₂I₂	0.55	180	...	...	...
Pt(PBr₃)₂Cl₂	3.77	25.5	...	...	...
Pt(AsEt₃)₂Cl₂	0.57	176	3070	1180	14.2
Pt(SbEt₃)₂Cl₂	34.4	1.90	380	2410	9.4
Pt(SbEt₃)₂I₂	21	290	...	...	...
Pd(SbEt₃)₂Cl₂	6.0	15.7	...	...	...

* From reference 28.

ization to the *trans* form is accompanied by the release of benzene. Something of the order of two moles of benzene liberated per mole of *cis* complex converted would be sufficient to account for the observed entropy increase. It was estimated that the total bond energy of the *cis* isomer is approximately 10 kcal greater than that of the corresponding *trans* complex. This is explained in terms of the contribution made by π bonding to the total bond energy.

The influence of π bonding for a typical set of isomers, *cis-* and *trans-*Pt(PR₃)₂Cl₂, is schematically represented in Fig. 5. The size of the dots designate the contribution of π bonding to the total bond strength. Both Cl and P have vacant d orbitals so that they can both accept electrons from the platinum to form dd-π bonds. Since phosphorus has a greater *trans* effect than does chlorine, it is assumed that Pt—P has more double bond character than has Pt—Cl. Whenever the phosphorus atoms are attached in *trans* positions they compete with one another for the d_{yz} (the P—Pt—P bond is designated as the y axis) electron pair of the platinum, but if they are in *cis* positions each competes with the chloro group for the two sets of electron pairs (d_{xz} and d_{yz}). It therefore follows that these electron pairs will be more ef-

Fig. 5. π bonding in *cis-* and *trans-*Pt(PR₃)₂Cl₂. The extent of double bonding is represented by the size of the dots. (From reference 28.)

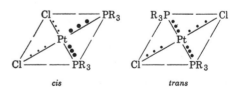

ficiently utilized in the latter case (*cis* isomer) because of the smaller tendency of chlorine to form π bonds compared to phosphorus.

Data in Table 2 also show the effect of various systematic changes in PtA_2X_2 on the *cis-trans* equilibrium. The percentage of *cis* isomer at equilibrium increases in the order As $<$ P $<$ Sb. The difference between the arsenic and phosphorus series is largely due to a change in the heat of isomerization, but that between the phosphorus and antimony series is due to a change in entropy. For a series in which only the alkyl groups change, the equilibrium lies increasingly towards the *trans* isomer as R goes from methyl to *n*-propyl and then levels off to *n*-pentyl. This stabilization of the *trans* form is probably mainly steric in origin because differences between the inductive effects of the alkyl groups is small for these complexes.[29] Replacement of chlorine by iodine in a given complex results in a large shift of the equilibrium towards the *trans* isomer. This is perhaps due to the greater double bond character in Pt—I compared to Pt—Cl such that its competition with phosphorus for the π electrons is favored over that of chlorine. Therefore, it is apparent from Fig. 5 that there will be a smaller difference in bond energy between any two iodo isomers than there is between the two corresponding chloro isomers. Finally a comparison of $Pt(SbEt_3)_2Cl_2$ with $Pd(SbEt_3)_2Cl_2$ reveals that the palladium(II) complex contains far less *cis* isomer at equilibrium than does the platinum(II) compound. In fact the amount of *cis* isomers in benzene solutions of phosphine and arsine complexes of palladium(II) is too small to detect by the method of dielectric constant measurements. This may be due to a greater amount of π bonding in the platinum(II) compared to palladium(II) complexes, which in turn creates a larger stabilizing effect in favor of the *cis* isomer.

Thus although *cis-trans* isomerizations of platinum(II) complexes are not common, they do occur. These isomerizations appear to require a trace of some catalyst. This suggests that the mechanism is intermolecular and involves a trigonal bipyramid intermediate as discussed for substitutions in "square" complexes (Chapter 4, Fig. 9). However, this reaction process leads to retention of configuration. In order that rearrangement, or in this case, isomerization, takes place it is necessary that at least two "dissociation" steps be involved (Fig. 6). The first step is the replacement of the chloro group by the catalyst trialkylphosphine to form $[Pt(PR_3)_3Cl]Cl$ (B). In the second step the reverse happens, and the complex $Pt(PR_3)_2Cl_2$ is formed along with the catalyst PEt_3. If this second step goes through trigonal bipyramid A, then the original *cis* isomer is regenerated, but, if it goes

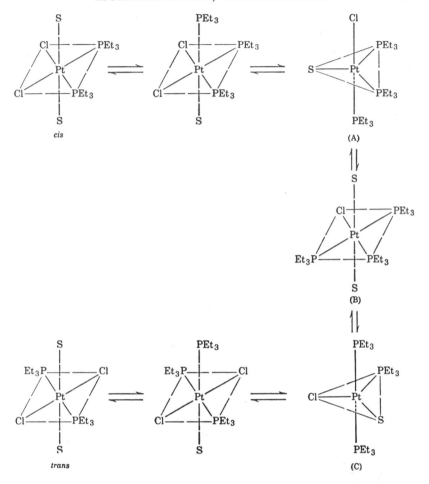

FIG. 6. Possible mechanism for the PR_3-catalyzed *cis-trans* isomerization of $Pt(PR_3)_2Cl_2$.

through C, then the *trans* isomer is formed. Mechanisms of this type
were suggested for the isomerization of $Pt(SEt_2)_2Cl_2$ in solutions
containing excess diethylsulfide [30] and for $Pd(NH_3)_2(NO_2)_2$ in aqueous
ammoniacal solutions containing nitrite ion.[31]

This tentative mechanism is consistent with the information now
available that (1) *cis-trans* isomerizations of the more labile nickel(II)
and palladium(II) square complexes are rapid, presumably as a result
of displacements involving the solvent, (2) the more inert platinum(II)

complexes isomerize only in the presence of a catalyst which is known to be a good displacing reagent, (3) "square" complexes in reality have a tetragonal structure, and (4) theoretical considerations favor a trigonal bipyramid intermediate for systems with π-bonding ligands. Other mechanisms that can lead to isomerization of square complexes without excessive atomic motion are an intramolecular rearrangement with a tetrahedral intermediate and an S_N1 process with a symmetrical planar trigonal intermediate. On the basis of our present knowledge neither one of these two mechanisms is as satisfactory as the proposed two-step process, but it is obvious that this awaits rigorous testing by kinetic and exchange experiments on these systems.

NITRITO-NITRO ISOMERIZATION

Nitrito (M—ONO) complexes of cobalt(III) were first described by Jørgensen,[32] who also observed that they rearrange to the corresponding nitro (M—NO$_2$) compounds. The suggestion [33] that nitrito complexes do not exist has been proven to be incorrect,[34] and there is indeed an abundance of experimental evidence in support of nitrito-nitro isomerizations in complex ions. The mechanism of formation of nitrito complexes was discussed earlier (p. 160). The discussion that follows will summarize what is known about the process of conversion of nitrito complexes into the corresponding stable nitro form.

Adell [35, 38] has made an extensive investigation of the nitrito-nitro isomerization. Some of his data are collected in Table 3. The rates of rearrangement were determined spectrophotometrically, and in all cases the data were found to give a first-order plot. Measurements were made on the solid salts as well as their aqueous solution, with the observed result that isomerization is ten to one hundred times faster in solution. This can be only approximate because the rate of isomerization of the solids depends on the anion portion of the salt, e.g., $[Co(NH_3)_5(ONO)]X_2$, where $X = Cl^-$, I^-, and NO_3^- in Table 3.* It was concluded that, since the solid salts isomerize, this must happen by an intramolecular process. Such need not necessarily be true of rearrangements in solution. However, it was suggested [39] that this must

---

* Although in the investigations by Adell (Table 3A) the solid-state reactions were regarded as first-order processes in which nitrito is completely converted to nitro, recent infrared studies (I. R. Beattie and D. P. N. Satchell, *Trans. Faraday Soc.*, **52**, 1590 (1956)) show that the isomerization of $[Co(NH_3)_5(ONO)]Cl_2$ in potassium chloride disks is essentially an equilibrium process. Therefore the data in Table 3A should be used with some reservations.

Table 3

Rates of Nitrito-Nitro Isomerization at 20°C

Complex	k_1, min^{-1}	k_2, min^{-1}	E_{a_1}, kcal/mole	E_{a_2}, kcal/mole	Reference
(A) Solids					
[Co(NH$_3$)$_5$(ONO)]Cl$_2$	5.5×10^{-5}	...	22.4	...	35
[Co(NH$_3$)$_5$(ONO)]I$_2$	1.0×10^{-5}	...	26.3	...	35
[Co(NH$_3$)$_5$(ONO)](NO$_3$)$_2$	2.7×10^{-4}	...	.21.9	...	35
trans-[Co(en)$_2$(NCS)-(ONO)]I	2.3×10^{-5}	...	25.5	...	35
trans-[Co(en)$_2$(NCS)-(ONO)]ClO$_4$	1.6×10^{-5}	...	25.1	...	35
trans-[Co(py)$_2$(NH$_3$)$_2$-(ONO)$_2$]NO$_3$	2×10^{-4}	4×10^{-5} *	19.9	24.7	36
cis-[Co(en)$_2$(ONO)$_2$]NO$_3$	3×10^{-4}	4×10^{-5} *	19.3	25.0	37
trans-[Co(en)$_2$(ONO)$_2$]-NO$_3$	3×10^{-5}	7×10^{-5} *	28.0	23.8	37
(B) Aqueous Solutions					
Co(NH$_3$)$_5$(ONO)$^{2+}$	1.0×10^{-3}	...	22.6	...	38
Co(NH$_3$)$_4$(H$_2$O)(ONO)$^{2+}$	2.3×10^{-2}	(30°C)			16
cis-Co(NH$_3$)$_4$(ONO)$_2$$^+$	1.1×10^{-2}		8.3		16
cis-Co(en)$_2$(NO$_2$)(ONO)$^+$	4.5×10^{-2}	(35°C)			39

* Dinitrito complexes rearrange stepwise in the solid; thus k_1 is the value estimated for the formation of nitrito-nitro, and k_2 for its conversion to the final product dinitro.

also be the mechanism in solution because the rates of isomerization in solutions containing no excess nitrite ion are far too great to be compatible with an intermolecular process. That this is correct was recently conclusively demonstrated by studies with oxygen 18.

Murmann and Taube [40] found that neither the oxygen attached to cobalt and nitrogen nor that attached only to nitrogen exchanges with the solvent or with added nitrite ion in the transformation

$$(NH_3)_5Co—*ONO^{2+}$$
$$\text{or} \quad \Big\rangle \xrightarrow[\text{NO}_2]{\text{H}_2\text{O}} (NH_3)_5Co—N*O_2^{2+} \qquad (9)$$
$$(NH_3)_5Co—ON*O^{2+}$$

The same result was obtained with cis-Co(en)$_2$(NO$_2$)(ONO)$^+$ Furthermore this optically active cation mutarotates, with no racemization, at the same rate as its isomerization to the dinitro complex.

These results furnish excellent proof of the fact that the nitrito ligand is not released from the immediate coordination sphere of the complex during its rearrangement to the nitro form. An S_Ni (*substitution, nucleophilic, internal displacement*) type mechanism has been suggested.

$$(NH_3)_5Co—ONO^{2+} \rightarrow (NH_3)_5Co\underset{N—O}{\overset{O}{<}} {}^{2+} \rightarrow (NH_3)_5Co—NO_2^{2+} \tag{10}$$

One other point of interest is the observation [38] that the rates of isomerization in aqueous solution are retarded by the presence of acid. Different acids show different effects, and the effectiveness decreases in the order $HCl > HClO_4 > HNO_3$. Although this acid retardation of the rate of isomerization at low acid concentration does not appear to be accompanied by decomposition, it was found [40] that, if nitrogen is bubbled through a reaction mixture with $\sim 0.07\ N$ acid, then one detects small quantities of oxides of nitrogen and the aqua complex. Since the rate of water exchange of $Co(NH_3)_5H_2O^{3+}$, in this acid region, is essentially independent of hydrogen ion concentration,[41] it would seem that the replacement of coordinated water by nitrite ion is not operative. It has been suggested [40] that the decreased rate of formation of $Co(NH_3)_5NO_2^{2+}$ in slightly acid solutions is due to an equilibrium which removes a portion of the nitrito complex,

$$(NH_3)_5Co—OH_2^{3+} + HNO_2 \underset{H_3O^+}{\overset{fast}{\rightleftharpoons}}$$

$$(NH_3)_5Co—ONO^{2+} \xrightarrow{slow} (NH_3)_5Co—NO_2^{2+} \tag{11}$$

That different acids have different effects for the same hydrogen ion concentration is perhaps due to salt or ion pair effects or both.

RACEMIZATION OF OCTAHEDRAL COMPLEXES

The racemization of optically active coordination compounds often is rapid compared to that of carbon compounds. It should of course be remembered that, just as there are carbon compounds which racemize rapidly, there are also coordination compounds which racemize very slowly. Labile complexes racemize rapidly, and in most cases it has not been possible to resolve ions of this type.[42]   However, the resolution of certain labile complexes such as $Al(C_2O_4)_3{}^{3-}$, $Ga(C_2O_4)_3{}^{3-}$, $Fe(C_2O_4)_3{}^{3-}$, $Cd(en)_3{}^{2+}$, and $Zn(en)_3{}^{2+}$ has been reported (Table 4).   Attempts to repeat the resolution of the aluminum(III) and iron(III) complexes were not successful.[42, 43] *   If these ions are indeed resolvable, then it must mean that interconversions of dextro and levo forms is slow, although the coordinated groups undergo rapid substitution.   In spite of these few exceptions it still is true that the bulk of the optically active complexes (Table 4) are found among the inert compounds.

The rate of loss of optical activity of aqueous solutions of these compounds varies from extremely rapid to extremely slow.   In many cases the rates are such that they can be followed by conventional techniques.   The question of how coordination compounds undergo this loss of optical activity has long been of interest to coordination chemists.   A consideration of molecular models reveals that octahedral complexes can racemize either by an intermolecular or an intramolecular process.   Examples of both processes will be cited, as well as one where both mechanisms contribute to the total racemization.

Intermolecular mechanism.   The term intermolecular is used here because it is felt that the more common usage of dissociation might imply an S_N1 process.   It is desirable to avoid this confusion, since in most cases the molecularity of these intermolecular reactions is not as yet known.   Whenever the term dissociation is used in the discussion that follows, it will refer only to the formation of a lower complex, e.g., $M(AA)_3 \rightleftharpoons M(AA)_2 + AA$, and implies nothing as to the role played by the solvent in this process.

Thomas[94] suggested that the racemization of $M(C_2O_4)_3{}^{3-}$ takes place by an intermolecular process involving a planar intermediate $M(C_2O_4)_2{}^{-}$.   The fact that such an intermediate is symmetrical would then account for the loss in optical rotation.   A more plausible intermediate would be the diaqua complex $M(C_2O_4)_2(H_2O)_2{}^{-}$, thus maintaining the coordination number of six for the central metal ion.   Regardless of the exact nature of the intermediate, its formation does permit rearrangements that can result in loss of optical activity.

The intermolecular mechanism of racemization has been established

---

* Recent studies on the chromatographic resolution of metal complexes on starch at $-35\,°C$ failed for the complexes $Al(C_2O_4)_3{}^{3-}$, $Zn(en)_3{}^{2+}$, $Cd(en)_3{}^{2+}$, and $Ni(en)_3{}^{2+}$, but some optical rotation was detected for a solution of $Fe(C_2O_4)_3{}^{3-}$ (H. Krebs, J. Diewald, H. Arlitt, and J. A. Wagner, *Z. anorg. u. allgem. Chem.*, **287**, 98 (1956).

Table 4

Some Optically Active Six-Coordinated Complex Ions [a]

Compound	$[\alpha]_D$	Reference	Remarks [b]
Aluminum(III):			
$K_3[Al(C_2O_4)_3]3H_2O$	34°	44	$t_{1/2}$ (R.T.) 1–50 hr; failure to resolve complex [42,43]
$K_3[Al(C_6H_4O_2)_3]1.5H_2O$	61.7	45	
$[Al(CH=N(CH_2)_2NHCH_2\!-\!\!\overset{O}{\underset{C_6H_5}{}})_2]NO_3$	124.4	46a	$t_{1/2}$ (R.T.) 2-3 hr in methanol
Arsenic(V):			
$K[As(C_6H_4O_2)_3]\cdot H_2O$	460	47	no rac. in alkali for hours at R.T. but rapid in acid
Cadmium(II):			
$[Cd(en)_3]Cl_2$	113.7	48	complete rac. in solution in 1.5 hr, in solid in 2 hr
Chromium(III):			
$K_3[Cr(C_2O_4)_3]\cdot 1H_2O$	1,300 [c]	49, 50	$t_{1/2}$ (18.2°C) = 67 min
$K[Cr(en)(C_2O_4)_2]\cdot 2H_2O$	578	50	$t_{1/2}$ (19°C) = 8.4 min
$[Cr(en)_2C_2O_4]Cl\cdot 3H_2O$	266	50	no rac., decomposition after 12 hr at 18°C
$[Cr(en)_3]I_3$	60	51	no rac., R.T.
$[Cr(en)_2Cl_2]Cl$	140 [d]	52	$t_{1/2}$ (R.T.) $\sim$ 1 hr
Cobalt(III):			
$K_3[Co(C_2O_4)_3]\cdot H_2O$	2,620	50, 53	$t_{1/2}$ (37.5°C) = 66 min
$Co(aeoc)_3$ [b]	300	54	rac. soln. 12 hr; solid more than 3 days; rac. of $Cr(aeoc)_3$ slower, $Fe(aeoc)_3$ very fast
$[Co(en)_2C_2O_4]Cl\cdot 3H_2O$	646	50, 55	no rac. after 5 days at 18°C; decomp. on long boiling
$[Co(en)_3]Cl_3$	155	56, 57	no rac. in 1 day at 90°C but rac. complete in 2 min in presence of charcoal

Compound		Ref.	Notes
[Co(en)₂Cl₂]Cl	630	9, 58, 59	in H₂O at 30°C $t_{1/2}$ M.R. = 23 min, $t_{1/2}$ rac. = 430 min; in CH₃OH at 35.8°C $t_{1/2}$ (rac.) = 110 min
[Co(en)₂F₂]NO₃	220	60	$t_{1/2}$ M.R. (25°C) = 23 hr, $t_{1/2}$ rac. = 58 hr
[Co(en)₂(NO₂)Cl]Cl	52	9, 61	M.R. complete in 4–5 hr, not rac. after 2 mo
[Co(en)₂(NCS)Cl]ClO₄·H₂O	560	9, 62	M.R. complete in 2 days, not rac. after 50 days
[Co(en)₂(NH₃)Br]Br₂·2H₂O	46	9, 63	20% M.R. in 20 days, not rac. after 5 mo
$\left[Co \left\langle \begin{array}{c} H \\ O \end{array} \right\rangle Co(NH_3)_4 \right]_3 Br_6 \cdot 2H_2O$	2,620	64	rapid rac. in water, slower in 50% acetone
$\left[Co \left\langle \begin{array}{c} H \\ O \end{array} \right\rangle Co(en)_2 \right]_3 (SbOC_4H_4O_6)_6$ α, ·18H₂O	3,920	65	$t_{1/2}$ (40°C) α = 2.5 hr, β = 25 hr
β, ·9H₂O	3,620		
K[Co(EDTA)]·3H₂O	150	66, 67	$t_{1/2}$ (100°C) = 170 min
$Co \left[CH{=}N(CH_2)_3SCH_2{-} \right]_2$	11,800	19	M.R. in alcohol at 70°C, then slower rac.
$Co \left[CH{=}N(CH_2)_2NHCH_2{-} \right]_2$	250	46a	
[Co(trien)Cl₂]Cl	100	46a	
[Co(en)₂(dabp)]Cl₃	α, 70 / β, 60	46b	no rac. dabp = 2,2-diaminobiphenyl

Table 4 (Continued)

Compound	$[\alpha]_D$	Reference	Remarks [b]
Gallium(III):			
$K_3[Ga(C_2O_4)_3]\cdot 3H_2O$	16.5	68	10% rac. in 2 hr at R.T., failure to resolve complex [43b]
Germanium(IV):			
$K_2[Ge(C_2O_4)_3]$	80	69	complete rac. (R.T.) in 1–2 days
Iridium(III):			
$K_3[Ir(C_2O_4)_3]\cdot 2H_2O$	82	70	no rac.
$K_3Ir(C_2O_4)_2Cl_2]$	24	70	H_2O soln. at 130°C isomerizes to *trans*
$[Ir(en)_3]Br_3\cdot 3H_2O$	50	71	no rac.
$[Ir(en)_2(NO_2)_2]Br$	26	71	no rac.
Iron(II) and (III):			
$K_3[Fe(C_2O_4)_3]\cdot 3H_2O$	356	72	$t_{1/2}$ (R.T.) 15 min; failure to resolve complex [42,43]
$[Fe(bipy)_3](ClO_4)_2\cdot 2H_2O$	4,800	73, 74	$t_{1/2}$ (25°C) = 38 min
$[Fe(bipy)_3](ClO_4)_3\cdot 3H_2O$	260 [c]	74	$t_{1/2}$ (25°C) = 2.4 min
$[Fe(phen)_3](ClO_4)_2\cdot 3H_2O$	1,432	75	$t_{1/2}$ (25°C) = 35 min
$[Fe(phen)_3]^{3+}$	...	76	$t_{1/2}$ (25°C) = 0.4 min
	2,000	77	rac. (100°C) ~ 2 min
	545	46	
Nickel(II):			
$[Ni(bipy)_3]Cl_2\cdot 6H_2O$	529 [c]	78	$t_{1/2}$ (24.7°C) = 10 min
$[Ni(phen)_3](ClO_4)_2$	1,460	79	$t_{1/2}$ (25°C) = 34 hr
$[Ni(CH_3—phen)_3]Br_2\cdot 7H_2O$	600	80	$t_{1/2}$ (34.8°C) = 9.7 hr

Osmium(II), (III):			
[Os(bipy)₃]I₂·3H₂O	81	0	$[\alpha]_{5461} = 2200$, no rac.
[Os(bipy)₃](ClO₄)₃·H₂O	82	0	$[\alpha]_{5461} = 250$, no rac.
[Os(phen)₃](ClO₄)₂·H₂O	83	0	$[\alpha]_{5461} = 3670$, no rac.
[Os(phen)₃](ClO₄)₃·H₂O	74	0	$[\alpha]_{5461} = 400$, no rac.
Platinum(IV):			
[Pt(en)₃]Cl₄·3H₂O	84	86	no rac.
[Pt(pn)₃]Cl₄·H₂O	85	180	no rac.
[Pt(en)₂Cl₂](d-C₁₀H₁₄SO₄Br)₂	86	+65.5	M.R. to $[\alpha]_D = +55.5$ at 100°C with $t_{\frac{1}{2}} \sim 20$ hr
Rhodium(III):			
K₃[Rh(C₂O₄)₃]·H₂O	87	0	$[\alpha]_{6563} = 26.4$; $[\alpha]_{5876} = 114$; no rac.
Na[Rh(NHSO₂NH)₂(H₂O)₂]	88	8.8	no rac. at R.T.; 30% rac. (decomp.) at 100°C in 1 hr
[Rh(en)₃]I₃	89	50	no rac.
Ruthenium(II), (III):			
[Ru(bipy)₃]I₂·3H₂O	90	819	no rac.
[Ru(phen)₃](ClO₄)₂·2H₂O	91	979	no rac.
[Ru(bipy)₃]³⁺	90	465	rapid rac. at R.T.
[Ru(phen)₃]³⁺	91	311	rapid rac. at R.T.
Titanium(IV):			
(NH₄)₂[Ti(C₆H₄O₂)₃]	92	790	rapid rac.
Zinc(II):			
[Zn(en)₃]Cl₂	93	94	rac., soln. 2.3 hr; solid, 6 hr

a For a more complete listing of optically active octahedral complexes see F. Basolo, *Chem. Revs.*, **52**, 459 (1953).
b $t_{\frac{1}{2}}$ is half-life for loss of optical rotation (rac.); M.R. is mutarotation; no rac. means no change in optical rotation of a solution on standing at R.T. (room temperature) for several days.
c $[\alpha]_{5461}$.
d White light.
e $[\alpha]_{5270}$.
f Red light.

in two cases. One of these is the racemization of dextro tris(1,10-phenanthroline)nickel(II) and dextro tris(2,2′-bipyridine)nickel(II) ions in aqueous solution.[95] The other is that of levo *cis*-bis(ethylene-diamine)dichlorocobalt(III) ion in methanol solution,[59] where the loss of optical rotation is largely due to isomerization rather than racemization. The conclusion had been reached[96] that the nickel(II) complexes racemize by an intramolecular process. This mechanism was assigned because the rates of racemization were not altered by the presence of excess chelating agent. It was presumed[96] that the rate of racemization should decrease upon addition of excess chelating agent if an intermolecular mechanism, $Ni(phen)_3^{2+} \rightleftharpoons Ni(phen)_2^{2+} + phen$, is involved, because of the increased rate of the backward reaction. However, it is clear that, if the bis complex were either symmetrical or very rapidly lost its optical activity, then the presence of chelating agent would not be expected to change the rate of racemization.[95] It was further observed that the rates of dissociation and racemization are the same, which is the best diagnosis of an intermolecular mechanism.

The dissociation was observed in solutions of relatively high acid concentration because the 1,10-phenanthroline or 2,2′-bipyridine formed in dissociation

$$Ni(AA)_3^{2+} \overset{slow}{\rightleftharpoons} Ni(AA)_2^{2+} + (AA) \tag{12}$$

reacts rapidly with the acid

$$H^+ + (AA) \overset{fast}{\rightleftharpoons} H(AA)^+ \tag{13}$$

Since the products formed differ in color from the reactants, the rate of dissociation was conveniently followed by measurements of optical density at predetermined wavelengths. These results were compared with the rates of racemization determined at the same experimental conditions. The rate constants for racemization were based on the reactions

$$d\text{-}Ni(AA)_3^{2+} \overset{k}{\rightleftharpoons} \text{optically inactive products} \underset{k}{\rightleftharpoons} l\text{-}Ni(AA)_3^{2+} \tag{14}$$

such that the rate constant, k, is obtained from the slope, m, of the usual first-order plot, by the relationship $k = -2.303m$. Alternatively if the reaction is considered a direct inversion

$$d\text{-}Ni(AA)_3^{2+} \underset{k'}{\overset{k'}{\rightleftharpoons}} l\text{-}Ni(AA)_3^{2+} \tag{15}$$

then k' is found from the same plot to be given by $k' = -\frac{1}{2}(2.303m)$. The first method allows a direct comparison of rate constants, k, for dissociation and racemization. Some of the results obtained are illustrated in Fig. 7. The identical rates and activation energies for the two processes clearly show that in acid solution the racemization does proceed by dissociation, an intermolecular mechanism. The question then arises as to whether this is still true in neutral solution where the dissociation cannot be measured by this technique. There are two indications that the mechanism of racemization in water is the same as in acid: the first is that the activation energies for dissociation in acid and for racemization in water are the same, and the second is the continuous similar behavior of the two rates as a function of acidity. Final proof that this is correct was obtained recently [97] by exchange studies using radiocarbon in 1,10-phenanthroline. These studies also show that the intermolecular mechanism persists in alkaline solutions up to pH $\sim$13.

The actual configuration of the complex ion resulting from dissociation is not known, nor is anything known about the exact nature of the rearrangements which lead to a loss of optical rotation. It is apparent from the discussion in the previous chapter that several hypotheses are

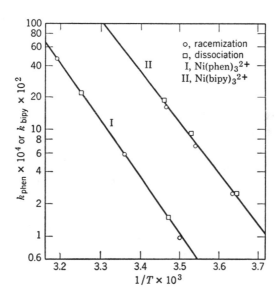

Fig. 7. Temperature dependence for reactions of $Ni(phen)_3{}^{2+}$ and $Ni(bipy)_3{}^{2+}$. (From reference 95.)

consistent with the observations, the only limitation being that the dissociated product is either symmetrical or loses its optical activity rapidly with respect to the rate at which recombination occurs. This restriction is imposed by the observation that excess chelating agent does not retard the rate of racemization.

Brown and Ingold [59] report another example of racemization occurring by an intermolecular process. They find that the rate of loss of optical activity ($k = 1.35 \pm 0.03 \times 10^{-4}$ sec^{-1}) at 35.8°C of a methanol solution of l-Co(en)$_2$Cl$_2^+$ is, within experimental error, equal to the rate of radiochlorine exchange of one chloro group. The simplest mechanism consistent with this observation is that the complex dissociates to a symmetrical five-coordinated intermediate; thus each dissociation leads directly to a loss of optical rotation. The chloride ion then re-enters the complex, 82% of the time forming the *trans* isomer and 18% of the time the racemic *cis* isomer. Therefore this is more a case of isomerization than racemization and was described earlier (p. 244). It is further of interest that the rate of loss of optical activity of methanolic l-*cis*-Co(en)$_2$Cl$_2^+$ is essentially the same in the presence of various reagents (X = Cl$^-$, Br$^-$, NCS$^-$, and NO$_3^-$) which lead to the formation of Co(en)$_2$ClX$^+$. Thus it would appear that all these reactions proceed through the same symmetrical intermediate.

The loss of optical rotation of l-*cis*-Co(en)$_2$Cl$_2^+$ in water solution was studied earlier,[9] and its behavior differs markedly from that in methanol. Although the replacement of coordinated chloride ion in methanol leads directly to loss of optical rotation, its replacement by water in an aqueous solution takes place essentially with retention of configuration. Since it is believed that both the acid hydrolysis reaction in water solution and the chloride exchange in methanol proceed by an S_N1 mechanism, it is obvious that the fate of the five-coordinated intermediate must not be the same. This difference can be explained on the basis that the donor ability of water is much greater than that of methanol. Therefore a water molecule in the outer sphere of the complex will readily slip into the position vacated by the chloro group without permitting any rearrangement. A similar behavior can be expected for methanol, but, because of the more labile Co—O bond, it is likely that there is extensive and rapid exchange of coordinated methanol with the solvent, thus greatly enhancing the possibility of rearrangement.

Mathieu [9] also found that the rate of racemization of the d-*cis*-Co(en)$_2$(H$_2$O)Cl^{2+}, obtained by acid hydrolysis of the dichloro complex, does not depend upon the rate of replacement of the remaining chloro group. In acid solution the racemization rate is approximately twenty-five times faster than the rate of replacement of chloride ion ($t_{1/2}$ at 30°C for racemization, 7 hr; for acid hydrolysis, 167 hr), whereas in alkaline buffers the rate of release of chloride ion may exceed the rate of loss of optical rotation. It was suggested that racemization was due to the dissociation of the aqua complex resulting in the formation of a symmetrical five-coordinated intermediate $Co(en)_2Cl^{2+}$, the same as that designated for the methanol system (Fig. 2). This same intermediate resulting from the acid hydrolysis of d-cis-$Co(en)_2Cl_2^+$ yields the aquachloro complex primarily with retention of configuration. It therefore follows that, if the water exchange mechanism for the racemization of d-cis-$Co(en)_2(H_2O)Cl^{2+}$ is correct, the rate of water exchange must exceed the rate of racemization. Unfortunately studies are not as yet available on the rate of water exchange.

Recent kinetic studies on this system [10a] indicate that the loss of optical rotation does not result from the formation of a symmetrical five-coordinated intermediate but rather is due to *trans* isomerization (Fig. 8). This is based on the observation that the acid hydrolysis of cis-$Co(en)_2Cl_2^+$ yields a mixture of cis- and $trans$-$Co(en)_2(H_2O)$-Cl^{2+}. Mathieu [9] reports that the rate of loss of optical activity of l-cis-$Co(en)_2Cl_2^+$ is ten times slower than its rate of acid hydrolysis. Therefore, since the loss in activity may result either from the formation of the *trans* aquachloro product or its racemic *cis* isomer, it follows that the rate of formation of $trans$-$Co(en)_2(H_2O)Cl^{2+}$ is at most one-tenth the rate of acid hydrolysis. This means that for the reaction sequence represented by

$$l\text{-}cis\text{-}Co(en)_2Cl_2^+ \text{ (A) } \xrightarrow{k}$$

$$d\text{-}cis\text{-}Co(en)_2(H_2O)Cl^{2+} \text{ (B) } \xrightarrow{k'} trans\text{-}Co(en)_2(H_2O)Cl^{2+} \text{ (C)} \quad (16)$$

$K = k'/k = 0.1$, providing this mechanism is correct. Then the maximum concentration of B can be shown to be [98]

$$B_{max} = A_0 K^{K/1-K} \quad (17)$$

and the time at which this is reached by

$$t_{max} = \frac{1}{k(K - 1)} \ln K \quad (18)$$

At 25°C t_{max} is 170 min and B_{max} is $0.77A_0$. The results obtained by this calculation (77% cis- and 23% $trans$-$Co(en)_2Cl_2^+$) are in good agree-

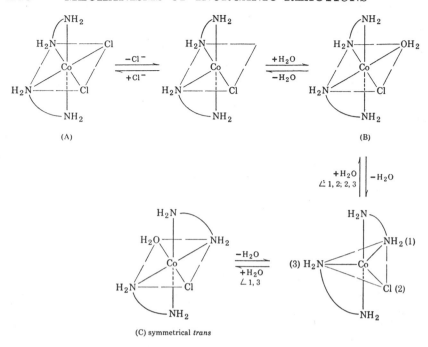

(A)

(B)

$+H_2O$
$\angle$ 1, 2; 2, 3 ‖ $-H_2O$

(3) H_2N

(C) symmetrical *trans*

FIG. 8. Loss of optical rotation of an aqueous solution of *l-cis*-Co(en)$_2$Cl$_2$+ by way of optically inactive *trans*-Co(en)$_2$(H$_2$O)Cl.

ment with the experimentally observed mixture of 79% *cis* and 21% *trans*, and it can therefore be concluded that the original assumption that the loss of optical rotation is a result of the formation of *trans*-Co(en)$_2$(H$_2$O)Cl^{2+} is essentially correct. The racemization results in methanol may also be explained by the formation of an unstable *trans*-Co(en)$_2$(CH$_3$OH)Cl^{2+} and need not involve a symmetrical five-coordinated species.

The rates of loss of optical rotation of aqueous solutions of Co(en)$_2$-XCl complexes where X = NH$_3$, NO$_2^-$, or NCS$^-$ [9] and of *d-cis*-Co(en)$_2$F$_2^+$ [60] have also been investigated.* In all cases the change in optical rotation takes place in two discrete steps. First, as with the dichloro complex just discussed, there is a change to the optical rotation of the aqua complexes and then a racemization of these com-

---

* The rate of loss of optical rotation of an aqueous solution of *l-cis*-Cr(en)$_2$-Cl$_2^+$ has also been found [52b] to take place in two steps similar to that of the analogous cobalt(III) complex.

plexes. The rates of racemization of the complexes $Co(en)_2(H_2O)X$ decrease in the following order of X: $Cl^- > F^- > NO_2^- \sim NCS^- > NH_3$. The rates of water exchange of the aqua complexes are not known, but the rates of acid hydrolysis of cis-$Co(en)_2Cl_2^+$ and of cis-$Co(en)_2(NO)_2Cl^+$ are approximately the same, suggesting that the rates of water exchange of cis-$Co(en)_2(H_2O)Cl^{2+}$ and of cis-$Co(en)_2$-$(H_2O)NO_2^{2+}$ are at least of the same order of magnitude. Yet the aquachloro complex racemizes roughly one hundred times faster than the aquanitro ion. This means that, if the racemization is a result of water exchange, then such exchange in the aquanitro complex takes place with retention of configuration a greater percentage of the time than does exchange in the aquachloro complex. It is further of interest to note that, of the complexes in this series, the aquahalo complexes racemize more readily than the aquathiocyanato, aquanitro, and aqua-amine complexes. One suggestion is that in the last three cases, the water exchange is an S_N2 process. Alternatively it may just mean that the five-coordinated intermediates of $Co(en)_2X$, where $X = Cl^-$ and F^-, retain their configuration a smaller percentage than do the species where $X = NCS^-$, NO_2^-, and NH_3. This is in keeping with π bonding [10b] involving p-electrons on the ligand and the vacant d orbital of the five-coordinated central ion. Such π-bonding can occur with the halo intermediate, thus tending to stabilize a trigonal bipyramid structure which in turn leads to rearrangement.

Intramolecular mechanism. The possibility that complex ions may racemize by an intramolecular mechanism was first suggested by Werner.[99] It has been shown that this is correct for the systems trioxalatocobalt(III) and -chromium(III) ions and also in part for tris(1,10-phenanthroline) and tris(2,2'-bipyridine)iron(II) and -iron-(III) ions. The oxalato complexes have been the subject of extensive studies by Johnson [42] and his students. He took issue with earlier statements [94] that these compounds racemize by an intermolecular process and cited as evidence against this the fact that (1) he was unable to detect any dissociation of $Co(C_2O_4)_3^{3-}$ or $Cr(C_2O_4)_3^{3-}$ in aqueous solution, (2) salts of these complex ions undergo racemization even in the solid state [100] and (3) the rate of racemization is not decreased by the presence of oxalate ion.[101] The last two pieces of evidence, 2 and 3, cannot be accepted as proof that an intermolecular mechanism in water solution is not possible. This question of mechanism was finally settled by studies [102] on the rate of oxalate ion exchange in the systems $Co(C_2O_4)_3^{3-}-^*C_2O_4^{2-}$ and $Cr(C_2O_4)_3^{3-}-^*C_2$-

$O_4{}^{2-}$. No oxalate exchange occurs under conditions that give complete racemization, so it must be concluded that racemization of these ions takes place by an intramolecular mechanism. It is of interest to note that the labile complexes $Al(C_2O_4)_3{}^{3-}$ and $Fe(C_2O_4)_3{}^{3-}$ undergo complete exchange with radiooxalate ion in the time of mixing. There are some differences of opinion [42, 43, 44, 72] as to the resolvability of these complex ions.

The rate of carbonate ion exchange in the system $Co(en)_2CO_3{}^{-}$ - $*CO_3{}^{2-}$ was found to be much more rapid than the rate of racemization of d-$Co(en)_2CO_3{}^{-}$ under the same experimental conditions.[103] Furthermore the racemization reaction bears little kinetic relationship to the exchange, e.g., addition of borate to the reaction mixture inhibits the exchange but accelerates the racemization. Thus it was concluded that racemization must involve an intramolecular mechanism since it clearly does not parallel the carbonate exchange process. However, the system is complicated in that each species of complex ion present at equilibrium racemizes independently such that the total rate expression is

$$\text{Rate} = k_1[Co(en)_2(CO_3)H_2O^+] + k_2[Co(en)_2(CO_3)OH])$$
$$+ k_3[Co(en)_2(HCO_3)H_2O^{2+}] + k_4[Co(en)_2(H_2O)_2{}^{3+}] \quad (19)$$

Certainly in view of these different complex species it is entirely possible that an intermolecular mechanism takes place through either carbonate or water exchange (or both). That racemization is much slower than exchange may just mean that a large percentage of the time exchange takes place with retention of configuration.

Another example of racemization of octahedral complexes by an intramolecular mechanism was observed for the complex ions $Fe(phen)_3{}^{2+}$, $Fe(bipy)_3{}^{2+}$, and $Fe(phen)_3{}^{3+}$. The rates of racemization [104] of these ions are greater than the rates of dissociation.[105] This means that racemization must, at least in part, involve an intramolecular process. Kinetic studies on the racemization and dissociation of the iron(II) complexes, with the same experimental conditions, suggest a dual mechanism.[106a] The data obtained on the iron(II) complexes and, for comparison, the nickel(II) complexes are summarized in Table 5. The intermolecular racemization rates are the spectrophotometrically determined rates of dissociation. Since each dissociation of the nickel(II) complexes leads to loss of optical activity, it is a reasonable assumption that the same behavior is shown by the analogous iron(II) complexes. In any event the fact that the racemiza-

Table 5 *

Rates of Individual Processes Leading to Racemization at 25°C

Complex	Intramolecular Racemization			Intermolecular Racemization		
	k, min^{-1}	E_a, kcal	$\Delta S\ddagger$, eu	k, min^{-1}	E_a, kcal	$\Delta S\ddagger$, eu
Fe(phen)$_3^{2+}$	3.9×10^{-2}	29	21	4.2×10^{-1}	32.1	28
Fe(bipy)$_3^{2+}$ †	1.6×10^{-2}	26	12	4.7×10^{-2}	27.4	17
Ni(phen)$_3^{2+}$	$<6.0 \times 10^{-5}$	...	...	6.0×10^{-4}	25.0	2
Ni(bipy)$_3^{2+}$ †	$<1.4 \times 10^{-1}$	...	...	1.1	21.8	6

* From reference 106a.
† These are the limiting rates in 1 M HCl.

tion is more rapid than the dissociation shows that racemization also takes place by some intramolecular process. The observed rate of racemization will then be the sum of the two rates, and the rate of intramolecular racemization can be obtained by subtracting the rate of dissociation from the total rate. Limiting values designated (Table 5) for the intramolecular racemization of the nickel(II) complexes are based on the failure to observe any racemization by this process.

It is somewhat surprising that the very similar iron(II) and nickel-(II) complexes should racemize by different mechanisms. The two sets of complexes have the same charge and size but differ in stability and bond type: the iron(II) complexes are diamagnetic with d^2sp^3 bonding, or spin paired, whereas nickel(II) complexes are paramagnetic with sp^3d^2 bonding, or spin unpaired. Davies [107] suggests that the intramolecular racemization of the iron(II) complexes may result from a process of expansion which permits loss of optical activity. Thus the interatomic distances between the donor atom and the metal may be increased beyond that of a d^2sp^3 hybrid bond, the system undergoing a change in bond type to something approaching ionic bonding. Such an excited state might well rearrange prior to returning to the original stable state. On the basis of this interpretation, the racemization can be represented by the equilibria:

$$Fe(AA)_3^{2+} \underset{k_2}{\overset{k_1}{\rightleftarrows}} Fe\text{---}(AA)_3^{2+} \underset{k_4}{\overset{k_3}{\rightleftarrows}} Fe\text{---}(AA)_2 + AA \qquad (20)$$

It is apparent that if $k_2 > k_3$ the racemization will occur by an intramolecular process, if $k_2 < k_3$ an intermolecular mechanism is involved, and if $k_2 \sim k_3$ both mechanisms may contribute to the observed rate of racemization.

In terms of the crystal field theory the nature of this expanded state can be put more clearly. It would simply be the higher energy spin-free state of the complex which would have greater bond distances and hence weaker bonding as required. The energy required to attain it would not be excessive because of the lowered electron repulsion. The large entropy gain shown in Table 5 would be due also to the greater freedom of the ligands in this excited state. This explanation fits in neatly with the observation that nickel(II) does not show any intramolecular racemization since such an excited state is not possible for nickel(II) which is already spin free. Hence only the dissociation mechanism is available to it. It may be noted that the activation energies are greater for the d^6 iron(II) system than for the d^8 nickel(II) systems in the dissociation process. This is also in agreement with crystal field theory. Thermodynamic data also show that the former complexes are energetically more stable. Thus, for the formation of $Fe(phen)_3^{2+}$ ΔH^0 is -30 kcal and ΔS^0 is -3.8 eu, and for $Ni(phen)_3^{2+}$ ΔH^0 is -26.8 kcal and ΔS^0 is $+19.3$ eu.[108] The entropy factor, however, favors the nickel(II) complex and may be understood in terms of the large decrease in mobility of the ligands in going from paramagnetic $Fe(H_2O)_6^{2+}$ to diamagnetic $Fe(phen)_3^{2+}$.

The exact nature of the intramolecular rearrangement leading to racemization is not known. A consideration of molecular models reveals that there are several ways that such a process can happen, and each appears to involve approximately the same energy. Some of the methods that have been suggested are diagramed in Fig. 9. Although it is difficult to obtain experimental proof of the exact nature of these rearrangement processes, in a few cases evidence is available which supports one or the other of the proposed paths. Werner [99] suggested the rupture of one (A) or two (B) bidentate ligands followed by the reattachment of the open ends. Kinetic studies [106a] on the dissociation and racemization of $Fe(bipy)_3^{2+}$ suggest that a bond rupture path does make some contribution to the total rate of racemization. The intramolecular racemization of this ion can take place in two ways. One method, like that of $Fe(phen)_3^{2+}$, which presumably involves shifting, but not breaking, of Fe—N bonds is essentially independent of acid concentration. A second process would involve an intramolecular racemization of the complex with one of the chelate rings open. Since the lifetime of this species decreases with increasing acid concentration (p. 154), it follows that the rate of racemization through such

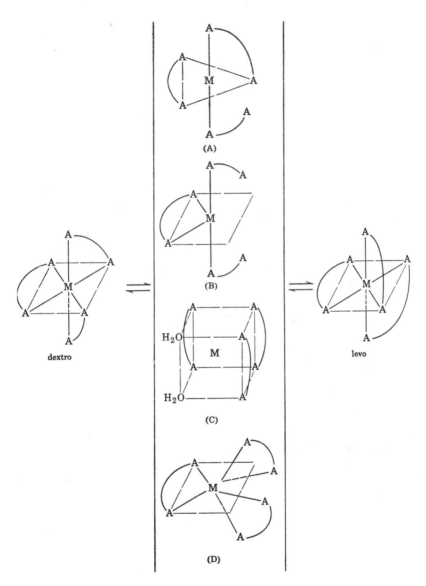

Fig. 9. Rearrangements proposed for intramolecular mechanism of racemization of octahedral complexes.

a route decreases with increasing acidity and approaches zero at high acidity. Such a decrease in intramolecular racemization was observed with increasing acidity, thus supporting path A. At high acid concentrations a constant residual intramolecular rate remained which is attributed to path D.

Considering only paths A and B, evidence has been cited in support of B. It was suggested that the cobalt(III) oxalate chelate rings can open because $Co(C_2O_4)_3^{3-}$ does racemize, whereas the cobalt(III) ethylenediamine ring does not open since $Co(en)_3^{3+}$ does not racemize.[56] Therefore the racemization of $Co(en)_2C_2O_4^+$ would support the view that only one ring need be opened (A), but failure of this compound to racemize would be consistent with path B. It was found that the loss of optical activity of this complex is a result of decomposition rather than racemization. On the basis of this observation it was concluded that two chelate rings must be opened (B). This conclusion is not justified because the original assumption to consider only A and B may not be correct.

An oxygen-18 exchange study which does shed some light on the racemization process of $Cr(C_2O_4)_3^{3-}$ was recently reported.[106d] It was observed that acid-catalyzed oxygen exchange in the system $Cr(C_2O_4)_3^{3-}$-$H_2{}^*O$ is much faster than is oxalate exchange in $Cr(C_2O_4)_3^{3-}$-${}^*C_2O_4^{2-}$. This exchange between the solvent oxygen and the coordinated oxalato oxygen is believed to occur by attack on the carbonyl carbon. In such a case, if the chelate ring remains intact, then only the carbonyl oxygen will undergo exchange (p. 162), which means a total of six oxygen atoms exchanging per complex ion. Instead it was found that all twelve oxygen atoms are exchanged. Therefore, the chelate rings must open and close many times prior to complete exchange with ${}^*C_2O_4^{2-}$. From this observation it follows that the racemization of $Cr(C_2O_4)_3^{3-}$ may well take place by a path which requires the opening of one or more chelate rings, e.g., A, B, etc., Fig. 9. It should be mentioned, however, that the rate of racemization is much faster than the rate of oxygen exchange.

Another suggestion [109] is that the racemization of octahedral complexes may result from an addition of solvent to expand the coordination number to eight, allowing the formation of a symmetrical cubic structure (C). The exact nature of the role played by the solvent is not known, but that it is of some importance will be shown later. It is found that the water of crystallization has an effect on the racemization of certain solid oxalato salts.[100] For example, when d- or l-$K_3Cr(C_2O_4)_3 \cdot 2H_2O$ is heated at 120°C in evacuated sealed tubes, the optical activity is essentially lost in several hours, whereas this loss takes several months with the anhydrous salt. It was suggested that the water enters the coordination sphere to give an unstable "expanded" complex which may either be symmetrical or rapidly lose its optical activity.

Finally the possibility of intramolecular rearrangement (D) without expansion of coordination number and without opening up of chelate rings was suggested by Rây and Dutt.[110] They argue that, since all six bonds in complexes of the type $M(AA)_3$ are equivalent, if bonds break, then there is no reason why two such bonds attached to the same chelate group should not occasionally be broken at the same time and thus lead to some dissociation. Since dissociation is not observed, it is assumed that the rearrangement can take place without the rupture of a bond. Also in support of this view is the indication from infrared measurements of complex compounds that the resistance towards bending is less than towards the stretching of bonds,[111] this being the accepted precursor of dissociation. Therefore the activation energy is expected to be less for a process that requires no breaking of bonds. A good illustration that intramolcular racemization can take place without the opening of chelate rings is afforded by the cations $Fe(phen)_3{}^{2+}$ [106a] and $Fe(phen)_3{}^{3+}$.[104] This would appear to be true in these cases because of the geometry of the 1,10-phenanthroline molecule, which is a fixed planar structure with the nitrogen atoms only 2.5 A apart. Therefore this molecule cannot readily behave as a unidentate group, and the intramolecular process may involve the movement of these chelate rings about the central atom. Kinetic studies on the acid dissociation of $Ni(phen)(H_2O)_4{}^{2+}$ [106b] and base dissociation of $Fe(phen)_3{}^{2+}$ [106c] have, however, recently been interpreted in terms of a unidentate 1,10-phenanthroline intermediate.

Finally it should be mentioned that three different investigators [112,157] have recently independently suggested still an alternative mechanism for an intramolecular process without the rupture of any metal-ligand bonds. According to their suggestion the octahedron is visualized as a trigonal antiprism (Fig. 10). It is apparent then that if one of the trigonal planes (top one in Fig. 10) is allowed to rotate through 60° there is generated a trigonal prism. This excited and somewhat expanded state is symmetrical for complexes of the type $M(AA)_3$ so that its formation automatically leads to racemization. Bailar [157] points out that this same process can also provide a path for intramolecular isomerization (Fig. 11).

Although there seem to be these rearrangement paths available

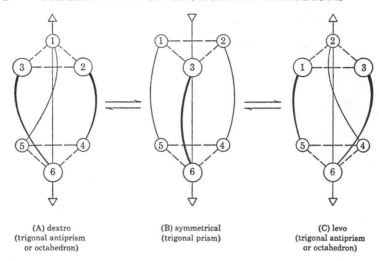

(A) dextro	(B) symmetrical	(C) levo
(trigonal antiprism	(trigonal prism)	(trigonal antiprism
or octahedron)		or octahedron)

FIG. 10. Intramolecular racemization of $M(AA)_3$ without bond rupture through a symmetrical intermediate (B). Octahedra A and C are viewed as trigonal antiprisms. The rotation of the top trigonal plane through 60°, counterclockwise for A and clockwise for C, gives the optically inactive trigonal prism B.

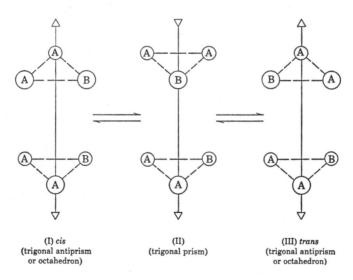

(I) *cis*	(II)	(III) *trans*
(trigonal antiprism	(trigonal prism)	(trigonal antiprism
or octahedron)		or octahedron)

FIG. 11. Intramolecular isomerization of MA_4B_2 via trigonal prism II. Octahedra I and III are viewed as trigonal antiprisms. The clockwise rotation of the top trigonal plane through 60° for the *cis* isomer (I) yields II; continued rotation through another 60° gives the *trans* isomer (III).

for intramolecular racemization and isomerization without metal-ligand bond rupture, there is no experimental evidence at present that requires this mechanism. Certainly all of the examples of isomerization that have been investigated can be explained on the basis of an intermolecular process. However, there is some indication that the acid independent portion of the intramolecular racemization of $Fe(bipy)_3^{2+}$ and the intramolecular racemization of $Fe(phen)_3^{2+}$ and $Fe(phen)_3^{3+}$ take place without metal-ligand bond cleavage.[106a]

Effect of environment. The rates of racemization of some complex ions are altered by changes of salt concentration or of solvent. Although there are now some quantitative data on these effects, their exact nature is not yet well understood. The most extensive studies of salt effects were made by Beese and Johnson [101] and by Rây and Dutt [110] on the anionic complex trioxalatochromate(III) and the cationic tris(biguanidinium)cobalt(III) respectively (Table 6). In

Table 6 *

Salt Effects on the Rates of Inversion of $Cr(C_2O_4)_3^{3-}$ and $Co(bigH)_3^{3+}$

$Cr(C_2O_4)_3^{3-}$		$Co(bigH)_3^{3+}$	
Solution	$k \times 10^3$, sec^{-1}, 18.2°C	Solution	$k \times 10^3$, sec^{-1}, 46.2°C
H_2O	0.173	H_2O	0.246
KOH, 0.54 M	0.484	NaOH, 0.0025 M	12.2
HCl, 0.98 M	2.47	HCl, 0.0005 M	0.137
KCl, 0.50 M	0.213	KCl, 0.1 M	0.145
CaCl$_2$, 0.01 M	0.47	CaCl$_2$, 0.0005 M	0.097
MnCl$_2$, 0.01 M	0.42	CuCl$_2$, 0.0005 M	0.0346
Co(NO$_3$)$_2$, 0.01 M	0.73	LaCl$_3$, 0.0005 M	0.0395
Ni(NO$_3$)$_2$, 0.01 M	1.58	ThCl$_4$, 0.0005 M	0.0520
CuSO$_4$, 0.01 M	2.49	[Co(NH$_3$)$_4$CO$_3$]Cl, 0.0005 M	0.0755
ZnSO$_4$, 0.01 M	1.18	[Co(NH$_3$)$_5$Cl]Cl$_2$, 0.0005 M	0.0975
La(NO$_3$)$_3$, 0.001 M	0.719	[Co(NH$_3$)$_6$]Cl$_3$, 0.0005 M	0.0869

* From references 101 and 110.

both cases it is reported that except for the hydroxide ion the anion has little or no effect on the rate of racemization. This acceleration of rate by the hydroxide ion is apparently a result of base hydrolysis leading to a decomposition of the complexes. That other anions show no specific effect on the anionic complex of chromium(III) is not surprising; what is unexpected is that anions have little or no effect on the cationic cobalt(III) complex. However, the rate of racemization of $Co(bigH)_3^{3+}$ is essentially the same in solutions containing the same concentration of chloride, bromide, iodide, or nitrate salts of potassium. Bivalent anions could not be tested because these formed precipitates with the complex.

The rates of racemization of these two complexes is markedly altered by different cations, that of $Cr(C_2O_4)_3^{3-}$ being accelerated, whereas that of $Co(bigH)_3^{3+}$ is retarded. The possible formation of ion pair or outer sphere complexes (Chapter 9) between cations and $Cr(C_2O_4)_3^{3-}$ may be responsible for its enhanced rate of racemization. This interpretation is also in keeping with the observation that the effect increases with increasing charge on the cation. The charge of the cation is of such importance and its effect on the rate so great that studies on the rates of racemization might be used to furnish some information on the nature of the cations in solution. For example, mercury(I) behaves as a divalent ion, Hg_2^{2+}, mercury(II) chloride has very little effect because it is a weak electrolyte, and chromium(III) and aluminum(III) behave like divalent ions for they are largely present as the basic ions, $CrOH^{2+}$ and $AlOH^{2+}$.* The cationic retardation of the rate of racemization of $Co(bigH)_3^{3+}$ is indeed puzzling. It is very unlikely that this effect, like that just described for the chromium(III) complex, can be a result of electrostatic interaction because, first, the complex and the cations are of like charge and would tend to repel each other, and, second, the effect increases with increased cationic charge, which is contrary to electrostatic forces. Since the biguanidine ligand has additional nitrogens that might behave as donor atoms, there is the possibility that the cation becomes attached to one or more of these nitrogens, thus forming a binuclear complex. However, such an argument is not convincing in view of the fact that inert complex cations, such as $Co(NH_3)_6^{3+}$, have approximately the same effect as do metal ions of corresponding charge (Table 6).

A similar but smaller cationic acceleration of the rates of racemization of $Cr(en)(C_2O_4)_2^-$ and $Co(C_2O_4)_3^{3-}$ compared to $Cr(C_2O_4)_3^{3-}$ has been observed.[50] It was also found [104] that the addition of salt has only a very slight retardation effect on the rate of racemization of $Ni(phen)_3^{2+}$, but the rate is slightly increased in the presence of

---

*It has been pointed out (J. H. Carter, thesis, University College London, London, England, 1956) that the effectiveness of the bivalent ions follows their natural order of stability. This suggests that the accelerated rates result from complex formation with the added ions.

alkali. However, in the case of $Ni(bipy)_3^{2+}$ a specific anion effect was observed, the rates of racemization being increased by hydroxide, chloride, and fluoride ions, whereas sulfate and nitrate ions have no effect. Similar results were obtained [112b] for the rates of dissociation of $Fe(bipy)_3^{2+}$ in methanol solution indicating that perhaps the increase in rate with the smaller ions may be due to the fact that they can enter the five-coordinated intermediate (p. 156) and prevent the reclosing of the opened 2,2′-bipyridine chelate ring. Since the rate of dissociation of $Fe(phen)_3^{2+}$ in methanol solution is also accelerated by chloride ion, it would appear that a more plausible interpretation of this behavior in non-aqueous systems is the formation of ion pairs.[112b] Although the salt effect on the rate of racemization of $Fe(phen)_3^{2+}$ in water is very slight, the addition of acid or salt to a solution of $Fe(phen)_3^{3+}$ results in a very pronounced decrease in rate.[104,113a] In the case of the iron(III) complex spectroscopic studies [113a] show the formation of ion pairs. Furthermore it should be mentioned that the optical activity of $Fe(phen)_3^{2+}$, unlike that of $Ni(phen)_3^{2+}$, is rapidly lost in alkali due to decomposition.[104]

The effects described above are those of ordinary salts. Much greater effects have been observed with large ions or compounds. This phenomenon is related to the so-called *Pfeiffer effect*,[114] which was recently discussed in terms of "configurational activity" [115] (p. 285). In many cases the rates of racemization of diastereoisomeric salts are slower than those of ordinary salts of the labile component. This is in accord with the observation that stable optically active centers in a given molecule seem to stabilize labile centers in the same molecule. Kinetic studies reveal that diastereoisomeric pairs, *d*-A, *l*-B and *l*-A, *l*-B, may racemize at different rates. This inequality in rates, due to differences in free energies of the diastereoisomers, was shown by Turner and Harris [116] to be the basis of the phenomenon of *first-order asymmetric transformation*. That free energy differences may exist between solid diastereoisomeric compounds or diastereoisomeric salts in non-dissociating solvents is understandable, but it is surprising that they may also occur in dissociating solvents. However, it has been observed [110] that the rates of loss of optical activity of aqueous solutions of dextro and levo tris(biguanidinium)cobalt(III) chloride dextro tartrate are slightly different. Similarly the rates of racemization of $Ni(phen)_3^{2+}$ in the presence of optically active ions and also in the presence of large optically inactive ions are different [117] (Table 7).

It will be noted that regardless of whether or not the large ions are optically active, they cause a considerable retardation in the rate of

Table 7 *

Effect of Optically Active Ions and of Large Ions on the Racemization Rates of d- and l-Ni(phen)$_3^{2+}$

Solution	Temp., °C	$k_d \times 10^4$, min^{-1}	$k_l \times 10^4$, min^{-1}	$K = k_d/k_l$	E_d, cal	E_l, cal	$\log PZ_d$, sec^{-1}	$\log PZ_l$, sec^{-1}
H$_2$O †	25.0	3.35	...	...	25,000	...	13.4	...
4% ammonium d-bromocamphor-sulfonate	24.85	1.53	1.71	0.895	26,300	25,800	13.7	13.4
2% d-cinchoninium sulfate	24.95	3.25	2.87	1.13	24,960	25,330	13.0	13.2
5% ammonium d-camphorsulfonate	25.0	2.03	2.15	0.945	...	...	...	...
2% ammonium naphthalenesulfonate †	25.0	1.63	...	...	27,200	...	14.3	...
2% triphenylmethylarsonium chloride †	25.0	2.92	...	...	26,300	...	13.9	...

* From reference 117.

† The racemization rates in these cases with no other optically active ions present are the same for the two enantiomorphs.

racemization of $Ni(phen)_3^{2+}$. This shows that the slower loss of optical rotation of diastereoisomeric salts over the simple salts of labile ions need not be ascribed, as is often done, to a stabilizing effect due to the optical activity of the other component but instead to its large size. This effect is attributed to the association of the large ions with the complex by the operation of van der Waals' dispersion interaction forces. Spectral evidence has recently been found for such interaction between the complex $Fe(phen)_3^{2+}$ and camphor sulfonate ion, and dialysis studies show an interaction between the complex ion and polystyrene sulfonate ion.[113b] Regardless of the mechanism of racemization, it does seem that the rate of racemization of the associated complex ion may differ from that of the free complex, either as a result of a modification of the metal-ligand bond or of alterations in entropy between the initial and activated states. In this connection it is of interest to note that the rates of dissociation of some complex ions are likewise affected by large ions. For example, it has been observed [113b] that the rate of dissociation of $Fe(phen)_3^{2+}$ is decreased by large anions but increased by large cations. Moreover, certain polyelectrolytes have an effect on this rate, and all of these materials likewise alter the rate of racemization.

The rate of loss of optical rotation of complex ions is also dependent upon the nature of the solvent. Werner [99] observed that the addition of acetone to water solutions of $Cr(C_2O_4)_3^{3-}$ retards its rate of racemization. However, the addition of acetone to an aqueous solution of $Co(C_2O_4)_3^{3-}$ results in a slightly accelerated rate of racemization.[50] Schweitzer and Rose [118] made a more detailed study of the racemization rate of $Cr(C_2O_4)_3^{3-}$ in binary solvents of water containing different mole fractions of methanol, ethanol, 1-propanol, 2-propanol, acetone, and 1,4-dioxane. In all cases there is a smooth decrease in rate with an increase in organic solvent. It was not possible to establish any definite relationships between solvents.

Racemization rates of $Ni(bipy)_3^{2+}$, $Ni(phen)_3^{2+}$, $Fe(bipy)_3^{2+}$, and $Fe(phen)_3^{2+}$ in aqueous-non-aqueous solvent mixtures and in non-aqueous solvents have been reported.[96, 112b, 119] The racemization rates of the iron(II) complexes are greater in primary alcohols and nitrobenzene, whereas those of the nickel(II) complexes are smaller.[119] Detailed kinetic data for $Ni(phen)_3^{2+}$ as well as the dielectric constants and viscosities of the solvents are summarized in Table 8.* These data show clearly that there is no simple correlation between the rate of racemization and either the dielectric constant or the viscosity of a solvent. Furthermore these solvents of extremely different coordi-

Table 8 *

Inversion Rates of $Ni(phen)_3^{2+}$ at 25°C in Different Solvents

Solvent	Dielectric Constant, 25°C	Viscosity, mp 25°C	$k \times 10^4$, min^{-1}	E_a, kcal	log PZ
Water	80.0	8.95	3.4	24.9 ± 0.3	13.0 ± 0.3
Methanol	33.7	5.5	2.2	23.7	11.9
Ethanol	25.7	11.0	1.2	24.7	12.4
n-Propanol	21.8	20.0	1.1	25.6	12.3
Acetone	21.4	3.1	3.0	24.6	12.7
Pyridine	12.5	8.9	4.6	26.0	13.9
Nitrobenzene	35.0	18.0	0.34	26.1	12.9
Ethylene glycol	41.2	181.0	0.40	27.5	14.0

* From reference 119.

nating properties do not greatly alter the activation energies and frequency factors for the loss of optical rotation of the complex ion. This indicates that the racemization processes in all of these systems are not too different. Since racemization of $Ni(phen)_3^{2+}$ in aqueous solution takes place by a dissociation mechanism,[95] this would indicate that the same process is involved in the other solvents. Recent exchange studies [97] on the system $Ni(phen)_3^{2+}$-*phen show that the rate of ligand exchange is the same as the rate of racemization in nitrobenzene and also in absolute alcohol. Thus racemization in these two solvents must also involve a dissociation process.

The inversion rates of $Ni(phen)_3^{2+}$ in binary solvents of water with methanol and acetone are shown in Fig. 12. It had been suggested that a duality in mechanism may be responsible for the minimum in the curve.[120a] This could then result from a decrease in rate of dissociation and an increase in rate of intramolecular rearrangement with increasing amount of organic solvent. Such behavior would not, however, account for the maxima in these curves. Furthermore it has recently been observed [97] that the rates of ligand exchange and of racemization are identical for a particular solvent regardless of whether it be water, ethanol, or a water-ethanol mixture. Thus the dissociative mechanism must be operative throughout the water-organic solvent systems. One possible explanation for the minima in these curves is the formation of ion pairs in the organic-rich solvents.[112b] Since the ion-pair species reacts more rapidly than the parent complex, the initial decrease in rate due to a change in solvent is followed by an increase in rate due to a greater concentration of ion pairs. This may also explain the

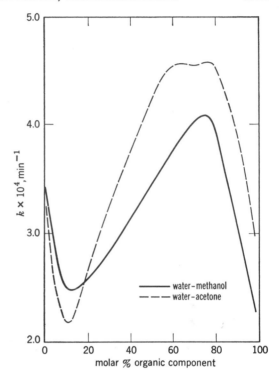

FIG. 12. Rates of racemization of d-Ni-(phen)$_3^{2+}$ as a function of water–organic solvent composition at 25°C. (From reference 119.)

——— water–methanol
- - - - water–acetone

$k \times 10^4$, min^{-1}

molar % organic component

maxima in these curves, because the rate of reaction of the ion pair likewise will decrease with increasing organic solvent.

Investigations [112b] of the rates of dissociation and racemization of Fe(bipy)$_3^{2+}$ and Fe(phen)$_3^{2+}$ in water-methanol systems show that the intramolecular mechanism makes a greater contribution to the observed rate of racemization with increasing concentration of methanol. It was also observed that the rate of racemization of Fe(bipy)$_3^{2+}$ in methanol and methanol-rich solvents, unlike that in water, is almost independent of acid concentration. This is to be expected if the contribution made by a dissociation mechanism to the rate of loss of optical activity is negligible.

One other factor that has a large effect on the rate of racemization of certain coordination compounds is the presence of decolorizing charcoal. This heterogeneous catalysis of reactions of cobalt(III) ammines, first reported by Schwarz and Kronig,[121] is described on p. 355. Douglas [57] observed that the optical rotation of an aqueous solution of dextro tris(ethylenediamine)cobalt(III) chloride is unchanged after 24 hr on a steambath, whereas in the presence of decolorizing carbon racemization is complete in 2 min at 90°C.*

Effect of electron transfer. The subject of electron transfer is discussed in Chapter 7. That an electron transfer reaction can greatly catalyze the racemization of complex ions has been clearly demonstrated for the systems $Os(bipy)_3^{2+}$ ᵃⁿᵈ ³⁺ [122] and $Co(en)_3^{2+}$ ᵃⁿᵈ ³⁺ [123] The two systems differ in that the Os(II) and Os(III) complexes are both inert and do not undergo racemization, whereas the Co(II) complex is labile and does not retain any optical activity and the Co(III) complex is inert and does not readily racemize. Therefore the enhanced rates of racemization produced by electron transfer occur by a different process for each of these two systems. In the first place complete racemization of the inert osmium(II) and (III) complexes will occur only if equivalent amounts of the two with different generic configurations, D-Os$(bipy)_3^{2+}$ and L-Os$(bipy)_3^{3+}$ or vice versa, are mixed. Thus the rapid electron transfer offered by the equilibrium

$$D\text{-}Os(bipy)_3^{2+} + L\text{-}Os(bipy)_3^{3+} \rightleftharpoons L\text{-}Os(bipy)_3^{2+} + D\text{-}Os(bipy)_3^{3+}$$

$$(21)$$

will result in a rapid loss of optical rotation. Dwyer and Gyarfas [122] report that such a solution, 5×10^{-4} M with respect to both ions, was completely inactive in less than 15 sec at 25°C. This method was suggested as a means of studying the rate of electron transfer.

The racemization of $Co(en)_3^{3+}$, instead, requires only catalytic amounts of $Co(en)_3^{2+}$. Since the cobalt(II) complex is configuratively labile, the racemization path must involve conversion of D-Co$(en)_3^{3+}$ into D-Co$(en)_3^{2+}$, which racemizes instantly. This means that the simultaneously formed cobalt(III) complex is racemic. Busch [123] has made use of this behavior in the resolution of dl-Co$(en)_3^{3+}$ to obtain in excess of 150% of the amount of the dextro or levo isomer originally present. This was made possible by the addition of $Co(en)_3^{2+}$ to catalyze the racemization of $Co(en)_3^{3+}$. Thus, as the less soluble diastereoisomer d-[Co$(en)_3$]Cl d-$C_4H_4O_6$ separates from solution, the remaining l-Co$(en)_3^{3+}$ is catalytically racemized, providing more of

---

* It was recently observed (D. S. Popplewell, thesis, Sheffield University, 1956) that the rate of exchange in the system $Co(en)_3^{3+}$-*en on charcoal is slower than the rate of racemization of d-Co$(en)_3^{3+}$ under these same conditions. Therefore the racemization must, at least in part, take place by an intramolecular process.

the dextro form, which then crystallizes. It had previously been observed [99,75] in other systems that virtually all of a labile complex may be separated as the least soluble diastereoisomer because of the fact that the more soluble form racemizes to continually supply some of the less soluble isomer. Such a process is termed a *second-order asymmetric induction*. Finally, it is of interest to note that the failure to resolve $Co(phen)_3^{3+}$ and $Co(bipy)_3^{3+}$ has perhaps been due to the presence of catalytic amounts of the corresponding cobalt(II) complexes and the very rapid rate of electron transfer in these systems (see footnote, p. 288).

RACEMIZATION OF TETRAHEDRAL COMPLEXES

In addition to the numerous optically active carbon compounds, other elements may form optically active tetrahedral compounds.[124] However, optically active tetrahedral metal complexes have been reported only for B(III), Be(II), Zn(II), and Cu(II). Examples of these are shown in Table 9. These complexes are all labile and in most cases racemize so rapidly that it has not been possible to separate the complex from the resolving agent. Thus the optical activity of the complex was observed in the form of its diastereoisomer, which rapidly mutarotates to a constant optical rotation. For example, it has been suggested [131] that the quinine salts of zinc(II), cadmium(II), and mercury(II) complexes of 1-chlorobenzene-3,4-dithiolate mutarotate at such a rate that this is not detectable even at $-35°C$. It should be noted that all of these complexes contain two chelate rings giving rise to a spiran-type [124] optical activity (Fig. 13). That such complexes are resolvable was used as proof of their tetrahedral structure, since a planar configuration would result in the formation of optically inactive geometric isomers.

The mechanism of racemization of these coordination compounds is not known. However, just as is true of the octahedral complexes, this may involve either (1) an intramolecular or (2) an intermolecular process. Werner [132] did suggest an intramolecular mechanism for the loss of optical activity of asymmetric carbon compounds through the formation of a symmetrical planar intermediate. Although this has been found to be incorrect for organic compounds,[133] it cannot be excluded as a possible mechanism for the more loosely bonded coordination compounds. However, since these complexes are all known to be labile, it would appear more probable that the rapid loss of optical rotation takes place by an intermolecular process. The observation

Table 9

Optically Active Tetrahedral Complexes [a]

Compound	$[\alpha]_D$	Reference	Remarks [b]
Brucine bis(γ-chloropyrocatechol)borate(III)	−19.7	125	after 10 days $[\alpha]_D = -14.0$
Strychnine bis(β-nitropyrocatechol)borate(III)	−55.2	125	after 8 days $[\alpha]_D = -58.3$
Brucine bis(hydroxyisobutyrato)borate(III)	−48.9	126	after 12 days $[\alpha]_D = -42.0$
Brucine bis(benzoylpyruvato)beryllate(II)	+25.1	127	M.R. to $[\alpha]_D = +5; t_{1/2}(20°C) = 13$ min (CHCl₃), $= 74$ min (C₂H₅OH)
Brucine bis(benzoylpyruvato)beryllate(II)	−11.8	127	M.R. to $[\alpha]_D = +5; t_{1/2}(20°C) = 9$ min (CHCl₃)
Dimethylammonium bis(benzoylpyruvato)beryllate	...	127	rac. at 20°C in C₂H₅OH, $t_{1/2} = 6$ min
Bis(d-benzoylcamphor)beryllium(II)	+449	128	M.R. to $[\alpha]_{5461} = +381; t_{1/2}(25°C) \sim 28$ hr (CCl₄, CHCl₃)
Bis(benzoylacetonato)beryllium(II)	~+1	129	Completely rac. in 9 hr at R.T.
Brucine bis(benzoylpyruvato)zincate(II)	+20.1	127	M.R. to $[\alpha]_D = +4; t_{1/2}(20°C) = 8.5$ min (CHCl₃)
Potassium bis(8-quinolinato-5-sulfonic acid)–zincate(II)	−40	130	total rac. of aqueous solution at 100°C in 4 hr
Strychnine bis(benzoylpyruvato)cuprate(II)	+27.6	127	M.R. to $[\alpha]_D = +4.2; t_{1/2}(20°C) = 10$ min (CHCl₃)

[a] Although the optical activity of the Zn(II) and Cu(II) was attributed to a tetrahedral structure of these complexes, it should be remembered that both of these ions are known to exhibit a coordination number of six. Therefore, it is possible that the optical activity observed may result from some asymmetric six-coordinated species.

[b] M.R. is mutarotation, R.T. is room temperature, and rac. is racemization.

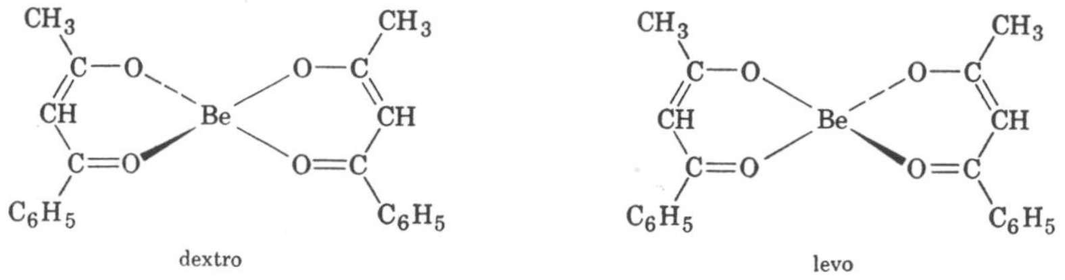

Fig. 13. Mirror image isomers of bis(benzoylacetonato) beryllium(II).

that the mutarotation of bis(d-benzoylcamphor) beryllium (II) in either carbon tetrachloride or chloroform solution requires a catalyst does indicate an intermolecular mechanism.[128,134] The question of mechanism will have to be settled by studies such as a comparison of the rate of ligand exchange with the rate of racemization.

CONFIGURATIONAL ACTIVITY

It is well known that, for certain types of organic compounds, the addition of an optically active compound to a solution of a racemic compound may result in a gradual change in optical rotation of the final solution. This slow change in optical rotation of the solution to some constant value is called a *first-order asymmetric transformation* [116] and is attributed to the following changes:

$$dl\text{-A} + l\text{-B}$$
$$\downarrow \text{fast}$$
$$d\text{-A} \cdot l\text{-B} \rightleftharpoons l\text{-A} \cdot l\text{-B} \qquad (22)$$
$$\underset{50\%}{} \qquad \underset{50\%}{}$$
$$\downarrow \text{slow}$$
$$d\text{-A} \cdot l\text{-B} \rightleftharpoons l\text{-A} \cdot l\text{-B}$$
$$\underset{x\%}{} \qquad \underset{(100-x)\%}{}$$

It is believed that the diastereoisomers differ in stability because of the different spatial demands of the two isomers; thus at equilibrium they are present at different concentrations. Although such an explanation is acceptable for diastereoisomeric molecules in solution, it has been suggested [135] that this cannot account for the same behavior of ionic systems in dissociating solvents.

Thus Pfeiffer and Quehl [136] observed first-order asymmetric transformations with coordination compounds in ionized salt solutions. They found that the optical rotation of a solution of zinc d-camphor-π-sulfonate changed from $\alpha_D = +0.98°$ to $+0.09°$ upon addition of three moles of 1,10-phenanthroline. Likewise a solution of zinc sulfate and cinchonine hydrochloride with an optical rotation of $\alpha_D = +5.29°$ changed to $-1.89°$ upon addition of 1,10-phenanthroline. The addition of 2,2′-bipyridine gave similar results of smaller magnitude, whereas neither ammonia nor pyridine had any effect. This is to be expected since neither $Zn(NH_3)_6{}^{2+}$ nor $Zn(py)_6{}^{2+}$ can be optically active. Somewhat unexpected is the observation that the addition of ethylenediamine has no effect, although $Zn(en)_3{}^{2+}$ is asymmetric. This so-called *Pfeiffer effect* is observed with 1,10-phenanthroline and 2,2′-bipyridine complexes [136,137] of Mn(II), Fe(II), Co(II), Ni(II), Zn(II), Cd(II), Cu(II),[138] and Co(III) [139] (see footnote, p. 288).

Dwyer, O'Dwyer, and Gyarfas [135] attribute this effect to what they have named *configurational activity*. This term is used to designate that the thermodynamic activities of optical antipodes in solution are affected differently upon the addition of optically active ions. In labile systems, such as for the above-mentioned complexes, the equilibria

$$d\text{-}M(AA)_3{}^{2+} \rightleftharpoons l\text{-}M(AA)_3{}^{2+} \tag{23}$$

are rapidly established. Since at equilibrium solutions of such salts are optically inactive, the concentration of the two antipodes must be equal. Furthermore, from the equal solubility of $d\text{-}[M(AA)_3]X_2$ and $l\text{-}[M(AA)_3]X_2$, where X^- is optically inactive, it follows that the thermodynamic activities of the complex ions are the same. However, if X^- is optically active, then the activity coefficients of the enantiomorphic salts may differ, so that the solution may be optically active due to different concentrations of the two antipodes. Thus at equilibrium, in the presence of optically active ions, since

$$\gamma_{d\text{-}M(AA)_3{}^{2+}} \neq \gamma_{l\text{-}M(AA)_3{}^{2+}} \tag{24}$$

then

$$[d\text{-}M(AA)_3{}^{2+}] \neq [l\text{-}M(AA)_3{}^{2+}] \tag{25}$$

It is suggested [135] that the steric factor invoked to account for the behavior of organic compounds in non-polar solvents is not applicable to these ionized salt solutions. In the ionized solutions, diastereoisomeric molecules are not present and perhaps there are also no ion pairs, e.g., dilute solutions in which the two optically active species are both cations. If this is correct, then some long-range effects may be sufficient to account for the behavior in aqueous salt solution. Whatever the reason for these effects, the fact remains that they do exist as is shown by experimental studies on (1) the solubilities of enantiomers, (2) the redox potentials of optically active systems, and (3) the rates of racemization of diastereoisomers.

The solubilities of d- and of l-$[Ru(phen)_3](ClO_4)_2$ in water and in solutions of sodium chloride are the same. However, in a 1% ammonium d-bromocamphorsulfonate solution the solubilities of the d and l complexes are 0.237 and 0.240 g/100 ml of solvent respectively, and in 2% sodium potassium d-tartrate the solubilities are 0.219 and 0.225 g/100 ml of solvent respectively.[141a] Because of these differences in solubility it is possible to resolve racemic complexes by recrystallizing simple salts of enantiomers in the presence of optically active ions.[135] This method was used to obtain optically active fractions of $[Ni(bipy)_3]I_2$ and $[Ru(bipy)_3]I_2$ from solutions containing ammonium d-bromocamphorsulfonate. The resolution of racemic tris-(acetylacetonato)cobalt(III), a non-electrolyte, was also achieved by extraction from a solution containing optically active tris(ethylenediamine)cobalt(III) iodide. Thus prefential interactions likewise exist between asymmetrically arranged dipoles of a non-electrolyte and an optically active ion.

The redox potentials of d-$Os(bipy)_3^{2+}/d$-$Os(bipy)_3^{3+}$ and of l-$Os(bipy)_3^{2+}/l$-$Os(bipy)_3^{3+}$ were measured in water and in solutions of electrolytes, such as sodium nitrate, and found to be the same within experimental error of ± 0.2 mv. However, in the presence of optically active anions the potentials of the d and l redox systems are different.[141b] In solutions of ammonium d-camphorsulfonate, at an ionic strength of 0.01, the differences in potentials are 1.2 and 2.5 mv, respectively. The redox potentials of the d- and l-osmium systems are also different in the presence of either d- or l-$[Co(en)_3](NO_3)_3$, thus demonstrating that specific interactions exist between ions of the same charge.

That rates of racemization of ionized diastereoisomers may differ was first reported for d- and l-tris(biguanidinium)cobalt(III) chloride d-tartrate.[110] Similarly the rates of racemization of d-$Ni(phen)_3^{2+}$ and of l-$Ni(phen)_3^{2+}$ differ when in the presence of optically active anions or cations [117] (Table 7). Differences of activation energies and entropies of activation for the racemization of the two antipodes, in the presence of either d-bromocamphorsulfonate or d-cinchonium ions, are in good agreement with values obtained from equilibrium studies on the same systems.

The interpretation of these results in terms of differences in thermodynamic activity coefficients of the two antipodes when in presence of a third optically active ion is based upon there being no associated species in these ionized solutions. Even so the differences must result from some steric effect, since the presence of a large, but symmetrical, ion has a considerable (but equal) effect on the activities of the two antipodes. A long-range steric effect would be unusual, and it is tempting to suggest that some type of association, approaching ion-pair formation, may exist in these "ionized" salt solutions.

Cryoscopic, refractometric, and spectrophotometric measurements [139] on the Pfeiffer-effect systems show that an unusually high degree of association is present. For example, the stepwise dissociation

$$Zn(phen)_3^{2+} \cdot 2BCS^- \rightleftharpoons Zn(phen)_3^{2+} \cdot BCS^- + BCS^- \qquad (26)$$

$$Zn(phen)_3^{2+} \cdot BCS^- \rightleftharpoons Zn(phen)_3^{2+} + BCS^- \qquad (27)$$

where BCS^- is d-bromocamphorsulfonate ion, is less than 50% complete even in dilute solutions. Thus it has recently been suggested [140] that *differential association* is the primary mechanism of the Pfeiffer effect. According to this concept the dextro and levo antipodes of a complex are associated to different extents with the stable optically active ion. This preferential association is attributed to van der Waals' forces together with the effects of size, shape, and electrical asymmetry. The principal fact cited in support of this view is that the effect is observed with cobalt(III) complexes which are believed to be optically inert and therefore do not rapidly establish equilibrium.* For labile systems the preliminary differential association is then immediately followed by a change in concentration to the new equilibrium values.

The best argument against ionic associations is afforded by the cation-cation systems, which also show a first-order asymmetric transformation. However, since the charges on the complex cation are not localized but are spread out as fractional charges over the peripheral atoms of the ligands,[142] the electrostatic repulsive forces between cations may not be too large. Furthermore the effect is observed with

---

* Recent studies [97b, 120b] show that the methods generally used to prepare salts of $Co(phen)_3^{3+}$ and $Co(bipy)_3^{3+}$ yield products which are contaminated with the corresponding cobalt(II) compounds. It has also been observed that the rate of electron transfer in these systems is very fast, which means that the otherwise inert cobalt(III) complexes are rendered labile by the presence of the analogous cobalt(II) compounds. This is perhaps the reason that $Co(phen)_3^{3+}$ and $Co(bipy)_3^{3+}$ have not as yet been resolved and suggests that resolution from an acid medium where the cobalt(II) complex catalyst cannot exist may be possible.

big cationic alkaloids, where the positive charge may possibly remain far removed from the point of interaction with the complex cation. It is also noteworthy that large symmetrical cations or anions have a much greater effect on the rates of reaction of complex ions than do ordinary salts, e.g., large cations accelerate the rate of dissociation of $Fe(phen)_3^{2+}$, whereas large anions retard the rate.[113b] Such results indicate that large ions, regardless of charge, may be somewhat associated in solution. Although there is no evidence of association between $Fe(phen)_3^{2+}$ and small ordinary ions, e.g., Cl^-, NO_3^-, dialysis studies permit an estimate of the association constant ($K = 4 \times 10^4$ at 25°C) of the complex with polystyrenesulfonate ion (mol wt. $\sim$ 142,-000). It would be of interest to know the relative importance of the electrostatic and van der Waals' forces in these interactions and also the role of the size, shape, and charge distribution of the ions.[143]

STEREOSPECIFIC REACTIONS OF COORDINATION COMPOUNDS

Coordination compounds containing optically active ligands have been studied by several investigators and found to exhibit specific stereochemical effects. For example, octahedral complexes of the type $M(AA)_3$, where AA is optically active, are expected to exist in eight forms:

D*ddd*	L*ddd*
D*ddl*	L*ddl*
D*dll*	L*dll*
D*lll*	L*lll*

(D and L are used to represent the experimental optical rotation of the complex, and d and l designate the optical rotation of the asymmetric ligands when not coordinated). However, attempts to isolate all eight isomers from reaction mixtures of racemic 1,2-propanediamine (pn) or racemic trans-1,2-cyclopentanediamine (cptdin) with Co(III), Pt(IV), or Rh(III) have not been successful. Instead, only two forms were obtained for any one complex, e.g., D-Co(d-pn)$_3^{3+}$, L-Co(l-pn)$_3^{3+}$;[144a] D-Co(l-cptdin$_3^{3+}$, L-Co(d-cptdin)$_3^{3+}$;[145] D-Pt(l-pn)$_3^{4+}$, L-Pt(d-pn)$_3^{4+}$;[146] D-Rh(l-cptdin)$_3^{3+}$, L-Rh(d-cptdin)$_3^{3+}$.[145] It has also been shown that the two isomers obtained by the resolution of these reaction products from the racemic diamines are identical with those produced by the reaction of the metal ion with the dextro and the levo diamines separately.[145b, 146] Attempts to prepare isomers containing dextro and levo antipodes of the same donor molecule have not been successful. The reaction of L-[Co(d-cptdin)$_2$Cl$_2$]Cl with l-cptdin does not yield L-[Co(d-cptdin)$_2$(l-cptdin)]Cl$_3$ except perhaps as a very reactive intermediate.[145]

$$3\text{L-[Co(d-cptdin)}_2\text{Cl}_2]\text{Cl} + 3l\text{-cptdin} \rightarrow$$

$$3\text{L-[Co(d-cptdin)}_2(l\text{-cptdin)]Cl}_3 \rightarrow$$

$$2\text{L-[Co(d-cptdin)}_3]\text{Cl}_3 + \text{D-[Co(l-cptdin)}_3]\text{Cl}_3 \quad (28)$$

Although there appears to be a pronounced tendency to form only two of the eight possible isomers, Dddd and Llll or Dlll and Lddd, the more soluble geometric isomer of tri-d-alaninecobalt(III) has been separated into two forms, Dddd and Lddd.[147] It was suggested [145b, 148] that this may be due to the extreme stability of the cobalt(III) alanine chelate rings, which makes the rearrangement from a less stable to a more stable form difficult. Another similar example of the isolation of more than two isomers from such systems is the recent resolution of the hexol complex,[149a]

$$\left(\text{Co} \left[\begin{array}{c} \begin{array}{c} \text{H} \\ \text{O} \end{array} \\ \diagdown \\ \begin{array}{c} \text{O} \\ \text{H} \end{array} \end{array} \right] \text{Co(en)}_2 \right)_3^{6+}$$

to obtain four of the possible eight isomers. In this tetranuclear complex the optically active bidentate group is

$$\begin{array}{c} \text{H} \\ \text{O} \\ \diagup \diagdown \\ \qquad\qquad \text{Co(en)}_2{}^+ \\ \diagdown \diagup \\ \text{O} \\ \text{H} \end{array}$$

and it is believed that the four isomers isolated are Dddd, Dlll, Lddd, and Llll. Attempts to determine the optical activity of the donor groups in the polynuclear complex by means of acid hydrolysis to yield optically active Co(en)$_2$(H$_2$O)$_2{}^{2+}$ were not successful. Hydrolysis was accompanied by racemization. It is of interest to note that the rates of racemization of these two pairs of diastereomers differ by a factor of ten ($k_{40°C} = 1.1 \times 10^{-4}$ and 1.1×10^{-5} sec^{-1}).

Dwyer [149b] has started a detailed investigation of the systems $M(pn)_3^{3+}$. Preliminary systematic fractionation of 550 g. of DL[Co(dl-pn)$_3$]I$_3 \cdot$ H$_2$O as the chloride d-tartrate has already permitted the separation of six different isomers. These isomers are believed to be the following three sets of dl- pairs:

(1) *cis* or *trans* Dddd and Llll; $[\alpha]_D = \pm 24°$
(2) *cis* or *trans* Dddd and Llll; $[\alpha]_D = \pm 33°$
(3) *cis* or *trans* Dlll and Lddd; $[\alpha]_D = \sim \pm 120°$

The *cis* and *trans* structures refer to the relative positions of the methyl groups of the chelate rings in the octahedral complex as shown in Fig. 14. That each isomer has either all d- or all l-propylenediamine was verified by a decomposition of the complex and a determination of the optical rotation of the resulting diamine. Furthermore that isomer 3 has the unexpected combination Dlll and Lddd was confirmed by the charcoal-catalyzed mutarotation of Dddd followed by fractionation of the iodides. Three fractions were obtained corresponding to isomers 1, 2, and 3. Since isomer 3 was levorotatory it must be Lddd. This same experiment was repeated starting with Llll to yield a dextrorotatory 3 corresponding to Dlll. It has been suggested [149c] that it would be of interest to measure the change in optical rotation of a solution of one of these isomers, e.g., Dddd, after the addition of catalytic amounts of Co(d-pn)$_3^{2+}$. Such a study as this might make possible an estimate of the equilibrium concentrations of the various isomers. The rate of change of optical rotation would also provide a way to determine the rate of electron transfer in these systems.

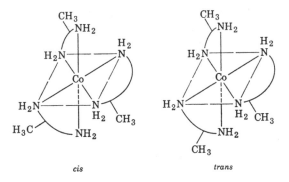

FIG. 14. Geometrical isomers of the tris(propylenediamine)cobalt(III) cation.

A similar, but less pronounced, effect is observed if the complex contains only two optically active coordinating groups. It has been shown [145] that cis-Co(cptdin)$_2$Cl$_2{}^+$ exists in only two of the six possible forms, DllCl$_2$ and LddCl$_2$. Whenever an aqueous solution of $trans$-[Co(d-cptdin)$_2$Cl$_2$]Cl is concentrated, it yields only cis-L-[Co(d-cptdin)$_2$Cl$_2$]Cl rather than a mixture of the two isomers, DddCl$_2$ and LddCl$_2$. However, it has been possible to obtain both DllCO$_3$ and LllCO$_3$ forms of Co(l-pn)$_2$CO$_3{}^+$.[150a] The DllCO$_3$ isomer is produced by concentration to dryness of an aqueous solution of the chloride at room temperature, whereas evaporation at 85°C yields LllCO$_3$.[150b]

Finally, complexes containing only one optically active donor group also exhibit the same stereospecificity but to a much smaller extent. A good illustration of this is afforded by the two reactions,[145]

DL-[Co(en)$_2$Cl$_2$]Cl + dl-cptdin $\rightarrow$

$$\text{D-[Co(en)}_2(l\text{-cptdin)]Cl}_3 + \text{L-[Co(en)}_2(d\text{-cptdin)]Cl}_3 \quad (29)$$

DL-[Co(en)$_2$Cl$_2$]Cl + d-cptdin $\rightarrow$

$$\text{D-[Co(en)}_2(d\text{-cptdin)]Cl}_3 + \text{L-[Co(en)}_2(d\text{-cptdin)]Cl}_3 \quad (30)$$

The stereospecific tendency for such a system is demonstrated by the first reaction, which yields only two of the possible four isomers (Dd, Dl, Ld, and Ll). However, the second reaction does show that it is also possible to obtain the Dd and presumably also the Ll isomers. Although it is possible to introduce d-1,2-cyclopentanediamine into either D- or L-Co(en)$_2$Cl$_2{}^+$, the d-diamine cannot be introduced into D-Co(l-cptdin)$_2$Cl$_2{}^+$ as mentioned earlier. Thus there is a more pronounced difference between a dextro and levo isomer of the same compound than exists between an optically active molecule and a totally different substance in those cases where it is attempted to introduce them all together into the same dissymmetrical spatial configuration. The previous presence of an unrelated diamine in the complex is a less serious hindrance to the entrance of an optically active diamine than is the presence of the same diamines but of enantiomorphous arrangement. This characteristic behavior appears to be somewhat analogous to the highly specific action of optically active ferments and enzymes on attackable substrates of enantiomorphous configuration.

Bailar [148] and his students have utilized this stereospecific behavior of coordination compounds both to prepare optically active complexes and to resolve diamines, carboxylic acids, and amino acids. They were able to prepare optically active $Co(en)_3^{3+}$, $Co(en)_2Cl_2^+$, and $Co(en)_2(NO_2)_2^+$ from the product obtained by the reaction of DL-Co-$(en)_2CO_3^+$ with d-tartaric acid.[151]   This reaction yields a mixture of D-$Co(en)_2(d$-tart$)^+$ and L-$Co(en)_2(d$-tart$)^+$, and it was found that the two diastereomers differ greatly in reactivity.   When this mixture is shaken with ethylenediamine at room temperature, part of the material reacts within two hours to give d-$Co(en)_3^{3+}$; the remainder does not react even in twelve hours.   As much as a 70% yield of d-Co-$(en)_3^{3+}$ is obtained, so that either the two isomers of $\overline{Co}(en)_2(d$-tart$)^+$ are not present in equal amount or the less reactive is converted to the more reactive as it is consumed by reaction with ethylenediamine. Similarly reactions with hydrochloric acid and with calcium nitrite yield d-$Co(en)_2Cl_2^+$ and d-$Co(en)_2(NO_2)_2^+$ respectively.   The same procedure but forming the d-antimonyltartrato instead of the d-tartrato complex was used to prepare l-$Co(en)_2Cl_2^+$ and l-$Co(trien)Cl_2^+$.[152] The method has not been found to work for complexes with only one replaceable group such as $Co(en)_2(NH_3)Cl^{2+}$, or with optically active ions such as d-α-bromocamphor-π-sulfonate which would not readily enter the coordination sphere.

The treatment of $Co(l$-pn$)_2CO_3^+$ with d- and with l-tartaric acid gives $Co(l$-pn$)_2(d$-tart$)^+$ and $Co(l$-pn$)_2(l$-tart$)^+$ respectively, but the two isomers differ markedly in reactivity.[153]   Both will react with l-propylenediamine to yield $Co(l$-pn$)_3^{3+}$, but, at 70°C, the latter reacts completely in 40 min, whereas the former requires 2 hr.   This difference in reactivity was further demonstrated by the partial resolution of racemic tartaric acid.   Whenever the reaction product obtained from the reaction of $Co(l$-pn$)_2CO_3^+$ with racemic tartaric acid is allowed to react with l-propylenediamine, the tartrate ion liberated in the initial stages of the reaction has a levorotation.

A slightly different method has been used for the partial resolution of racemic tartaric acid [154] as well as certain other organic acids.[155] The method consists of allowing 100% excess of the racemic acid to react with $Co(l$-pn$)_2CO_3^+$.   One enantiomorph of the acid enters the coordination sphere more readily than the other.   This results in the resolution of the racemic acid, since the coordinated and uncoordinated acid fractions can be removed from solution separately.   The same method was used to resolve a racemic mixture of propylenediamine or alanine with copper(II), nickel(II), or cobalt(III) complexes of d-tartrate, l-glutamate, or d-gluconate ions.[156]   The degree of resolution achieved was low, not over 5% for the copper(II) and nickel(II) complexes nor over 20% with cobalt(III) complexes.

The stereospecific behavior of coordination compounds containing optically active ligands is generally attributed to the formation of a preferred dissymmetrical configuration about the central atom. Jaeger [145b] points out that complexes of the type $M(AA)_3$ possess a rather high degree of symmetry D_3 (the symmetry of d- and l-quartz), provided the substituents themselves have a single binary symmetry axis. In other cases, such as $M(d-AA)_2(l-AA)$, this degree of symmetry of the complex must be much less even if the condition just mentioned be fulfilled. In such a case the complex ions will have but a single polar binary axis C_2. Thus the observed stereospecificity is believed to result from the tendency to generate the least unsymmetrical asymmetric isomer.

Mention was made earlier of the observation that the reaction of cobalt(III) with d-1,2-propanediamine and with l-$trans$-1,2-cyclopentanediamine yields D-$Co(d$-pn$)_3{}^{3+}$ and D-$Co(l$-cptdin$)_3{}^{3+}$ respectively.[145] That the observed optical rotation of these complex ions must be caused chiefly by the dissymmetrical configuration about the cobalt(III) ion is shown by a comparison of their rotatory dispersion curves with that for the analogous ethylenediamine complex, $Co(en)_3{}^{3+}$ (Fig. 15). The marked similarity between these curves suggests that the source of optical rotation is essentially the same

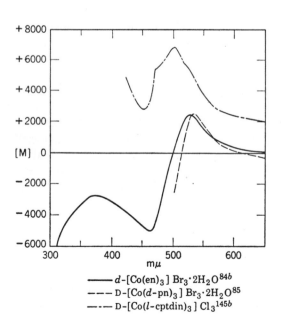

FIG. 15. Rotatory dispersion curves.

——— d-[Co(en)$_3$] Br$_3$·2H$_2$O [84b]
‒ ‒ ‒ D-[Co(d-pn)$_3$] Br$_3$·2H$_2$O [85]
‒·‒·‒ D-[Co(l-cptdin)$_3$] Cl$_3$ [145b]

in the three cations. Since in $Co(en)_3^{3+}$ the optical activity must arise from the asymmetric arrangement of the chelate rings about the cobalt, this is likewise the presumed source for the complexes which contain optically active diamines. Additional support of this is afforded by the data shown in Table 10.[144a, 146]

Table 10 *

Optical Rotation of Platinum(II), (IV) Complexes Containing l-1,2-Propanediamine

Compound	$[M]_D^{25°}$
$[Pt(l\text{-pn})(NH_3)_2]Cl_2$	+94.1
$[Pt(l\text{-pn})en]Cl_2$	+96.3
$[Pt(l\text{-pn})_2]Cl_2$	+192.0
$[Pt(l\text{-pn})_3]Cl_4$	+1025

* From reference 146.

The molecular rotation due to each molecule of l-1,2-propanediamine separately introduced into the square platinum(II) complexes is approximately +96°. Therefore coordination of three molecules of l-1,2-propanediamine may be expected to give a molecular rotation of approximately +288°. Instead, the observed molecular rotation for D-$[Pt(l\text{-pn})_3]Cl_4$ is +1025°, which suggests that much of the surplus observed is due to the fixed asymmetry of the ligands about the platinum(IV). Perhaps a much better comparison would be one in which the oxidation state of platinum is kept constant, e.g., $Pt(l\text{-pn})(NH_3)_4^{4+}$, $trans\text{-}Pt(l\text{-pn})_2(NH_3)_2^{4+}$, and $Pt(l\text{-pn})_3^{4+}$.[157]

One other interesting observation in support of asymmetric induction in these systems is afforded by the reaction of d-Co(EDTA)$^-$ with ethylenediamine[67] and with racemic propylenediamine.[158] The reaction with ethylenediamine yields d-$Co(en)_3^{3+}$, which means that at least to some extent the asymmetry of the complex is maintained during the reaction. It seems plausible that the same retention of configuration would result for the analogous reaction with propylenediamine. In addition it is observed that in this reaction there is a selectivity towards the dextro form of the diamine. This therefore suggests that the particular asymmetric arrangement in question about the cobalt(III) prefers one antipode of racemic propylenediamine over the other.

In direct opposition to this concept of asymmetric induction about the central metal ion due to the coordination of optically active ligands is the recent interpretation of data on the dispersion ratio of several complexes (Table 11).[159] The term dispersion ratio means simply the

Table 11

Dispersion Ratio of Metal-Diamine Complexes

Complex	$\alpha_{4705}/\alpha_{5880}$	Reference
$[Zn(l\text{-}pn)_2]Cl_2$	1.74	159b
$[Pt(d\text{-}pn)_2]Cl_2$	1.74	144b
$[Pt(l\text{-}pn)_3]Br_4$	1.74	159b
$[Rh(d\text{-}ptn)_3]I_3$ [a]	1.75	160
$[Rh(l\text{-}cptdin)_3]Cl_3$	1.74	145a
$[Pt(en)_3]Cl_4$	1.68	161
$[Rh(en)_3]I_3$	1.44	162
$[Rh(m\text{-}ptn)_3]I_3$	2.08	160

[a] ptn = 2,4-n-pentanediamine.

ratio of the optical rotations of a compound at two different wavelengths. It is apparent from the data in Table 11 that the dispersion ratio at 4705 and 5880 A is the same for all of the compounds which contain optically active ligands. This dispersion ratio differs from the values observed for complexes with optically inactive ligands, the most striking comparison being that of $[Rh(d\text{-}ptn)_3]I_3$ and $[Rh(m\text{-}ptn)_3]I_3$. It was suggested [159] that such a difference must mean that the source of optical activity in metal complexes with optically active diamines is different than that for the resolved metal complexes with inactive diamines. One other thing to note about the data in Table 11 is that the dispersive power seems independent of the metal ion, even should it become a center of asymmetry, and of the optically active diamine. The diamines alone (not coordinated) also show a constant dispersion ratio. Because of this constant dispersion ratio, it has been presumed that the optical activity of the complex arises only from the ligands and not from any induced asymmetry around the central metal ion. It should be pointed out however that all of the complexes listed in Table 11 are colorless and that therefore the dispersion ratio is reported only for a wavelength region some distance removed from the absorption bands of the complex ions. Certainly in the absorption band wavelength region there are many known examples of similar complexes which contain optically inactive or optically active ligands having analogous rotatory dispersion curves (Fig. 12). Thus it would be of interest to determine the ultraviolet rotatory dispersion curves of the complexes in Table 11; of particular interest would be a comparison of $[Rh(d\text{-}ptn)_3]I_3$ and $[Rh(m\text{-}ptn)_3]I_3$.

There is at present therefore evidence both for and against induced asymmetry around the central metal ion arising from the coordination of optically active ligands. Further study is required in order to settle this question. If the presence of optically active ligands in a complex does cause it to take on a fixed asymmetry, then the stereospecific reactions which have been observed for these systems are readily understood. However, if this is not the case, then the coordination of l-AA with a metal ion does not yield $D\text{-}[D\text{-}M(l\text{-}AA)]_3$ but instead $D\text{-}[DL\text{-}M(l\text{-}AA)_3]$, where D and L are used to represent the generic configuration of the complex. Thus the reaction of $DL\text{-}Co(en)_2CO_3{}^+$ with d-tartaric acid would yield $L\text{-}[DL\text{-}Co(en)_2(d\text{-}tart)]^+$. Yet, as was mentioned earlier, a reaction of the resulting d-tartrato complex with ethylenediamine yields as much as 70% $d\text{-}Co(en)_3{}^{3+}$. However, such a result does not necessarily require that there be a prior induced asymmetry about the cobalt(III) ion. It can equally well be accounted for on the basis of a slight difference in either the stability or the reactivity of the two diastereomers. Thus all of the stereospecific reactions described in this section can be understood without invoking the argument of induced asymmetry.

A somewhat related effect is that reported for the acid hydrolysis rates of $trans\text{-}Co(bn)_2Cl_2{}^+$ where bn is either racemic or $meso$-2,3-butanediamine.[163] The complex with the $meso$-diamine reacts thirty times faster than that with the racemic diamine. This difference in reactivity is attributed to crowding of the two methyl groups on the same side of the chelate ring in the $meso$-diamine leading to strain in the complex.

REFERENCES

1. S. M. Jørgensen, *J. prakt. Chem.*, **39**, 16 (1889); **41**, 449 (1890).
2. A. Werner, *Ber.*, **44**, 3278 (1911).
3. A. Werner, *ibid.*, **44**, 2452 (1911).
4. M. Delepine, *Compt. rend.*, **175**, 1409 (1922).
5. M. Delepine, *Anales soc. españ. fis. y quim.*, **27**, 485 (1929).
6. H. D. K. Drew and N. H. Pratt, *J. Chem. Soc.*, **1937**, 506.
7. H. D. K. Drew and H. J. Tress, *J. Chem. Soc.*, **1932**, 2328; **1933**, 1335.
8. G. W. Ettle and C. H. Johnson, *J. Chem. Soc.*, **1939**, 1490.
9. J. P. Mathieu, *Bull. soc. chim.*, [5]4, 687 (1937).
10. (*a*) R. G. Pearson, R. E. Meeker, and F. Basolo, *J. Am. Chem. Soc.*, **78**, 2673 (1956). (*b*) R. G. Pearson and F. Basolo, *ibid.*, **78**, 4878 (1956).
11. D. D. Brown and R. S. Nyholm, *J. Chem. Soc.*, **1953**, 2696.

12. R. F. Trimble, Jr., *J. Am. Chem. Soc.*, **76**, 6321 (1954).
13. A. Uspensky and K. Tschibisoff, *Z. anorg. u. allgem. Chem.*, **164**, 326 (1927).
14. T. Uemura and N. Hirosawa, *Bull. Chem. Soc. Japan*, **13**, 377 (1938); F. Basolo, *J. Am. Chem. Soc.*, **72**, 4393 (1950).
15. J. Bjerrum and S. E. Rasmussen, *Acta Chem. Scand.*, **6**, 1265 (1952).
16. R. G. Yalman and T. Kuwana, *J. Phys. Chem.*, **59**, 298 (1955).
17. A. Werner, *Ann.*, **406**, 261 (1914).
18. G. E. Cunningham, R. W. Burley, and M. T. Friend, *Nature*, **169**, 1103 (1952); R. E. Hamm, *J. Am. Chem. Soc.*, **75**, 609 (1953).
19. F. P. Dwyer, N. S. Gill, E. C. Gyarfas, and F. Lions, *J. Am. Chem. Soc.*, **74**, 4188 (1952).
20. D. P. Mellor, *Chem. Revs.*, **33**, 137 (1943).
21. L. Tschugaeff, *J. Russ. Phys. Chem. Soc.*, **42**, 1472 (1910); K. A. Jensen, *Z. anorg. u. allgem. Chem.*, **229**, 265 (1936); W. Klemm and K. H. Raddatz, *Z. anorg. u. allgem. Chem.*, **250**, 207 (1942); A. A. Grinberg and V. M. Shulman, *Compt. rend. acad. sci. U.R.S.S.*, **1**, 218 (1933); F. G. Mann, D. Crowfoot, D. Gottiker, and N. Wooster, *J. Chem. Soc.*, **1935**, 1642.
22. S. Sugden, *J. Chem. Soc.*, **1932**, 246.
23. H. J. Cavell and S. Sugden, *ibid.*, **1935**, 621.
24. F. P. Dwyer and D. P. Mellor, *J. Am. Chem. Soc.*, **57**, 605 (1935).
25. H. D. K. Drew, *J. Chem. Soc.*, **1929**, 560.
26. E. G. Cox, W. Wardlaw, and K. C. Webster, *ibid.*, **1936**, 775.
27. F. W. Pinkard, E. Sharratt, W. Wardlaw, and E. G. Cox, *ibid.*, **1934**, 1012.
28. J. Chatt and R. G. Wilkins, *ibid.*, **1952**, 273, 4300; **1953**, 70; **1956**, 525.
29. J. Chatt, L. A. Duncanson, and L. M. Venanzi, *ibid.*, **1955**, 4461.
30. H. D. K. Drew and G. H. Wyatt, *ibid.*, **1934**, 56; J. V. Quagliano and L. Schubert, *Chem. Revs.*, **50**, 220 (1952).
31. H. B. Jonassen and N. L. Cull, *J. Am. Chem. Soc.*, **73**, 274 (1951); H. B. Jonassen, T. O. Sistrunk, J. R. Oliver, and G. F. Helfrich, *ibid.*, **75**, 5216 (1953); H. B. Jonassen and T. O. Sistrunk, *J. Phys. Chem.*, **59**, 290 (1955).
32. S. M. Jørgensen, *Z. anorg. Chem.*, **5**, 169 (1893).
33. J. Lecomte and C. Duval, *Bull. soc. chim.*, [5]**12**, 678 (1945); R. Duval, C. Duval, and J. Lecomte, *ibid.*, [5]**14**, 1048 (1947).
34. M. Linhard, H. Seibert, and M. Weigel, *Z. anorg. u. allgem. Chem.*, **278**, 287 (1955); B. Adell, *ibid.*, **279**, 220 (1955); R. B. Penland, F. J. Lane and J. V. Quagliano, *J. Am. Chem. Soc.*, **78**, 887 (1956).
35. B. Adell, *Z. anorg. u. allgem. Chem.*, **271**, 49 (1952).
36. B. Adell, *Acta Chem. Scand*, **4**, 1 (1950).
37. B. Adell, *ibid.*, **5**, 54, 941 (1951).
38. B. Adell, *Svensk Kem. Tidskr.*, **56**, 318 (1944); **57**, 260 (1945).
39. R. G. Pearson, P. M. Henry, J. G. Bergmann, F. Basolo, *J. Am. Chem. Soc.*, **76**, 5920 (1954).
40. R. K. Murmann and H. Taube, *ibid.*, **78**, 4886 (1956).
41. H. Taube and A. C. Rutenberg, *J. Chem. Phys.*, **20**, 825 (1952).
42. C. H. Johnson, *Trans. Faraday Soc.*, **31**, 1612 (1935).
43. (a) M. Delepine, *Bull. soc. chim.*, **1**, 1256 (1934). (b) F. P. Dwyer and A. M. Sorgeson, *J. Phys. Chem.*, **60**, 1331 (1956).
44. W. Wahl, *Ber.*, **60**, 399 (1927); G. J. Burrows and K. H. Lauder, *J. Am. Chem. Soc.*, **53**, 3600 (1931).

45. W. D. Treadwell, G. Szobados, and E. Haimann, *Helv. Chim. Acta,* **15,** 1049 (1932).
46. (*a*) B. Das Sarma and J. C. Bailar, Jr., *J. Am. Chem. Soc.,* **77,** 5476, 5480 (1955). (*b*) F. McCullough, Jr., and J. C. Bailar, Jr., *ibid.,* **78,** 714 (1956).
47. R. F. Weinland and J. Heinzler, *Ber.,* **52,** 1322 (1919).
48. P. Neogi and G. K. Mukherjee, *J. Indian Chem. Soc.,* **11,** 225 (1934).
49. A. Werner, *Ber.,* **45,** 3061 (1912); F. M. Jaeger, *Rec. trav. chem.,* **38,** 250 (1919).
50. E. Bushra and C. H. Johnson, *J. Chem. Soc.,* **1939,** 1937.
51. A. Werner, *Ber.,* **45,** 865 (1912).
52. (*a*) A. Werner, *Ber.,* **44,** 3138 (1911). (*b*) J. Selbin and J. C. Bailar, Jr., *J. Am. Chem. Soc.,* **79,** 4285 (1957).
53. F. M. Jaeger, *Rec. trav. chim.,* **38,** 247 (1919).
54. F. P. Dwyer and E. C. Gyarfas, *Nature,* **168,** 29 (1951).
55. A. Werner and J. Basshart, *Ber.,* **47,** 2178 (1914).
56. A. Werner, *ibid.,* **45,** 121 (1912).
57. B. E. Douglas, *J. Am. Chem. Soc.,* **76,** 1020 (1954).
58. A. Werner, *Ber.,* **44,** 3280 (1911); J. C. Bailar, Jr., *Inorg. Syntheses,* **II,** 223 (1946).
59. D. D. Brown and C. K. Ingold, *J. Chem. Soc.,* **1953,** 2680.
60. W. R. Matoush and F. Basolo, *J. Am. Chem. Soc.,* **78,** 3972 (1956); F. Basolo W. R. Matoush, and R. G. Pearson, *ibid.,* **78,** 4883 (1956).
61. A. Werner, *Ber.,* **44,** 3278 (1911).
62. W. Tupizina, thesis, Zurich, 1915; *Gmelin's Handbuch der anorganischen Chemie,* Verlag Chemie, Berlin, 1930, No. 58B, p. 273.
63. A. Werner and E. Schalze, *Ber.,* **44,** 1896 (1911).
64. A. Werner, *ibid.,* **47,** 3090 (1914).
65. H. Goodwin, E. C. Gyarfas, and D. P. Mellor, private communication.
66. D. H. Busch and J. C. Bailar, Jr., *J. Am. Chem. Soc.,* **75,** 4574 (1953).
67. F. P. Dwyer, E. C. Gyarfas, and D. P. Mellor, *J. Phys. Chem.,* **59,** 296 (1955).
68. P. Neogi and N. K. Dutt, *J. Indian Chem. Soc.,* **15,** 83 (1938).
69. T. Moeller and N. C. Nielsen, *J. Am. Chem. Soc.,* **75,** 5106 (1953).
70. M. Delepine, *Compt. rend.,* **159,** 239 (1914); **175,** 1409 (1922).
71. A. Werner and A. P. Smirnoff, *Helv. Chim. Acta,* **3,** 472 (1920).
72. W. Thomas, *J. Chem. Soc.,* **121,** 196 (1922).
73. A. Werner, *Ber.,* **45,** 433 (1912).
74. F. P. Dwyer and E. C. Gyarfas, *J. Am. Chem. Soc.,* **74,** 4699 (1952).
75. F. P. Dwyer and E. C. Gyarfas, *J. Proc. Roy. Soc. N. S. Wales,* **83,** 263 (1949).
76. F. P. Dwyer and E. C. Gyarfas, *ibid.,* **83,** 263 (1949).
77. F. P. Dwyer, N. S. Gill, E. C. Gyarfas, and F. Lions, *J. Am. Chem. Soc.,* **75,** 3834 (1953).
78. G. T. Morgan and F. H. Burstall, *J. Chem. Soc.,* **1931,** 2213.
79. F. P. Dwyer and E. C. Gyarfas, *J. Proc. Roy. Soc. N. S. Wales,* **83,** 232 (1949).
80. G. F. Svatos, thesis, Northwestern University, 1952.
81. F. H. Burstall, F. P. Dwyer, and E. C. Gyarfas, *J. Chem. Soc.,* **1950,** 953.
82. F. P. Dwyer and E. C. Gyarfas, *J. Am. Chem. Soc.,* **73,** 2322 (1951).
83. F. P. Dwyer, N. A. Gibson, and E. C. Gyarfas, *J. Proc. Roy. Soc. N. S. Wales,* **84,** 68 (1951).

84. (a) J. P. Mathieu, *Bull. soc. chim.,* **6,** 1258 (1939); (b) *J. chim. phys.,* **33,** 78 (1936).

85. A. P. Smirnoff, *Helv. Chim. Acta,* **3,** 177 (1920).

86. L. F. Heneghan and J. C. Bailar, Jr., *J. Am. Chem. Soc.,* **75,** 1840 (1953).

87. A. Werner, *Ber.,* **45,** 1954 (1914).

88. F. G. Mann, *J. Chem. Soc.,* **1933,** 412.

89. A. Werner, *Ber.,* **45,** 1229 (1912).

90. F. P. Dwyer and E. C. Gyarfas, *J. Proc. Roy. Soc. N. S. Wales,* **83,** 174 (1949).

91. F. P. Dwyer and E. C. Gyarfas, *Nature,* **163,** 918 (1949); *J. Proc. Roy. Soc. N. S. Wales,* **83,** 170 (1949).

92. A. Rosenheim, B. Raibmann, and G. Schendel, *Z. anorg. u. allgem. Chem.,* **196,** 168 (1931).

93. P. Neogi and G. K. Mukherjee, *J. Indian Chem. Soc.,* **11,** 681 (1934).

94. W. Thomas, *J. Chem. Soc.,* **119,** 1140 (1921); W. Thomas and R. Frazer, *ibid.,* **123,** 2973 (1923); E. K. Rideal and W. Thomas, *ibid.,* **121,** 196 (1922).

95. F. Basolo, J. C. Hayes, and H. M. Neumann, *J. Am. Chem. Soc.,* **75,** 5102 (1953).

96. G. K. Schweitzer and J. M. Lee, *J. Phys. Chem.,* **56,** 195 (1952); N. R. Davies and F. P. Dwyer, *Trans. Faraday Soc.,* **48,** 244 (1952); **49,** 180 (1953).

97. (a) R. G. Wilkins and M. J. G. Williams, *J. Chem. Soc.,* **1957,** 4514. (b) P. Ellis, R. G. Wilkins, and M. J. G. Williams, *ibid.,* **1957,** 4456.

98. A. A. Frost and R. G. Pearson, *Kinetics and Mechanism,* John Wiley & Sons, New York, 1953, p. 155.

99. A. Werner, *Ber.,* **45,** 3061 (1912).

100. C. H. Johnson and A. Mead, *Trans. Faraday Soc.,* **31,** 1621 (1935).

101. N. W. D. Beese and C. H. Johnson, *Trans. Faraday Soc.,* **31,** 1632 (1935).

102. F. A. Long, *J. Am. Chem. Soc.,* **61,** 570 (1939); **63,** 1353 (1941).

103. J. S. Holden and G. M. Harris, *ibid.,* **77,** 1934 (1955).

104. N. R. Davies and F. P. Dwyer, *Trans. Faraday Soc.,* **48,** 244 (1952); **49,** 180 (1953); **50,** 820 (1954).

105. S. Ruben, M. D. Kamen, M. B. Allen, and P. Nahinsky, *J. Am. Chem. Soc.,* **64,** 2297 (1942); T. S. Lee, I. M. Kolthoff, and D. L. Leussing, *ibid.,* **70,** 3596 (1948); J. H. Baxendale and P. George, *Trans. Faraday Soc.,* **46,** 736 (1950).

106. (a) F. Basolo, J. C. Hayes, and H. M. Neumann, *J. Am. Chem. Soc.,* **76,** 3807 (1954). (b) D. W. Margerum, R. I. Bystroff, and C. V. Banks, *ibid.,* **78,** 4211 (1956). (c) D. W. Margerum, *ibid.,* **79,** 2728 (1957). (d) D. R. Llewellyn and J. H. Carter, private communication.

107. N. R. Davies, *Revs. Pure and Applied Chem.,* **4,** 66 (1954).

108. J. E. Dickens, thesis, Oxford, 1954.

109. R. Charonnat, *Ann. chim.,* **16,** 202 (1931).

110. P. Rây and N. K. Dutt, *J. Indian Chem. Soc.,* **18,** 289 (1941); **20,** 81 (1943).

111. P. Faust and J. V. Quagliano, *J. Am. Chem. Soc.,* **76,** 5346 (1954); G. M. Barrow, R. H. Krueger, and F. Basolo, *J. Inorg. Nuclear Chem.,* **2,** 340 (1956)

112. (a) W. G. Gehman, thesis, Pennsylvania State University, State College, Pa., 1954. (b) L. Seiden, thesis, Northwestern University, Evanston, Ill., 1957.

113. (a) J. E. Dickens, F. Basolo, and H. M. Neumann, *J. Am. Chem. Soc.,* **79,** 1286 (1957). (b) A. Jensen, F. Basolo, and H. M. Neumann, *ibid.,* 1958, in press.

114. P. Pfeiffer and K. Quehl, *Ber.*, **64**, 2667 (1931); **65**, 560 (1932).
115. F. P. Dwyer, M. F. O'Dwyer, and E. C. Gyarfas, *Nature*, **167**, 1036 (1951).
116. E. E. Turner and M. M. Harris, *Quart. Revs. London*, **1**, 299 (1948).
117. N. R. Davies and F. P. Dwyer, *Trans. Faraday Soc.*, **50**, 24 (1954).
118. G. K. Schweitzer and J. L. Rose, Jr., *J. Phys. Chem.*, **56**, 428 (1952).
119. N. R. Davies and F. P. Dwyer, *Trans. Faraday Soc.*, **50**, 1325 (1954).
120. (a) H. M. Neumann, private communication. (b) B. R. Baker, thesis, Northwestern University, Evanston, Ill., 1958.
121. R. Schwarz and W. Kronig, *Ber.*, **56**, 208 (1923).
122. F. P. Dwyer and E. C. Gyarfas, *Nature*, **166**, 481 (1950).
123. D. H. Busch, *J. Am. Chem. Soc.*, **77**, 2747 (1955).
124. R. L. Shriner, R. Adams, and C. S. Marvel in H. Gilman, *Organic Chemistry*, 2nd ed., John Wiley & Sons, New York, 1943, Vol. I, pp. 400–434.
125. J. Boeseken and J. A. Mijs, *Rec. trav. chim.*, **44**, 758 (1925).
126. J. Boeseken, H. D. Muller, and R. T. Jophangjauw, *ibid.*, **45**, 919 (1926).
127. W. H. Mills and R. A. Gotts, *J. Chem. Soc.*, **1926**, 3121.
128. H. Burgess and T. M. Lowry, *ibid.*, **1924**, 2081.
129. D. H. Busch and J. C. Bailar, Jr., *J. Am. Chem. Soc.*, **76**, 5352 (1954).
130. J. C. I. Lin and J. C. Bailar, Jr., *ibid.*, **73**, 5432 (1951).
131. W. H. Mills and R. E. D. Clark, *J. Chem. Soc.*, **1936**, 175.
132. A. Werner, *Lehrbuch der Stereochemie*, Gustav Fischer, Jena, 1904, p. 48.
133. G. W. Wheland, *Advanced Organic Chemistry*, John Wiley & Sons, New York, 1949, pp. 250–253.
134. T. M. Lowry and R. C. Traill, *Proc. Roy. Soc. London*, **A132**, 398 (1931).
135. F. P. Dwyer, M. F. O'Dwyer, and E. C. Gyarfas, *Nature*, **167**, 1036 (1951); F. P. Dwyer and E. C. Gyarfas, *ibid.*, **168**, 29 (1951); E. C. Gyarfas, *Revs. Pure and Appl. Chem.*, **4**, 73 (1954).
136. P. Pfeiffer and K. Quehl, *Ber.*, **64**, 2667 (1931); **65**, 560 (1932).
137. P. Pfeiffer and Y. Nakasuka, *Ber.*, **66**, 410 (1933).
138. N. Davies and F. P. Dwyer, *J. Proc. Roy. Soc. N. S. Wales*, **86**, 64 (1953).
139. R. C. Brasted, thesis, University of Illinois, Urbana, Ill., 1942.
140. V. Landis, thesis, University of Minnesota, Minneapolis, Minn., 1956.
141. (a) F. P. Dwyer, E. C. Gyarfas, and M. F. O'Dwyer, *J. Proc. Roy. Soc. N. S. Wales*, **89**, 146 (1956). (b) G. T. Barnes, J. R. Backhouse, F. P. Dwyer, and E. C. Gyarfas, *ibid.*, **89**, 151 (1956).
142. L. Pauling, *J. Chem. Soc.*, **1948**, 1461.
143. J. O'M. Bockris, J. Bowler-Reed, and J. A. Kitchener, *Trans. Faraday Soc.*, **47**, 184 (1951).
144. (a) L. Tschugaeff and V. Sokoloff, *Ber.*, **40**, 177 (1907); (b) **42**, 55 (1909).
145. (a) F. M. Jaeger and H. B. Blumendal, *Z. anorg. u. allgem. Chem.*, **175**, 161, 198, 200, 220 (1928). (b) F. M. Jaeger, *Optical Activity and High Temperature Measurements*, McGraw-Hill Book Co., New York, 1930.
146. A. P. Smirnoff, *Helv. Chim. Acta*, **3**, 177, 181, 194 (1920).
147. J. Lifschitz, *Z. physik. Chem.*, **114**, 493 (1925).
148. J. C. Bailar, Jr., *Record Chem. Progr. Kresge-Hooker Sci. Lib.*, **10**, 17 (1949).
149. (a) H. Goodwin, E. C. Gyarfas, and D. P. Mellor, unpublished results. (b) F. P. Dwyer, private communication. (c) D. H. Busch, private communication.

150. (a) J. C. Bailar, Jr., and J. P. McReynolds, *J. Am. Chem. Soc.*, **61,** 3199 (1939). (b) M. Martinette and J. C. Bailar, Jr., *ibid.*, **74,** 1054 (1952)

151. H. B. Jonassen, J. C. Bailar, Jr., and E. H. Huffman, *ibid.*, **70,** 756 (1948).

152. B. Das Sarma and J. C. Bailar, Jr., *ibid.*, **77,** 5480 (1955).

153. J. C. Bailar, Jr., H. B. Jonassen, and A. D. Gott, *ibid.*, **74,** 3131 (1952).

154. H. Hamilton, thesis, University of Illinois, Urbana, Ill., 1947.

155. A. D. Gott and J. C. Bailar, Jr., *ibid.*, **74,** 4820 (1952).

156. B. Das Sarma and J. C. Bailar, Jr., *ibid.*, **78,** 895 (1956).

157. J. C. Bailar, Jr., International Conference on Coordination Chemistry, Rome, September, 1957; private communication.

158. S. Kirschner, Y. K. Wei, and J. C. Bailar, Jr., *J. Am. Chem. Soc.*, **79,** 5877 (1957).

159. (a) T. D. O'Brien and R. C. Toole, *ibid.*, **76,** 6009 (1954); (b) **77,** 1368 (1955).

160. C. J. Dippel and F. M. Jaeger, *Rec. trav. chim.*, **50,** 547 (1931).

161. J. P. Mathieu, *Bull. soc. chim.*, **6,** 1258 (1939).

162. F. M. Jaeger, *Rec. trav. chim.*, **38,** 11 (1919).

163. R. G. Pearson, C. R. Boston, and F. Basolo, *ibid.*, **75,** 3089 (1953).

1 Oxidation-reduction reactions

The classical definition of oxidation and reduction in terms of gain or loss of oxygen has in modern times been abandoned in favor of the concept of electron loss (oxidation) and electron gain (reduction). It is now customary to discuss an oxidative process in terms of an ion-electron or half-cell equation, e.g.,

$$Fe^{2+} \rightarrow Fe^{3+} + e \tag{1}$$

The implication that redox reactions occur by coupled electron-loss and electron-gain steps may be quite incorrect as far as mechanism is concerned. Operationally we define oxidation-reduction reactions in terms of changes in oxidation states or oxidation numbers. The alleged transfer of electrons is a bookkeeping device for effecting the changes in oxidation states and for balancing the equations. Since the oxidation states are themselves calculated according to an arbitrary and sometimes unrealistic set of rules, there may be little relation between what is shown in the two half-cell equations representing a redox reaction and what actually occurs when the reagents are mixed.

For example, the reaction of a halogen with alkali such as

$$I_2 + OH^- \rightarrow I^- + IOH \tag{2}$$

is clearly an oxidation-reduction reaction by the usual rules (the oxidation number of iodine changing from zero to $+1$ and -1. Mechanistically, however, this reaction can be classified as a typical S_N2 reaction with the nucleophile hydroxide ion displacing iodide ion from the electrophile iodonium ion, I^+. Or it can be considered a typical acid-base reaction involving the Lewis acid I^+. Edwards [1] has a discussion of many redox reactions considered as displacement processes.

Particularly in aqueous solution it is usually possible to imagine atom or group transfer, rather than electron transfer, as occurring in a redox reaction. For example, iron(II) ion may act as a reducing agent by transferring a hydrogen atom from its hydration shell to a substrate:

$$Fe(H_2O)_6^{2+} + R \cdot \rightarrow Fe(H_2O)_5OH^{2+} + RH \tag{3}$$

Iron(III) ion may act as oxidizing agent by transferring hydroxyl radical to a substrate:

$$Fe(H_2O)_6^{3+} + R \cdot \rightarrow Fe(H_2O)_5^{2+} + H^+ + ROH \tag{4}$$

In general, transfer of a positive group or atom is equivalent to the transfer of electrons, and transfer of a negative group or atom is equivalent to the taking up of electrons.

The problem, then, in studying the mechanism of an oxidation-reduction reaction, is to find out if atom transfer or electron transfer occurs, which atoms are transferred or how many electrons are transferred, and what intermediates, stable or unstable, are formed. A complete study would include a detailed picture of the transition state for all steps involved. Not only the composition but also the geometry of the transition state is desired.

ELECTRON TRANSFER REACTIONS

In view of the preceding discussion it is fair to raise the question as to whether or not simple electron transfer reactions exist. In the case of gaseous systems the evidence is clear that direct electron transfer between molecules does occur.[2] In a number of cases the probability of transfer, expressed as a collision diameter, is known. Even monatomic molecules can have large effective diameters for accepting an electron in certain cases. The values found can be several times the diameters determined by viscosity measurements.[3]

In particular electron transfer is very efficient when occurring between a rare gas molecule and its ion,

$$A + A^+ \rightarrow A^+ + A \tag{5}$$

This is because of the operation of a quantum mechanical resonance effect. The modern picture of an electron in an atomic orbit as an electron cloud with charge density falling off with distance from the nucleus enables us to understand how it may occasionally be found far from the nucleus. However, even if an electron comes much closer to another nucleus than to its original parent, it will only transfer if the law of conservation of energy can be maintained. This condition exists if the two atoms, except for the transferring electron, are identical, as in reaction 5.

It can be shown [4] that the frequency with which an electron transfers between two identical nuclei is given approximately by the interaction energy of the system divided by Planck's constant. Since the interaction energy depends on the extent to which the orbitals centered on the two nuclei overlap each other, we see that the rate of electron transfer is large for two orbitals which occupy much the same region in space. There are also symmetry restrictions depending on the sign of the wave function associated with the orbital and the energy restriction mentioned earlier. The simultaneous transfer of two or more electrons becomes less probable.

The situation in a solution in the liquid state is more complicated. The same restrictions operate as before, but now not even approximate quantum mechanical calculations can be made because of the large number of particles that must be considered. From a qualitative view it seems reasonable that an electron transfer which would go readily in the gas phase between two particles will be hindered by the presence of solvent molecules. This is because such molecules prevent the extension into space of the orbitals on the exchanging particles. In particular the ligands of a complex ion (unless of special character) will act as good insulating groups for electrons and orbitals of the central metal ion.

The energy requirement will not be as stringent in the liquid phase, however, because the large number of energy levels possible for a system of interacting particles will make it easier to find configurations which allow energy to be conserved. Interestingly enough, the transition which was easiest in the gas phase, between an atom and its ion, now becomes more difficult. For any two central particles which differ only by one unit of charge, interaction with the environment will be different enough so that unequal energies will result if an electron transfers. [5]

It might be thought that rearrangement of the coordinated groups could occur simultaneously with the movement of the electron. This is forbidden, however, according to the Franck-Condon principle, [6] which states that the motion of nuclei is so slow compared to that of electrons that an electron transfer occurs without any appreciable movement of the nuclei.

The situation can be made clearer by considering a specific case involving the aqua iron(III) and iron(II) ions:

$$Fe(H_2O)_6{}^{3+} + Fe(H_2O)_6{}^{2+} \rightarrow \overset{*}{F}e(H_2O)_6{}^{2+} + \overset{*}{F}e(H_2O)_6{}^{3+} \quad (6)$$

The star indicates an ion in an energy-rich state. The unstarred ions have the average energies characteristic of their species. If electron transfer occurred between two such average energy ions, then energy-rich products would be formed. This is because the average ions of each charge type would have the ligand water molecules, in particular, held by them at a distance which leads to a minimum potential energy. This distance would be different for the two charge types, being smaller for the more highly charged ion. If electron transfer occurred, the water molecules would be at the wrong distance from the central ion, either too close or too far, and the potential energy would be increased. These energy-rich ions would then lose energy to the medium by collision, liberating heat.

$$\overset{*}{F}e(H_2O)_6{}^{3+} + \overset{*}{F}e(H_2O)_6{}^{2+} \rightarrow Fe(H_2O)_6{}^{3+} + Fe(H_2O)_6{}^{2+} + heat$$
$$(7)$$

The whole process of equation 6 plus equation 7 is a violation of the law of conservation of energy in that heat energy is created.

A way in which the proposed reaction can occur is to rearrange the hydration shells of the ions to some intermediate position before electron transfer occurs. This requires energy from the solution, but an equivalent amount of energy will be released when the products revert to the average state.

For conservation of energy both ions can rearrange to various intermediate configurations. The most favorable intermediate will be the one requiring the least amount of energy to form, since this rearrangement energy constitutes a barrier which must be surmounted before electron transfer can occur.[7] The least energy will be required to form two identical configurations so that electron transfer involves a symmetrical transition state intermediate between the Fe^{2+} and Fe^{3+} arrangements. It is of interest to try to evaluate the magnitude of the energy involved.

The hydration energies of divalent cations of the transition metals are of the order of 450–500 kcal, and for trivalent cations about 1100 kcal as discussed in Chapter 2. This suggests that some alarmingly large energies may be needed to put the hydration shells of both kinds of ions in some intermediate configuration. However, this is not the case as can be shown by using the simple electrostatic model used for calculating coordinate bond energies in Chapter 2.

This model gave the potential energy of an ion and its first hydration layer in terms of the charge on the ion, the dipole moment and polarizability of water, and the distance, r, of the ligands from the central ion. The energy of all other layers of water was given by the Born charging equation. For ions such as $Fe(H_2O)_6^{2+}$ and $Fe(H_2O)_6^{3+}$, the total energy is given explicitly as a function of the distance r, the equilibrium value of which was taken as 2.21 A for iron(II) and 2.05 A for iron(III).

The energy increase on changing r for both ions to some common value can easily be calculated. For example, to change r for iron(II) to 2.05 A requires 34 kcal per mole, a gain in potential energy of 43 kcal in the first layer being partially offset by a decrease of 9 kcal in the Born energy. If both ions are changed so that r is 2.08 A, about 33 kcal are needed, 10 kcal for iron(III) and 23 kcal for iron(II). Nevertheless this is probably the value of r which is easiest for both ions to achieve.

The reason for this is that the potential energy calculations were made as if the particles were all at rest. Thus zero-point and thermal vibrational energies were neglected. These would amount to about 1.5 kcal per bond in the systems considered. (Metal-ligand vibrational frequencies are of the order of 400 cm^{-1} as a rule.) Thus the bond distance, r, in iron(III) can vary from 2.05 A to 2.08 A as a result of bond vibration without any need to supply additional energy. Making an additional allowance for the vibrational energy of iron(II) as 1.5 kcal per bond, the calculated rearrangement energy becomes 14 kcal.

It would seem then that the symmetry required for electron exchanges involves supplying the reactants with 10–15 kcal of activation energy before electron transfer can occur. The identification of the rearrangement energy calculated above with activation energy should not be considered as very accurate because of the simple model used and because of other temperature-dependent factors that exist. For example, in discussing the interaction of an ion with dipolar molecules there are entropy changes which should not be neglected.[8]

In the event that electron transfer takes place between two ions which are not the same, as is the more common case, an examination of the process shown in equations 6 and 7 shows that exothermic reactions are greatly favored. That is, since heat is to be evolved anyway, the lack of energy conservation shown in 6 and 7 is no longer necessarily a factor. It is necessary only that the products be formed in some suitably activated state to release the correct amount of heat on thermal equilibration.[5] On the other hand endothermic reactions will be strongly hindered, both the heat of reaction and the rearrangement energy being required.

Another important restriction on the transfer of an electron from one molecule to another is that no overall change in electron spin should occur. That is, the spins of the other electrons in the system must be undisturbed by the electron that transfers. This can be important for a metal ion in a complexing environment such that one oxidation state of the metal is spin paired and the other oxidation state is spin free. It will be recalled that this is frequently the case for complexes in which the ligands have fairly strong crystal fields but not strong enough to couple the electrons in the lower valence state of the metal, e.g., $Co(NH_3)_6{}^{3+}$ and $Co(NH_3)_6{}^{2+}$.

In such a case it is required that electron transfer occur between the ions when at least one ion is in an excited state.* The best path would have the ligand distances equal and the magnetic properties the same except for the exchanging electron. Presumably the easiest way for this to occur in the case mentioned would be to decrease the Co—N distance in the case of cobalt(II). This would increase the crystal field strength and induce the coupling of all electrons but one. Transfer of this electron from one of the higher d orbitals, such as $3d_{x^2-y^2}$, to a corresponding orbital in cobalt(III) would then occur.

The electron tunneling hypothesis. Considerable insight into the electron transfer process in solution is given by the electron tunneling theory developed by Weiss [9] and by Marcus, Zwolinski, and Eyring.[7] The possibility of an electron leaking through a potential energy barrier that would be classically impenetrable is a well-known quantum mechanical phenomenon. The result is that the electron can transfer at distances considerably greater than would correspond to actual collision of the reactants. The tunneling effect is thus related to the extension in space of the electronic orbitals mentioned in connection with gas phase transfer processes.

Figure 1 shows schematically a potential energy diagram for illustrating barrier leakage. The energy is plotted as a function of the dis-

---

* There will be a reaction between the unexcited ions accompanied by the rearrangement of spins of other electrons. This process, being forbidden, will go very slowly and usually contribute little to the actual reaction.

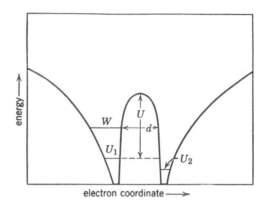

FIG. 1. Electron transfer by penetration of a potential energy barrier. U_1 and U_2 refer to the ground states of the electron in cations 1 and 2 respectively. (From reference **7**.)

tance of the electron from the centers of the two ions involved in the transfer. If the barrier is approximated as a triangular one, the probability of transfer, K, is given by the Gamow equation [10]

$$K = e^{-(8\pi d/3h)[2m(U-W)]^{1/2}} \tag{8}$$

where U = height of the barrier, W = kinetic energy of the electron, m = electron mass, d = width of the barrier at the height of penetration, and h = Planck's constant.

W can be equated to the ionization potential of the electron in the initial state, but U is more difficult to evaluate. The shape of the curve is a function of the distance between the two ions and the nature of the medium between the ions as well as of the ions themselves. The energy barrier is not the same nor is it directly related to the energy used to rearrange the hydration shells mentioned earlier. It is assumed that any such rearrangement has already occurred in constructing Fig. 1.

As an approximation Marcus, Zwolinski, and Eyring considered an electron moving in the coulomb field of two cations and calculated the potential energy by the simple coulomb equation

$$U' = \frac{q_1 q_2}{Dd} - \frac{eq_1}{Dx} - \frac{eq_2}{D(d-x)} \tag{9}$$

where q_1 and q_2 are the charges on each of the ions not counting the electron, D is the dielectric constant of the solvent, x is the distance of the electron from the cation of charge q_1. From 9 and from U_1 it is possible to calculate the barrier U as a function of d. This distance is picked to give the best balance between repulsion of the two cations as given by the first term of 9 and the probability of transfer as given by 8. U_1 is the ground state potential energy of the electron on cation 1.

More specifically the rate constant for electron transfer is written according to the transition state theory [11] as

$$k = K \frac{RT}{Nh} e^{-\Delta F^{\ddagger}/RT} \tag{10}$$

where K is the transmission coefficient given by equation 8, and where $\Delta F^{\ddagger}$ includes the free energy of rearrangement, if any, and the electrostatic repulsion term. The value of d is now picked to maximize k. Using reasonable values of W and U, it is possible to get reasonable values for k for a number of reactions if the energy of rearrangement is chosen as 8 kcal. The values of d range from 3.4 A to 9.3 A for ions of varying charge. The energy barriers are of the order of several electron volts.

However, this particular calculation must be regarded as merely informative rather than as essentially correct. The use of the coulomb law for the potential is very crude, especially since the critical distance d is based on it as well. In particular the theory would predict no barrier for a reaction involving an ion and a neutral molecule (or two oppositely charged ions).

Platzman and Franck [12] take the view that electron transfer will not occur at distances as large as calculated above. They also point out correctly that the coulomb law is not reliable if the two ions must approach each other so closely that the first hydration shells are perturbed, much larger energies being required in such a case. Thus their arguments leave no mechanism for electron transfer. These authors are unduly pessimistic, however, since it is also concluded that oppositely charged ions will likewise have to surmount very large potential barriers before the bare ions can come in contact. This opinion is contradicted by the rapidity with which simple ions form complexes in solution.

One further feature of the electron tunneling theory is that the transmission factor K is not markedly temperature dependent (in which barrier leakage phenomena differ from thermal barrier crossing processes). Hence from equation 10, there will be a contribution to the apparent entropy of activation.

$$\Delta S_t = R \ln K \tag{11}$$

Since the probability of transmission is always less than unity this will be a negative entropy term. Its magnitude from the calculations of Marcus, Zwolinski, and Eyring is of the order of -15 eu.

Before leaving this introductory survey of electron transfer in solution, one further possibility should be considered for the mechanism of transfer. Suppose the reducing agent ejects an electron into the solvent, which then solvates it and holds it until the oxidizing agent picks it up? It does appear to be true that solvated electrons exist in liquid ammonia.[13] However, in water it seems certain that such electrons would rapidly reduce water to hydrogen

$$e + H_2O \rightarrow \tfrac{1}{2}H_2 + OH^- \tag{12}$$

(compare the reaction of sodium in water and in liquid ammonia), and this mechanism for electron transfer is ruled out in aqueous solutions.[5]

Furthermore spectroscopic evidence exists that the removal of an electron to the solvent would be very difficult for most reducing agents. The ultraviolet absorption spectra of negative ions in water is interpreted as involving the removal of an electron from the ion to a bound state partly on the halogen atom and partly in the hydration layer.[12] The energy involved even for iodide ion is very large (about 120 kcal).

ATOM TRANSFER REACTIONS

Turning now to the other possibility for oxidation-reduction reactions involving atom or group transfer, we are in a more familiar field as far as kinetic theory is concerned. If the transfer of an atom is rate determining, then the usual adiabatic assumption can be made that the electrons can easily follow the motions of the nuclei. Thus the peculiar restrictions on electron transfer no longer apply (except for the spin restriction). We are dealing, in short, with ordinary chemical reactions. They will not, however, be without some unusual features.

Evidence for atom transfer comes from several sources. In oxidation-reduction reactions of oxy anions it is possible to show oxygen atom transfer using oxygen-18 labeling, providing that rapid exchange with the solvent oxygen does not occur.[14] In this way atom transfer has been demonstrated for the oxidation of SO_3^{2-} with ClO^-, ClO_2^-, ClO_3^-, and BrO_3^- and in the oxidation of NO_2^- with $HClO$.[14] Such reactions can be regarded as nucleophilic attacks on an oxygen atom acting as a Lewis acid or electrophile, an anion being displaced.

$$\left[\begin{array}{c} O \\ \diagdown \\ N\text{-}\text{-}\text{-}{}^{18}O\text{---}Cl \\ \diagup \quad\quad | \\ O \quad\quad\quad H \end{array} \right]^{-} \xrightarrow{H_2O} \left[\begin{array}{c} O \\ \diagdown \\ N\text{---}{}^{18}O\text{-}\text{-}\text{-}Cl \\ \diagup \quad\quad | \\ O \quad\quad\quad H \end{array} \right]^{-} \rightarrow$$

$$\begin{array}{c} O \\ \diagdown \\ N\text{---}{}^{18}O^{-} + HCl \quad (13) \\ \diagup \\ O \end{array}$$

By the ingenious selection of Cr^{2+} as a reducing agent, Taube and his co-workers have been able to demonstrate the transfer of a large number of univalent atoms and groups.[15] The essential feature is that chromium(II) complex ions are labile but the complexes of chromium(III) are inert. Hence, if atom transfer occurs during the oxidation of chromium(II), the atom will remain as part of the coordination sphere of the chromium(III) long enough to be detected. Using $CrCl^{2+}$, $FeCl^{2+}$, $AuCl_4^-$, and $Co(NH_3)_5Cl^{2+}$ as oxidizing agents, the transfer of chlorine atoms has been shown.[15] Using $Co(NH_3)_5X$ as an oxidant, the transfer of X has been demonstrated for X = NCS^-, N_3^-, PO_4^{3-}, acetate, oxalate, $P_2O_7^{4-}$, Br^-, and SO_4^{2-}.[16]

Regardless of the charge of the transferred group, it acts as a univalent radical since the change in oxidation number of the chromium is always from plus two to plus three. Thus these reactions can be classified as free radical displacements. Note the similarity of the reactions

$$H + Br_2 \rightarrow HBr + Br \quad\quad\quad (14)$$

$$Cr^{2+} + Br_2 \rightarrow CrBr^{2+} + Br \quad\quad\quad (15)$$

14 being a step in the free radical chain reaction between H_2 and Br_2 and 15 being a reaction demonstrated by Taube.

An interesting point in chromium(II) reductions occurs in the reaction with the complex ion $IrCl_6^{2-}$. Here the products are $Cr(H_2O)_6^{3+}$ and $IrCl_6^{3-}$. Although the possibility for chlorine atom transfer exists as in previous cases, it does not occur. Taube explains this by the greater stability of $IrCl_6^{3-}$ compared to $Cr(H_2O)_5Cl^{2+}$, whereas in the other examples the chromium(III) complex is more stable than the iron(II) or cobalt(II) complexes. Thus the atom transfer is not a necessary part of these reactions, which may in fact go by electron transfer in every case. Transfer of a group immediately following will then depend on the relative stabilities of the possible products.

That transfer does happen in many cases demonstrates, however, that bridging of the chromium(II) ion to the oxidizing agent is a necessary part of the reaction.

$$(NH_3)_5Co(III)Cl\text{---}Cr(II)(H_2O)_5 \tag{16}$$

The close approach of the metal ions allowed by bridging accounts for the increase in rate of the redox reaction when a good bridging group is present. Thus the reaction between $Cr(H_2O)_6{}^{2+}$ and $Cr(H_2O)_6{}^{3+}$, using radioactive isotope labeling, is extremely slow, whereas the exchange between $Cr(H_2O)_6{}^{2+}$ and $Cr(H_2O)_5Cl^{2+}$ is very rapid.[17] Atom transfer occurs in the latter case.

Evidence also exists for hydrogen atom transfer in reactions particularly of aqua and hydroxo complexes.[18] By studying the electron transfer reaction (by isotope labeling) between iron(II) and iron(III) in heavy water, it was found that the rate of reaction between $Fe(H_2O)_6{}^{2+}$ and both $Fe(H_2O)_6{}^{3+}$ and $Fe(H_2O)_5OH^{2+}$ was slowed by a factor of two compared to ordinary water. Such a reduced rate is characteristic of a reaction in which a hydrogen atom must move. For example, $k_H/k_D = 1.4 - 2.6$ for the reaction of alkali metals in H_2O and D_2O.[19]

A picture of the transition state is given by Hudis and Dodson [18] as follows:

$$\begin{matrix} & & \text{H} & & & & \\ & & | & & & & \\ (H_2O)_5Fe^{(II)} & \!\!-\!\! & \text{O} & \!\!-\!\!\text{H}\cdots\!\text{O}\!-\! & Fe^{(III)}(H_2O)_5 \\ & & | & & & & \\ & & \text{H} & & & & \end{matrix} \tag{17}$$

in which the dotted line indicates the direction of atom transfer.

Reynolds and Lumry [20] consider that $(H_2O)_5Fe(H_3O)^{3+}$ is a reducing agent as well, and that one or more molecules of water lie between the two hydration shells both in 17 and 18:

$$\begin{matrix} & \text{H} & & \text{H} & & \text{H} & \\ & | & & | & & | & \\ (H_2O)_5Fe^{(II)}\!-\! & \text{O} & \!-\!\text{H}\cdots\!\! & \text{O} & \!\!-\!\text{H}\cdots\!\! & \text{O} & \!-\!Fe^{(III)}(H_2O)_5 \\ & | & & & & | & \\ & \text{H} & & & & \text{H} & \end{matrix} \tag{18}$$

There is no evidence for an acid catalysis in this particular reaction, which would indicate that the protonated species is not very effective. Nevertheless the authors point out that the principle of microscopic reversibility [21] in this type of exchange reaction demands a symmetrical intermediate such as shown in 18.

For this reason there is some uncertainty as to the details of the process when the two aqua ions undergo exchange. Since an isotope effect of two (using deuterium) is found for this reaction, it is presumed that atom transfer occurs:

$$(H_2O)_5Fe^{(II)}\underset{\underset{H}{|}}{\overset{\overset{H}{|}}{-O-H\cdots O}}-Fe^{(III)}(H_2O)_5 \qquad (19)$$

The difficulty is that the principle of microscopic reversibility then requires that the reverse process also happen. This corresponds to a hydrogen atom transfer from the species $Fe(H_2O)_5(H_3O)^{3+}$ to the species $Fe(H_2O)_5OH^{2+}$.

The overall mechanism of exchange is thus related to the equilibrium

$$Fe(H_2O)_6{}^{3+} + Fe(H_2O)_6{}^{2+} \underset{k_2}{\overset{k_1}{\rightleftharpoons}} Fe(H_2O)_5(H_3O)^{3+} + Fe(H_2O)_5OH^{2+}$$
$$(20)$$

The equilibrium principle gives the relationship

$$k_1[Fe(H_2O)_6{}^{3+}][Fe(H_2O)_6{}^{2+}] = k_2[Fe(H_2O)_5(H_3O)^{3+}][Fe(H_2O)_5OH]^{2+}$$
$$(21)$$

The rate constant for electron transfer is equal to $2k_1$, since both the forward and reverse reactions of 21 lead to isotopic exchange if one valence state of the iron is labeled by using radioactive iron-55.

Since reaction 20 does occur to some extent, it is of interest to see if it can conceivably be rapid enough to account for the observed rates of isotopic exchange. An estimate can be made in the following way. The ratio of k_1/k_2 is equal to the equilibrium constant for 20. Since this is simply an acid-base proton transfer, disregarding the exchange feature, the equilibrium constant can also be set equal to K_aK_b/K_w. K_a is the acid ionization constant of $Fe(H_2O)_6{}^{3+}$, known to be about 1.0×10^{-3} at 25°C. K_w is the ion product of water, 1.0×10^{-14}, and K_b is the basic ionization constant of $Fe(H_2O)_6{}^{2+}$. This last is unknown but may be approximated by considering the base constant [22] of $Fe(H_2O)_5OH^+$, which is 2×10^{-6}. The difference in the basicity of OH^- and H_2O is 17 pK units. This would make K_b for $Fe(H_2O)_6{}^{2+}$ very roughly 10^{-23}.

Thus we calculate $k_1/k_2 = (10^{-3})(10^{-23})(10^{14}) = 10^{-12}$. The experimental value of k_1 is 2 M^{-1} sec^{-1} at 25°C (see Table 1). This makes $k_2 \simeq 10^{12}$ M^{-1} sec^{-1}. All that can be said is that this is not an impossible value of k_2 considering the crudity of the calculation. Collision theory puts an upper limit on k_2 as approximately 10^{10} since this is the rate at which the two ions would diffuse towards each other and encounter. Atom transfer must occur at nearly every encounter on this basis. Certainly the pair of reactants $Fe(H_2O)_5(H_3O)^{3+}$ and $Fe(H_2O)_5OH^{2+}$ would be very reactive. There are other possibilities which avoid invoking reaction 20. One is that atom transfer does not occur, and that the isotope effect is due to some solvation phenomenon. The other is that a proton is transferred from iron(III) to iron(II) at the same time that a hydrogen atom is transferred from iron(II) to iron(III) (as in 19).

There is some photochemical data bearing on hydrogen atom transfers from aqua ion reducing agents.[23] Illumination with ultraviolet light of the bivalent cations of the first transition period leads to the photoreduction of water.

$$M(H_2O)_6^{2+} \xrightarrow{h\nu} M(H_2O)_5OH^{2+} + H \qquad (22)$$

The hydrogen atoms may be detected by their reaction with various substances. Figure 2 shows the oxidation potential of the couple M^{2+}/M^{3+} plotted against the energy of the long wavelength limit for the photoreduction of water with several of the elements.

The slope of the straight line is 23.5 kcal/volt, which is very close to the theoretical value of 23.06 kcal/ev. This means that the energy just capable of removing a hydrogen atom from the aqua complex is equal to the energy involved when each of the bivalent cations reduces a common oxidant to within an additive constant. The implication that hydrogen atom transfer is the common reduction mechanism is strong but not conclusive. The high energy requirement for releasing a hydrogen atom as in 22 makes it clear that the atom transfer in a redox reaction must be a short-pathed, synchronous act.*

One-electron and two-electron transfers. It was mentioned earlier that quantum mechanical calculations indicate rather low probability for simultaneous transfer of two or more electrons. The term simultaneous is ambiguous. Experimentally we can only tell if a reaction involving a change in oxidation number greater than unity proceeds

---

* Atom transfer may not be short pathed if a number of water, or similar, molecules are fixed in a rather rigid structure. This may be the case for the hydration layer of a protein molecule. Long-range redox reactions in biochemical systems are discussed by Reid (*Excited States in Chemistry and Biology*, Academic Press, Inc., New York, 1957, p. 115).

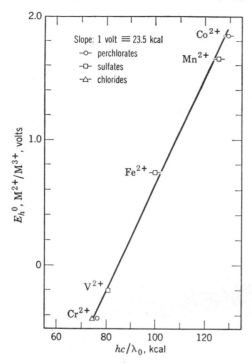

Fig. 2. E^0 of the M^{2+}/M^{3+} couple for the first transition series plotted against the energy of the long wavelength limit for the electron transfer spectra of the divalent aqua cations. (From reference 23.)

by steps by detecting the intermediates in some fashion. On the basis of several such intermediates (such as the semiquinones) Haber and Weiss [24] and Michaelis [25] promoted the general doctrine of compulsory one-electron steps in oxidation-reduction reactions.

Two comments may be made on this doctrine. First, if atom or group transfer occurs, then it is clear that changes in oxidation number greater than one may occur. Second, at the present time there is no good evidence that simultaneous, or near-simultaneous, transfer of more than one electron in a true electron transfer reaction ever occurs.*

It will be noted that the several kinds of atom transfer reactions that have been mentioned can be classified as either acid-base or free radical reactions depending on whether a change in oxidation state of two units or one unit occurs in the individual step. Since chemical reactions in general are usually acid-base, free radical, or electron transfer, it would appear that changes of oxidation number greater than two will not

---

* A possible example is the oxidation of Hg by Tl^{3+} (A. M. Armstrong and J. Halpern, *Can. J. Chem.*, **35**, 1020 (1957)). However, other explanations are possible.

occur in a single step of any redox reaction. This seems to be the case.[26]

Higginson [27] suggests the following semiempirical rules:

(a) Species derived from the transition elements will react with each other by a series of univalent changes.

(b) Species derived from the non-transition elements will react with each other in a series of bivalent changes *unless* at least one of the reactants is a free radical, in which case univalent change occurs.

(c) Species derived from a transition element and a non-transition element will react with each other by either univalent or bivalent changes, univalent changes being more common.

These rules are not to be construed as assuming anything about the mechanism, whether atom or electron transfer. One consequence of these rules concerning valency changes is that unusual valences are to be expected for intermediates in redox reactions.

EXPERIMENTAL RESULTS

Turning now to a consideration of experimental data, Table 1 gives the results of a number of kinetic studies on redox reactions of complex ions. The data are presented in terms of the assumed reactants, the second-order rate constant at 25°C, the Arrhenius activation energy, the entropy of activation, and the difference in standard oxidation potentials of the reactants when known. Each of these entries requires some comment.

The reactants that have been selected are those best fitting the rate data as a function of the various concentrations. However, there is often a choice of reactants. For example, the pair of reactants Fe^{2+}-$FeCl^{2+}$ cannot be distinguished kinetically from the three reactants Fe^{2+}-Fe^{3+}-Cl^-. Similarly the dependence of rate on pH has been interpreted in terms of reasonable oxy and hydroxo complexes believed to exist over the pH range studied. Several choices are usually possible in such cases, and chemical intuition has been freely used to pick the most reasonable combination, but there is no assurance that it is the correct one. The reason for this difficulty lies in the various mobile equilibria that exist, such as

$$Fe^{3+} + Cl^- \rightleftharpoons FeCl^{2+} \tag{23}$$

$$H_2O_2 \rightleftharpoons H^+ + O_2H^- \tag{24}$$

Table 1

Rates of Redox Reactions at 25 °C

Reaction	k, $M^{-1}\text{sec}^{-1}$	E_a, kcal	$\Delta S^{\ddagger}$, eu	ΔE^0, volts	Reference
Fe^{2+}-Fe^{3+}	4.0	9.9	−25	0.0	30
Fe^{2+}-$FeOH^{2+}$	3.2 × 10³	7.4	−18	−0.66	30
Fe^{2+}-$FeCl^{2+}$	38	8.8	−24	−0.04	30
Fe^{2+}-$FeCl_2^{+}$	65	10	−20	−0.04	30
Fe^{2+}-FeF^{2+}	40	9.1	−21	−0.31	31
Fe^{2+}-FeF_2^{+}	11	9.5	−22	−0.54	31
Fe^{2+}-H_2O_2	54	10	−15	1.00	20
Fe^{2+}-$C(CH_3)_3OOH$	13	9.2	−22	...	20
Fe^{2+}-$S_2O_8^{2-}$	70	12	−8	1.28	20
Fe^{2+}-Tl^{3+}	1.6 × 10⁻ᵃ	18.4	−7	0.48	32
Fe^{2+}-$C_6H_5C(CH_3)_2OOH$	18	10.0	−18	...	20
$Fe(EDTA)^{2-}$- $C_6H_2C(CH_3)_2OOH$	2 × 10³	10	−10	...	20
$FeP_2O_7^{2-}$- $C_6H_5C(CH_3)_2OOH$	4 × 10²	9	−16	...	20
$Fe(phen)_3^{2+}$-$TlOH^{2+}$	7 × 10⁻³	20	−2	0.18	33
NpO_2^{+}-NpO_2^{2+}	100	8.3	−24	0.0	34
VOH^{2+}-VO^{2+}	1	10.7	−24	...	35
Tl^{+}-Tl^{3+}	4.3 × 10⁻⁵	14.7	−33	0.0	36
Tl^{+}-$TlOH^{2+}$	3.4 × 10⁻⁴	...	...	0.07	36
HQ^{-}-Fe^{3+}	3.3 × 10¹⁰	20	+53	0.68	38
HO_2^{-}-Fe^{3+}	5 × 10³	28	+50	0.02	39
HO_2^{-}-Co^{3+}	4 × 10¹²	18	+55	1.09	40
HO_2^{-}-$Fe(terpy)_3^{3+}$	1 × 10¹⁰	11	+23	...	40
HO_2^{-}-$Fe(CN)_5CO^{2-}$	4 × 10⁸	9	+9	...	40
HO_2^{-}-$Fe(bipy)_3^{3+}$	3 × 10⁷	7	−5	0.31	40
Fe^{2+}-Q	6.5 × 10⁻²	8.2	−39	−0.07	38
$Ru(bipy)_3^{2+}$-$Ce(SO_4)_3^{2-}$	1 × 10⁴	...	...	~0	33
Fe^{2+}-$TlOH^{2+}$	0.20	...	...	0.55	32
Cr^{2+}-Cr^{3+}	~10⁻⁵	...	...	0.0	41
Cr^{2+}-$CrCl^{2+}$	10 at 0°	...	...	...	17
Tl^{+}-Co^{3+}	2.5 × 10⁻³	26.4	+22	0.59	37
Cr^{2+}-$CrOH^{2+}$	0.7	...	...	0.22	41
$Co(phen)^{2+}$-$Co(phen)_3^{3+}$	6.0 at 0°	...	...	...	73
$Co(en)_3^{2+}$-$Co(en)_3^{3+}$	4.5 × 10⁻⁵	14.3	−33	0.0	42
$Co(EDTA)^{2-}$-$Co(EDTA)^{-}$	4 × 10⁻⁷	22	−17	0.0	74a
$Co(NH_3)_6^{2+}$-$Co(NH_3)_6^{3+}$	very slow			0.0	42
$Co(C_2O_4)_3^{4-}$-$Co(C_2O_4)_3^{3-}$	very slow			0.0	74a
$Fe(CN)_6^{4-}$-H_2O_2	very slow			1.41	32
MnO_4^{2-}-MnO_4^{-}	3.6 × 10³	10.5	−10	0.0	44
$Fe(CN)_6^{4-}$-$Fe(CN)_6^{3-}$	7.4 × 10²	4.7	−41	0.0	45
$Mo(CN)_8^{4-}$-$Mo(CN)_8^{3-}$	very fast at 2°			0.0	46
Fe^{2+}-$IrCl_6^{2-}$	very fast at 18°			0.25	33
Fe^{2+}-$Fe(phen)_3^{3+}$	very fast at 18°			0.37	33
Fe^{2+}-$Ru(bipy)_3^{3+}$	very fast at 18°			0.53	33
$Fe(bipy)_3^{2+}$-Ce^{4+}	very fast at 18°			0.55	33
$Fe(phen)_3^{2+}$-Ce^{4+}	very fast at 18°			0.47	33
$Fe(phen)_3^{2+}$-$Ce(SO_4)_3^{2-}$	very fast at 18°			0.1	32
$Fe(bipy)_3^{2+}$-$Fe(phen)_3^{3+}$	very fast at 18°			0.08	33
$Fe(bipy)_3^{2+}$-$Ru(bipy)_3^{3+}$	very fast at 18°			0.24	33
$Fe(CN)_6^{4-}$-$Fe(phen)_3^{3+}$	very fast at 18°			0.78	33
$Fe(CN)_6^{4-}$-$Ru(bipy)_3^{3+}$	very fast at 18°			0.94	33
$Fe(CN)_6^{4-}$-$IrCl_6^{2-}$	very fast at 18°			0.66	33
$Mo(CN)_6^{4-}$-$IrCl_6^{2-}$	very fast at 18°			0.28	33
$Mn(CN)_6^{4-}$-$Mn(CN)_6^{3-}$	very fast			0.0	47
$IrCl_6^{3-}$-$IrCl_6^{2-}$	very fast at 1°			0.0	48
$W(CN)_8^{4-}$-$W(CN)_8^{3-}$	very fast at 1°			0.0	49
V^{2+}-V^{3+}	very fast at 2°			0.0	50
Co^{2+}-Co^{3+}	0.75 at 0°			0.0	51
Co^{2+}-$Co(NH_3)_6^{3+}$	very slow			−1.79	52
$Co(en)_3^{2+}$-$Co(NH_3)_6^{3+}$	~10⁻²			0.32	42
$Co(NH_3)_6^{2+}$-$Co(en)_3^{3+}$	very slow			−0.32	42
$Os(bipy)_3^{2+}$-$Os(bipy)_3^{3+}$	fast at 5°			0.0	53
$Fe(phen)_3^{2+}$-$Fe(phen)_3^{3+}$	very fast at 0°			0.0	54
Eu^{2+}-Eu^{3+}	very slow			0.0	64
$CuCl_2^{-}$-$CuCl_4^{2-}$	5 × 10⁷			0.0	57b

Symbols: phen = 1,10-phenanthroline, HQ^{-} = hydroquinone anion, terpy = 2,2′,2″-terpyridine, bipy = 2,2′-bipyridine, en = ethylenediamine, EDTA = ethylenediaminetetraacetate.

Rate data will not tell us whether the left-hand or right-hand components of such equilibria are involved in the activated complex.

The rate constants given also depend on the particular assignment of reactants made and would be incorrect if the reactants were chosen wrongly. If equilibria such as 23 and 24 are involved, the corresponding equilibrium constants must usually be known to get the rate constants from the experimental data. The exception would be if, under the conditions of the experiments, almost all of the added reagent existed in the form assumed to be the reactant.

The Arrhenius activation energy is derived from the equation $k = Ae^{-E_a/RT}$, where A is the so-called frequency factor. The entropy of activation is derived from the theory of absolute reaction rates,[28] the equation being

$$k = \frac{RT}{Nh} e^{-\Delta H^{\ddagger}/RT} e^{\Delta S^{\ddagger}/R} \tag{25}$$

The heat of activation, $\Delta H^{\ddagger}$, is less than the activation energy, E_a, by RT or 0.6 kcal for reactions in solution.

The value of ΔE^0 is a convenient way of showing the equilibrium constant for the reaction. A positive value refers to a favorable equilibrium constant. The value of ΔE^0 also depends on the choice of reactants and products. For a number of reactions ΔE^0 is zero. These are for isotope exchange reactions, which are usually studied using a radioactive isotope to label one of the two oxidation states of the element. Strictly speaking ΔE^0 would not be identically zero for such a reaction

$$A^n + {}^*A^m \rightleftharpoons {}^*A^n + A^m \tag{26}$$

because of small isotope effects favoring the heavier isotope in one state or another. However, except for the lightest elements, these effects can be neglected.

If radioisotopes are used, the reaction is followed by separating the two oxidation states and measuring the radioactivity in each form. The McKay [29] equation should be followed

$$\ln (1 - x/x_\infty) = -Rt(a + b)/ab \tag{27}$$

where x is the activity at time t of the form originally inactive, x_∞ is the equilibrium value of the activity, and a and b are the analytical concentrations of the two forms of the element which remain constant during the run. R is the rate of the exchange reaction and is equal to some function of the various concentrations involved and one or more rate and equilbrium constants. For a simple bimolecular reaction

$$R = kab \qquad (28)$$

In such studies care must be taken that the separation technique used does not induce the exchange reaction and give erroneous rates.

It has been shown that, if separation-induced exchange is incomplete but constant and reproducible, the rate of exchange can still be found.[55] However, the time required for separation, either physical or chemical, greatly limits the range of velocities that can be studied. Dwyer and Gyarfas [53] have used an ingenious method to eliminate the necessity for separation. If the exchanging species can be obtained with at least one form optically active, then exchange can be followed by studying changes in optical rotation.

Another method that may be useful for very rapid electron transfers in systems where the equilibrium constant is close to unity involves nuclear magnetic resonance spectroscopy.[56] If one of the atoms in a reactant has a nuclear moment, then the frequency of resonance absorption will vary somewhat with the oxidation state of the reactant. In favorable cases a rapid change in oxidation state will cause a broadening of the absorption line from which the rate constant can be calculated.[57]

Evidence for electron transfer. Even after the reactants have been identified and something about the rate and energetics of the reaction is known, as given in Table 1, it still remains a major problem to decide between an atom transfer or electron transfer mechanism. In a number of cases it seems reasonably clear that an electron transfer must be involved. These are the cases of two substitution inert complexes such as $Fe(CN)_6^{4-}$-$Fe(CN)_6^{3-}$, MnO_4^{2-}-MnO_4^-, $IrCl_6^{3-}$-$IrCl_6^{2-}$ and the like. In a number of such systems the overall rate of reaction is much greater than any possible mechanism based on dissociation and atom transfer.

In some cases where only one reactant is non-labile, electron transfer again seems to be the only possible mechanism. For example, $Co(en)_3^{3+}$ is inert but $Co(en)_3^{2+}$ is labile. However, the rate in this case is independent of pH and of excess ethylenediamine [42] and cannot involve free Co^{2+} or the conjugate base of $Co(en)_3^{3+}$. The conjugate base containing a nitrogen atom with an unshared pair of electrons could otherwise offer a bridging path for hydrogen atom transfer. For this reason (possible bridging) all the reactions of aqua and hydroxo complexes are uncertain. Also reactions of a halo complex of either an inert or labile complex with a labile complex offers the possibility of halogen atom transfer, e.g., $Fe^{2+} - FeCl^{2+}$ and $Cr^{2+} - CrCl^{2+}$.

Considering the example where electron transfer is indicated, excellent agreement with the theoretical arguments presented earlier is found. Reactions with favorable free energy changes, and hence usually exothermic, proceed rapidly in most cases. For the isotope exchange reactions, the rate is relatively great for two ions of very similar geometry so that little rearrangement is needed to symmetrize the transition state, for example, $Mn(CN)_6^{4-}$-$Mn(CN)_6^{3-}$ and $Fe(phen)_3^{2+}$-$Fe(phen)_3^{3+}$. This will generally be the case for complexes differing by one electron in the low energy d orbitals not used in ligand bonding, such as d_{xy}. The rates will be the greatest if the ligands are unsaturated and π bonding, metal to ligand, occurs. This will stabilize the lower valence state more than the higher, and hence the geometries will be more nearly equal. Thus the exchange in $Fe(CN)_6^{4-}$-$Fe(CN)_6^{3-}$ will be faster than in $Fe(H_2O)_6^{2+}$-$Fe(H_2O)_6^{3+}$, even though an electron from a low energy orbital is transferred in each case.

If the geometry of the two ions is very different, however, the reaction is slow, as predicted. This is the case for ions where the electron to be transferred occupies one of the high energy d orbitals used to hold a ligand, such as $d_{x^2-y^2}$. The prime examples are Co(II)-Co(III) in their various complexes and Cr(II)-Cr(III). In the case of the cobalt complexes such as $Co(NH_3)_6^{2+}$ and $Co(NH_3)_6^{3+}$, the cobalt-nitrogen bond distances are known to be quite dissimilar.[58] Another restriction on exchanges between Co(II) and Co(III) is the differing electron multiplicities as mentioned earlier.

It is interesting to note that $Co(en)_3^{2+}$ exchanges slowly with $Co(en)_3^{3+}$ but more rapidly with $Co(NH_3)_6^{3+}$. This is because the latter reaction is exothermic due to the greater stability of $Co(en)_3^{3+}$.

$$Co(en)_3^{2+} + Co(NH_3)_6^{3+} \rightarrow Co(NH_3)_6^{2+} + Co(en)_3^{3+} + heat \quad (29)$$

The reverse reaction of (29) does not occur with any measurable velocity.

Also $Co(C_2O_4)_3^{4-}$, or perhaps $Co(C_2O_4)_2^{2-}$, reacts slowly with cerium(IV), an electron transfer agent, and rapidly with H_2O_2 and ClO^-, which are probably atom transfer agents.[43] This indicates the advantage of a bridged intermediate.

Aqua and hydroxo complexes. Co^{3+} exchanges fairly fast with Co^{2+} (compared to Cr^{3+}-Cr^{2+}), in spite of the difference in structure. However, the aqua cobalt(III) is very unstable, being a powerful oxidizing agent (aqua chromium(III) is stable). It has been suggested that the normal diamagnetic structure of cobalt(III) complexes is fairly easily excited to a paramagnetic structure using outer d orbitals for binding water molecules.[59] (In crystal field terminology, the spin-

	3d	4s	4p	4d
$Co(H_2O)_6{}^{3+}$ (diamagnetic)	⊙ ⊙ ⊙ [⊙ ⊙	⊙	⊙ ⊙ ⊙]	○ ○
$Co(H_2O)_6{}^{3+}$ (paramagnetic)	⊙ ⊙ ⊙ ⊙ ⊙	[⊙	⊙ ⊙ ⊙]	⊙ ⊙

free state can be formed easily because the field strength of water ligands is weak enough so that the energy decrease on using only the more stable $3d$ orbitals is just about equal to the extra pairing energy of the electrons.) This form would exchange rapidly with cobalt(II) complexes which are also paramagnetic. The rapid exchange of water observed [60] for $Co(H_2O)_6{}^{3+}$ using oxygen-18 labeling may be due to this excited, paramagnetic form, which would be labile, or to the electron exchange reaction with $Co(H_2O)_6{}^{2+}$, since the latter is always present in preparations of $Co(H_2O)_6{}^{3+}$. It will be recalled that $Cr(H_2O)_6{}^{3+}$ exchanges water slowly with the solvent.

The general similarity in rates, activation energies, and entropies of activation for the reactions of iron(II) ion is cited by Reynolds and Lumry [20] as evidence for a common hydrogen atom transfer mechanism. The similarities hold even when the Fe(II) is complexed with *versene*, $Fe(EDTA)^{2-}$, and with pyrophosphate ion so that electrostatic factors do not seem important. Furthermore there is an isotope effect for the reduction of cumene hydroperoxide, $C_6H_5C(CH_3)_2OOH$, with Fe^{2+}. The rate is reduced by a factor of two when run in heavy water.[20] Certainly a pure electron transfer mechanism for so many diverse reagents would have widely varying rates.

It will be noticed that reductions of Tl(III) are somewhat slower than corresponding reactions involving other metal ions. Since Tl(I) is the next stable valence state, it might be argued that these reactions go by a two-electron transfer and are slow for that reason. However, there is evidence that Tl(II) is formed as an intermediate in some of these reactions.

The reaction of Tl^{3+} with Fe^{2+} is first order in each reactant during most of the reaction indicating a rate-determining step as either

$$Fe^{2+} + Tl^{3+} \rightleftharpoons Fe^{3+} + Tl^{2+} \tag{30}$$

or

$$Fe^{2+} + Tl^{3+} \rightleftharpoons Fe^{4+} + Tl^{+} \tag{31}$$

The second-order rate constant declines after the first 60% of reaction. This indicates that the reversal of 30 or 31 begins to compete with the follow-up step,

$$Fe^{2+} + Tl^{2+} \rightarrow Fe^{3+} + Tl^+ \tag{32}$$

or

$$Fe^{2+} + Fe^{4+} \rightarrow 2Fe^{3+} \tag{33}$$

It was found that the initial addition of Fe^{3+} slowed down the reaction markedly, whereas Tl^+ had no effect on the rate.[61] This indicates that 30 and 32 constitute the mechanism. It was also shown that including the reverse of reaction 30, and using the steady-state approximation, $d[Tl^{2+}]/dt = 0$, leads to an analytical relation between concentrations and time which was linear for 93% of the reaction.[61]

The rate also depends on the pH in a manner which shows that another reaction must be considered.

$$TlOH^{2+} + Fe^{2+} \rightleftharpoons TlOH^+ + Fe^{3+} \tag{34}$$

This is similar to the exchange reaction between Tl(III)-Tl(I) which, by analogy, depends on the reactions

$$Tl^{3+} + Tl^+ \rightleftharpoons 2Tl^{2+} \tag{35}$$

$$TlOH^{2+} + Tl^+ \rightleftharpoons TlOH^+ + Tl^{2+} \tag{36}$$

$$Tl^{2+} + Tl^{3+} \rightleftharpoons Tl^{3+} + Tl^{2+} \tag{37}$$

$$Tl^{2+} + Tl^+ \rightleftharpoons Tl^+ + Tl^{2+} \text{ etc.} \tag{38}$$

In these two reactions of Tl(III), the observed rate constant depends on $[H^+]$ in a way given approximately by either of the two equations

$$k = A + \frac{B}{[H^+]} \tag{39}$$

or

$$k = \frac{A}{B + [H^+]} \tag{40}$$

where A and B are constants. If Tl^{3+} and $TlOH^{2+}$ are indeed the reactive forms of Tl(III), the theoretical expression for the observed rate would be

$$k = \frac{k_1[H^+] + k_2 K_h}{K_h + [H^+]} \tag{41}$$

where k_1 is the rate constant for the reaction of Tl^{3+}, k_2 is the rate constant for $TlOH^{2+}$, and K_h the first hydrolysis constant of Tl^{3+}, that is, for the reaction

$$Tl^{3+} + H_2O \rightleftharpoons TlOH^{2+} + H^+ \tag{42}$$

Equation 41 can reduce to either 39 or 40 depending on the relative magnitudes of $[H^+]$ and K_h. The values of $[H^+]$ are quite large covering the range from $0.5\ M$ to either $3\ M$ or $6\ M$ for the Fe^{2+} reaction and the exchange reaction. An incorrect estimate of 6.4 for K_h led to considerable difficulty in the early work on these reactions. However, Rossotti [62] has shown that Biedermann's accurate value of 0.073 for K_h [63] fits the data quite well and allows an assignment of the values of k_1 and k_2 shown in Table 1 from the magnitudes of A and B in equation 39.

It is true that the experimental data still do not exclude the possibility that the reactants are, for example, Fe^{2+} and $FeOH^+$ with Tl^{3+}. Even $TlOH$, although unstable, may be considered as a reactant. However, K_h for Fe^{2+} is very small (5×10^{-9}) [22] and, if the OH group is needed to serve as a bridge for either atom or electron transfer, it can be supplied more readily by $TlOH^{2+}$.

It will be noticed in Table 1 that the entropies of activation are generally negative and substantial. In the tunneling theory of Marcus, Zwolinski, and Eyring, this is explained by a small value of the transmission coefficient, K. However, it is only for a few exchange reactions that an electron transfer seems certain for the systems where $\Delta S^{\ddagger}$ has been measured.

In a few cases $\Delta S^{\ddagger}$ is large and positive. These are generally reactions between tripositive cations and an anion where cancellation of charge in forming the transition state would lead to an entropy increase. This is presumably because of the release of oriented solvent molecules from the ions. A close approach of the reactants is indicated, for example,

$$Co^{3+} + HO_2^- \rightleftharpoons CoO_2H^{2+} \tag{43}$$

$$CoO_2H^{2+} \rightarrow Co^{2+} + \cdot O_2H \tag{44}$$

$$Co^{3+} + \cdot O_2H \rightarrow CoO_2H^{3+} \tag{45}$$

$$CoO_2H^{3+} \rightarrow Co^{2+} + O_2 + H^+ \tag{46}$$

with 43 representing a step in which the anion of hydrogen peroxide becomes part of the hydration sphere of the cation. Reaction 44 would be rate determining, and 43 would account for the entropy increase.

It may be noted that the overall entropy change of a reaction equivalent to 43 plus 44 is estimated as $+58$ eu,[39]

$$Fe^{3+} + HO_2^- \rightarrow Fe^{2+} + \cdot O_2H \qquad (47)$$

Again it is possible that the reagents are actually H_2O_2 and $CoOH^{2+}$ in the system above. This is not consistent with the entropy change, nor is the pathway easy to imagine for the detailed reaction. Furthermore reagents which do not have acidic hydrogens, such as $Fe(CN)_5CO^{2-}$ and $Fe(bipy)_3^{3+}$, have the same pH dependence as Fe^{3+} and Co^{3+} and form a continuous rate pattern. This indicates O_2H^- as a common reagent.

The effect of anions on the rate. The greater rate of reaction of hydroxo complexes compared to aqua complexes may be due to the existence of a hydrogen atom transfer process as already mentioned. Another explanation stresses the similarity to the effect of small negative ions such as F^- and Cl^- in speeding up certain redox reactions. Several examples are shown in Table 1 where it has been assumed that complexes such as $FeCl^{2+}$ are formed first. In addition chloride accelerates the Eu(II)-Eu(III) exchange [64] and fluoride ion catalyzes the Ce(III)-Ce(IV) exchange.[65] In the reaction of Co(III) and Tl(I), sulfate ion can be a catalyst.[37] In the reactions of Cr^{2+} where bridging seems general, the order of effectiveness of various groups is $OH^- > Br^- > Cl^- \simeq F^- > SO_4^{2-} > H_2O > RCOO^-$.

In addition to the bridging mechanism, for which good evidence exists in the case of Cr^{2+}, other ways in which a negative ion may influence the rate can be imagined. Libby [5] stressed the importance of reducing the coulombic repulsions between two cations with an intervening negative ion. On this basis alone, a negative ion anywhere in the vicinity might be beneficial. Also the negative ion might complex the reducing agent as it is oxidized, generally stabilizing it in the higher valence state, e.g.,[16]

$$F^- + Ce^{3+} + Ce^{4+} \rightarrow F-Ce^{3+} + Ce^{3+} \qquad (48)$$

Thus Cr(II) may be complexed with ions such as $P_2O_7^{4-}$ and Cl^- when it acts as a reducing agent. This is in addition to any anion that it may bridge to.

There are observations against this line of reasoning, however. Thus chloride ion does not increase the rate between $Co(en)_3^{2+}$-$Co(en)_3^{3+}$ nor between $Cr(H_2O)_6^{2+}$-$Cr(H_2O)_6^{3+}$. Furthermore the reaction between $Ru(bipy)_3^{2+}$ and Ce^{4+} is too fast to measure, but between $Ru(bipy)_3^{2+}$ and $Ce(SO_4)_3^{2-}$ it is much slower.[33] In the last case we see an example where complexing of the oxidized form stabilizes it so that it does not react as readily.

In general the available rate data on redox reactions do not show that coulombic attractions and repulsions play a dominant role. This is not to imply that these electrostatic effects do not exist, but rather that other factors are of greater importance. For example, the rate of exchange between NpO_2^{2+} and NpO_2^+ is nearly constant over the range of dielectric constant from 88 to 68.[66] The electron tunneling theory would predict a decrease in rate by a factor of 10 for this change.

Accepting a bridge mechanism, there are still several ways in which the rate can be increased. First, there is the coulombic repulsion as indicated. Second, there is the symmetrizing of the transition state if one ligand is shared in common. Perhaps most important is that an easier pathway for an electron transfer is made in that a bridging atom is held on both sides by chemical bonds through which an electron can easily move (compare the molecular orbital theory of valency). There will still be Franck-Condon restrictions on the electron motion, however. Finally, if the bridging atom or group is transferred, this may be a faster process than the electron transfer.

The relative importance of all these factors cannot easily be assessed. It is not possible to tell (in any case except that involving the hydrogen atom) whether the electron transfers first followed by the movement of the negative ion in the opposite direction, or whether only the atom or group is transferred. The order of efficiency found for the halide ions indicates that two opposing factors are at work, the tendency to form a bridge, $F^- > Cl^- > Br^-$, and the tendency either to transmit an electron, or to undergo homolytic bond breaking, $Br^- > Cl^- > F^-$.

In the case of $Tl(III)-Tl(I)$ again an interesting effect occurs [36,67] with Cl^- and CN^-. Small amounts of these ions inhibit the rate of the reaction. A reduction to $\frac{1}{200}$ of the original rate in the absence of cyanide ion is found at a ratio of $[CN^-]/Tl(III) = 3.5$. This is a minimum value, and addition of more cyanide ion increases the rate approximately as the cube of the cyanide ion concentration. At 0.5 M cyanide ion, the rate is 60 times as great as in the absence of cyanide. The only reasonable interpretation seems to be that complexes such as $TlCN^{2+}$ and $Tl(CN)_2^+$ are inert, whereas complexes such as

$Tl(CN)_4^-$ and possibly $Tl(CN)_2^-$ are reactive. The similar results with chloride ion give a minimum at $[Cl^-]/[Tl(III)] = 1.5$, and the rise is about second order in $[Cl^-]$.

Since something is known about the stability constants of chloride complexes of $Tl(III)$,[36] it can be said that the most reactive species is $TlCl_4^-$. The dependence on chloride ion concentration indicates that $Tl(I)$ participates as the weak complex $TlCl_2^-$. A symmetrical bridge structure for the transition state can be written in this case:

$$\left[\begin{array}{ccc} Cl & Cl & Cl \\ & Tl & Tl \\ Cl & Cl & Cl \end{array}\right]^{2-} \tag{49}$$

There is a strong correspondence here to the exchanges between $Sb(III)$-$Sb(V)$ [68] and $Sn(II)$-$Sn(IV)$,[69] which also occur between species containing large numbers of chloride ions. Although not definite, it appears that $SnCl_4^{2-}$ and $SnCl_6^{2-}$ may be involved as well as $SbCl_6^-$ and either $SbCl_4^-$ or $SbCl_3$. In any event a reasonable interpretation of all the evidence seems to be that for systems involving a change of two in the oxidation state during exchange, a single univalent anion bridge is not sufficient, and two are required.*

It is of interest to note that bridged complexes of mixed valency such as shown in 49 are believed to be responsible for the intense colors frequently developed when two valency states of an element are present.[69,70] Such optical interaction has been shown for $Sb(III)$-$Sb(V)$, $Sn(II)$-$Sn(IV)$, $Fe(II)$-$Fe(III)$, and $Cu(I)$-$Cu(II)$.[71] It is not clear if the species responsible for the color is involved in the electron exchange reaction, but it may not be.[69]

It has been reported by two groups that Fe^{3+} and $Fe(CN)_6^{4-}$ do not give electron transfer even after long periods in spite of a favorable free energy change.[72] The insoluble reaction product, Turnbull's blue, is intensely colored. The difference, if any, between this material and Prussian blue, formed from Fe^{2+} and $Fe(CN)_6^{3-}$, is not certain. Since the insoluble material must be decomposed to see if exchange has occurred, all that has really been demonstrated is that exchange of cyanide ions has not taken place.

---

*An exception may be the exchange of platinum(II) and platinum(IV) complexes. See p. 167.

In addition to the increased rate of apparent electron transfer produced by bridging groups, there is a little more information available as to how the nature of the insulating ligands can affect the ease of oxidation-reduction. In the reactions of Cr^{2+} with complexes of Co(III) it has been shown that $Co(en)_2phen^{3+}$ is faster than $Co(en)_3^{3+}$ by a factor of 20 or so.[16] Also for $Co(NH_3)_5X$, when X is acetate, succinate, butyrate, or crotonate, the rates are about the same (about one-tenth of the rate when X is water). However, when X is oxalate or maleate, the rate is several hundred times faster. It seems that a conjugated system of double bonds can aid in the transfer of an electron. A reasonable intermediate would be

$$\underset{\substack{\| \\ O}}{Co^{(III)}-O-C}-\overset{\overset{\displaystyle H}{|}}{C}=\overset{\overset{\displaystyle H}{|}}{C}-\underset{\substack{\| \\ O}}{C}-O-Cr^{(II)} \tag{50}$$

Even more impressive is the recent observation[73] that the rate of exchange in the system $Co(phen)_3^{3+}$-$Co(phen)_3^{2+}$ is some 10^5 times faster than for $Co(en)_3^{3+}$-$Co(en)_3^{2+}$. Another factor is probably responsible for most of this large rate difference. It was said earlier that cobalt(III)-cobalt(II) exchange probably necessitates converting cobalt(II) to an excited state with all electrons paired but one. The stronger the crystal field strength of the ligands, the more easily this can be done. As it turns out, 1,10-phenanthroline has a larger crystal field strength than any other of the common ligands except cyanide ion. This accounts for the ease of electron transfer. The same theory explains why $Co(en)_3^{3+}$-$Co(en)_3^{2+}$ exchanges more rapidly than $Co(NH_3)_6^{3+}$-$Co(NH_3)_6^{2+}$ and $Co(oxalate)_3^{3-}$-$Co(oxalate)_3^{4-}$.

Arranging the ligands in order of increasing crystal field strength H_2O < oxalate < EDTA < NH_3 < en < 1,10-phen, one finds that electron transfer is rapid at either end of the series and slowest in the middle.[74] This is because, in the limits of zero crystal field, cobalt(III) becomes paramagnetic, as is cobalt(II), and, at high crystal field, cobalt(II) becomes spin paired as is cobalt(III). Presumably electron transfer would be most rapid for systems such as CoF_6^{3-}-CoF_6^{4-} and $Co(das)_3^{3+}$-$Co(das)_3^{2+}$. In the former case both of the hexafluoro complexes are paramagnetic, whereas in the latter case the o-phenylenebis(dimethylarsine) complexes are both of the spin-paired type.[75]

REFERENCES

For general discussions, see B. J. Zwolinski, R. J. Marcus, and H. Eyring, *Chem. Revs.*, **55**, 151 (1955); F. S. Dainton et al., "Kinetics and Mechanism of Inorganic Reactions in Solution," the Chemical Society, *Special Publ. No.* 1, London, 1954.

1. J. O. Edwards, *Chem. Revs.*, **50**, 455 (1952).
2. H. D. Smyth, O. P. Harnwell, T. R. Hogness, and E. G. Lunn, *Nature*, **119**, 85 (1927).
3. J. A. Hornbeck, *J. Phys. Chem.*, **56**, 829 (1952); J. B. Hasted, *Proc. Roy. Soc. London*, **A227**, 476 (1955).
4. H. Eyring, J. Walter, and G. E. Kimball, *Quantum Chemistry*, John Wiley & Sons, New York, 1944, pp. 192–199.
5. W. F. Libby, *J. Phys. Chem.*, **56**, 863 (1952).
6. E. U. Condon, *Am. J. Phys.*, **15**, 365 (1947).
7. R. J. Marcus, B. J. Zwolinski, and H. Eyring, *J. Phys. Chem.*, **58**, 432 (1954); see also R. A. Marcus, *J. Chem. Phys.*, **24**, 970 (1956).
8. R. E. Powell and W. M. Latimer, *J. Chem. Phys.*, **19**, 1139 (1951).
9. J. Weiss, *Proc. Roy. Soc. London*, **A222**, 128 (1954).
10. N. F. Mott and I. N. Sneddon, *Wave Mechanics and Its Applications*, Clarendon Press, Oxford, 1948.
11. S. Glasstone, K. Laidler, and H. Eyring, *The Theory of Rate Processes*, McGraw-Hill Book Co., New York, 1941, p. 189.
12. R. Platzman and J. Franck, *Z. Physik*, **138**, 411 (1954).
13. J. Kaplan and C. Kittel, *J. Chem. Phys.*, **21**, 1429 (1953).
14. H. Taube, *Record Chem. Progr. Kresge-Hooker Sci. Lib.*, **17**, 25 (1956).
15. H. Taube, H. Myers, and R. L. Rich, *J. Am. Chem. Soc.*, **75**, 4118 (1953); H. Taube and H. Myers, *ibid.*, **76**, 2103 (1954).
16. H. Taube, *ibid.*, **77**, 4481 (1955).
17. H. Taube and E. L. King, *ibid.*, **76**, 4053 (1954).
18. J. Hudis and R. W. Dodson, *ibid.*, **78**, 911 (1956).
19. K. B. Wiberg, *Chem. Revs.*, **55**, 713 (1955).
20. W. L. Reynolds and R. Lumry, *J. Chem. Phys.*, **23**, 2560 (1955).
21. A. A. Frost and R. G. Pearson, *Kinetics and Mechanism*, John Wiley & Sons, New York, 1953, pp. 202–204.
22. D. L. Leussing and I. M. Kolthoff, *J. Am. Chem. Soc.*, **75**, 2476 (1953).
23. F. S. Dainton, *J. Chem. Soc.*, **1952**, 1533.
24. F. Haber and J. Weiss, *Proc. Roy. Soc. London*, **A147**, 332 (1934).
25. L. Michaelis, *Trans. Electrochem. Soc.*, **71**, 107 (1937).
26. F. H. Westheimer, *The Mechanism of Enzyme Action*, The Johns Hopkins Press, Baltimore, 1954, p. 321.
27. W. C. E. Higginson and J. W. Marshall, *J. Chem. Soc.*, **1957**, 447.
28. S. Glasstone, K. Laidler, and H. Eyring, *The Theory of Rate Processes*, McGraw-Hill Book Co., New York, 1941.
29. H. A. C. McKay, *Nature*, **142**, 997 (1938); A. C. Wahl and N. A. Bonner, *Radioactivity Applied to Chemistry*, John Wiley & Sons, New York, 1951, Chapter 1.

30. J. Silverman and R. W. Dodson, *J. Phys. Chem.*, **56**, 846 (1952).
31. J. Hudis and A. C. Wahl, *J. Am. Chem. Soc.*, **75**, 4153 (1953).
32. C. E. Johnson, *ibid.*, **74**, 959 (1952).
33. P. George and D. H. Irvine, *J. Chem. Soc.*, **1954**, 587.
34. D. Cohen, J. C. Sullivan, and J. C. Hindman, *J. Am. Chem. Soc.*, **76**, 352 (1954).
35. S. C. Furman and C. S. Garner, *ibid.*, **74**, 2333 (1952).
36. R. J. Prestwood and A. C. Wahl, *ibid.*, **71**, 3137 (1949); G. Harbottle and R. W Dodson, *ibid.*, **73**, 2442 (1951).
37. K. G. Ashurst and W. C. E. Higginson, *J. Chem. Soc.*, **1956**, 343.
38. J. H. Baxendale, H. R. Hardy, and L. H. Sutcliffe, *Trans. Faraday Soc.*, **47**, 963 (1951).
39. W. G. Barb, J. H. Baxendale, P. George, and K. R. Hargrave, *ibid.*, 491.
40. J. H. Baxendale, *Kinetics and Mechanism of Inorganic Reactions in Solution*, The Chemical Society, *Special Publ. No.* 1, London, 1954, p. 43.
41. A. Anderson and N. A. Bonner, *J. Am. Chem. Soc.*, **76**, 3826 (1954).
42. W. B. Lewis, C. D. Coryell, and J. W. Irvine, *J. Chem. Soc. Suppl. Issue No.* 2, S386 (1949).
43. A. W. Adamson, private communication.
44. J. C. Sheppard and A. C. Wahl, *J. Am. Chem. Soc.*, **75**, 5134 (1953); A. C. Wahl, private communication.
45. A. C. Wahl and C. F. Deck, *ibid.*, **76**, 4054 (1954); A. C. Wahl, private communication.
46. R. L. Wolfgang, *ibid.*, **74**, 6144 (1952).
47. A. W. Adamson, *J. Phys. Chem.*, **56**, 858 (1952).
48. E. N. Sloth and C. S. Garner, *J. Am. Chem. Soc.*, **77**, 1440 (1955).
49. E. L. Goodenow and C. S. Garner, *ibid.*, **77**, 5272 (1955).
50. W. R. King, Jr., and C. S. Garner, *ibid.*, **74**, 3709 (1952).
51. N. A. Bonner and J. P. Hunt, *ibid.*, **74**, 1866 (1952).
52. S. A. Hoshowsky, O. G. Holmes, and K. J. McCallum, *Can. J. Research*, **27B**, 258 (1949).
53. F. P. Dwyer and E. C. Gyarfas, *Nature*, **166**, 1181 (1950).
54. L. Eimer and A. I. Medalia, *J. Am. Chem. Soc.*, **74**, 1592 (1952).
55. R. J. Prestwood and A. C. Wahl, *ibid.*, **71**, 3137 (1949).
56. J. E. Wertz, *Chem. Revs.*, **55**, 829 (1955).
57. (a) C. R. Bruce, R. E. Norberg, and S. I. Weissman, *J. Chem. Phys.*, **24**, 473 (1956). (b) H. M. McConnell and H. E. Weaver, Jr., *ibid.*, **25**, 307 (1956).
58. W. Biltz, *Z. anorg. u. allgem. Chem.*, **164**, 246 (1927).
59. H. L. Friedman, J. P. Hunt, R. A. Plane, and H. Taube, *J. Am. Chem. Soc.*, **73**, 4028 (1951).
60. H. L. Friedman, H. Taube, and J. P. Hunt, *J. Chem. Phys.*, **18**, 757 (1950).
61. K. G. Ashurst and W. C. E. Higginson, *J. Chem. Soc.*, **1953**, 3044.
62. F. J. C. Rossotti, *J. Inorg. Nuclear Chem.*, **1**, 159 (1955).
63. G. Biedermann, *Arkiv Kemi*, **5**, 441 (1953).
64. D. J. Meier and C. S. Garner, *J. Phys. Chem.*, **56**, 853 (1952).
65. H. C. Hornig and W. F. Libby, *ibid.*, 869.
66. D. Cohen, J. C. Sullivan, E. S. Amis, and J. C. Hindman, *J. Am. Chem. Soc.*, **78**, 1543 (1956).
67. E. Penna-Franca and R. W. Dodson, *ibid.*, **77**, 2651 (1955).

68. N. A. Bonner, *ibid.,* **71,** 3909 (1949) ; H. M. Neumann, *ibid.,* **76,** 2611 (1954) ; H. M. Neumann and H. Brown, *ibid.,* **78,** 1843 (1956).

69. C. B. Amphlett, *Quart. Revs. London,* **8,** 219 (1954) ; C. L. Browne, R. P. Craig, and N. Davidson, *J. Am. Chem. Soc.,* **73,** 1946 (1951).

70. N. V. Sidgwick, *The Chemical Elements and Their Compounds,* Oxford, 1950, p. 1339.

71. N. Davidson et al., *J. Am. Chem. Soc.,* **69,** 2076 (1947) ; **71,** 3809; **72,** 5557.

72. R. C. Thompson, *ibid.,* **70,** 1045 (1948) ; C. Haenny and G. Rochat, *Helv. Chim. Acta,* **32,** 2441 (1949).

73. H. M. Neumann and B. R. Baker, private communication; P. Ellis, R. G. Wilkins, and M. J. G. Williams, *J. Chem. Soc.,* **1957,** 4456.

74. (*a*) A. W. Adamson and K. S. Vorres, *J. Inorg. Nuclear Chem.,* **3,** 206 (1956)
    (*b*) L. E. Orgel, Tenth Solvay Conference, Brussels, May, 1956.

75. H. F. Burstall and R. S. Nyholm, *J. Chem. Soc.,* **1952,** 3570.

8

Catalytic effects
of coordination
compounds

A very large number of reactions are known in which coordination compounds, or rather the metal ions which form coordination compounds, act as catalysts. At the end of the reaction the metal ion can be recovered, though possibly in a changed oxidation state and coordinated with different groups than originally. However, these are secondary effects, and the efficiency of very small amounts of the metal ion justifies the use of the term catalyst. It will be seen to be characteristic of these reactions that intermediate coordination compounds are formed which undergo further reaction.

Two broad classifications exist for these reactions: acid-base and oxidation-reduction. These will be discussed in terms of acid catalysis by metal ions and catalysis of homogeneous reduction and homogeneous oxidation reactions. In all of these categories the most important and interesting examples are no doubt to be found in biological systems. However, such systems are beyond the scope of this discussion. Several excellent reviews of the role of metal ions in enzyme systems are fortunately available.[1] Many of the simple examples that will be mentioned here may be considered as models for biological cases.

ACID-BASE CATALYSIS

The activity of complex ions in acid-catalyzed reactions comes about in a very straightforward manner. If we have a reaction that is catalyzed by hydrogen ion, or other acids, then it will generally be catalyzed by metal ions, which are also acids in the Lewis sense. In fáct even reactions which are catalyzed only by hydrogen ion and not by acids such as acetic acid molecules (specific catalysis) will still be catalyzed by metal ions. This is because hydrogen ion and metal ions are acids of the same type.

There are a number of ways in which acid catalysis may occur.[2] For the reactions of interest to us here, the major effect may be considered to be that of the acid adding on to a substrate in such a way as to drain electrons toward the site of attachment. This then facilitates reaction at some other part of the substrate. An example is furnished by the work of Pedersen[3] on the bromination of acetoacetic ester catalyzed by cupric ion:

$$CH_3-\overset{O}{\underset{\|}{C}}-CH_2-\overset{O}{\underset{\|}{C}}-OC_2H_5 + Cu^{2+} \underset{\overset{}{\longleftarrow}}{\overset{fast}{\longrightarrow}} CH_3-\overset{\overset{\displaystyle Cu}{\diagup\,\diagdown}}{\overset{+O\quad\quad O+}{\underset{\|\quad\quad\|}{}}}-CH_2-\overset{}{}-OC_2H_5 \tag{1}$$

$$CH_3-\overset{\overset{\displaystyle Cu}{\diagup\,\diagdown}}{\overset{+O\quad\quad O+}{\underset{\|\quad\quad\|}{}}}-CH_2--OC_2H_5 + B \xrightarrow{slow}$$

$$CH_3-\overset{}{\underset{\|}{C}}=CH-\overset{\overset{\displaystyle Cu}{\diagup\,\diagdown}}{\overset{O\quad\quad O+}{\underset{\quad\quad\|}{}}}-OC_2H_5 + BH^+ \tag{2}$$

followed by rapid reaction of the enolate with bromine. Here B is any base in the solution. The effect of copper ion is quite pronounced, 0.007 M Cu^{2+} causing a doubling of the rate. Only a small amount of the reactive complex is rapidly formed in 1. The rate-determining step is 2, but the net rate depends on the stability of the complex formed in 1. In agreement with this, Pedersen found that in the similar bromination of a cyclic ketoester,[4] the catalytic power of several cations fell in the order $Cu^{2+} > Ni^{2+} > La^{3+} > Zn^{2+} > Pb^{2+} > Mn^{2+} > Cd^{2+} > Ca^{2+} > Ba^{2+} > H^+$. This is in good agreement with the expected order of stabilities of the respective complexes.

The decarboxylation of certain keto acids is another reaction catalyzed by metal ions. The decomposition of acetoacetic acid (I) is not so catalyzed but that of oxaloacetic acid (II) is.[5]

$$CH_3-\overset{O}{\underset{\|}{C}}-CH_2-\overset{O}{\underset{\|}{C}}-OH \qquad\qquad HO-\overset{O}{\underset{\|}{C}}-\overset{O}{\underset{\|}{C}}-CH_2-\overset{O}{\underset{\|}{C}}-OH$$
$$\text{(I)} \qquad\qquad\qquad\qquad\qquad\qquad \text{(II)}$$

From pH and other behavior,[6] it is clear that the reactive species is a complex of the dianion

$$\underset{\substack{\text{C}\\\parallel\\\text{O}}}{\underset{\text{O}}{\overset{\text{O}}{\text{C}}}}\underset{\text{C}}{\overset{\overset{\text{M}}{\diagup\diagdown}}{\overset{\text{O}^+}{\text{C}}}}-\text{CH}_2-\underset{}{\overset{\overset{\text{O}}{\parallel}}{\text{C}}}-\text{O}^- \rightarrow \underset{\substack{\text{C}\\\parallel\\\text{O}}}{\overset{\text{O}}{\text{C}}}\underset{\text{C}}{\overset{\overset{\text{M}}{\diagup\diagdown}}{\overset{\text{O}}{\text{C}}}}=\text{CH}_2 + \text{CO}_2 \qquad (3)$$

$$\underset{\substack{\text{C}\\\parallel\\\text{O}}}{\overset{\text{O}}{\text{C}}}\underset{\text{C}}{\overset{\overset{\text{M}}{\diagup\diagdown}}{\overset{\text{O}}{\text{C}}}}=\text{CH}_2 \xrightarrow{\text{H}^+} \underset{\substack{\text{C}\\\parallel\\\text{O}}}{\overset{\text{O}}{\text{C}}}\underset{\text{C}}{\overset{\overset{\text{M}}{\diagup\diagdown}}{\overset{\text{O}^+}{\text{C}}}}-\text{CH}_3 \qquad (4)$$

This complex may not be the most stable one that can be formed, but presumably it exists in some degree. Hydrogen ion can replace the metal ion, M^{2+}, since the monoanion decarboxylates readily. However, too much hydrogen ion (or too much metallic ion catalyst) will cause a decrease in the rate because unreactive species will be formed.[7]

In a similar fashion oxalosuccinic acid [5b] and acetonedicarboxylic acid [8] show catalysis by metal ions for their decarboxylations. Good correlation exists between catalytic efficiency and the complex-forming ability of the metal, the order in the first case being

$$\text{Al}^{3+} > \text{Fe}^{3+} > \text{Cu}^{2+} > \text{Fe}^{2+} > \text{Zn}^{2+} > \text{Mg}^{2+} > \text{Mn}^{2+} > \text{Ca}^{2+}$$

Recently it has been found [9] that metal ions catalyze the hydrolysis of the esters and amides of α-amino acids. From tracer studies using oxygen 18 it appears that a complex is formed which leads to the addition of water to the carbonyl,[10] e.g.,

$$\underset{\underset{\text{Cu}}{\diagdown\diagup}}{\underset{\text{H}_2\overset{+}{\text{N}}}{\text{R}'-\text{C}}}\underset{\overset{+}{\text{O}}}{\overset{\overset{\parallel}{\text{C}}}{\text{C}}}-\text{OR} + \text{H}_2\text{O} \rightleftharpoons$$

$$\underset{\underset{\underset{+}{\text{Cu}}}{\mid}}{\underset{\text{H}_2\overset{+}{\text{N}}}{\text{R}'-\text{C}}}\underset{\underset{\underset{\text{H}}{\mid}}{\overset{\mid}{\text{O}}}}{\overset{\overset{\overset{\text{H}}{\mid}}{\text{O}}}{\text{C}}}-\text{OR} \rightarrow \underset{\underset{\underset{+}{\text{Cu}}}{\mid}}{\underset{\text{H}_2\overset{+}{\text{N}}}{\text{R}'-\text{C}}}\underset{}{\overset{\overset{\text{O}}{\parallel}}{\text{C}}}-\text{OH} + \text{ROH} \qquad (5)$$

This is to be compared to the ordinary acid-catalyzed hydrolysis of esters:[2]

$$R'\overset{\overset{\overset{\text{H}}{\underset{|}{\text{O}^+}}}{\|}}{\text{C}}\!-\!OR + H_2O \rightleftarrows R'\overset{\overset{\text{H}}{\underset{\underset{\text{H}}{\overset{+}{\text{O}}}}{\underset{|}{\text{C}}}}}{\text{C}}\!-\!\overset{\text{H}}{\underset{+}{\text{O}}}R \rightarrow R'\overset{\overset{\text{O}}{\|}}{\text{C}}\!-\!OH + ROH + H^+ \tag{6}$$

The effect of cupric ion in reaction 5 is much greater than that of an equivalent amount of hydrogen ion, however. Thus at 0.01 M Cu^{2+} the half-life is 10–30 min for several examples, whereas the acid-catalyzed reaction is extremely slow.[10]

The reason for this superiority is clearly the fact that the metal ion has a greater coordination number than hydrogen ion. Thus in $R'\!-\!\overset{|}{\underset{\underset{+}{\text{NH}_3}}{\text{C}}}\!-\!\overset{\overset{\text{O}}{\|}}{\text{C}}\!-\!OR$

the proton cannot interact with the carbonyl group except by the less efficient electrostatic induction. In general it will be found that two or more points of attachment for the metal ion are needed for it to display catalytic activity.

In line with this reasoning is the observation[11] that Schiff bases are easily hydrolyzed if made part of a chelate system such as

$$\tag{7}$$

Thus the reaction above occurs with cupric ion, nickel ion, and with hydrogen ion. However, if the aldehyde moiety is coordinated to the metal ion as in

then cleavage of the Schiff base will be retarded.[11c] These reactions are reminiscent of those found by Pfeiffer,[12] in which copper and nickel chelates of Schiff bases formed from salicylaldehyde and esters of optically active α-amino acids were shown to undergo rapid racemization, ester exchange, and oxidative deamination.

The racemization and deamination are understandable in terms of the prototropic tautomerism of these aldimine systems (Schiff bases).

$$
\underset{R}{} \overset{H}{\underset{|}{C}} = N - \overset{H}{\underset{|}{\underset{H}{C}}} - \overset{O}{\overset{\|}{C}} - OR' \xrightleftharpoons{\text{base}} \underset{R}{} \overset{H}{\underset{|}{C}} - N = \overset{H}{\underset{|}{\underset{H}{C}}} - \overset{O}{\overset{\|}{C}} - OR' \qquad (8)
$$

Hydrolysis of the new tautomer will now lead to a transamination

$$
\underset{R}{} \overset{H}{\underset{|}{\underset{H}{C}}} - N = \overset{H}{\underset{|}{C}} - \overset{O}{\overset{\|}{C}} - OR' + H_2O \xrightarrow{\text{acid}} \underset{R}{} \overset{H}{\underset{|}{\underset{H}{C}}} - NH_2 + O = \overset{H}{\underset{|}{C}} - \overset{O}{\overset{\|}{C}} - OR'
$$

$$(9)$$

Both the tautomerism and the hydrolysis will be catalyzed by metal ions. This mechanism appears to operate in the case of transaminations produced by pyridoxal on amino acids.[13]

In summary, it is expected that metal ions will catalyze reactions which are acid catalyzed *provided* chelation of some kind is possible. In such cases metal ions will usually be much more effective than hydrogen ion. If only a single point of attachment is possible (simple esters and amides), then hydrogen ion catalysis will be more important. Thus hydrogen ion usually has the greatest affinity of all cations for basic, monodentate ligands.

The efficiency of the metal ion will depend on its complex-forming ability as a rule. However, other factors, such as the rate of reaction of the intermediate complex, will certainly enter in. Also metal ions that are too effective in complexing may be catalytically inactive. This occurs in the case of Al^{3+} and Be^{2+}, which do not influence the rate of bromination of acetoacetic ester.[4] Presumably the explanation is that they are too highly stabilized by other ligands to interact with the weakly basic keto ester. A similar explanation has been given by Klotz[14] for the high efficiency of the weak complexes of Mg^{2+} and Mn^{2+} in activating enzyme systems.

CATALYSIS OF OXIDATION REACTIONS

The role played by complexes in the previous case of acid-catalyzed reactions was purely that of a generalized acid and depended on complex-forming ability. Except for this ability there was no distinction between transition, inner transition, and representative elements. The second kind of catalytic behavior to be discussed is confined almost entirely to the transition elements since the key feature is the ability to exist in solution in more than one oxidation state. Ability to complex plays a secondary, but still necessary, role.

If a given oxidizing agent and reducing agent have the proper redox potentials (or standard free energies) to react with each other, the reaction may still be slow. This is particularly true in the case of organic reducing agents. In such a case a metallic ion of variable valence may greatly accelerate the rate by providing an easier reaction path. Essentially alternate reactions of the ion with an oxidizing agent and a reducing agent occur.

Generally this will involve complexing of the metal ion with the other reagents. Such coordination often greatly increases the ease with which an electron transfer can occur.[15] An example is the catalytic effect of $Mn(III)$ on the reaction between chlorine and oxalate ion. The key step is the internal oxidation-reduction of $MnC_2O_4^+$, followed by reaction with chlorine.[16]

$$MnC_2O_4^+ \rightarrow Mn^{2+} + CO_2 + CO_2^- \tag{10}$$

$$CO_2^- + Cl_2 \rightarrow CO_2 + Cl + Cl^- \tag{11}$$

$$Cl + Mn^{2+} \rightarrow Cl^- + Mn^{3+} \tag{12}$$

Trivalent manganese is again free to react with oxalate ion.

The decomposition of hydrogen peroxide in the presence of transition metal ions is an important example. After much controversy and some revision, the classical mechanism of Haber and Weiss [17] finally seems to fit all of the known data.[18] Hydrogen peroxide is both the oxidizing and reducing agent and ferrous or ferric iron is an example of the catalyst. The steps involved are

$$Fe^{2+} + H_2O_2 \rightleftharpoons FeOH^{2+} + OH \tag{13}$$

$$OH + H_2O_2 \rightarrow H_2O + HO_2 \tag{14}$$

$$HO_2 + H_2O_2 \rightarrow H_2O + O_2 + OH \tag{15}$$

$$Fe^{3+} + H_2O_2 \rightleftharpoons Fe^{2+} + HO_2 + H^+ \tag{16}$$

$$Fe^{3+} + HO_2 \rightarrow Fe^{2+} + O_2 + H^+ \tag{17}$$

$$Fe^{2+} + OH \rightarrow FeOH^{2+} \tag{18}$$

Depending on the pH, further reactions can be written involving O_2H^- and O_2^- derived by proton loss from H_2O_2 and HO_2. For 16 and 17 the reactions involving the anions are the important ones.

We are dealing here with a free radical chain reaction involving 13 or 16 as initiating steps, 14 and 15 as chain carriers, and 17 and 18 and the reverse of 13 and 16 as chain breakers. A great many details of the rates of the individual reactions are known.[18]

Because the reactive radicals OH and HO_2 are formed it is also possible to use the mixture to oxidize a number of organic substances (Fenton's reagent).[18,19] Similar reactions can be written for other metal ions of variable valence in place of iron(II) and for organic peroxides * and hydroperoxides in place of H_2O_2.[18] In fact the general scheme shown can be considered a model for most oxidations catalyzed by heavy metal ions. This will become clear from the following discussion on autoxidation.

Autoxidation of organic substances. The term autoxidation is used to denote the reaction of oxidizable materials with molecular oxygen unaccompanied by the phenomena of flame and high temperature. The reaction takes place slowly, homogeneously in the case of liquids, is inhibited by easily oxidized materials such as phenols, aromatic amines, and secondary alcohols, and is greatly accelerated by the presence of small amounts of metal ions from the transition series.

The reaction is an undesirable one in many cases such as the deterioration of edible fats, lubricating oils, high polymers such as rubber, and so on. It is desirable in the case of the hardening of drying oils, the oxidation of reactive impurities (such as mercaptans) in mixtures, and particularly in the industrially important air oxidation of hydrocarbons to more valuable intermediates.

It has long been known that it is the metals of variable valence that are effective in these reactions. Thus copper, cobalt, iron, manganese, and nickel salts are good catalysts, whereas aluminum, magnesium, zinc, and lead salts are inactive or very poor catalysts. Since metals used in the construction of equipment can form their ions by corrosion, the latter metals may be preferable to the former for many cases where oxidizable materials contact the equipment. If oxidation is desired, the usual practice is to add the metal in the form of a salt of ill-defined constitution such as naphthenate, resinate, or stearate for reasons of solubility in the organic phase.

* $R+$ is not formed in place of $H+$ in reactions 16 and 17, however.

To illustrate autoxidation generally, a discussion of the oxidation of hydrocarbons will be given.[20] Cobalt(II) salts are the preferred catalysts, and small amounts of organic peroxides or hydroperoxides are usually added to prevent the induction period which is otherwise encountered.[21] The reaction may go at room temperature or up to 150°C or so. Pressure may be atmospheric or higher. Only a small amount of dissolved oxygen is actually reacting, but this is sufficient if a reservoir in the gas phase is available. The reaction is slow with saturated hydrocarbons, but unsaturation greatly activates it, as do most negative groups.

The start of the reaction coincides with the oxidation of cobalt(II) to cobalt(III). Starting with cobalt(III) may eliminate the need for added peroxides.[22] The major initial product is hydroperoxides, later accompanied by peroxides, alcohols, ketones, and carboxylic acids. The rate of the reaction expressed as $-dO_2/dt$ is generally independent of the oxygen pressure or concentration, and may be between first and second order in the hydrocarbon and between zero and first order in the catalyst concentration. That is, the rate generally increases with catalyst concentration at low concentrations but tends to become independent of added catalyst at higher concentrations.[20a]

The essential steps appear to be those of the following free radical chain mechanism (RH is the hydrocarbon):

$$Co^{2+} + ROOH \rightarrow Co^{3+} + OH^- + RO\cdot \qquad (19)$$

$$Co^{3+} + ROOH \rightarrow Co^{2+} + H^+ + ROO\cdot \qquad (20)$$

$$ROO\cdot + RH \rightarrow ROOH + R\cdot \qquad (21)$$

$$R\cdot + O_2 \rightarrow ROO\cdot \qquad (22)$$

$$RO\cdot + RH \rightarrow ROH + R\cdot \qquad (23)$$

$$2ROO\cdot \rightarrow \text{inactive products} \qquad (24)$$

and other chain-terminating steps involving the combination of free radicals.* Equations 19 and 20 represent initiating steps which also perpetuate the catalyst. Reactions 21 and 22 are the main chain-carrying steps leading to hydroperoxide. Some of the hydroperoxide is used up to regenerate the catalyst. Further oxidation and decomposition of the hydroperoxide and alcohol, ROH, can occur, so that too much oxidation leads to a reduced yield of the hydroperoxide.

* For recent work on the details of the mechanism of autoxidation, see G. A. Russell, *J. Am. Chem. Soc.*, **79**, 3871 (1957), and earlier papers.

Reactions 19 and 22 are generally fast and do not influence the over-all rate, which depends chiefly on 21 and on the relative rates of chain initiation in 20 and the various chain-breaking steps. Because of the complicated mechanism the observed rate equation can take on various forms depending on the hydrocarbon and the experimental conditions.

The reactions involving the metal ion usually involve prior co-ordination of the metal and the hydroperoxide. The role of the catalyst in both forming and decomposing hydroperoxide was first clearly pointed out by Ivanov.[23] Since the rate of the chain-initiating step depends on the product of metal ion and peroxide, and since peroxide is destroyed by metal ion in two ways, it is possible that the rate be-comes independent of metal ion concentration after a point. Further, a reaction such as

$$Co^{2+} + ROO\cdot \rightarrow CoOOR^{2+} \tag{25}$$

essentially the reverse of 20, could become a chain-interrupting step at higher metal ion concentrations.

The effect of inhibitors, such as β-naphthol, is to break the chains by combining with the active free radicals in some as yet not completely specified manner.[24] The chains must be very long as judged by the influence of very small amounts of inhibitor. Some inhibitors simply retard the reaction, reducing the overall rate. Others completely stop it until they are themselves used up. This leads to induction periods of varying duration.

There are other ways in which the metal ion can enter into the reaction. For example Co(III) if not strongly complexed, as the aqua ion or in acetic acid, will oxidize directly many organic molecules,[20a] e.g.,

$$Co^{3+} + RCHO \rightarrow Co^{2+} + RCO + H^+ \tag{26}$$

Also cobalt(II) probably forms an addition product with oxygen mole-cule,

$$Co^{2+} + O_2 \rightarrow CoO_2^{2+} \tag{27}$$

the addition product being a free radical. The stability and fate of such an adduct depends on the environment, particularly on the other ligands surrounding the cobalt(II).

For example Calvin[25] has shown that for certain chelate compounds of cobalt(II) quite stable addition compounds such as in 27 can be obtained both in solution and, particularly, in the solid state. In these cases reaction 27 is reversible. For ordinary ligands such as ammonia,

CoO_2^{2+} may be a precursor in the usual air oxidation of cobalt(II) to cobalt(III). Thus frequently binuclear peroxo complexes are formed which are suggestive of a CoO_2^{2+} intermediate: [26]

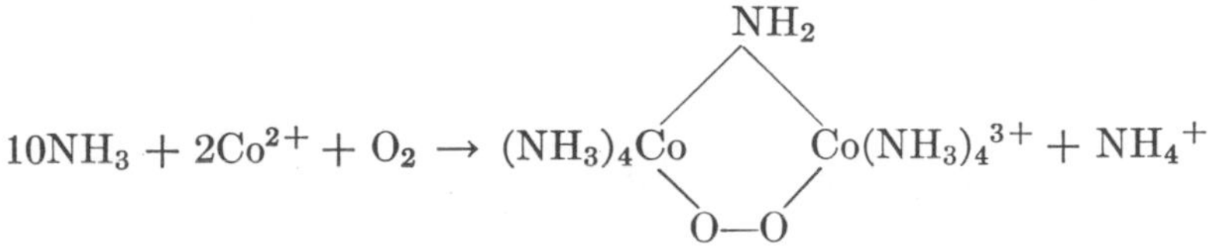

$$10NH_3 + 2Co^{2+} + O_2 \rightarrow (NH_3)_4Co \overset{\displaystyle NH_2}{\underset{\displaystyle O-O}{\diamond}} Co(NH_3)_4{}^{3+} + NH_4{}^+$$

(28)

Whether or not such oxygen adducts play a role in autoxidation remains to be demonstrated. There is, of course, the case of oxyhemoglobin, which is the iron analog of Calvin's stable cobalt adduct, and which plays a vital part in biochemical oxidation.

Important industrial applications of air oxidations of hydrocarbons include the formation of terephthalic acid from p-xylene.[27] The diacid

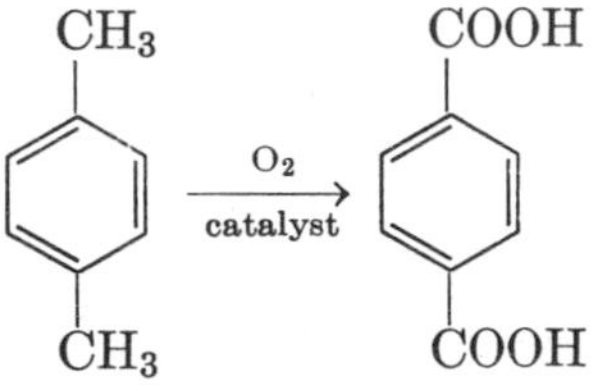

$$\underset{\displaystyle CH_3}{\overset{\displaystyle CH_3}{\bigcirc}} \xrightarrow[\text{catalyst}]{O_2} \underset{\displaystyle COOH}{\overset{\displaystyle COOH}{\bigcirc}}$$

(29)

is used in the production of polymers for synthetic fibers. Also the production of cumene hydroperoxide from cumene (isopropylbenzene), and the manufacture of other hydroperoxides, is carried out on a large

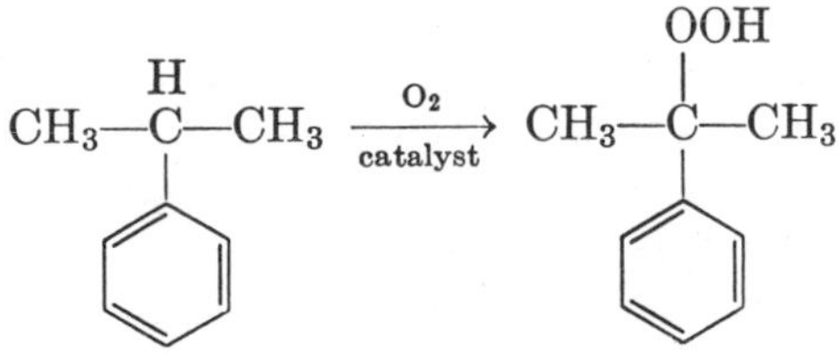

$$CH_3{-}\underset{\displaystyle \bigcirc}{\overset{\displaystyle H}{C}}{-}CH_3 \xrightarrow[\text{catalyst}]{O_2} CH_3{-}\underset{\displaystyle \bigcirc}{\overset{\displaystyle OOH}{C}}{-}CH_3$$

(30)

scale. The hydroperoxides are used as convenient sources of free radicals particularly to initiate polymerization reactions.[28] Either thermal decomposition or metal ion-catalyzed decomposition may be used. A particularly important application is the acid-catalyzed cleavage of cumene hydroperoxide to form commercially important amounts of phenol and acetone.[29]

$$\text{(31)}$$

HOMOGENEOUS CATALYTIC HYDROGENATION

In recent years a number of examples of the metal ion activation of molecular hydrogen in solution have been reported.[30] Following earlier observations by Ipatieff, the first example studied was that of Calvin.[31] He showed that, in quinoline solution, copper(I) salts of organic acids catalyze the reduction by dissolved hydrogen of copper(II) salts and benzoquinone. The details of this reaction have been elucidated in subsequent papers.[32]

It is found that the reaction is homogeneous, is independent of the concentration of the oxidizing agent, and follows the rate law

$$\text{Rate} = k[\text{Cu A}]^2[\text{H}_2] \qquad (32)$$

where A^- is the anion of the organic acid. The interpretation is that molecular hydrogen is split by a dimer of copper(I), or in a termolecular process, to a hydride-like species which is a very active reducing agent. A schematic mechanism would be

$$2\text{Cu(I)} + \text{H}_2 \rightleftharpoons 2\text{Cu(I)} \cdot \text{H or } [\text{Cu(I)} \cdot \text{H}]_2 \qquad (33)$$

$$\text{Cu(I)} \cdot \text{H} + \text{Cu(II)} \xrightarrow{\text{fast}} 2\text{Cu(I)} + \text{H}^+ \qquad (34)$$

with the splitting rate determining. The representation $\text{Cu(I)} \cdot \text{H}$ is not intended to be a complete formula of the intermediate.

In the absence of an oxidizing agent the reversibility of 33 is shown by the ability of the system to catalyze the *ortho-para* hydrogen conversion [33] and the exchange of deuterium isotope with a hydrogen donor in solution.[34] The activation energy for the splitting of H_2 is 13.0 kcal when A^- is acetate.[32d] As expected, D_2 reacts somewhat slower than H_2 with an activation energy of 13.7 kcal. In general the system is very sensitive to the presence of various possible ligands in the system which may deactivate Cu(I).

In a similar fashion it is found [35] that Ag^+ in aqueous solution can catalyze the reduction by hydrogen of a number of oxidizing agents such as $Cr_2O_7{}^{2-}$ and Ce^{4+}. Again there is independence of the oxidizing agent and a rate equation

$$\text{Rate} = k[Ag^+]^2[H_2] \tag{35}$$

suggesting the interaction of a dimer. The activation energy in this case is 15.8 kcal. It is of interest that this is much less than the estimated overall heats of either of the reactions

$$Ag^+ \text{ (aq.)} + H_2 \text{ (g.)} \rightarrow AgH \text{ (aq.)} + H^+ \text{ (aq.)} \tag{36}$$

whose ΔH^0 is $+30$–35 kcal,[36] or

$$2Ag^+ \text{ (aq.)} + H_2 \rightarrow Ag_2 + 2H^+ \text{ (aq.)} \tag{37}$$

whose ΔH^0 is $+46$ kcal.[35] This suggests that a species such as AgH^+ is involved.

Though the simultaneous splitting of H_2 by two metal ions seems to be a favored mechanism, it is not the only one. Thus in water Cu^{2+} and Hg^{2+}, and their acetato complexes, activate H_2 in such a way as to cause homogeneous reduction of oxidizing agents.[35,36] The behavior is similar to that of Ag^+ except that the rate law shows only a first-order dependence on the metal ion concentration. This may be attributed to the divalent character of these ions. This is not the complete story, however, because, in pyridine and in dodecylamine, copper(I) and silver(I) acetate activate hydrogen by a process which is also first order in Cu(I) and Ag(I).[37] The cuprous system catalyzes the reduction of cupric acetate and causes deuterium exchange. The silver ion system is reduced to metallic silver. These results show that a dimer of a monovalent ion is not required to split molecular hydrogen.

With dimeric species, a homolytic bond breaking to give two hydrogen atoms bonded to metal seems most plausible. With a single monovalent ion it is probable that a heterolytic split to H^- and H^+ occurs with the metal ion taking up the hydride ion and the basic solvent taking up the proton [38]

$$Ag^+\text{---}H\text{---}H\text{---}B \rightarrow AgH + BH^+ \tag{38}$$

It has been shown [39] that strong bases can in fact split the hydrogen molecule into H^- and H^+. Thus, if B is hydroxide ion or amide ion, the metal ion may not be necessary for reaction 38, its place being taken by H_2O or NH_3.

Also a fairly straightforward calculation can be made of the energies required for heterolytic and homolytic splitting in water. The reaction

$$H_2 \text{ (aq.)} \rightarrow 2H \cdot \text{ (aq.)} \qquad (39)$$

requires about 100 kcal, whereas the ionic splitting

$$H_2 \text{ (aq.)} \rightarrow H^+ \text{ (aq.)} + H^- \text{ (aq.)} \qquad (40)$$

requires only about 33 kcal. This is based on heats of hydration for the proton of -260 kcal, for hydride ion of -108 kcal, and for H_2 of -2 kcal. Consequently, unless two hydrogen atoms can simultaneously be accepted by some species in solution, the ionic splitting should be favored in solvents of high polarity.

A more detailed study of the activation of H_2 by $Cu(H_2O)_6^{2+}$ in $HClO_4$ solution reveals that the kinetic order of copper(II) changes from one to two as the acidity increases.[30b] At the same time a decrease in rate is observed. The following mechanism can account for these facts:

$$Cu^{2+} + H_2 \underset{k_2}{\overset{k_1}{\rightleftharpoons}} CuH^+ + H^+ \qquad (41)$$

$$CuH^+ + Cu^{2+} \overset{k_3}{\longrightarrow} 2Cu^+ + H^+ \qquad (42)$$

$$2Cu^+ + \text{substrate} \overset{\text{fast}}{\longrightarrow} \text{products} + 2Cu^{2+} \qquad (43)$$

Application of the steady-state method, assuming CuH^+ a reactive intermediate, gives the rate equation:

$$\text{Rate} = \frac{k_1 k_3 [H_2][Cu^{2+}]^2}{k_3[Cu^{2+}] + k_2[H^+]} \qquad (44)$$

The ratio of k_2/k_3 was found to be 0.25 at 110°C. This mechanism can explain a number of phenomena such as the effect of the nature of the solvent and of added anions on the rates and kinetic orders. Thus the proton and the metal ion will be stabilized to varying degrees by the solvent or by anions. Competition of these stabilized forms for CuH^+ determines the characteristics observed. In aqueous solution the effect of various complexing agents is shown in Table 1.

It can be seen that the more basic simple anions produce high rates of reduction of the substrates (such as $Cr_2O_7^{2-}$, IO_3^-, Ce^{4+}). This can be attributed to the stabilization of the hydrogen ion, so that k_2 is diminished. Chelating agents such as glycine, however, are inhibitors for the catalytic reaction. This is because copper(II) ion is now most stabilized, and k_3 and/or k_1 is diminished. Very similar

Table 1

Effect of Complexing Agents on the Catalytic Activity of Cu^{2+} in Aqueous Solution

Ligand	Relative Activity	Ligand	Relative Activity
Butyrate	150	Chloride	2.5
Propionate	150	Perchlorate	1.0
Acetate	120	Glycine	0.5
Sulfate	6.5	Ethylenediamine	0.1

Data from reference 30b.

results have been observed for the copper(I)- and silver(I)-catalyzed reactions.[34,38]   Table 2 gives a summary of data on homogeneous hydrogenation reactions.

The oxo reaction.   The most important example of homogeneous hydrogenation is the so-called oxo or hydroformylation reaction.[40] The system, composed of cobalt salts, carbon monoxide, molecular hydrogen, and organic substrate, undergoes a variety of reactions in the liquid state.   Some examples are

$$\text{Hydroformylation} \quad \diagdown\!\!/C{=}C\diagdown\!\!/ + CO + H_2 \rightarrow \diagdown\!\!/CH{-}\overset{\displaystyle H}{\underset{\displaystyle |}{C}}{-}\overset{}{C}{=}O \quad (45)$$

$$\text{Hydrogenation} \quad \diagdown\!\!/C{=}C\diagdown\!\!/ + H_2 \rightarrow \diagdown\!\!/CH{-}CH\diagdown\!\!/ \quad (46)$$

$$\text{Homologation} \quad {-}CH_2OH + CO + 2H_2 \rightarrow {-}CH_2{-}CH_2OH + H_2O \quad (47)$$

$$\text{Hydrogenolysis} \quad R_2CHOH + H_2 \rightarrow R_2CH_2 + H_2O \quad (48)$$

Temperatures are 90–200°C and pressures from 100 to 400 atmospheres. It has been shown that dicobalt octacarbonyl and cobalt hydrocarbonyl are formed under the reaction conditions.   Furthermore it has been shown [41] that cobalt hydrocarbonyl plus the organic substrate will, at room temperature and pressure, give the same products as are formed in the oxo reaction.   Hence it seems reasonably sure that $HCo(CO)_4$ is the active agent to consider in some of the reactions that occur.

This interesting substance was first prepared by Coleman and

Table 2

Summary of Homogeneous Hydrogenation Reactions

Catalytic Species	Solvent	Reaction Studied	Temperature Range	Kinetics for $-d[H_2]/dt$	$\Delta H^{\ddagger}$, kcal	$\Delta S^{\ddagger}$, eu
CuOAc	quinoline	reduction of Cu(II) or quinone; *para* H_2 conversion	25–117°	$k[H_2][Cu(I)]^2$	13–16	−20
CuOAc	pyridine	Cu(II) $\rightarrow$ Cu(I)	100	$k[H_2][Cu(I)]$		
AgOAc	pyridine	Ag(I) $\rightarrow$ Ag(0)	25–78	$k[H_2][Ag(I)]$	12–14	−25
Co$_2$(CO)$_8$	benzene, ether, etc.	hydroformylation, hydrogenation, etc.	90–200			
Ethylene–platinous chloride	toluene, acetone	$C_2H_4 + H_2 \rightarrow C_2H_6$	<0			
Cu(OAc)$_2$	aqueous HOAc	Cu(II) $\rightarrow$ Cu(I) or $Cr_2O_7^= \rightarrow Cr^{+++}$,	80–140	$k[H_2][Cu(II)]$	24	−7
Cu^{++}	aqueous HClO$_4$	$Cr_2O_7^= \rightarrow Cr^{+++}$, etc.	80–140	$k[H_2][Cu^{++}]$	26	−10
Ag$^+$	aqueous HClO$_4$	$Cr_2O_7^= \rightarrow Cr^{+++}$	30–70	$k[H_2][Ag^+]^2$	15	−22
Hg^{++}	aqueous HClO$_4$	$Hg^{++} \rightarrow Hg_2^{++}$	65–100	$k[H_2][Hg^{++}]$	18	−12
Hg$_2^{++}$	aqueous HClO$_4$	$Hg_2^{++} \rightarrow Hg(0)$	65–100	$k[H_2][Hg_2^{++}]$	20	−10
MnO$_4^-$	aqueous HClO$_4$	$MnO_4^- \rightarrow MnO_2$	30–70	$k[H_2][MnO_4^-]$	14	−17
Ag$^+$ + MnO$_4^-$	aqueous HClO$_4$	$MnO_4^- \rightarrow MnO_2$	30–60	$k[H_2][Ag^+][MnO_4^-]$	9	−26
Co(CN)$_2$	water	H_2 absorption	25	$k[H_2][Co(II)]^2$		
OH$^-$	water	*para* H_2 conversion or D$_2$ exchange	80–110	$k[H_2][OH^-]$	23	−7
NH$_2^-$	ammonia	*para* H_2 conversion or D$_2$ exchange	−50	$k[H_2][NH_2^-]$		

Source: J. Halpern, *Quart. Revs. London*, **10**, 463 (1956).

Blanchard.[42] It is an unstable liquid which decomposes according to
the equation

$$2HCo(CO)_4 \rightarrow H_2 + Co_2(CO)_8 \qquad (49)$$

The decomposition is second order, and hence the substance is relatively
stable in the gas phase where its partial pressure is small.[43] The assumption is that formation of the hydrocarbonyl in the liquid states
occurs by the reversal of 49. This does not occur in the gas phase,
however.[43]

Dicobalt octacarbonyl has the bridge structure

$$
\begin{array}{c}
O \\
\parallel \\
C \\
\diagup \quad \diagdown \\
(CO)_3Co \!\!-\!\!\!-\!\!\!-\!\! Co(CO)_3 \\
\diagdown \quad \diagup \\
C \\
\parallel \\
O
\end{array}
$$

evidence being presented for two kinds of CO groupings, a carbonyl
type and a carbon monoxide type, chiefly from infrared spectra.[44]
This is similar to other metal carbonyls such as iron enneacarbonyl.[45]
The bridge CO is similar to an organic carbonyl group. Those carbon
monoxide molecules that are not bridging donate a pair of electrons
from carbon to the metal. It is also believed that d electrons from the
metal form π bonds back to carbon.[46] The chief canonical structures
(resonating forms) would be

$$\bar{M}\!:\!\overset{+}{C}\!:\!:\!\overset{..}{O}\!: \leftrightarrow M\!:\!:\!C\!:\!:\!\overset{..}{O}\!: \leftrightarrow \bar{M}\!:\!C\!:\!:\!:\!\overset{+}{O}\!:$$

Since five of the coordination positions of cobalt are occupied by CO
groups, the sixth position is still free, though the orbital corresponding
to it contains a single electron. The two cobalt atoms are then close
enough to couple the spins of the two electrons forming a weak metal-
metal bond. It is this bond which would probably first be broken
in forming $HCo(CO)_4$, a homolytic split of H_2 occurring.

In aqueous solution $HCo(CO)_4$ is a strong acid, being completely
ionized in a saturated solution, $0.056\ M$.[43] In view of this it is remarkable that nuclear magnetic resonance studies [44b] show that the proton
signal occurs at such a frequency as to indicate a hydride ion-like
environment.

The anion $Co(CO)_4^-$ is stable towards decomposition. Electron diffraction studies [47] show a tetrahedral arrangement of the four CO groups around the cobalt atom. The location of the hydrogen atom is uncertain. For example, the infrared spectrum of $HCo(CO)_4$ and $DCo(CO)_4$ is the same in the 2–22 μ region.[43, 44b] The best structure that can be written is probably one with the hydrogen buried in one of the tetrahedral faces and loosely bonded to Co, C, and O.[48]

The explanation for the acidity and general activity then, is that the hydrogen is only loosely held and may, depending on circumstances, come off as H^+, H^-, or H atom. The electronic structure of the anion $Co(CO)_4^-$ is as follows:

with one electron in the $3d$ level having been contributed by hydrogen atom or some other reducing agent. The $4s$ and $4p$ electrons come from the four CO ligands.

A kinetic study of the oxo reaction proper, which is the hydroformylation reaction, shows that the reaction is first order in olefin and approximately first order in the amount of cobalt present.[49] The rate increases with increasing hydrogen pressure and decreases with increasing carbon monoxide pressure.[50] A mechanistic sequence which fits the data obtained with different ratios of hydrogen and CO pressure is as follows for cyclohexene as the olefin: [51]

$$C_6H_{10} + Co_2(CO)_8 \rightleftharpoons Co_2(CO)_7 \cdot C_6H_{10} + CO \qquad (50)$$

$$Co_2(CO)_7 \cdot C_6H_{10} + H_2 \rightarrow Co_2(CO)_7 \cdot C_6H_{10} \cdot H_2 \qquad (51)$$

$$Co_2(CO)_7 \cdot C_6H_{10} \cdot H_2 \rightarrow C_6H_{11}CHO + Co_2(CO)_6 \qquad (52)$$

$$Co_2(CO)_6 + 2CO \rightarrow Co_2(CO)_8 \qquad (53)$$

The reverse of reaction 50 and reaction 51 compete with each other to account for the results.

The reaction rate is virtually independent of solvent, is faster for terminal olefins than for internal olefins, and is slowed down by chain branching in the olefin.[52] A plausible structure for the intermediate which leads to product is

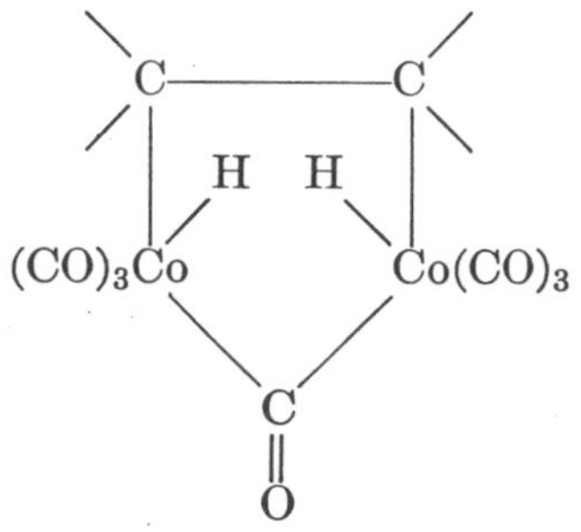

$$\text{(CO)}_3\text{Co} \diagdown\text{C}\diagdown \underset{\overset{|}{\text{C}}}{\overset{\text{H}\quad\text{H}}{\text{\ }}} \diagup\text{C}\diagup \text{Co(CO)}_3$$

Such an intermediate could also be formed from two moles of hydro-carbonyl and the olefin. A base, such as triethylamine, will completely inhibit the reaction,[41] so that the anion $Co(CO)_4{}^-$ is not effective in any way. It is of interest that both pentene-1 and pentene-2 give the same products in the oxo reaction.[40d] Also if the reaction is interrupted for a terminal olefin, it is found that some isomerization to internal olefin has occurred.[53] Hence the adduct shown as $Co(CO)_7 \cdot C_6H_{10}$ in reaction 50 is capable of isomerizing the olefin by hydrogen atom transfer.

The oxo process has been studied extensively, not only because it is important commercially, but because it is a homogeneous model for the even more important heterogeneous Fischer-Tropsch process.[54] Iron is a more versatile catalyst for the Fischer-Tropsch syntheses than cobalt. For example, one reaction catalyzed by precipitated iron, activated by small amounts of alkali, is the water-gas shift

$$H_2O + CO \xrightarrow{\text{Fe}} H_2 + CO_2 \tag{54}$$

this reaction is of importance in the commercial preparation of hydrogen.

A homogeneous model for the water-gas shift involves the use of iron pentacarbonyl as a catalyst.[55] When $Fe(CO)_5$ is treated with an aqueous solution of NaOH, the following reaction occurs:[56]

$$Fe(CO)_5 + 3NaOH \rightarrow NaHFe(CO)_4 + Na_2CO_3 + H_2O \tag{55}$$

Thus the anion $HFe(CO)_4{}^-$ of iron hydrocarbonyl, $H_2Fe(CO)_4$, is formed. In stronger alkali $Fe(CO)_4{}^{2-}$ would be produced.[56] At high carbon monoxide pressures an aqueous solution containing $HFe(CO)_4{}^-$ can catalyze the reaction of water and CO to form hydrogen and carbon dioxide, the water-gas shift reaction.

It has been shown that a dimer is formed from $HFe(CO)_4{}^-$, which can then lose hydrogen as molecular hydrogen [57] (reaction 56). The

$$
\left[\begin{array}{c} O \\ \parallel \\ C \\ (CO)_3Fe\!-\!H \quad H\!-\!Fe(CO)_3 \\ C \\ \parallel \\ O \end{array}\right]^{2-} \rightarrow \left[\begin{array}{c} O \\ \parallel \\ C \\ (CO)_3Fe\!-\!\!-\!\!-\!Fe(CO)_3 \\ C \\ \parallel \\ O \end{array}\right]^{2-} + H_2
$$

(56)

anion $Fe_2(CO)_8{}^{2-}$ is presumably the species which can then split water and, in the presence of CO, regenerate the anion $H_2Fe_2(CO)_8{}^{2-}$. The analogy between these bridged species of iron and the cobalt compounds involved in the oxo reaction is striking. As might be expected these iron compounds can also catalyze the oxo reaction.[57] However, the usual product instead of being aldehyde is alcohol.[58] This is reasonable in view of the expected great reducing properties of the species H_2Fe_2-$(CO)_8{}^{2-}$.

One other topic of related interest: it has been shown in the case of the complex ion formed between cobalt(II) .and cyanide ion that the formula is $Co(CN)_5{}^{3-}$ in aqueous solution and a dimer of this in the solid state.[59] The solid is diamagnetic, but in solution the ion is paramagnetic with one unpaired electron. Such a species is expected to be very reactive, being oxidized easily by air and slowly reducing water. It reacts with bromine and iodine by an atom transfer mechanism. This can be shown since the cobalt(III) complex formed is inert.[60]

$$Co(CN)_5{}^{3-} + X_2 \rightarrow Co(CN)_5X^{3-} + X \qquad (57)$$

$$Co(CN)_5{}^{3-} + X \rightarrow Co(CN)_5X^{3-} \qquad (58)$$

If dimerization occurs in solution, to a small extent as compared to the solid, it is expected that such a dimer could activate molecular hydrogen. Evidence for such activation has recently been given, since hydrogen gas is absorbed by a solution of $Co(CN)_5{}^{3-}$ (forming $HCo(CN)_5{}^{3-}$, perhaps) and deuterium exchange with D_2 occurs.[61]

METAL ION–OLEFIN COMPLEXES

Another class of interesting and industrially important complexes are those formed between certain metals and metal ions and olefinic, aromatic, and acetylenic compounds.[62] The most stable systems of this type are formed by d^{10} atoms and ions such as Ni(0), Cu(I), Ag(I), and Hg(II), and by d^8 atoms and ions such as Fe(0), Rh(I), Ni(II), Pd(II), and Pt(II).[63] Gold would undoubtedly form such complexes in either its plus one or plus three oxidation states, but it is too easily reduced to the metal.

There is very little doubt that the unsaturated group is held to the metal by essentially a double bond, in which unsaturation electrons from the organic molecule form a σ coordinate bond to the metal and the metal in turn donates a pair of d electrons to the organic molecule through a π bond.[64] The best formulation of the bonds in such a system is that due to Dewar.[65] The problem is to form bonding orbitals from the set of atomic orbitals consisting of p orbitals on each carbon atom and an s, or $(s + p)$ hybrid, and a d orbital on the metal.

Figure 1 shows the atomic orbitals involved and the convenient way of representing the two lowest molecular orbitals that can be formed from them. Remembering the criterion of matching signs for the wave functions in regions of overlap, it is clear that an s orbital on the metal will combine with the hybrid obtained by adding together the two carbon p orbitals. This is the bonding M.O. of the carbon-carbon double bond. The d orbital of the metal will combine with the hybrid obtained by changing the sign of one carbon p orbital and then adding. This corresponds to the antibonding M.O. of the double bond. Schematically the silver ion–ethylene complex may be represented by

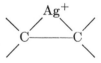

Fig. 1. The double bonding in a silver ion–olefin complex. (From reference 65.)

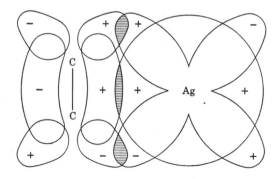

if it is kept in mind that considerable double bond character for the carbon-carbon linkage still remains.

This representation of the complex is not to be confused with the original one given by Winstein and Lucas in which the d electrons of the metal were not considered.[66] It is obviously different from those of the complexes formed between unsaturated systems and such ions as H^+ and Al^{3+}, or generalized acids such as BF_3, $SnCl_4$, $TiCl_4$. These systems are of interest in that they are the intermediates in the cationic type of polymerization, but we shall not discuss them further here.[67]

The bonding of the silver ion to olefin is reasonably strong. Thus the heat of the reaction

$$C_2H_4(CCl_4) + Ag(H_2O)_n^+ \rightarrow AgC_2H_4(H_2O)_{n-1}^+ + H_2O \qquad (59)$$

is about 6 kcal exothermic.[66] Neglecting the differences in the heat of solution of the olefin in water and in carbon tetrachloride, this gives a figure for the metal ion–ethylene coordinate bond as between 20 kcal and 30 kcal.[68] The uncertainty lies in not knowing whether n is 6 or 4 in correcting for the hydration energy of the silver ion.

The importance of the d type of bonding from the metal is brought out by the fact that the stability of the platinum-olefin complexes decreases in the order $PtC_2H_4Cl_3^- \simeq PtC_2H_4ACl_2 > PtC_2H_4A_2Cl^+ > PtC_2H_4A_3^{2+}$, where A is a neutral ligand. Thus negative charge on the complex stabilizes the olefin portion in a way consistent with the concept of electron donation to the olefin.[64] It is of interest to note that, for these square planar complexes of platinum(II), the carbon-carbon axis of ethylene is perpendicular to the plane of the ring.[69] This minimizes the repulsion of the ethylene for the ligands *cis* to it and allows for π bonding from the metal.

The olefin complexes of copper(I) are more stable than those of silver(I) in agreement with the ease of oxidation of each metal to the divalent state.[70] Likewise, platinum(II) complexes are more stable than those of palladium(II). Sometimes the complexes of the divalent cations are more stable than those of the monovalent ions, e.g., Hg^{2+}-cyclohexene is more stable than Ag^+-cyclohexene.[71] This indicates a greater importance of the σ bond (olefin to metal bonding) than the π bond (metal to olefin bonding) in such cases.

Substitution of almost any kind on ethylene makes it a poorer coordinating species.[64] *cis*-Olefins form more stable complexes than *trans*-olefins. Acetylenes form slightly less stable complexes with silver ion than olefins do, but more stable than those of aromatic systems.[72] The complexes of silver with acetylenes and of mercury with acetylenes and olefins containing hydrogen atoms on the unsaturated carbons are quite strong acids, the C—H presumably being ionized.

$$H—C{\overset{\overset{\displaystyle Ag^+}{\diagup\diagdown}}{=\!=\!=}}C—H \rightarrow H—C{\equiv}C—Ag + H^+$$

or

$$H—C{\overset{\overset{\displaystyle Ag^+}{\diagup\diagdown}}{=\!=\!=}}C^- + H^+ \qquad (60)$$

The silver complexes of olefins are stabilized towards hydration and isomerization [66] in contrast to the complex formed between H^+ and olefins.[73] The mercury complexes of acetylene, etc., are catalytic for the hydration of the organic molecule under suitable conditions (strong acid). However, the mechanism of this reaction is not simple. In

$$H—C{\overset{\overset{\displaystyle Hg^{2+}}{\diagup\diagdown}}{=\!=\!=}}C—H + H_2O \rightarrow \overset{H}{\underset{H}{\diagdown\diagup}}C{=}C\overset{OH}{\underset{H}{\diagup\diagdown}} + Hg^{2+} \qquad (61)$$

$$\downarrow$$

$$CH_3CHO$$

glacial acetic acid a more straightforward reaction occurs, which involves reaction of the mercury complex with acetic acid or perhaps rearrangement of the complex.[74]

$$R—C{\equiv}C—R + H^+ + Hg(OAc)_2 \rightarrow R—C{\overset{\overset{\displaystyle \overset{+}{H}gOAc}{\diagup\diagdown}}{=\!=\!=}}C—R + HOAc \qquad (62)$$

$$R—C{\overset{\overset{\displaystyle \overset{+}{H}gOAc}{\diagup\diagdown}}{=\!=\!=}}C—R + HOAc \rightarrow R—\overset{H}{\underset{|}{C}}{=}\overset{OAc}{\underset{|}{C}}—R + HgOAc^+ \qquad (63)$$

In the case of olefins [71, 75a] and aromatics,[75b] stable organomercury compounds may be formed,

$$\overset{+}{H}gOAc$$

$$\underset{/}{\overset{\backslash}{C}}\!-\!-\!-\!\underset{\backslash}{\overset{/}{C}} + OAc^- \rightarrow \underset{/}{\overset{\backslash}{C}}\!-\!\underset{\backslash}{\overset{/}{C}} \qquad (64)$$

$$OAc$$

$$C_6H_6 \cdot HgNO_3{}^+ \rightarrow C_6H_5HgNO_3 + H^+ \qquad (65)$$

A different class of catalytic activity appears in the synthesis of acrylonitrile from acetylene and hydrocyanic acid catalyzed by cuprous chloride.[76] The mechanism of this condensation has not been worked

$$H\!-\!C\!\equiv\!N + H\!-\!C\!\equiv\!C\!-\!H \xrightarrow{Cu^+} \underset{H}{\overset{H}{\underset{/}{\overset{\backslash}{C}}}}\!=\!\overset{H}{\underset{|}{C}}\!-\!C\!\equiv\!N \qquad (66)$$

out, and it may be that the cuprous ion is exerting only an acid type of catalytic effect, with the isomeric acid $H\!-\!N\!=\!C$ acting as a nucleophilic agent as acetate ion and acetic acid do in reactions 64 and 63.

Alternatively, the mode of action may be similar to that shown by nickel complexes in catalyzing condensations of acetylene and its derivatives.[62b] For example, acetylene in non-aqueous media such as tetrahydrofuran condenses to cyclooctatetraene under the influence of nickel(II) cyanide, as discovered by Reppe.

$$4C_2H_2 \xrightarrow{Ni(CN)_2} C_8H_8 \qquad (67)$$

The condensation of acetylene, carbon monoxide and water, alcohol, or amines to form derivatives of acrylic acid is catalyzed by nickel carbonyl. Reactions occur at low temperature (40°C):

$$CO + ROH + H\!-\!C\!\equiv\!C\!-\!H \xrightarrow{Ni(CO)_4} \underset{H}{\overset{H}{\underset{/}{\overset{\backslash}{C}}}}\!=\!\overset{H}{\underset{|}{C}}\!-\!\overset{O}{\underset{\|}{C}}\!-\!OR \qquad (68)$$

The nickel carbonyl is clearly the transfer agent for CO since it forms metallic nickel as reaction proceeds. However, it is possible to add acid to form salts of nickel(II) and hydrogen, and then to regenerate nickel carbonyl by carbon monoxide under pressure.

$$5CO + NiCl_2 + H_2O \rightarrow Ni(CO)_4 + 2HCl + CO_2 \qquad (69)$$

Also, by using higher temperatures and pressures, it is possible to operate the process continuously so that the nickel carbonyl acts as a true catalyst.

Many similar condensations of olefins and acetylenes have been claimed by Reppe.[62b] It is of interest that such substances as triphenyl phosphine and iodide ion are activators for the catalysis by nickel carbonyl.[77] This is an indication that it is necessary to displace some CO from $Ni(CO)_4$ to cause reaction, since it has been shown that only ligands capable of forming double bonds with metals can cause such displacements easily [78] (see also p. 39).

Longuet-Higgins and Orgel [79] have recently made the interesting suggestion that complexed cyclobutadiene is an intermediate in some of these condensations (such as the formation of cyclooctatetraene). It is pointed out that, if two molecules of acetylene add to nickel either as tetrahedral nickel(0) or square planar nickel(II), the π orbitals of the carbons are close enough for intermolecular interaction. The

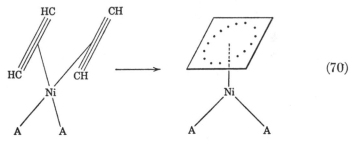

(70)

resultant bonding can be described in terms of an M.O. treatment. In the structure shown above, each acetylene is acting only as a unidentate group and two other ligands would be attached to nickel. Reasoning by analogy it is possible that complexed cyclopropenone is an intermediate in the condensations of carbon monoxide and acetylene.

HETEROGENEOUS CATALYSIS IN REACTIONS OF METAL COMPLEXES

That reactions of metal complexes are subject to heterogeneous catalysis was first reported by Schwarz and Kronig.[80] They observed that when an aqueous solution of hexamminecobalt(III) chloride is shaken with either silica gel or decolorizing charcoal it readily dissociates to a pentammine complex; on prolonged treatment cobalt(III) hydroxide is formed. Similar catalytic effects were also found for reactions of complexes of chromium(III) [81] and of platinum(II), (IV) ions.[82]   Other catalysts that have been used are Raney nickel,[83] colloidal palladium,[84] and mercury.[84]

Bjerrum [84] utilized the catalytic property of charcoal to determine the stability of cobalt(III) ammine compounds.   Thermodynamic data on the aqueous system Co(III)-NH_3-NH_4^+ cannot be obtained because the reactions involved are extremely slow so that equilibrium is not established.   Thus $Co(NH_3)_5OH^{2+}$ in an ammonia-ammonium ion–buffered solution remains completely unchanged for several weeks. However, the same solution in the presence of charcoal yields $Co(NH_3)_6^{3+}$ in the course of a few hours.   The use of charcoal as a catalyst thus allowed the system to reach equilibrium, and potentiometric measurements were made to determine the overall formation constant of $Co(NH_3)_6^{3+}$ ($\log K_T = 35.21$ at 30°C in 2 N salt solution). In spite of this large formation constant, the oxidation of an ammoniacal cobalt(II) salt solution yields largely pentamminecobalt(III) salt instead of the more stable hexammine compound.   This is in part due to the lower stability of the cobalt(II) ammines so that prior to oxidation the reaction mixture contains some pentamminecobalt(II) ion.   There need not necessarily be a large concentration of this ion; all that is required is that it be more readily oxidized than the hexamminecobalt(II) ion.   In such a case, as the pentammine complex is oxidized more is formed because cobalt(II) ammines are labile.   Therefore a large amount of $Co(NH_3)_5OH^{2+}$ is produced which, in the absence of a catalyst, does not react to yield the more stable $Co(NH_3)_6^{3+}$.   However, under the same reaction conditions, but with added charcoal, the product is almost exclusively the hexamminecobalt(III) salt.[84]

Additional investigations on the use of a catalyst for the synthesis of chromium(III) and cobalt(III) ammines are reported by Bailar and Work.[83]   The usual procedure for the preparation of $[Cr(en)_3]Cl_3$ is to use anhydrous materials, since water molecules coordinated to chromium are not displaced by amines under ordinary conditions. However, in the presence of charcoal, hydrated chromium(III) chloride and aqueous ethylenediamine react to yield the hexammine salt.   Neither ammonia nor nitro groups are readily replaced when coordinated to cobalt(III).   Although $Co(en)_2(NH_3)_2^{3+}$ does not react with nitrite ion alone, in the presence of charcoal it is converted into $Co(en)_2(NO_2)_2^+$. Similarly the unreactive $Co(NH_3)_6^{3+}$ ion will react with nitrite ion when charcoal is present to yield $Co(NH_3)_3(NO_2)_3$.   The reaction of l-$Co(en)_2Cl_2^+$ with nitrite ion, either in the presence or absence of a catalyst, yields d-$Co(en)_2(NO_2)_2^+$.   Likewise, d-$Co(en)_2(NH_3)Cl^{2+}$

gives d-Co(en)$_2$(NH$_3$)NO$_2{}^{2+}$ whether or not a catalyst is used. Although only qualitative, these results do suggest that the reaction mechanism is similar for the catalyzed and uncatalyzed reactions.

No systematic study has as yet been made on the relative catalytic effects of different materials nor on the effect towards different complexes and different types of reactions. However, fragmentary observations can be brought together to indicate some of the general trends. In the first place charcoal and Raney nickel are better catalysts for reactions of cobalt(III) complexes than are silica gel, mercury, and colloidal palladium (the last two require the presence of some cobalt(II) ions). For example, in the absence of a catalyst, ammonium hydroxide converts [Co(en)$_2$Cl$_2$]Cl to [Co(en)$_2$(NH$_3$)Cl]Cl$_2$ readily, but the replacement of the second chlorine proceeds slowly. In the presence of silica gel conversion to [Co(en)$_2$(NH$_3$)$_2$]Cl$_3$ is complete in thirty minutes; with either charcoal or Raney nickel the same effect is produced in two minutes.[83] The surface of the reaction vessel may also affect the rate of reaction of cobalt(III) complexes. Both the absorption spectrum and

$$pH \text{ of solutions of either } Co(en)_2(H_2O)_2{}^{3+} \text{ or } (en)_2Co \overset{\displaystyle OH}{\underset{\displaystyle OH}{\diagup\diagdown}} Co(en)_2{}^{4+}$$

gradually change upon standing, this change being much more rapid in a glass container than it is in a paraffined vessel.[85] Similarly air oxidation of Co(II)-en yields binuclear peroxo complexes in paraffined reaction flasks but mononuclear cobalt(III) compounds if a glass container is used.[86]

Numerous examples are reported of induced ligand or metal ion exchange where precipitation methods of separation are used.[87] These examples indicate that catalytic surface effects are fairly common for reactions of coordination compounds. Certainly these effects must vary in degree all the way from being very small to very large. For example, although charcoal greatly catalyzes reactions of cobalt(III) compounds, it has only a very slight effect on the rate of decomposition of Cr(NH$_3$)$_6{}^{3+}$.[88]

The rates of isomerization[89] and of racemization[90] of cobalt(III) complexes are markedly catalyzed by charcoal. The conversion of $trans$-Co(en)$_2$(H$_2$O)$_2{}^{3+}$ to the cis isomer is ten times faster in the presence of charcoal than in its absence. The optical rotation of a solution of d-Co(en)$_3{}^{3+}$ is unchanged after 24 hr at 90°C, but, with added decolorizing carbon, the optical activity is completely lost in two minutes. This loss of optical rotation is not accompanied by a change in the absorption spectrum of the solution; it is thus due to racemization, not decomposition. Furthermore the rate of ethylene-diamine exchange in the system $Co(en)_3^{3+}$-*en is slower than the racemization, which must therefore involve an intramolecular mechanism.[91] It is also observed that the carbon becomes a less effective catalyst as time progresses.[90] Recent studies show that both the racemization and decomposition of d-$Co(C_2O_4)_3^{3-}$ are accelerated by the presence of charcoal and that Raney nickel causes a rapid decomposition of $Co(en)_3^{3+}$ and $Co(C_2O_4)_3^{3-}$.[92]

There has been some interest recently in the application of hydrogen reduction of salt solutions at high temperatures and pressures to the commercial production of metals.[93] In this connection colloidal graphite was found to catalyze the reduction of ammoniacal cobalt(II) sulfate solutions.[94] The results of kinetic studies on this system are consistent with a proposed mechanism that involves adsorption of hydrogen and cobalt(II) complex on the catalyst surface.

Similarly, due to the industrial importance of the hydroformylation reaction, as mentioned earlier, and to the general current interest in transition metal compounds with M—C bonds, there has been a renewed interest in studies of metal carbonyls. For example, Keeley and Johnson [95] find that the half-lives of radiocarbon monoxide exchange with various metal carbonyls in benzene solution are $Fe(CO)_5$, > 260 hr; $Fe_3(CO)_{12}$, > 130 hr; $Co_2(CO)_8$, < 2 min; $Co_4(CO)_{12}$, > 35 hr; $Ni(CO)_4$, < 2 min. In the absence of solvent, Webb [96] finds that at 25°C or below there is no exchange in the system $Fe(CO)_5$-*CO. However, the exchange of carbon monoxide in this system is subject to heterogeneous catalysis. Of the catalysts studied at 0°C, these show the following decrease in order of catalytic activity $(Fe_2O_3$-$Fe_3O_4) > Pt > Ni > Fe > Cu > Al_2O_3$. It would appear that all the active catalysts have electron acceptor properties and that the most active ones have incompletely filled d orbitals. It was also observed that the exchange reaction is completely stopped by covering the catalyst surface with more than a monolayer of iron pentacarbonyl. The interpretation of this is that part of the iron pentacarbonyl is available for exchange on the most active portions of the catalyst surface but that a second part is less mobile and restricted to exchange on less active sites, or must reach the active sites by a relatively slow transport process.

Heterogeneous catalysis, in fields other than coordination chemistry, has been extensively investigated and several theories proposed to account for the observed results.[97] It is generally agreed that the reactants are activated by adsorption on the surface of the catalyst. A similar process of dissociative adsorption may account for the catalysis of reactions of coordination compounds. This can be illustrated for a substitution reaction in a complex of the type MA_5X, which is adsorbed on the catalyst surface to give a path for breaking

$$
\begin{array}{ccc}
MA_5 & & \\
\vdots & & \\
X & \longrightarrow & X \quad MA_5 \\
\vdots & & \vdots \quad\vdots \\
\underset{\text{Catalyst}}{\sim\!\sim\!\sim\!\sim} & & \underset{\text{Catalyst}}{\sim\!\sim\!\sim\!\sim}
\end{array}
\tag{71}
$$

the M—X bond. The mechanistic details of substitution reactions on the catalyst surface are not at present understood. It is of interest that this type of catalysis has rarely been reported for substitution reactions of organic compounds.

In some systems the catalytic effect may result from a catalyzed electron transfer mechanism. There is, for instance, some evidence that the effectiveness of a catalyst in reactions of cobalt(III) complexes is markedly improved by the presence of cobalt(II) ions.[84] Since cobalt(II) complexes are labile, a mechanism which involves a rapid transfer of electrons would provide a path for the reaction of the inert cobalt(III) complexes. The reaction sequence would be

$$
Co(II) + C \rightarrow Co(III) + C^- \tag{72}
$$

$$
Co(III)X + C^- \rightarrow Co(II)X + C \tag{73}
$$

$$
Co(II)X \rightarrow Co(II) + X \tag{74}
$$

where C stands for the charcoal surface.

Anionic olefin polymerization. Metal alkyls when used alone catalyze the polymerization of ethylene [98] but only to the formation of low molecular weight polymers which have little value. Recently Ziegler [99] has reported the low pressure polymerization of ethylene to very high molecular weight polyethylene which is, of course, of considerable industrial importance. Catalysts for this process result from the reaction of a metal alkyl with some transition metal compound. The first catalysts described by Ziegler, often called the Ziegler catalysts and most widely studied, are those obtained by reacting titanium tetrachloride with aluminum trialkyls. This reaction is rather complicated and is as yet not entirely understood. However, it seems to involve the following steps:

$$TiCl_4 + Al(C_2H_5)_3 \rightarrow Al(C_2H_5)_2Cl + TiCl_3C_2H_5 \qquad (75)$$

$$TiCl_3C_2H_5 \rightarrow TiCl_3 + C_2H_5 \cdot \qquad (76)$$

$$2C_2H_5 \cdot \rightarrow C_2H_4 + C_2H_6 \qquad (77)$$

Possibly further reduction to titanium(II) also occurs. In the inert hydrocarbon solvents used, an insoluble mixed halide-alkyl complex of aluminum and titanium is formed of variable composition. This material is the active catalyst for the polymerization of ethylene, presumably acting as a heterogeneous catalyst.

Natta and his co-workers [100] have extended these observations and have had remarkable success in the production of stereospecific polymers. For example, olefins such as propylene have been polymerized in such a way as to yield long linear head-to-tail chains consisting

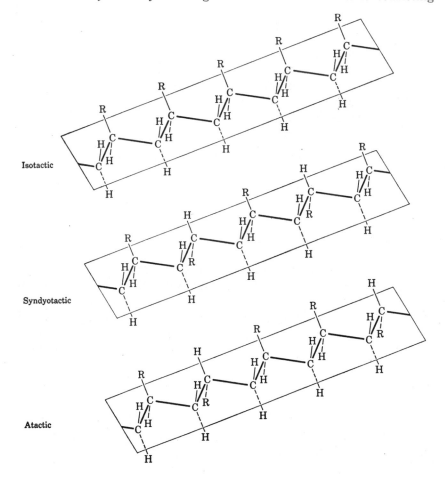

of sequences of monomeric units having the same steric structure. These polymers, which are called *isotactic* polymers, crystallize easily, whereas those with monomeric units of different steric arrangement arranged at random do not crystallize well. These latter polymers are called *atactic*. Polymers of regular, alternating structure called *syndyotactic* polymers are also known.

Though some free radicals are produced in forming the catalyst, the bulk of the polymerization certainly seems to be an anionic process. For example, with a constant supply of olefin, a constant rate of polymerization can be obtained showing that the catalyst is not used up as it would be in a radical-initiated process. The mechanism for both the initiation and propagation steps probably involves addition of a carbanion to an adsorbed olefin molecule. The adsorption may be unsymmetrical so that the olefin double bond is polarized. For example,

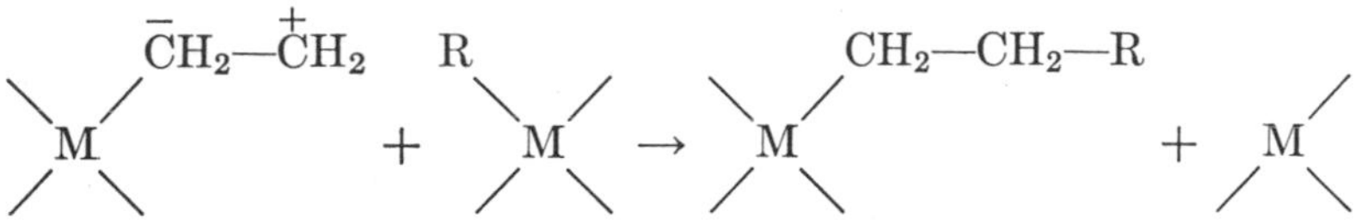

$$\overset{-}{C}H_2\!-\!\overset{+}{C}H_2 \quad R \qquad\qquad CH_2\!-\!CH_2\!-\!R$$

$$(78)$$

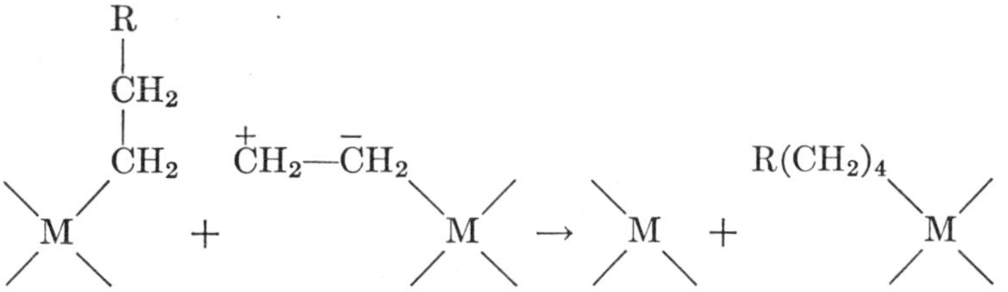

$$(79)$$

It is not known whether the carbanion is initially on the same metal atom as the olefin or on a different but adjacent metal atom. It is attractive to consider that a bridged complex involving two different metal atoms is involved. The unsymmetrical bridge may then exist in a polar form suitable for adsorbing and polarizing the olefin and transferring the carbanion:

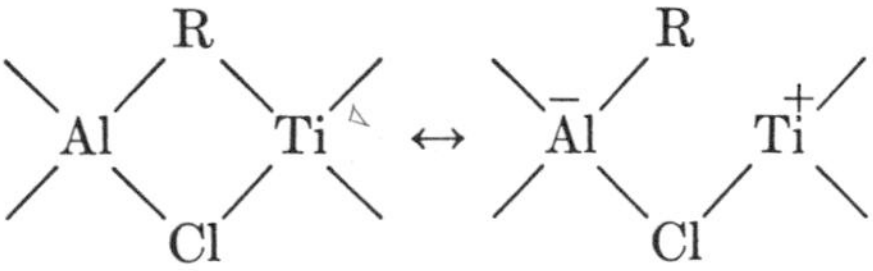

$$(80)$$

Although it is not known which metal adsorbs the olefin and which metal transfers the carbanion, it may be that the well-known instability of simple alkyl compounds of the transition metals favors the ionic form shown above. This would explain the role played by titanium(III) in the catalyst. However, titanium(IV) tends to form more stable alkyl derivatives.[101]

It is well known [102] that aluminum alkyls can form dimers with alkyls acting as bridging groups. Such compounds, as mentioned earlier, are poor catalysts, either alone or in the presence of aluminum chloride. This may be due to the bridged dimers being non-polar since two identical metal atoms are involved. Thus there is an advantage in having two different metals in the bridge to favor an ionic structure such as 80.

That bridged structures may be responsible for the catalytic activity of these systems is supported by the observation that the analogous bridged complexes

$$(C_5H_5)_2Ti \underset{Cl}{\overset{Cl}{<}} \underset{C_2H_5}{\overset{C_2H_5}{>}} Al \quad \text{and} \quad (C_5H_5)_2Ti \underset{Cl}{\overset{Cl}{<}} \underset{C_2H_5}{\overset{Cl}{>}} Al$$

are efficient catalysts even in homogeneous solution.[103] Surprisingly some of the titanium at least must be oxidized to the tetravalent state to give an active catalyst.[104] Finally, other di- or trivalent transition metal halides of a layer-lattice structure will also enhance the catalytic

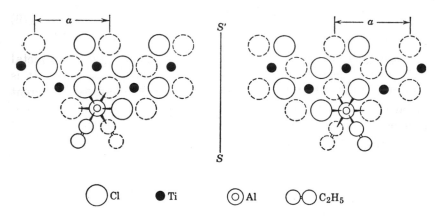

$\bigcirc$ Cl   ● Ti   ◎ Al $\bigcirc\bigcirc$ C$_2$H$_5$

FIG. 2. Schematic model of how adsorption of $AlCl(C_2H_5)_2$ on the border of the basal plane of a crystal of $TiCl_3$ ($a = 6.12$ A) may give rise to enantiomorphous active centers. SS' defines a plane separating the enantiomorphs. (From reference 105.)

activity of aluminum alkyls. However, a metal such as platinum which forms stable metal-olefin complexes does not give an effective catalyst.

Stereospecific polymerization is believed to result from the steric properties of the aluminum alkyl bridged to the crystalline titanium (III) chloride surface.[105] The schematic models represented in Fig. 2 show that the aluminum becomes six-coordinated when adsorbed on the titanium (III) chloride crystalline lattice. Since the example shown corresponds to a complex of the type cis-Al(AA)$_2$X$_2$, it is asymmetric and is formed as a racemic mixture. This structure is such that the olefin will tend to approach the aluminum in the least sterically hindered fashion. If one particular approach is sterically favored, then the net result is the production of an isotactic polymer. It is of interest that, when the catalyst is adsorbed on amorphous carriers, then amorphous atactic polymers are obtained. Presumably an optically active polymer would result if the catalyst were adsorbed on an optically active carrier such as dextro or levo quartz.

REFERENCES

1. (a) A. E. Martell and M. Calvin, *Chemistry of the Metal Chelate Compounds,* Prentice-Hall, New York, 1952, Chapter 8. (b) A. L. Lehninger, *Physiol. Revs.,* **30,** 393 (1950). (c) R. J. P. Williams, *Biol. Revs. Cambridge Phil. Soc.,* **28,** 381 (1953).
2. For an analysis see A. A. Frost and R. G. Pearson, *Kinetics and Mechanism,* John Wiley & Sons, New York, 1953, Chapter 9.
3. K. Pedersen, *Acta Chem. Scand.,* **2,** 252 (1948).
4. K. Pedersen, *ibid.,* **2,** 385 (1948).
5. (a) H. A. Krebs, *Biochem. J. London,* **36,** 303 (1942). (b) A. Kornberg, S. Ochoa, and A. H. Mehler, *J. Biol. Chem.,* **174,** 159 (1948).
6. R. Steinberger and F. H. Westheimer, *J. Am. Chem. Soc.,* **73,** 429 (1951); K. Pedersen, *Acta Chem. Scand.,* **6,** 285 (1952); F. J. Speck, *J. Biol. Chem.,* **178,** 315 (1948).
7. R. J. P. Williams, *Nature,* **171,** 304 (1953).
8. J. E. Prue, *J. Chem. Soc.,* **1952,** 2331.
9. H. Kroll, *J. Am. Chem. Soc.,* **74,** 2036 (1952); I. M. Klotz and B. Campbell, private communication; L. Meriwether and F. H. Westheimer, *J. Am. Chem. Soc.,* **78,** 5119 (1956).
10. M. L. Bender and B. W. Turnquest, *J. Am. Chem. Soc.,* **79,** 1889 (1957).
11. (a) G. L. Eichhorn and J. C. Bailar, Jr., *J. Am. Chem. Soc.,* **75,** 2905 (1953). (b) G. L. Eichhorn and I. M. Trachtenberg, *ibid.,* **76,** 5183 (1954). (c) G. L. Eichhorn and N. D. Marchand, *ibid.,* **78,** 2688 (1956).
12. P. Pfeiffer, W. Offermann, and H. Werner, *J. prakt. Chem.,* **159,** 313 (1941).

13. J. Baddiley, *Nature,* **170,** 711 (1952); D. E. Metzler and E. E. Snell, *J. Am. Chem. Soc.,* **74,** 979 (1952).
14. I. M. Klotz and W. C. Loh Ming, *J. Am. Chem. Soc.,* **76,** 805 (1954).
15. (*a*) F. R. Duke, *ibid.,* **69,** 3054 (1947). (*b*) F. R. Duke and A. A. Forist, *ibid.,* **71,** 2790 (1949).
16. H. Taube, *ibid.,* **69,** 1418 (1947), **70,** 1216 (1948); F. R. Duke, *ibid.,* **69,** 2885 (1947).
17. F. Haber and J. Weiss, *Proc. Roy. Soc., London,* **A147,** 332 (1934).
18. (*a*) N. Uri, *Chem. Revs.,* **50,** 375 (1952). (*b*) W. L. Reynolds and I. M. Kolthoff, *J. Phys. Chem.,* **60,** 969, 996 (1956).
19. J. Weiss, *J. Phys. Chem.,* **41,** 1107 (1937).
20. For general discussions see (*a*) C. E. H. Bawn, *Discussions Faraday Soc.,* **14,** 181 (1953); *J. Oil & Colour Chemists' Assoc.,* **36,** 443 (1953); (*b*) A. Robertson and W. A. Waters, *Trans. Faraday Soc.,* **42,** 201 (1946); L. Bateman, *Quart. Revs. London,* **8,** 147 (1951).
21. J. P. Wibaut and A. Strang, *Koninkl. Ned. Akad. Wetenschap., Proc.,* **B54,** 102 (1951).
22. R. Lombard and L. Rammert, *Bull. soc. chim. France,* **23,** 36 (1956).
23. K. I. Ivanov, V. K. Savinova, and E. G. Mikhailova, *Compt. rend. acad. sci. U.R.S.S.,* **25,** 34, 40 (1939).
24. See, for example, G. S. Hammond, C. E. Boozer, C. E. Hamilton, and J. N. Sen, *J. Am. Chem. Soc.,* **77,** 3238 (1955); R. F. Moore and W. A. Waters, *J. Chem. Soc.,* **1954,** 243.
25. See reference 1*a,* Chapter 8; also M. Ardon and G. Stein, *J. Chem. Soc.,* **1956,** 2095.
26. A. Werner and A. Mylius, *Z. anorg. Chem.,* **16,** 1245 (1898).
27. P. W. Sherwood, *Chimie & industrie,* **71,** 300 (1954).
28. F. A. Bovey, I. M. Kolthoff, A. I. Medalia, and E. J. Meehan, *Emulsion Polymerization,* Interscience Publishers, New York, 1955; R. J. Orr and H. L. Williams, *J. Am. Chem. Soc.,* **78,** 3273 (1956); E. Collinson and F. S. Dainton, *Nature,* **177,** 1224 (1956).
29. W. E. Vaughan and F. E. Seubold, *J. Am. Chem. Soc.,* **75,** 3790 (1953); C. Plummer, *Petroleum Engr.,* **25,** No. 10, C27 (1953).
30. For reviews see (*a*) G. A. Mills and S. Weller, *Advances in Catalysis,* Vol. VIII, 1955, Academic Press, N. Y.; (*b*) J. Halpern, *Quart. Revs. London,* **10,** 463 (1956).
31. M. Calvin, *Trans. Faraday Soc.,* **34,** 1181 (1938).
32. (*a*) M. Calvin, *J. Am. Chem. Soc.,* **61,** 2230 (1939). (*b*) W. K. Wilmarth, M. K. Barsh, and S. S. Dharmotti, *ibid.,* **74,** 5035 (1952). (*c*) M. Calvin and W. K. Wilmarth, *ibid.,* **78,** 1301 (1956). (*d*) W. K. Wilmarth and M. K. Barsh, *ibid.,* **78,** 1305 (1956).
33. W. K. Wilmarth and M. K. Barsh, *ibid.,* **75,** 2237 (1953).
34. S. Weller and G. A. Mills, *ibid.,* **75,** 769 (1953); L. W. Wright and S. Weller, *ibid.,* **76,** 3345 (1954).
35. A. H. Webster and J. Halpern, *J. Phys. Chem.,* **60,** 280 (1956); O. J. Korinek and J. Halpern, *ibid.,* 285.
36. J. Halpern and E. Peters, *J. Chem. Phys.,* **23,** 605 (1955); E. Peters and J. Halpern, *J. Phys. Chem.,* **59,** 793 (1955).
37. L. Wright, S. Weller, and G. A. Mills, *ibid.,* **59,** 1060 (1955).

38. W. K. Wilmarth and A. F. Kapanan, *J. Am. Chem. Soc.,* **78,** 1308 (1956).

39. W. K. Wilmarth, J. C. Dayton, and J. M. Fluornoy, *ibid.,* **75,** 4549 (1953); W. K. Wilmarth and J. C. Dayton, *ibid.,* **75,** 4553 (1953).

40. (*a*) O. Roelen, U. S. Pat. 2,327,066 (1943). (*b*) H. Adkins and G. Krsek, *J. Am. Chem. Soc.,* **70,** 383 (1948). (*c*) I. Wender, M. Orchin, and H. H. Storch, *ibid.,* **72,** 4842 (1950). (*d*) A. Keulemans, A. Kwantes, T. van Bavel, *Rec. trav. chim.,* **67,** 298 (1948).

41. I. Wender, H. W. Sternberg, and M. Orchin, *ibid.,* **75,** 3041 (1953).

42. G. W. Coleman and A. A. Blanchard, *ibid.,* **58,** 2160 (1936); W. Hieber and H. Schulten, *Z. anorg. u. allgem. Chem.,* **232,** 29 (1937).

43. H. W. Sternberg, I. Wender, R. A. Friedel, and M. Orchin, *ibid.,* **75,** 2717 (1953).

44. (*a*) J. W. Cable, R. S. Nyholm, and R. K. Sheline, *ibid.,* **76,** 3373 (1954). (*b*) R. A. Friedel, I. Wender, S. L. Shufler, and H. W. Sternberg, *ibid.,* **77,** 3951 (1955).

45. R. K. Sheline and K. S. Pitzer, *ibid.,* **72,** 1107 (1950).

46. L. Pauling, *The Nature of the Chemical Bond,* Cornell University Press, Ithaca, N. Y., 1940, p. 250.

47. R. V. G. Ewens and M. W. Lister, *Trans. Faraday Soc.,* **35,** 681 (1939).

48. W. F. Edgell and G. Gallup, *J. Am. Chem. Soc.,* **77,** 5762 (1955).

49. G. Natta and R. Ercoli, *Chimica e industria Milan,* **34,** 503 (1952).

50. G. Natta, R. Ercoli, S. Castellano, and P. H. Barbieri, *J. Am. Chem. Soc.,* **76,** 4049 (1954).

51. A. R. Martin, *Chemistry & Industry,* **1954,** 1536.

52. I. Wender, S. Metlin, H. W. Steinberg, S. Ergun, and H. Greenfield, *J. Am. Chem. Soc.,* **78,** 4520 (1956).

53. F. Asinger and O. Berg, *Ber.,* **88,** 445 (1955).

54. H. H. Storch, N. Golumbic, and R. B. Anderson, *The Fischer-Tropsch and Related Syntheses,* John Wiley & Sons, New York, 1951.

55. J. W. Reppe, *Ann.,* **582,** 121 (1953); W. Hieber and F. Leutert, *Z. anorg u. allgem. Chem.,* **204,** 145 (1932).

56. P. Krumholz and H. M. A. Stettiner, *J. Am. Chem. Soc.,* **71,** 3035 (1949).

57. H. W. Sternberg, R. Markby, and I. Wender, *ibid.,* **79,** 6116 (1957); W. Hieber and G. Brendel, *Z. anorg. u. allgem. Chem.,* **289,** 324 (1957).

58. J. W. Reppe and H. Vetter, *Ann.,* **582,** 133 (1953).

59. A. W. Adamson, *ibid.,* **73,** 5170 (1951); W. Hieber, R. Nast, and C. Bartenstein, *Z. anorg. u. allgem. Chem.,* **272,** 32 (1953).

60. A. W. Adamson, *ibid.,* **78,** 4260 (1956); G. Schwarzenbach, *Helv. Chim. Acta,* **32,** 839 (1949).

61. S. Weller, private communication; M. E. Winfield, *Revs. Pure and Appl. Chem.,* **5,** 217 (1955).

62. For general reviews see (*a*) M. H. Bigelow and J. W. Copenhaver, *Acetylene and Carbon Monoxide Chemistry,* Reinhold Publishing Corp., New York, 1949; (*b*) J. W. Reppe, "Acetylene Chemistry," *P. B. Report* 18852-S, Charles A. Meyer and Co., New York, 1949.

63. J. Chatt, *Cationic Polymerization,* P. H. Plesch, ed., Heffner and Sons, Cambridge, 1953, p. 56

64. J. Chatt, *ibid.,* p. 40; *Nature,* **177,** 852 (1956).

65. M. J. S. Dewar, *Bull. soc. chim. France,* **18,** C79 (1951).

66. S. Winstein and H. J. Lucas, *J. Am. Chem. Soc.,* **60,** 836 (1938).

67. See *Catonic Polymerization,* reference 63, for several papers and reviews; J. J. Throssell, S. P. Sood, M. Szwarc, and V. Stannett, *J. Am. Chem. Soc.,* **78,** 1122 (1956).

68. D. D. Eley, reference 63, p. 6.

69. J. A. Wunderlich and D. P. Mellor, *Acta Cryst.,* **7,** 130 (1954); J. N. Dempsey and N. C. Baenziger, *J. Am. Chem. Soc.,* **77,** 4985 (1955).

70. R. M. Keefer, L. J. Andrews, and R. E. Kepner, *J. Am. Chem. Soc.,* **71,** 2381, 3906 (1949).

71. H. J. Lucas, F. R. Hepner, and S. Winstein, *ibid.,* **61,** 3102 (1939).

72. W. S. Dorsey and H. J. Lucas, *ibid.,* **78,** 1665 (1956).

73. R. W. Taft, Jr., *ibid.,* **74,** 4372 (1952); R. W. Taft, Jr., E. L. Purlee, P. Reiz, and C. A. DeFazio, *ibid.,* **77,** 1584 (1955).

74. H. Lemaire and H. J. Lucas, *ibid.,* **77,** 939 (1955).

75. (*a*) J. Chatt, *Chem. Revs.,* **48,** 7 (1951). (*b*) See F. H. Westheimer, E. Segal, and R. Schramm, *J. Am. Chem. Soc.,* **69,** 773 (1947) for a review.

76. C. W. Bradley and H. S. Davis, *Chem. Abstr.,* **40,** 1867 (1946).

77. J. D. Rose and F. S. Statham, *J. Chem. Soc.,* **1950,** 69.

78. R. S. Nyholm and L. N. Short, *ibid.,* **1953,** 2670.

79. H. C. Longuet-Higgins and L. E. Orgel, *ibid.,* **1956,** 1969.

80. R. Schwarz and W. Kronig, *Ber.,* **56,** 208 (1923).

81. N. Shilov and B. Nekrasov, *Z. physik. Chem.,* **118,** 79 (1925); B. Nekrasov, *J. Russ. Phys. Chem. Soc.,* **58,** 207 (1926).

82. I. I. Zhukov and O. P. Shipulina, *Kolloid-Z.,* **49,** 126 (1929).

83. J. C. Bailar, Jr., and J. B. Work, *J. Am. Chem. Soc.,* **67,** 176 (1945).

84. J. Bjerrum, *Metal Ammine Formation in Aqueous Solution,* P. Haase and Son, Copenhagen, 1941, pp. 235–251.

85. S. E. Rasmussen and J. Bjerrum, *Acta Chem. Scand.,* **9,** 735 (1955).

86. C. E. Schäffer, private communication.

87. A. C. Wahl and N. A. Bonner, *Radioactivity Applied to Chemistry,* John Wiley & Sons, New York, 1951, Chapter 1, p. 16 (authors of this chapter are O. E. Myers and R. J. Prestwood).

88. J. Bjerrum and C. G. Lamm, *Acta Chem. Scand.,* **9,** 216 (1955).

89. J. Bjerrum and S. E. Rasmussen, *ibid.,* **6,** 1265 (1952).

90. B. E. Douglas, *J. Am. Chem. Soc.,* **76,** 1020 (1954).

91. D. S. Popplewell, thesis, Sheffield University, 1956.

92. B. E. Douglas, private communication.

93. J. G. Baraguanth and J. B. Chalelain, *Mining and Metallurgy,* **26,** 391 (1945); F. A. Forward, *Mining Eng.,* **5,** 577 (1953).

94. T. M. Kaneko and M. E. Wadsorth, *J. Phys. Chem.,* **60,** 457 (1956).

95. D. F. Keeley and R. E. Johnson, *Abstr. Amer. Chem. Soc. Meeting,* Miami, Florida, April, 1957.

96. A. N. Webb, private communication.

97. P. H. Emmett, *Catalysis, Fundamental Principles,* Part I, Reinhold Publishing Corp., New York, 1954.

98. For a recent review on polyethylene, see S. L. Aggarwal and O. J. Sweeting, *Chem. Revs.,* **57,** 665 (1957).

99. K. Ziegler, E. Holzkamp, H. Breil, and H. Martin, *Angew. Chem.,* **67,** 541 (1955); K. Ziegler, Belgian Patents 533,362 (May 16, 1955), 534,792 (Jan. 31, 1955), 534,888 (Jan. 31, 1955).
100. G. Natta, *Atti. accad. naz. Lincei,* [8]**4,** 61 (1955); G. Natta, P. Pino, G. Mazzanti, P. Longhi, *Gazz. chim. ital.,* **87,** 549 (1957).
101. D. F. Herman and W. K. Nelson, *J. Am. Chem. Soc.,* **75,** 3877, 3882 (1953); L. Summers and R. H. Uloth, *ibid.,* **76,** 2278 (1954).
102. G. E. Coates, *Organo-Metallic Compounds,* Methuen & Co., London, 1956, p. 75; E. G. Rochow, D. T. Hurd, and R. N. Lewis, *The Chemistry of Organometallic Compounds,* John Wiley & Sons, New York, 1957, p. 133.
103. G. Natta, P. Pino, G. Mazzanti, and U. Giannini, *J. Am. Chem. Soc.,* **79,** 2975 (1957).
104. D. S. Breslow and N. R. Newburg, *ibid.,* **79,** 5072 (1957).
105. G. Natta, English translation of a paper presented at the International Conference on the Chemistry of Coordination Compounds, Rome, Italy, September 15–21, 1957; *Angew. Chem.,* **68,** 393 (1956).

9 Miscellaneous topics

THE ABSORPTION SPECTRA OF COMPLEX IONS

Most of the complexes, including aqua ions, of the transition metals show two distinct kinds of absorption of light. The first kind occurs chiefly in the visible, though it may extend to the infrared and ultraviolet regions, and consists of one or more moderately well-defined bands of low intensity. Molar extinction coefficients are of the order of 0.1 to 100. The second kind of absorption occurs chiefly in the ultraviolet, though it may extend to the visible, and has much higher intensity, the molar extinction coefficients being of the order of 1000 to 10,000. One or more bands may be found, or often only a steadily increasing absorption with decreasing wavelength so that the maximum is not accessible. Figure 1 shows some typical spectra, that of two *luteo* cobalt(III) ions.

The visible, weak absorption is due to transitions involving only electrons on the central metal atom, chiefly the electrons which can be associated with orbitals formed from the d orbitals of the isolated metal atom. These may be called d-d transitions. Their occurrence is responsible for the usual colors associated with complex ions.

It would be very desirable to discuss the positions of the d-d bands with respect to energy levels derived from those found in the free, gaseous atoms and ions. About the latter a good deal is known from atomic spectroscopy.[1] It has been possible, in fact, to correlate the narrow absorption bands of the lanthanides and actinides with the $4f$ and $5f$ levels of the free ions.[2] In the transition metals the situation is more complicated, because the position of the bands varies greatly with the nature of the ligands making up the complex ion.

However, starting with Ilse and Hartmann, in the last few years a rather satisfactory general theory of the d-d spectra has been devel-

368

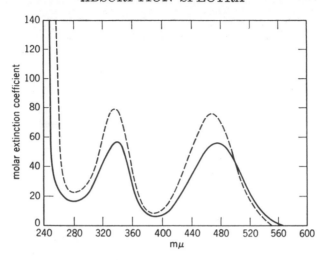

FIG. 1. Visible and near-ultraviolet absorption spectra of $Co(NH_3)_6{}^{3+}$ (solid line) and $Co(en)_3{}^{3+}$ (dashed line) in aqueous solution.

oped.[3] The theory utilizes the "crystal field" method of Bethe,[4] which was discussed in Chapter 2. The essential part of the theory is that the five d orbitals of the central atom, which are degenerate and equal in energy in an isolated, gaseous atom, are split into orbitals of different energy by the electrostatic fields of the anions or dipolar molecules that are the ligands. For an ion with an unfilled d shell, then, transitions can occur between these levels of different energy.

To calculate the splittings, a quantum mechanical perturbation calculation must be made. Since the unperturbed wave functions are not known exactly and since the true value of the perturbing electric field is not known, exact calculations cannot be made. Nevertheless a good deal of semiquantitative information can be gained by approximate calculations.

For example, the number of levels can be calculated. This depends only upon the geometric symmetry of the complex and the number of d electrons. A field of high symmetry gives fewer levels than a field of low symmetry. For a single d electron as many as five different energy levels can be split from the original set of five degenerate energy levels. This would occur for a very unsymmetrical arrangement of ligands.

The situation is illustrated for a single d electron in Fig. 2 for crystal fields of different symmetry. The quantum designations for the states

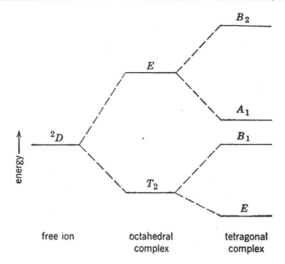

Fɪɢ. 2. Crystal field splittings of energy states of Ti^{3+} in regular complexes.

E, T_2, etc., are based on group theory symmetry properties. The original energy level, ^2D, is fivefold degenerate. In a field of cubic symmetry, such as in an octahedral complex with all ligands the same, splitting into two sets of levels occurs, the upper doubly degenerate (E) and the lower triply degenerate (T_2). These may be identified with the atomic levels $d_{x^2-y^2}$ and d_{z^2}, which form the set E, and d_{xy}, d_{yz}, and d_{xz}, which form the set T_2.

Recalling that the $d_{x^2-y^2}$ and d_{z^2} are the atomic orbitals used to form hybrid octahedral orbitals in sp^3d^2 hybridization, it is easy to see why the influence of negative ligands or dipoles raises the energy of an electron in these two levels more than that of an electron in the remaining three d levels. It is simply that electrostatic repulsion between the negative ligands and an electron is greater if the electron is in an orbital pointing at the ligands rather than if it is in an orbital tipped at 45° to the directions of the ligands.

A complex ion of tetragonal symmetry such as a square planar complex will cause a further differentiation between the d_{xy} orbital in the tetragonal plane and the d_{xz} and d_{yz}, as well as splitting apart the d_{z^2} and $d_{x^2-y^2}$ as shown in Fig. 2. This diagram is valid only for a single d electron or, with inversion, for nine d electrons (positive hole analogy). It is also valid for six and four d electrons in their states of highest multiplicity. However, in these cases there are states of lower multiplicity possible (some electrons paired), so that a complete diagram would be quite complicated, In the same way the systems d^2, d^3, d^7, and d^8 have a greater number of energy levels because of the various ways of assigning the electrons to orbitals, and because of interaction between levels of the same symmetry.[5]

A typical calculation of the energy difference between T_2 and E for an aqua ion with one d electron, such as $Ti(H_2O)_6^{3+}$, gives the result $\Delta E \simeq 5e\overline{a^4}\mu/r^6$. Here $\overline{a^4}$ is the average value for the fourth power of the radius of the d electron, μ is the permanent plus induced dipole moment of the water molecule, and r is the distance from the center of the dipole to the center of the ion. The radius of Ti^{3+} in the crystal state is 0.69 A, and the radius of a water molecule is 1.38 A. The sum of these gives r as 2.07 A, and μ is about 5 debyes. The spectrum of the ion shows a single weak band with a maximum at 20,300 cm^{-1} (4900 A).[3a] This corresponds to a quantum of energy equal to 55 kcal/mole. To make the calculated value of ΔE agree, it is necessary that $\overline{a^4}$ equal at least one A^4, which is too large but not very much so.

These calculations were based on the simplest possible model using point charges and dipoles and neglecting the environment of the ion except for the six water molecules. There is some justification for doing the latter since the spectra of complex ions in solution and in the solid state are usually very similar.

Generally speaking, however, it is not possible to make good calculations of the energy separations a priori.[7] The results are usually expressed in terms of some parameter, Dq, the crystal field strength, which may be given an interpretation in terms of properties of the ion and ligands. However, such interpretations often are not obvious, and Dq is best considered as a fitting constant to be obtained from some piece of spectral data. For complexes of lower symmetry, more than one parameter is needed (see also p. 79).

The greater the crystal field, the greater is the energy difference, ΔE or $10Dq$, between T_2 and E in Fig. 2. From experimental data on the position of the absorption bands, ΔE is of the order of 10,000 cm^{-1} for the bivalent aqua ions of the first transition series and 20,000 cm^{-1} for the trivalent ions.[6, 3b] For ammonia or ethylenediamine complexes, the corresponding figures are 12,500 cm^{-1} and 25,000 cm^{-1}.

The frequency of the maximum in the case of symmetrical complexes of Cu(II), Co(III), Cr(III), and Ni(II) ions gives the order of Dq as $CN^- > $ 1,10-phenanthroline $> NO_2^- > $ ethylenediamine $> NH_3 > NSC^- > H_2O > F^- > RCO_2^- > OH^- > Cl^- > Br^-$[3] (the Fajans-Tsuchida series). Unfortunately there seems no way of correlating this order with any single property of the ligands. Furthermore iron(III) and cobalt(II) sometimes require a different order, as do other ions.[7b]

Despite this shortcoming, the crystal field theory has been very successful in predicting the number of absorption bands and their relative positions for numerous complex ions. It gives a satisfactory general picture of d-d absorption. The weakness of absorption in this region is explained by the theory on the grounds that all of the transitions are formally forbidden in the free ion because of odd-even and angular momentum selection rules. These selection rules are broken down in part in the complexed ion.

In going to the second and third transition series, it is found that Dq or ΔE for a given ligand increases markedly. Thus the longest wavelength absorptions of $Rh(en)_3^{3+}$ and $Ir(en)_3^{3+}$ are in the ultraviolet, whereas for $Co(en)_3^{3+}$ they are in the visible.[8] Similarly it is found that the complexes of copper(II) are blue, whereas those of silver(II) are orange or yellow. At the same time in the series $3d$, $4d$ and $5d$ the electron pairing energy (Chapter 2, p. 45) decreases. That is, because of the increased size of the higher d orbitals, it is not as important that electrons occupy different orbitals. Thus Hund's rule of maximum multiplicity breaks down for the heavy atoms, and complexes of low magnetic moment are formed. This will influence both the structures of such complexes and the absorption spectra.

Charge transfer spectra. The intense absorption in the ultraviolet region mentioned earlier is of the so called "charge transfer" type.[9] The term refers to the characteristic feature that when light is absorbed an electron is transferred from one definite part of the system to another. Such spectra are characteristic of associated pairs of molecules, where one can identify a charge-donating group and a charge-accepting group, or alternatively, a Lewis base and a Lewis acid, or a reductant and an oxidant.

Examples are the organic complexes such as quinhydrone, iodine with aromatic hydrocarbons, and polynitro compounds with phenols, amines, etc. The approximate quantum mechanical theory of both the binding forces of such complexes and their absorption of light has been given by Mulliken.[10] The intensity of the absorption is due to the absence of hindering selection rules and to the large change in polarity accompanying the transition from the ground state to the photochemically activated state.

In inorganic chemistry, the ultraviolet spectra of solid salts such as NaCl, salts in the vapor state, and simple anions in solution are also of the charge transfer type.[9] In solution, sodium ion and the other alkali and alkaline earth ions do not show spectra in the accessible region of the ultraviolet. In each of the cases mentioned above an electron is believed to be transferred, upon excitation, from chloride ion to the set of sodium ions in the solid, to a single sodium ion in the vapor, and to the hydration sphere in the case of the ion in solution.

In the case of complex ions it is not always clear in which direction the charge transfer has occurred. Rabinowitch [11] has suggested that in the case of easily oxidized cations (or easily reduced ligands) the electron transfer of lowest energy is from cation to ligand.

$$M—L \xrightarrow{h\nu} M^+—L^- \tag{1}$$

In the reverse case of easily reduced cation (or easily oxidized ligand) the transfer is in the opposite direction.

$$M—L \xrightarrow{h\nu} M^-—L^+ \tag{2}$$

This concept is well supported by most of the evidence.

Figure 3 shows the spectra of some halogen complexes of Fe(III). These are clearly examples of the second case above, such as

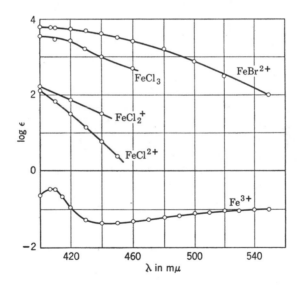

FIG. 3.   Visible absorption spectra of $Fe(H_2O)_6^{3+}$ and some halo derivatives in water. (E. Rabinowitch and W. H. Stockmayer, *J. Am. Chem. Soc.*, **64**, 335 (1942).)

$$FeCl^{2+} \xrightarrow{h\nu} Fe^{2+} + Cl \tag{3}$$

Thus the increased absorption at higher wavelengths in going from chlorine to bromine is understandable in terms of the lower electron affinity of bromine atom. The iodide ion complexes undergo spontaneous oxidation-reduction and cannot be studied. The effect of an increased number of halogen atoms on the intensity and wavelength is also reasonable. The detection of the chlorine atoms as indicated in equation 3 has been carried out by Evans and Uri.[12] In the case of the aqua complex of iron(II), the electron transfer is in the opposite direction.[13]

$$Fe(H_2O)_6{}^{2+} \xrightarrow{h\nu} Fe(H_2O)_5OH^{2+} + H \tag{4}$$

For the octahedral complexes of cobalt(III) and chromium(III) the charge transfer bands begin in the region of 2500 A for the hexammines. Replacement of ammonia by a halogen other than fluorine displaces this band to longer wavelengths so that it overlaps some of the weak *d-d* bands in the visible. This is consistent with an electron's being transferred from the ligand to the metal ion.

Photochemistry of complex ions. It is clear that the charge transfer processes discussed above are photochemical oxidation-reduction reactions. It is expected, then, that irradiation of solutions of complex ions with light of wavelengths within the region of the' charge transfer spectra will produce chemical change.

This is indeed the case, though relatively little quantitative work has been done in this area. Linhard [14, 15] observed that $Co(NH_3)_5I^{2+}$ and $Co(NH_3)_5N_3{}^{2+}$ are decomposed to Co(II) and to I_2 or N_2 on exposure to sunlight. The photolysis of $K_3M(CN)_6$ produced, presumably, cyanogen and a reduced form of the metal ion, and occurred most easily in the order Mn > Fe > Cr > Co.[16] The oxalato complexes such as $Fe(C_2O_4)_3{}^{3-}$, $Co(C_2O_4)_3{}^{3-}$, and the well-known uranyl oxalate actinometer produce carbon dioxide.[17] Ferric formate complex yields ferrous ion and carbon dioxide.[18]

In several instances it has been found that light induces the exchange of the ligands of a complex ion with labeled ligands in solution.[19] In the case of $PtCl_6{}^{2-}$ this probably occurs with the formation of chlorine atoms and Pt(III),[20] e.g.,

$$PtCl_6{}^{2-} \xrightarrow{h\nu} PtCl_5{}^{2-} + Cl \tag{5}$$

$$PtCl_5^{2-} + *Cl^- \rightarrow Pt*Cl_5^{2-} + Cl^- \qquad (6)$$

$$Pt*Cl_5^{2-} + PtCl_6^{2-} \rightarrow Pt*Cl_6^{2-} + PtCl_5^{2-} \qquad (7)$$

If a reduced form of a metal ion is in the complex, then the ligand can undergo a reduction, as opposed to the oxidations mentioned above. In particular, since we can have both the reaction [21]

$$FeOH^{2+} \xrightarrow{h\nu} Fe^{2+} + OH \qquad (8)$$

followed by

$$2OH \rightarrow H_2O_2 \rightarrow H_2O + \tfrac{1}{2}O_2 \qquad (9)$$

and reaction 4 followed by

$$2H \rightarrow H_2 \qquad (10)$$

it is seen that a photochemical decomposition of water is possible.[22] If such a process can be discovered that is efficient to the extent of a few per cent with visible light, it would be a very valuable energy source for the future. Such processes are not inefficient because the light fails to be absorbed, but because of the high incidence of back reactions and side reactions and because of deactivation of the photo-excited state.[22]

Photochemical change caused by absorption of light in the d-d region is much less probable than for the charge transfer region. This is because of the lower intensity of light absorption, the lower energy of the quantum absorbed, and the fact that the excitation is localized on the metal atom. However, it has been suggested that photochemically induced substitution reactions may occur after d-d excitation.[19b, 23]

$$Fe(CN)_6^{3-} \xrightarrow{h\nu} \overset{*}{Fe}(CN)_6^{3-} \qquad (11)$$

$$\overset{*}{Fe}(CN)_6^{3-} + H_2O \rightarrow Fe(CN)_5H_2O^{2-} + CN^- \qquad (12)$$

This has been demonstrated [24] for water exchange in the case of $Cr(H_2O)_6^{3+}$. As expected, the quantum yield is low, being of the order of 10^{-2}.

REFERENCES

1. C. E. Moore, "Atomic Energy Levels," Vols. 1 and 2, *Nat. Bur. Standards U. S. Cir.*, 1949 and 1952.
2. R. A. Satten, *J. Chem. Phys.*, **21**, 633 (1953); C. Klixbüll Jørgensen, *Kgl. Danske Videnskab. Selskab Mat. fys. Medd.*, **29**, No. 7, 11 (1955).

3. (a) F. E. Ilse and H. Hartmann, *Z. physik. Chem.*, **197**, 239 (1951); *Z. Naturforsch.*, **6a**, 751 (1951). (b) L. E. Orgel, *J. Chem. Phys.*, **23**, 1004 (1955). (c) C. J. Ballhausen, *Kgl. Danske Videnskab. Selskab Mat. fys. Medd.*, **29**, No. 4 (1954). (d) J. Bjerrum, C. J. Ballhausen, and C. Klixbüll Jørgensen, *Acta Chem. Scand.*, **8**, 1275 (1954). (e) C. Klixbüll Jørgensen, *ibid.*, **8**, 1502 (1954); **9**, 116 (1955).

4. H. Bethe, *Ann. Physik*, [5]**3**, 133 (1929).

5. R. Finkelstein and J. H. van Vleck, *J. Chem. Phys.*, **8**, 790 (1940); J. W. van Santen and J. S. van Wieringen, *Rec. trav. chim.*, **71**, 420 (1952); Y. Tanabe and S. Sugano, *J. Phys. Soc. Japan*, **9**, 753, 766 (1954).

6. (a) C. K. Jørgensen, *Acta Chem. Scand.*, **8**, 1502 (1954). (b) J. Owen, *Proc. Roy. Soc. London*, **A227**, 183 (1955).

7. (a) W. H. Kleiner, *J. Chem. Phys.*, **20**, 1384 (1952). (b) R. J. P. Williams, *J. Chem. Soc.*, **1956**, 8.

8. W. Kuhn and K. Bein, *Z. anorg. u. allgem. Chem.*, **216**, 321 (1936); L. E. Orgel, *J. Chem. Phys.*, **23**, 1819 (1955).

9. L. E. Orgel, *Quart. Revs. London*, **8**, 452 (1954).

10. R. S. Mulliken, *J. Am. Chem. Soc.*, **74**, 811 (1952); *J. Phys. Chem.*, **56**, 801 (1952).

11. E. Rabinowitch, *Revs. Mod. Phys.*, **14**, 112 (1942); R. J. P. Williams, *J. Chem. Soc.*, **1955**, 137.

12. M. G. Evans and N. Uri, *Nature*, **164**, 404 (1949); N. Uri, *Chem. Revs.*, **50**, 375 (1952).

13. J. Weiss, *Nature*, **136**, 794 (1935); F. S. Dainton, *J. Chem. Soc.*, **1952**, 1533.

14. (a) M. Linhard and M. Weigel, *Z. anorg. u. allgem. Chem.*, **266**, 49, 73 (1951). (b) For the theory of spectra of cobalt(III) complexes, see F. Basolo, C. J. Ballhausen, and J. Bjerrum, *Acta Chem. Scand.*, **9**, 810 (1955).

15. M. Linhard and H. Flygare, *Z. anorg. u. allgem. Chem.*, **262**, 328 (1950).

16. R. Schwartz and H. Weiss, *Ber.*, **58B**, 746 (1925); R. Schwartz and K. Tede, *ibid.*, **60B**, 69 (1927).

17. J. Vranek, *Z. Elecktrochem.*, **23**, 336 (1939); C. A. Parker, *Proc. Roy. Soc. London*, **220**, 104 (1952).

18. C. J. Ballhausen and J. Bjerrum, *Acta Chem. Scand.*, **9**, 810 (1955).

19. (a) A. W. Adamson, J. P. Welker, and M. Volpe, *J. Am. Chem. Soc.*, **72**, 4030 (1950). (b) A. G. MacDiarmid and N. F. Hall, *ibid.*, **75**, 5204 (1953); **76**, 4222 (1954).

20. H. Taube, *ibid.*, **76**, 2609 (1954).

21. H. Bates, M. G. Evans, and N. Uri, *Nature*, **166**, 869 (1950).

22. T. Rigg and J. Weiss, *J. Chem. Phys.*, **20**, 1194 (1952); L. J. Heidt and A. F. MacMillan, *J. Am. Chem. Soc.*, **76**, 2135 (1954).

23. A. W. Adamson, private communication.

24. R. A. Plane and J. P. Hunt, *J. Am. Chem. Soc.*, **79**, 3343 (1957).

"OUTER SPHERE" COMPLEXES OR ION PAIRS

Complex ions, like other charged particles, are particularly sensitive to their environment. In addition to having thermodynamic and kinetic properties which depend strongly on the solvent, they will interact strongly with ionic species in solution.

One important aspect of this will be shown by the changes in activity coefficients of the complex ions due to the general ion atmosphere effect, as given by the Debye-Hückel theory for dilute solutions.[1] The theory gives for the activity coefficient, γ_i, of a single ion

$$- \log \gamma_i = \frac{A z^2 \sqrt{\mu}}{1 + B\sqrt{\mu}} \tag{13}$$

where z is the charge on the ion, μ is the ionic strength, and A is a constant equal to 0.509 for water at 25°C and given more generally by $A = 1.82 \times 10^6/(DT)^{3/2}$, where D is the dielectric constant of the medium and T the absolute temperature. The constant B increases with the distance of closest approach of two ions. It is of the order of magnitude of unity and may be set equal to one or treated as semi-empirical.[2] Equation 13 often gives a reasonable interpretation of activity data up to $\mu = 0.1$.

That complex ions obey 13 as well as other ions has been amply demonstrated. In fact complex ions were often selected to test various conclusions of the Debye-Hückel theory since they can be selected to cover a wide range of charges, positive and negative, can be very stable, and can be nearly spherically symmetrical. The kinetic equivalent of the Debye-Hückel equation, the Brønsted-Bjerrum-Christiansen formulation,[3] was inspired and tested by the reactions of the cobalt(III) ammines. It is simply the application of equation 13 to the reactants and to the transition state, giving for a bimolecular reaction,

$$\ln k = \ln k_0 + \frac{2A z_1 z_2 \sqrt{\mu}}{1 + B\sqrt{\mu}} \tag{14}$$

where k is the specific rate constant, k_0 is the same for infinite dilution, and z_1 and z_2 are the charge on the two reactants.

At higher concentrations 13 and 14 will no longer be valid, and unfortunately many reactions of complex ions must be carried out in concentrated solutions. It has been customary to add a term linear in μ to equation 13 to extend its range. However, there is no good theoretical method for estimating the magnitude or even the sign of the coefficient of this linear term.

Furthermore at higher concentrations the whole concept of the ionic strength principle breaks down, that is, the principle stating that the properties of an ion depend on the ionic strength only and not on the specific ions that constitute the environment.[4] Thus it has been customary in some studies to keep the ionic strength constant at some maximum value by the addition of an "inert" electrolyte such as $NaClO_4$, and to assume that changes due to replacing part of the $NaClO_4$ by a reagent will be negligible. This procedure has been shown to be invalid for large amounts of salt substitution, say of $NaClO_4$ by $HClO_4$, if the reaction studied involves an ion of opposite sign to that being replaced (a negative ion in this case).[5] Thus there is no sure guide to the behavior of complex ions, or any other ions, at moderate to high concentrations.

In addition to the general effect on the activity coefficient discussed above, there is another kind of interaction of an ion with other ions in solution. This is a more specific effect involving only ions of opposite sign and consisting of the equilibrium formation of an ion pair between the two ions: [6]

$$A^+ + B^- \rightleftharpoons A^+, B^- \tag{15}$$

A characteristic association equilibrium constant will accompany this process

$$K_a = [A^+, B^-]/[A^+][B^-] \tag{16}$$

Generally the equilibrium will be reached instantaneously on mixing A^+ and B^-. Such interaction will obviously have a considerable effect on the activities and other properties of A^+ and B^-. Although the activity of A^+ or B^- is always lowered, the effect of ion-pair formation on any measured property of the solution will depend on the contribution of A^+, B^- to that property.

We will present a theory for the formation of ion pairs due to Bjerrum.[7] The theory will be seen to be valid for certain kinds of systems only. In particular it does not apply to cases in which AB is itself a complex with a very strong bond, either covalent or ionic, directly between two atoms, e.g., $FeCl^{2+}$, $TlOH$, or $Co(NH_3)_5Cl^{2+}$, where $Co(NH_3)_5^{3+}$ is considered as A^+.

The theory applies well to rather large, spherically symmetrical ions where the only interaction is a fairly weak electrostatic one. In particular, then, it applies very well to the interaction of a substitution inert complex ion, such as $Co(NH_3)_6^{3+}$, with any anion, X^-, such that an ion pair $Co(NH_3)_6^{3+}$, X^- is formed. The descriptive name "outer sphere complex," as opposed to an inner sphere complex such as $Co(NH_3)_5X^{2+}$, has been given to such ion pairs.[6b, 12b]

The Bjerrum theory of ion association starts with the Maxwell-Boltzmann distribution function for the number of ions of a second kind around a selected central ion

$$n_2 = n_0 \exp\left(-\frac{z_1 z_2 e^2}{DkTr}\right) \tag{17}$$

where n_2 is the number of ions per cubic centimeter of the second kind at a distance r from the first kind, z_1 and z_2 are the ion charges, e the charge on the electron, k is Boltzmann's constant, and n_0 the bulk concentration of the second kind of ion. Equation 17 assumes simple point charges in a continuous dielectric medium and ignores the effect of the ionic atmosphere.

If equation 17 is used to calculate the number of ions of opposite charge in a series of shells of constant thickness dr at various distances r from the central ion, a minimum is found at a distance

$$r = q = \frac{z_1 z_2 e^2}{2DkT} \tag{18}$$

This distance is 3.57 A for water at 25°C for a 1:1 electrolyte. Bjerrum now made the quite arbitrary assumption that any two ions closer together than q constitute an ion pair. This is the same thing as saying that the electrostatic energy of attraction must be equal to at least $2kT$.

The degree of association, $(1 - \alpha)$, can now be found by integrating the number of ions in all the shells from $r = q$ to $r = a$, where a is the distance of closest approach of the two oppositely charged ions.

$$(1 - \alpha) = 4\pi n_0 \int_a^q \exp\left(-\frac{z_1 z_2 e^2}{DkTr}\right) r^2 \, dr \tag{19}$$

The equilibrium constant is given by 16, which becomes

$$K_a^{-1} = \frac{c\alpha^2\gamma^2}{(1 - \alpha)\gamma_0} = \frac{1000\alpha^2 n_0\gamma^2}{(1 - \alpha)N\gamma_0} \tag{20}$$

where c is concentration in moles per liter, γ is the mean activity coefficient of the free ions, γ_0 is the activity coefficient of the ion pair, and N is Avogadro's number. From 19 and 20 it is now possible to evaluate the equilibrium constant, though it is necessary to use tabulated values of the integral (expressed in dimensionless form).[6a] In dilute solution where the γ's can be set equal to unity, K_a is quickly found from the tables.*

For a given solvent and temperature, the effect depends strongly on the charges of the ions and on the distance of closest approach a. In water at 25°C no ion-pair formation would occur for univalent electrolytes whose radii added up to more than 3.57 A. For ions smaller than this, the approach would be too close for the theory to be valid, as discussed earlier. The effective radius of the $Co(NH_3)_6^{3+}$ ion has been estimated at 2.5 A from crystallographic data.[8] Thus the a distance involved for, say, $Co(NH_3)_6^{3+}$, Cl^- is 4.3 A. Since q is 10.71 A for this case, extensive ion-pair formation should occur.

This is the case, as is shown by the results listed in Table 1, which

Table 1

Association Constants for Outer Sphere Complex Ions at 25°C

Ion Pair	K_a	ΔH^0	ΔS^0	Reference
$Co(NH_3)_6^{3+}$, Cl^-	74	3.7 kcal	21 eu	10
$Co(NH_3)_6^{3+}$, Br^-	46	2.1	15	10
$Co(NH_3)_6^{3+}$, I^-	17	1.6	11	10
$Co(NH_3)_6^{3+}$, N_3^-	20	-4.0	-7	10
$Co(en)_3^{3+}$, Br^-	21	2.0	13	10
$Co(en)_3^{3+}$, I^-	9	1.2	8	10
$Co(en)_3^{3+}$, N_3^-	11	-5.2	-13	10
$Co(NH_3)_6^{3+}$, OH^-	71	...	...	8
$Co(en)_3^{3+}$, OH^-	31	...	...	11
$Co(pn)_3^{3+}$, OH^-	19	...	...	11
$Co(dl\text{-}bn)_3^{3+}$, OH^-	11	...	...	11
$Co(NH_3)_6^{3+}$, SO_4^{2-}	2.2×10^3	0.40	16.6	12
$Co(NH_3)_5H_2O^{3+}$, SO_4^{2-}	1.9×10^3	0	16.4	12
$Co(NH_3)_6^{3+}$, $S_2O_3^{2-}$	1.8×10^3	...	...	13
$Cr(H_2O)_6^{3+}$, SCN^-	7	...	...	14
$Cr(H_2O)_6^{3+}$, Cl^-	13	...	...	15

Data at zero ionic strength except for those from reference 11.

gives values of the association equilibrium constant for a number of complex ions with simple anions. The solvent is water at 25°C. In

* More simply

$$K_a = A_0 \exp\left(-\frac{z_1 z_2 e^2}{DkTa}\right)$$

where A_0 is a constant of the order of unity which includes non-electrostatic factors (R. M. Fuoss and C. A. Kraus, *J. Am. Chem. Soc.*, **79**, 3304 (1957)).

the example $Co(NH_3)_6^{3+}$, OH^- the required value of a to give the observed equilibrium constant is 3.7 A, whereas the ionic radii are $2.5 + 1.4$ or 3.9 A.[8] The other examples are seen to fall into approximately the right places on this basis. The general effect of increasing the size of the anion is shown in the series $Cl^- > Br^- > I^- > N_3^-$. However, it must be noticed that OH^- is smaller than Cl^- and still has less affinity for a given complex ion. $Co(en)_3^{3+}$ is definitely larger than $Co(NH_3)_6^{3+}$, by 0.9 A according to Jenkins and Monk,[9] and thus forms less stable ion pairs.

The very large effect of increasing z to -2 for sulfate ion and thiosulfate ion shows up very clearly. In general, for ions of the sizes shown, ion-pair formation is easily detected for $-z_1z_2 = 3$ or greater. For $-z_1z_2 = 2$, ion pairs can only be inferred from indirect evidence [16] (see below). For $-z_1z_2 = 1$, it is not possible to find evidence for outer sphere complexes. This is the situation in water, but in methanol solvent cis-$Co(en)_2Cl_2^+$ forms ion pairs with chloride ion and acetate ion.[17] The change from $D = 78$ in water to $D = 32$ for methanol compensates for the reduction in z_1z_2 since the value of K_a for chloride ion is about 150 in methanol.

Interestingly enough the $trans$-$Co(en)_2Cl_2^+$ does not form a recognizable ion pair with Cl^- under the same conditions.[17] This is attributed to the dipole moment of the cis isomer favoring association of a negative ion in an outer sphere complex. The $trans$ isomer has no net dipole moment. Such an effect is not included in the Bjerrum theory. Neither is the reduced tendency for $Cr(H_2O)_6^{3+}$ to form outer sphere complexes compared to $Co(NH_3)_6^{3+}$ explained by the simple theory, since the sizes and charges are nearly the same. According to King and Postmus [14] this happens because $Co(NH_3)_6^{3+}$ with 18 protons presents a more favorable, positively charged periphery to a negative ion than does $Cr(H_2O)_6^{3+}$ with only 12 protons.

The methods by which the constants recorded in Table 1 are obtained are of interest. They have been found by conductivity studies,[18] by solubility studies,[9] by potentiometric data,[11] and by changes in reaction rate.[8] The most general and interesting method, however, is a spectrophotometric one utilizing changes in the near-ultraviolet region.

It is observed that addition of simple anions to solutions of complex ions of high cationic charge does not materially affect the absorption bands of the complex in the visible region (d-d bands). However, the charge transfer absorption region is often markedly changed. The change consists essentially of a shift of the intense band to longer wavelengths. Figure 4 illustrates the effect of the halide ions on the

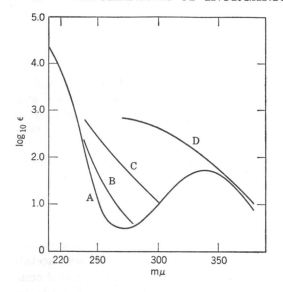

FIG. 4. Shifts in the ultra-violet absorptions spectrum of $Co(NH_3)_6^{3+}$ produced by ion-pair formation.

$A = Co(NH_3)_6^{3+}$
$B = Co(NH_3)_6^{3+}, Cl^-$
$C = Co(NH_3)_6^{3+}, Br^-$
$D = Co(NH_3)_6^{3+}, I^-$
(From reference 10.)

charge transfer spectrum of $Co(NH_3)_6^{3+}$. The shift can extend out into the visible in certain cases. Thus iodide ion causes $Ir(NH_3)_6^{3+}$ to change from colorless to yellow even though no chemical reaction occurs.[19]

Linhard[20] first proved that the spectral shifts shown in Fig. 4 are due to "outer sphere complexes." He established that the equilibrium

$$Co(NH_3)_6^{3+} + I^- \rightleftharpoons Co(NH_3)_6^{3+}, I^- \qquad (21)$$

was rapid and reversible and measured the association constant. The spectral change was shown to be due to the charge transfer absorption of the ion pair

$$Co(NH_3)_6^{3+}, I^- \xrightarrow{h\nu} Co(NH_3)_6^{2+}, I \qquad (22)$$

The shifts to longer and longer wavelengths shown in Fig. 1 for increasing size of the halide ion are in good agreement with this explanation.

It is usually easy to measure the equilibrium as in 21 by the changes in spectra in the 250–350 mμ region. The most accurate data in Table 1 were obtained in this way.[10,12] An exception would occur if the complex ion had a ligand of low electronegativity and if the anion had a high electronegativity. In this event the new spectrum would probably be hidden by the old. Taube and Posey[12b] have shown that the molecular extinction coefficients of the free ion and the ion pair are insensitive to ionic strength. They are, however, remarkably variable with the temperature. Thus the spectrum of the solution will change with temperature, not only because the equilibrium is shifted slightly, but also because the absorption per molecule changes considerably.

Taube and Posey [12b] provide a good example of the dual effect of ionic solutes on a complex ion. Thus the equilibrium,

$$Co(NH_3)_5H_2O^{3+} + SO_4^{2-} \rightleftharpoons Co(NH_3)_5H_2O^{3+}, SO_4^{2-} \qquad (23)$$

which is specific, occurs. The equilibrium is also sensitive to ionic strength since it involves charged species. Empirically it was found that the equation

$$\log K_a = 3.276 - \frac{6.10\sqrt{\mu}}{1 + 1.50\sqrt{\mu}} \qquad (24)$$

predicted the variation of the concentration equilibrium constant over a range from zero ionic strength to nearly one. The numerical value of K_a changes by 100-fold over this range. Equation 24 is the correct result of applying equation 13 to the thermodynamic equilibrium constant for reaction 23. Thus $z_1^2 + z_2^2 - (z_1 + z_2)^2 = 12$, and $12A = 6.10$ for water at 25°C. The constant B is treated as an adjustable constant.

The formation of outer sphere complexes usually has a pronounced effect on the kinetic properties of complex ions. In studying the sulfation reaction

$$Co(NH_3)_5H_2O^{3+} + SO_4^{2-} \rightleftharpoons Co(NH_3)_5SO_4^{+} + H_2O \qquad (25)$$

in which an "inner sphere" or normal complex is formed, the equilibrium 23 also occurred and was found to have a labilizing effect on the rate of 25.[12a] That is, the ion pair is more reactive than the free ion, $Co(NH_3)_5H_2O^{3+}$. The same effect was also found for the reverse reaction of 25. Another kinetic consequence of ion-pair formation in this reaction is that the forward rate of 25 is nearly independent of the sulfate ion concentration over a wide range. This is due to complete formation of the ion pair, $Co(NH_3)_5H_2O^{3+}, SO_4^{2-}$, over this range.

It is found that various anions speed up the acid hydrolysis [16,21] of $Co(NH_3)_5NCS^{2+}$, $Co(NH_3)_5Cl^{2+}$ and the water exchange [22] (using oxygen-18 labeling) of $Cr(H_2O)_6^{3+}$. In the first two cases ion pairs are not detected spectrophotometrically, presumably because of low concentrations. However, their presence is inferred and believed to be responsible for the increased reaction rates. In methanol [17] the increased rate of chloride ion release for cis-$Co(en)_2Cl_2^+$ caused by basic anions is attributed to ion-pair formation. Non-basic anions increase the rate only slightly even though more stable ion pairs are formed (see p. 150).

No increase in rate with even basic anions is found for $trans$-$Co(en)_2Cl_2^+$, which does not form ion pairs in methanol. In agreement with the general effect of charge and solvent on stability of outer sphere complexes, basic anions have no effect on the rate of aquation of cis- and $trans$-$Co(en)_2(NO_2)Cl^+$ in water.[23] Neither does chloride ion increase the rate of acid hydrolysis of cis-$Co(en)_2Cl_2^+$ in water.[24]

In water the increased rates are best explained by assuming that a reduction of the total positive charge of the cation enables a negative or dipolar ligand to dissociate more easily. The effect is not that of an S_N2 displacement of a ligand by the associated anion, since water rather than the anion ends up in the coordination sphere of the complex ion after the ligand is ejected.

In fact for the reaction of $Cr(H_2O)_6^{3+}$ with NCS^- to form $Cr(H_2O)_5NCS^{2+}$, increasing ionic strength slows down the reaction even though ion pairs are formed.[25] This is in agreement with the theory for oppositely charged ions (equation 14).

Except for the nature of the product, it is not possible to distinguish between a unimolecular reaction of an ion pair and a bimolecular reaction of an anion and the complex ion. In methanol the interpretation is more difficult because a complex such as $Co(en)_2(CH_3OH)_2^{3+}$ is very unstable and would not persist. Hence the observed product is one in which the basic anion has entered the inner coordination sphere, $Co(en)_2X_2^+$. By analogy, it seems most reasonable to assume that the ion pair is the reactant in this case as well.

For comparison with the outer sphere complexes of $Co(NH_3)_6^{3+}$ shown in Table 1, a list of data on inner sphere complexes of iron(III) is given in Table 2. It is seen that, for anions of strong acids such as Cl^-, Br^-, and SO_4^{2-}, the respective values of the equilibrium constants are rather similar. Thus it is expected that the ion pair $Fe(H_2O)_6^{3+}$, Cl^- would be about as stable as the complex $Fe(H_2O)_5Cl^{2+}$. However, for the basic anions OH^-, F^-, and N_3^-, the advantage of penetrating in close to the positive central ion is clearly shown. This is, of course, very similar to what happens in the reaction of these ions with H^+, the reaction by which we measure basicity in aqueous solution. For larger cations of smaller charge this

Table 2

Association Constants for Inner Sphere Complexes of Iron(III) at 25°C

Complex	K^a	ΔH^0	ΔS^0	Reference
$FeCl^{2+}$	30	8.5 kcal	35 eu	26, 27
$FeBr^{2+}$	4	6.1	23	26, 27
$FeNCS^{2+}$	960	...	...	26, 27
FeN_3^{2+}	1.3×10^4	-4.3	5	28
$FeOH^{2+}$	1×10^{12}	-1.2	50	27, 29
$FeSO_4^+$	7×10^3	...	...	26, 30
FeF^{2+}	3×10^3	3.3^b	...	31

^{a} At zero ionic strength.

^{b} Measured at $\mu = 0.5$; the value of K has been approximately corrected to $\mu = 0$.

advantage is lost. Thus TlOH, TlCl, TlBr, and TlNCS all have association constants between 3 and 7.[32]

Furthermore the inner complexes have a much greater tendency to add further anions forming $FeCl_2^+$, $FeCl_3$, and $FeCl_4^-$. Presumably another anion could add to a species such as $Co(NH_3)_6^{3+}$, Cl^-, but such aggregates have not yet been demonstrated. Their presence has been inferred from kinetic studies in some cases.

REFERENCES

1. For derivations and discussions see (a) R. A. Robinson and R. H. Stokes, *Electrolyte Solutions*, Academic Press, New York, 1955, Chapters 4 and 9; or (b) H. S. Harned and B. B. Owen, *Physical Chemistry of Electrolytic Solutions*, Reinhold Publishing Corp., New York, 1950, Chapter 2.
2. E. Guntelberg, *Z. physik. Chem.*, **123**, 199 (1926); E. A. Guggenheim, *Phil. Mag.*, **19**, 588 (1935).
3. See A. A. Frost and R. G. Pearson, *Kinetics and Mechanism*, John Wiley & Sons, New York, 1953, Chapter 7, for a discussion.
4. G. N. Lewis and M. Randall, *Thermodynamics*, McGraw-Hill Book Co., New York, 1923, Chapter 28.
5. L. G. Sillén and G. Biedermann, *Arkiv Kemi*, **5**, No. 40, 425 (1953).
6. (a) See reference 1a, Chapter 14, for a general introduction. (b) A. Werner, *Ann.*, **386**, 1 (1912). (c) A. R. Olson and T. R. Simonson, *J. Chem. Phys.*, **17**, 1167 (1949).
7. N. Bjerrum, *Kgl. Danske Videnskab. Selskab Mat. fys. Medd.*, **9**, 7 (1926).
8. J. A. Caton and J. E. Prue, *J. Chem. Soc.*, **1956**, 671.
9. I. L. Jenkins and C. B. Monk, *ibid.*, **1951**, 68.
10. M. G. Evans and G. H. Nancollas, *Trans. Faraday Soc.*, **49**, 363 (1953).
11. R. G. Pearson and F. Basolo, *J. Am. Chem. Soc.*, **78**, 4878 (1956).

12. (a) H. Taube and F. A. Posey, *ibid.*, **75**, 1463 (1953). (b) F. A. Posey and H. Taube, *ibid.*, **78**, 15 (1956).

13. F. G. R. Gimblett and C. B. Monk, *Trans. Faraday Soc.*, **51**, 793 (1955).

14. C. Postmus and E. L. King, *J. Phys. Chem.*, **59**, 1208 (1955).

15. R. E. Connick and M. S. Tsao, quoted in reference 14.

16. A. W. Adamson and R. G. Wilkins, *J. Am. Chem. Soc.*, **76**, 3379 (1954).

17. R. G. Pearson, P. M. Henry, and F. Basolo, *J. Am. Chem. Soc.*, **79**, 5379, 5382 (1957).

18. C. W. Davies, *J. Chem. Soc.*, **1930**, 2421.

19. N. V. Sidgwick, *The Chemical Elements and Their Compounds*, Oxford University Press, 1950, p. 1536.

20. M. Linhard, *Z. Elektrochem.*, **50**, 224 (1944).

21. F. J. Garrick, *Trans. Faraday Soc.*, **33**, 486 (1937); **34**, 1088 (1938).

22. R. A. Plane and H. Taube, *J. Phys. Chem.*, **56**, 33 (1952); J. P. Hunt and R. A. Plane, *J. Am. Chem. Soc.*, **76**, 5960 (1954).

23. F. Basolo, B. D. Stone, J. G. Bergmann, and R. G. Pearson, *ibid.*, **76**, 3079 (1954).

24. G. W. Ettle and C. H. Johnson, *J. Chem. Soc.*, **1939**, 1490.

25. C. Postmus and E. L. King, *J. Phys. Chem.*, **59**, 1217 (1955).

26. M. W. Lister and D. E. Rivington, *Can. J. Chem.*, **33**, 1572, 1591, 1603 (1955).

27. E. Rabinowitch and W. H. Stockmayer, *J. Am. Chem. Soc.*, **64**, 335 (1942).

28. N. Uri, *Chem. Revs.*, **50**, 375 (1952).

29. R. M. Milburn and W. C. Vosburgh, *J. Am. Chem. Soc.*, **77**, 1352 (1955).

30. R. A. Whiteker and N. A. Davidson, *J. Am. Chem. Soc.*, **75**, 3081 (1953); K. W. Sykes, *The Kinetics and Mechanism of Inorganic Reactions in Solution*, The Chemical Society, London, 1954, *Special Pub. No.* 1, p. 64.

31. H. W. Dodgen and G. K. Rollefson, *J. Am. Chem. Soc.*, **71**, 2600 (1949); H. H. Broene and T. DeVries, *ibid.*, **69**, 1644 (1947).

32. V. S. K. Nair and G. H. Nancollas, *J. Chem. Soc.*, **1957**, 318.

ACID-BASE PROPERTIES OF COMPLEX IONS

Complex ions, particularly those containing water and ammine ligands are frequently acids of measurable strength. In Table 3 are given some acid ionization constants determined in water for a number of aqua complexes. These constants are also called hydrolysis constants. They refer to the reaction

$$\cdot M(H_2O)^{m+} \rightleftharpoons MOH^{(m-1)+} + H^+ \tag{26}$$

The corresponding hydroxo complexes are then weak bases.

For the simple metal ions the determination of these acid constants is of fundamental importance since their behavior in various reactions as a function of pH is governed by their pK_a values. Also the acidic solutions produced by the dissolution of various salts of these ions in water is due to reaction 26. The older practice of estimating pK_a by

Table 3

Acid Ionization (Hydrolysis) Constants for Some Aqua Ions at 25°C

Ion	pK_a	Reference and Remarks
Tl^+	13.2	1; $\mu = 0$
Mg^{2+}	11.4	2; $\mu = 0$
Ca^{2+}	12.6	1; $\mu = 0$
Ba^{2+}	13.2	1; $\mu = 0$
Fe^{2+}	8.3	3; $\mu = 0$
Ni^{2+}	10.6	4; $\mu = 0$
Cu^{2+}	8.0	5; at 18°C; $\mu = 0$
Zn^{2+}	9.7	38
Cd^{2+}	9.0	39
Hg^{2+}	3.7	6; $pK_2 = 2.6$
Pb^{2+}	7.8	7; at 18°C; $\mu = 0$
Al^{3+}	4.9	2; at 15°C
Sc^{3+}	4.9	8
In^{3+}	4.4	9; $pK_2 = 3.9$
Tl^{3+}	1.1	10; $pK_2 = 1.5$
Cr^{3+}	3.9	2; at 15°C
Fe^{3+}	2.2	11; $\mu = 0$; $pK_2 = 3.3$
$CrCl_2(H_2O)_4{}^+$	5.7	12
$Co(NH_3)_5H_2O^{3+}$	5.7	13; at 15°C; $\mu = 0$
$Co(NH_3)_4(H_2O)_2{}^{3+}$	5.2	13; at 15°C; $\mu = 0$
$Co(NH_3)_3(H_2O)_3{}^{3+}$	4.7	13; at 15°C; $\mu = 0$
$Co(NH_3)_2(H_2O)_4{}^{3+}$	3.4	13; at 15°C; $\mu = 0$
$Rh(NH_3)_5H_2O^{3+}$	5.9	13; $\mu = 0$
$Cr(NH_3)_5H_2O^{3+}$	5.2	14; at 10°C
$Cr(NH_3)_4(H_2O)_2{}^{3+}$	5.5	14; at 10°C
cis-$Co(en)_2(H_2O)_2{}^{3+}$	6.1	15; $pK_2 = 8.2$
$trans$-$Co(en)_2(H_2O)_2{}^{3+}$	4.5	15; $pK_2 = 7.9$
cis-$Cr(en)_2(H_2O)_2{}^{3+}$	4.8	16; $pK_2 = 7.2$
$trans$-$Cr(en)_2(H_2O)_2{}^{3+}$	4.1	16; $pK_2 = 7.5$
cis-$Co(en)_2NO_2H_2O^{2+}$	6.3	17
$trans$-$Co(en)_2NO_2H_2O^{2+}$	6.4	17
cis-$Pt(NH_3)_2(H_2O)_2{}^{2+}$	5.6	18; at 20°C; $pK_2 = 7.3$
$trans$-$Pt(NH_3)_2(H_2O)_2{}^{2+}$	4.3	18; at 20°C; $pK_2 = 7.4$
$Pt(NH_3)_5(H_2O)^{4+}$	~4	19
$Pt(en)_2(H_2O)_2{}^{4+}$	strong acid	37

measuring the pH of solutions of these salts is completely unreliable, and the values shown in Table 3 refer to data obtained by analyzing titration curves. Unfortunately a wide variety of conditions have been used by different workers.

The accurate determination of pK_a values is rendered very difficult by the pronounced tendency of almost all hydroxo complexes to undergo olation. This is the name given to the formation of polynuclear complexes by splitting out of water between hydroxo groups

$$2MOH \rightarrow MOM + H_2O \qquad (27)$$

The oxygen atom between the two metal atoms may be protonated, forming a hydroxo bridge. Two metal atoms may be bound by more than one bridge. Such polymerization eventually leads to the formation of insoluble precipitates. For a discussion of this process and the methods used to obtain pK_a data, the papers of Sillén and his co-workers are most useful.[25]

Table 4 gives some data on the acid strengths of a number of ammine

Table 4

Acid Ionization Constants of Some Ammine Complexes at 25°C

Ion	pK_a	Reference
$Co(NH_3)_6^{3+}$	>14	20
$Co(en)_3^{3+}$	>14	20
$Rh(NH_3)_6^{3+}$	>14	21
$Rh(en)_3^{3+}$	>14	21
$Pt(NH_3)_6^{4+}$	7.9	22
$Pt(en)(NH_3)_4^{4+}$	6.2	22
$Pt(en)_3^{4+}$	5.5	22
$Pt(NH_3)_5Cl^{3+}$	8.1	22
$Pt(NH_3)_5Br^{3+}$	8.3	22
$Pt(NH_3)_5OH^{3+}$	9.5	22
$Pt(en)_2Cl_2^{2+}$	10.4	22
$Os(en)_3^{4+}$	strong acid	23; $pK_2 = 5.8$
$Au(en)_2^{3+}$	~ 6.5	24

complexes. As expected they are generally less acidic than are aqua complexes, just as ammonium ion is a weaker acid than hydronium ion. However, the factor between H_3O^+ and NH_4^+ is 10^{11}, whereas for the highly charged complexes the factor seems to be less, being only 10^4 for platinum(IV). In the case of cobalt(III) complexes such as $Co(en)_3^{3+}$, an interaction between hydroxide ion and the complex occurs [20, 26] which is due to the formation of an ion pair rather than to acid-base neutralization.

The effect of increasing positive charge on the complex is usually to increase acidity as expected. However, there are the remarkable examples of mercury(II) and indium(III) in which the second ionization constant, as shown by pK_2, is greater than the first. Thus in the sequence of reactions

$$Hg(H_2O)_2{}^{2+} \rightleftharpoons Hg(H_2O)OH^+ + H^+ \rightleftharpoons Hg(OH)_2 + 2H^+ \quad (28)$$

the second stage proceeds more easily than the first. This behavior may be related to the tendency of mercury(II) to form linear complexes. Thus it is possible that a change in coordination number from four to two occurs in stage two of reaction 28. A related phenomenon is the reaction of NH_3 with Ag^+, in which the formation constant for $Ag(NH_3)_2{}^+$ is greater than for $Ag(NH_3)^+$.

Before discussing the tables further it may be worth while to see what classical electrostatic theory tells us about the effect of size, charge, and substituents on the acidity of these ions. Fortunately many of them may be represented as spherical particles, which makes the problem tractable. The exact solution for the electrostatic potential of a system of charges in a spherical body of dielectric constant D_i immersed in a continuous medium of dielectric constant D has been worked out.[27]

The solution is rather involved, however, and the model leads to the wrong answer in some of the cases of interest to the inorganic chemist (the acidities of *cis-trans* isomers). A different model will accordingly be used consisting of a spherical cavity containing some point charges and immersed in a continuum of dielectric constant D. For this model an exact but simple solution of the potential for the case where $D \gg 1$ is possible.[28] The entire effect of the external medium can be replaced by a series of image charges outside of the sphere, one for each charge inside the sphere. The situation is shown in Fig. 5 for a charge at the center of the sphere, representing the charge on the central atom, and a single proton. If the radius of the sphere is a, and the distance of a charge, q_i, from the center is b, the image charge has the magnitude $-(D - 1)q_i a/bD$ and is at a distance a^2/b from the center.

The electrical work required to remove a proton from such a system is simply the total electrostatic interaction of the proton and its image with all the charges in the sphere, including the interaction of the proton with its own image. We now include the other ligands as a set of point charges and/or point dipoles within the sphere. As an approximation

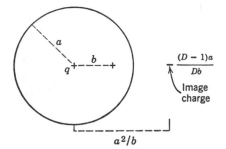

Fig. 5. Image charge of unit positive charge in spherical cavity of radius a. The central positive charge has an image at infinity which produces a potential of $-(D-1)q/Da$ in the cavity.

the values of the dipoles calculated in the gas phase for various ligands may be used (see Chapter 2). This is a good approximation for symmetrical complexes because the electric field due to the images of the ligand charges nearly vanishes. For unsymmetrical complexes the further polarization of the ligands must be considered.

If the proton is being removed from a water or ammonia molecule, it will leave behind a unit negative charge. This may be crudely represented in our model as a point negative charge in line with the proton and one angstrom unit nearer the center. Its distance from the center of the sphere may be taken as equal to the distance r of Chapter 2. The radius of the sphere on this basis is the crystallographic radius of the central ion plus the diameter of the ligand.

The entire scheme is now shown in Fig. 6. It is only necessary to use the one proton image in the calculations since the interaction of the image of a charge q_i with a charge q_j is the same as the interaction of the image of charge of q_j with q_i. The equations which relate the electrical interactions to the acid ionization constant are

$$\text{Work} = \tfrac{1}{2} \sum_i \phi_i q_i = -\Delta F_{\text{el}} = RT \ln K_a + \Delta F' \qquad (29)$$

where ϕ_i is the electric potential acting on every other charge within the sphere due to the proton and its image, and, in the case of the

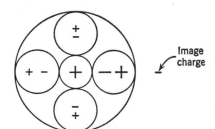

Fig. 6. Charges and dipoles which determine the acidity of a proton in an aqua complex. The image charge of the proton only is shown.

proton, the potential due to its own image and to every other charge plus its image. The term $\Delta F'$ includes any non-electrostatic contributions to the free energy change of ionization. This will include the covalent part of the OH bond which is broken. $\Delta F'$ also includes the change in free energy caused by putting the proton on some solvent molecule in the interior of the solution. Instead of trying to calculate this term, it may be simply noted that the negative free energy of hydration of the proton is about 260 kcal.[29]

Omitting further details of the calculation, the result for $Al(H_2O)_6^{3+}$, using the ionic radius of 0.57 A and 2.76 A for the diameter of the water molecule, is that the electrical free energy term in 29 is 276 kcal. The free energy of ionization of this acid is 7 kcal from Table 1. This implies that $\Delta F'$ is 269 kcal, which is of the right order of magnitude at least, since it must be greater than 260 kcal. Since the largest term in the calculated interaction is that of the proton on its adjacent negative charge, and since the model was very inaccurate for just this term, the agreement must not be taken seriously.

However, comparative values should be more valid. Thus for $Mg(H_2O)_6^{2+}$, a similar calculation, using 0.78 A for the ionic radius, gives $\Delta F_{el} = 287$ kcal, meaning that the divalent cation is a weaker acid by 11 kcal. The experimental difference in the free energies of ionization ($\Delta RT \ln K_a$) is 9.0 kcal. A calculation for $Tl(H_2O)_6^{3+}$ with an ionic radius of 1.05 A gives $\Delta F_{el} = 280$. Comparing this result with that for aluminum, it would appear that a larger ion should be a weaker acid than a smaller ion of the same charge. This is quite the opposite from the experimental results shown in Table 3. In fact it is usually true that the complexes of metals of high atomic weight are stronger acids, as shown also by the platinum metals. This may be attributed to the fact that the effective positive charge of the central ion which acts on the proton is larger than that which acts on the proton image (see Chapter 2). This would be expected for multielectronic atoms since the proton is closer to the nucleus than the second hydration sphere, which is responsible for the image charge.

It will be noticed from Fig. 6 that the dipoles of the other ligands are attractive for the proton. Thus larger dipole moments for these ligands will tend to make a weaker acid. In the case of NH_3 versus H_2O, the total dipole is some 15% greater for the former in the case of a trivalent ion of the size of cobalt(III) or chromium(III). This produces a theoretical weakening of the acid $Co(NH_3)_5H_2O^{3+}$ compared to $Co(H_2O)_6^{3+}$ of 3 kcal, or two powers of ten in the ionization constant. Our model is not good enough to calculate the acidity of an ammine complex such as $Co(NH_3)_6^{3+}$. It may also be noted that the acid strength of a tetrahedral complex should be greater than that of an octahedral complex because of the smaller number of attractive dipoles.

In Table 2 it may be noted that ethylenediamine complexes of platinum(IV) are more acid than ammonia complexes. This is somewhat unexpected inasmuch as $NH_2CH_2CH_2NH_3^+$ is a weaker acid than NH_4^+ by a factor of 8. However, an explanation can be given in terms of the bulky C_2H_4 group's preventing solvation of the protons in the coordinated NH_2 group. This will favor expulsion of the protons, or acid ionization. Using the spherical model, if the effect of going from $Co(NH_3)_6^{3+}$ to $Co(en)_3^{3+}$ is to increase the radius of the sphere a by only 0.4 A on the average, and if b, the proton distance, remains constant, it may be calculated that this solvation factor would increase the acid strength of the latter ion by 11 kcal of free energy. This corresponds to 10^8 in the equilibrium constant. Opposing this will be the inductive effect of the C_2H_4 portion, which is base strengthening. The net effect should be acid strengthening. In agreement with this conclusion it is found that $Co(en)_3^{3+}$ exchanges deuterium with a heavy water solvent faster than $Co(NH_3)_6^{3+}$ does.[30]

In the case of the parent ion, $NH_2CH_2CH_2NH_3^+$, the solvation-blocking properties of the alkyl chain are minimized because the ion is long and relatively extended. Access of the solvent molecules to the positive protons is not greatly hindered. However, NH_4^+ will still be more strongly solvated than the ethylenediammonium ion because of its small size and because it has four positive protons instead of three. The inductive effect predominates in this case, however. For the extreme case of a tertiary ammonium ion such as $(CH_3)_3NH^+$, the lack of solvation can be dominating. The general weakness of tertiary amines as bases has been accounted for in this way, though steric strain in the ion may play some role.[31]

The acid-strengthening effect of an alkyl group may also show up in positions remote from the alkyl substituent. Thus we find $+(CH_3)_3NCH_2COOH$ is a stronger acid than $+H_3NCH_2COOH$ by a factor of three.[32] The relative acid strengths of $Co(NH_3)_4(H_2O)_2^{3+}$, $Co(en)_2(H_2O)_2^{3+}$, and $Co(N\text{-}meen)_2(H_2O)_2^{3+}$ are 1:3:10, with the ligand $NH_2CH_2CH_2NHCH_3$ most acid strengthening.[33] It is the proton of the water in the last three ions which is acidic and not the nitrogen proton.

The interesting phenomenon of the greater strength of the *trans* diaqua complexes compared to *cis* for $Pt(NH_3)_2(H_2O)_2^{2+}$, $Cr(en)_2$-

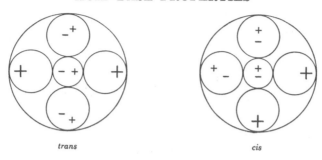

trans   *cis*

Fig. 7. Repulsion of two protons located *trans* and *cis* to each other. Dipoles induced in central atom and other ligands by second proton are shown.

$(H_2O)_2{}^{3+}$, and $Co(en)_2(H_2O)_2{}^{3+}$ can be explained by means of our model. The essential point is that we are not dealing with symmetric complexes in these cases, the aqua group being acid strengthening with respect to the ammine group. Hence polarization of the rest of the molecule by this group must be considered. Using the simpler case of two protons, Fig. 7 shows how the extra induced dipoles in the rest of the molecule caused by one proton are more repulsive for another proton in the *trans* position than in the *cis*. This effect can outweigh the direct interaction of the two protons (including their images), which is obviously greater for a *cis* arrangement than for a *trans*. This represents a more detailed picture of Grinberg's polarization theory of the *trans* effect (see Chapter 4).

The crystal field theory also makes some predictions about acid strengths. Since the crystal field strength of hydroxide ion is less than that of a water molecule, systems with large crystal field stabilizations should be weaker acids than otherwise since they suffer some loss of stabilization energy on replacing H_2O by OH^-. Thus we find Cr^{3+} aqua ion a weaker acid than Fe^{3+}. Since the property of being amphoteric depends upon forming a polyhydroxo complex in solution, the non-transition metals such as Al(III), As(III), and Zn(II) should dissolve in alkali more readily than the transition metals which are crystal field stabilized. However, Fe(III) and Cr(III) do not behave as expected, since it is the latter which appears to be more amphoteric.

Fe^{3+} has no crystal field stabilization since all five d orbitals are occupied. In the case of d^4 and d^9 systems ionization may be promoted [34] by crystal field effects since, if the OH^- is formed on the x axis, only the $d_{x^2-y^2}$ and d_{xy} levels are raised in energy, the others being lowered (see Table 5 of Chapter 2, square pyramid structures compared to octahedral). Thus if the complex is magnetically normal, the very unstable $d_{x^2 - y^2}$ level will be empty for d^4 or only half-filled for d^9. The resultant may be a greater crystal field stabilization for the hydroxo than for the aqua complex. This is borne out by the fact that Cu^{2+} is a stronger acid than its neighbors. Also ruthenium(IV) complexes are more acid than corresponding platinum(IV) complexes,[35] the latter being d^6. The d^4 system $Os(en)_3^{4+}$ is a strong acid, being completely ionized. However, its magnetic moment of 0.4 Bohr magnetons [23] shows that the occupancy of the d orbitals must be considered in more detail, as in the crystal field theory of Kotani.[36]

REFERENCES

1. R. P. Bell and M. H. Panckhurst, *J. Chem. Soc.*, **1956**, 2836.
2. G. Mattock, *Acta Chem. Scand.*, **8**, 777 (1954).
3. D. L. Leussing and I. M. Kolthoff, *J. Am. Chem. Soc.*, **75**, 2476 (1953).
4. K. H. Gayer and L. Woontner, *ibid.*, **74**, 1436 (1952).
5. K. J. Pedersen, *Kgl. Danske Videnskab. Selskab Mat. fys. Medd.*, **20**, No. 7 (1943).
6. S. Hietanen and L. G. Sillén, *Acta Chem. Scand.*, **6**, 747 (1952).
7. K. J. Pedersen, *Kgl. Danske Videnskab. Selskab Mat. fys. Medd.*, **22**, No. 10 (1945).
8. M. Kilpatrick and L. Pokras, *J. Electrochem. Soc.*, **100**, 85 (1953).
9. G. Biedermann, *Arkiv Kemi*, **9**, 227 (1956).
10. G. Biedermann, *ibid.*, **5**, 41 (1953).
11. B. O. A. Hedström, *Arkiv Kemi*, **6**, 1 (1953); R. M. Milburn, *J. Am. Chem. Soc.*, **79**, 537 (1957).
12. A. B. Lamb and G. R. Fonda, *J. Am. Chem. Soc.*, **43**, 1154 (1921).
13. J. N. Brønsted and K. Volqvartz, *Z. physik. Chem.*, **134**, 97 (1928).
14. W. K. Wilmarth, H. Graff, and S. T. Gustin, *J. Am. Chem. Soc.*, **78**, 2683 (1956).
15. J. Bjerrum and S. E. Rasmussen, *Acta Chem. Scand.*, **6**, 1265 (1952).
16. F. Woldbye, private communication.
17. F. Basolo, B. D. Stone, J. G. Bergmann, and R. G. Pearson, *J. Am. Chem. Soc.*, **76**, 3079 (1954).
18. K. A. Jensen, *Z. anorg. u. allgem. Chem.*, **242**, 87 (1939).
19. A. A. Grinberg and G. P. Faerman, *Z. anorg. u. allgem. Chem.*, **193**, 193 (1930).
20. R. G. Pearson and F. Basolo, *J. Am. Chem. Soc.*, **78**, 4878 (1956).
21. C. Klixbüll Jørgensen, *Acta Chem. Scand.*, **10**, 518 (1956).
22. A. A. Grinberg and K. I. Gil'dengershel, *Izvest. Akad. Nauk S.S.S.R.*, **1948**, 479.
23. F. P. Dwyer and J. W. Hogarth, *J. Am. Chem. Soc.*, **77**, 6152 (1955).
24. B. P. Block and J. C. Bailar, Jr., *ibid.*, **73**, 4722 (1951).
25. L. G. Sillén, *Acta Chem. Scand.*, **8**, 299, 318 (1954); L. G. Sillén and S. Hietanen, *ibid.*, 1607.

26. J. A. Caton and J. E. Prue, *J. Chem. Soc.*, **1956**, 671.
27. J. G. Kirkwood, *J. Chem. Phys.*, **2**, 351 (1934).
28. R. G. Pearson, unpublished calculations.
29. H. O. Pritchard, *Chem. Revs.*, **52**, 529 (1953).
30. J. S. Anderson, H. V. A. Briscoe, and N. F. Spoor, *J. Chem. Soc.*, **1943**, 361.
31. A. F. Trotman-Dickenson, *ibid.*, **1949**, 1286; R. G. Pearson and F. V. Williams, *J. Am. Chem. Soc.*, **76**, 258 (1954).
32. A. Neuberger, *Proc. Roy. Soc. London*, **A158**, 68 (1937); O. Weider, *Ber.*, **68B**, 263 (1935).
33. R. G. Pearson, R. E. Meeker, and F. Basolo, *J. Am. Chem. Soc.*, **78**, 709 (1956).
34. C. Klixbüll Jørgensen, Tenth Solvay Conference, Brussels, 1956.
35. R. Charonnat, *Ann. chim. Paris*, [10]**16**, 5, 123 (1931).
36. M. Kotani, *J. Phys. Soc. Japan*, **4**, 293 (1949); R. B. Johannesen and A. R. Lindberg, *J. Am. Chem. Soc.*, **76**, 5349 (1954).
37. P. H. Wilks, private communication.
38. I. M. Kolthoff and T. Kameda, *J. Am. Chem. Soc.*, **53**, 832 (1931).
39. Y. Marcus, *Acta Chem. Scand.*, **11**, 690 (1957).

EXCHANGE REACTIONS

Throughout this book reference is made to numerous applications of isotopically labeled substances in studies of reaction mechanisms. Techniques of this type are often the only means of testing certain theories on substitution reactions, isomerization, and oxidation-reduction reactions. Since these have already been discussed, it is not the intent of this section to do more than summarize briefly some of the information available on the rates of exchange in certain systems. Most of the material presented here is taken from a review article by Stranks and Wilkins.[1] For a more detailed treatment of isotopic tracer investigations of mechanisms and structures in inorganic chemistry the reader is referred to this review.

The general equation for an isotopic exchange reaction may be designated as

$$AX + *X \rightleftharpoons A*X + X \tag{30}$$

The rate of exchange of X is described by a first-order rate law

$$\text{Rate} = \frac{-2.303}{t} \frac{ab}{a+b} \log (1 - F) \tag{31}$$

where $a = [AX + A*X]$, $b = [*X + X]$, and $F =$ the fraction of exchange at time t. The functional dependence of the rate of exchange upon reactant concentrations must be determined by varying the concentrations. Perhaps the simplest approach is to study in turn the dependence of the rate on a single reactant concentration, the other concentrations being maintained constant.

In kinetic studies of exchange reactions involving coordination compounds, it is well to keep in mind that often the rate of exchange of the central metal ion is complicated by the stepwise equilibria

$$MX_n + *M \rightleftharpoons MX_{n-1} + *MX \rightleftharpoons \cdots \rightleftharpoons M + *MX_n \quad (32)$$

Not only does this lead to difficulties in the treatment of the rate data but also to the even more troublesome experimental difficulty of separating the exchanging species. This complication does not arise when the formation of intermediate complexes is unimportant because of their relatively low stability, so that the original complex can exist with significant concentrations of the free metal ion, e.g., $Fe(phen)_3^{2+}$ and $Ni(NH_2C(CH_3)_2C(CH_3)_2NH_2)_2^{2+}$. One other case where the formation of intermediate complexes is not important is, of course, where the central metal ion is coordinated to a single multidentate group, e.g., $Fe(EDTA)^-$ and $M(porphyrin)$. It is also apparent that the rate of exchange of metal ions in MX_n-$*M$ is not necessarily a true measure of the lability of the M—X bond. Certainly the probability of metal ion exchange is less than the corresponding probability of ligand exchange, which for a unidentate ligand requires only the rupture of one M—X bond. If in a particular complex the rate of the first M—X rupture is slow and that of subsequent M—X ruptures is fast, it follows that the rates of ligand and of metal ion exchange will be the same. However, in most systems this is not the case and the rate of ligand exchange is faster than that of metal ion exchange.

From the above discussion it can be said that studies of ligand exchange in complexes have definite advantages over the corresponding metal ion exchange study. The application of this technique to estimate the lability of a coordination compound is of particular importance here. A slow rate of substitution of one ligand (X) in a complex by a different ligand (Y) does not necessarily mean that the original complex is inert, since an apparent low rate of formation may result from an unfavorable equilibrium position for the reaction in question. This difficulty does not arise, however, with studies of isotopic ligand exchange. Since the heat of reaction for an isotopic exchange process is essentially zero, the free energy change for the process is derived almost entirely from the entropy of isotopic mixing and is therefore always negative. This means that at equilibrium there is a random distribution of isotopic ligands between the exchanging reactants, so that the rate of attainment of equilibrium is a direct measure of the lability of the M—X bonds.

The advantage of ligand exchange over metal exchange studies as a measure of complex lability is limited to the highest member in the coordination series, e.g., MA_6 where M has a coordination number of six. Metal exchange is best for the lowest member, e.g., MA, where investigations of ligand exchange are complicated by the formation of higher coordinated species. For example mercury(II) ion exchange in the system $HgCN^+-^*Hg^{2+}$ is slow,[61] so $HgCN^+$ is an inert complex. However, cyanide exchange in the system $HgCN^+-^*CN^-$ is expected to be rapid as it is in $Hg(CN)_2-^*CN^-$.[11] Estimates of the lability of the intermediate coordinated species by exchange studies is difficult whether it be done by either ligand or metal exchange.

Exchange data for some of the more common systems are summarized in Table 5, where examples are included of both ligand and metal ion exchange. The relative reactivities of metal complexes were discussed in some detail at the beginning of Chapter 3. The statements made there are seen to be in good agreement with most of the data collected in Table 5. On the basis of these data it is possible to make the following broad generalizations:

1. Transition metal complexes (crystal field stabilized) are more inert than are analogous non-transition metal compounds (non-crystal field stabilized), e.g., $Co(C_2O_4)_3{}^{3-}$ is inert whereas $Al(C_2O_4)_3{}^{3-}$ is labile.

2. Metal ions of the d^3, d^6, and d^8 systems are among the more inert complexes, e.g., Cr(III) and Co(III) complexes are not labile; the reactions of nickel(II) are slower than those of copper(II).

3. Coordination compounds of platinum metal ions are less reactive than the corresponding first member of the group VIII triad, e.g., $Fe(phen)_3{}^{2+}$ dissociates in acid whereas $Ru(phen)_3{}^{2+}$ and $Os(phen)_3{}^{2+}$ withstand boiling concentrated hydrochloric acid.

4. For the same metal ion, complexes which contain ligands of low crystal field strength are more labile than those with ligands of higher crystal field strength, e.g., compare inert cyano complexes with corresponding labile ammonia or halo compounds. This order is reversed in the system $PtX_4{}^{2-}$.

5. The larger the dentate character of a ligand the less labile its complexes, e.g., the lability of Cu(II) complexes decreases in the order ammonia > ethylenediamine > N,N'-ethylenebis(salicylaldimine) > pheophytin.

Table 5

Exchange Reactions of Some Metal Coordination Compounds [a,b]

Exchanging Species	[Complex], [Reactant], and Conditions	Exchange Rates	References
Aluminum group:			
$Al(H_2O)_6{}^{3+} - H_2{}^*O$	1.0, excess, pH 0	C, 3 min	2
$Al(C_2O_4)_3{}^{3-} - {}^*C_2O_4{}^{2-}$	0.03, 0.01, pH 4.5–6	C, 20 sec (35°C)	3
$Ga(H_2O)_6{}^{3+} - H_2{}^*O$	1.0, excess, pH 0	C, 2.5 min	2
Vanadium group:			
$V(CN)_6{}^{3-} - {}^*CN^-$	0.026, 0.026, pH 9	C, 1 min	4
Chromium group:			
$Cr(H_2O)_6{}^{2+} - H_2{}^*O$	0.4, excess, $0.4\,M$ HClO$_4$	C, 2 min	5
$Cr(H_2O)_6{}^{3+} - H_2{}^*O$ [c]	0.05–1.1, excess, 0.1–0.5 M HClO$_4$	28–58 hr	2, 5
$Cr(en)_3{}^{3+} - {}^*en$	0.1, 0.16, $1\,M$ HNO$_3$	N, 70 hr (40°C)	6
$Cr(H_2O)_5Cl - {}^*Cl^-$		slow	7
$Cr(NH_3)_5(N{}^*CS)^{2+} - {}^*SCN^-$ [c]	0.1, 0.2, pH 2.5	hours, (80°C)	8
$Cr(H_2O)_4Cl_2{}^+ - {}^*Cl^-$	1.6, 2.2	slow	9
$Cr(H_2O)_4SO_4{}^+ - {}^*SO_4{}^{2-}$		270 min (30°C)	10
$Cr(CN)_6{}^{4-} - {}^*CN^-$	0.026, 0.026, pH 11.3	C, 40 sec	4
$Cr(CN)_6{}^{3-} - {}^*CN^-$ [d]	0.05, 0.05, pH 10	24 days	4, 11
$Cr(CN)_6{}^{3-} - {}^*Cr(H_2O)_6{}^{3+}$	0.01, 0.01, pH 3–4	36 hr	12
$Cr(NCS)_6{}^{3-} - {}^*Cr(H_2O)_6{}^{3+}$	0.01, 0.01, pH ~1	N, 72 hr	12
$Cr(NCS)_6{}^{3-} - {}^*SCN^-$		slow	13
$Cr(C_2O_4)_3{}^{3-} - {}^*C_2O_4{}^{2-}$	0.06, 0.01	N, 25 min (35°C)	14
$Mo(CN)_8{}^{4-} - {}^*CN^-$ [d]	0.05, 0.05, pH 10	N, 11 days	11
$W(CN)_8{}^{4-} - {}^*CN^-$ [c]	0.01, 0.17, pH 11	~500 days (dark) ~11 days (light)	15
$W(CN)_8{}^{3-} - {}^*CN^-$ [d]	0.01, 0.17, pH 10.4	~500 days	15

Manganese group:			
$Mn(aeoc)_3-{}^*Mn^{2+}$	methanol	fast	16
$Mn(CN)_6^{4-}-{}^*CN^-$	0.026, 0.026, pH 11.8	C, 6 min	4
$Mn(CN)_6^{3-}-{}^*CN^{-c}$	0.01, 0.05, pH 9–11	35–80 min (0°C)	4, 11, 17
$Mn(C_2O_4)_3^{3-}-{}^*Mn^{2+}$	0.01, 0.01, pH 1	C, 5 sec	18
Iron group:			
$Fe(H_2O)_6^{3+}-H_2{}^*O$	1.0, excess, pH 0	C, 4 min	2
${}^*Fe(bipy)_3^{2+}-Fe(H_2O)_6^{2+c}$	0.01, 0.01, pH 1.5	~5 hr	19, 20
${}^*Fe(phen)_3^{2+}-Fe(H_2O)_6^{2+c}$	0.01, 0.02, pH 1.5	~97 min	19, 20
$Ferrihemoglobin-{}^*Fe(H_2O)_6^{3+}$	slightly acid	N, 30 hr	19
$Ferriprotoporphyrin-{}^*Fe(H_2O)_6^{3+}$	alcohol	N, 60 days	19
$Fe(CN)_6^{4-}-{}^*CN^{-cd}$	0.025, 0.025, pH 10.3	N, 77 hr (dark) $t^{1/2}$, 33 hr (light)	4
$Fe(CN)_6^{3-}-{}^*CN^{-d}$	0.05, 0.05, pH 10	N, 115 hr	4, 11, 21
$Fe(CN)_6^{3-}-{}^*Fe(H_2O)_6^{3+d}$	0.07, 0.14	N, 6 days	22
$Fe(CN)_5H_2O^{3-}-{}^*CN^{-d}$	0.025, 0.025, pH 10	38 hr (dark)	4
$Fe(CN)_5NO^{2-}-{}^*CN^{-d}$	0.025, 0.025, pH 10.3	134 hr (dark)	4
$Fe(C_2O_4)_3^{3-}-{}^*C_2O_4^{2-}$	0.06, 0.01, pH 4.5–6	C, 20 sec (35°C)	3, 21
$Fe(EDTA)^{2-}-{}^*Fe(H_2O)_6^{2+}$	0.01, 0.01, pH 2–5	C, 1 min	23
$Fe(EDTA)^--{}^*Fe(H_2O)_6^{3+c}$	0.006–0.025, 0.006–0.025, pH 1–2.5	25 min to 40 hr	23
$OsCl_6^{2-}-{}^*Cl$	0.06, 0.06, pH 1	N, 63 days (50°C)	24
Cobalt group:			
$Co(H_2O)_6^{2+}-H_2{}^*O$	1.55, excess, 3 M HClO₄	C, 2 min (0°C)	25
$Co(H_2O)_6^{3+}-H_2{}^*O$	0.5, excess, 4 M HClO₄	C, 2 min (0°C, Co^{2+})	25
${}^*Co(NH_3)_6^{3+}-Co(H_2O)_6^{2+}$	0.01, 0.01	N, 6 days (50°C)	26
${}^*Co(NH_3)_6^{3+}-Co(H_2O)_6^{3+}$	0.01, 0.01	N, 90 min	26
$Co(en)_3^{3+}-{}^*en$	0.04, 0.20, pH 7 charcoal catalyst	N, 65 hr (100°C) rate slower than rate of racemization	6 28

Table 5 (Continued)

Exchanging Species	[Complex], [Reactant], and Conditions	Exchange Rates	References
$Co(phen)_3^{2+}$-*$Co(H_2O)_6^{2+}$	0.005, 0.005	C, 30 sec (15°C)	27
$Co(terpy)_2^{2+}$-*$Co(H_2O)_6^{2+}$	0.005, 0.005	2.8 hr (15°C)	27
$Co(phen)_3^{3+}$-*phen	presence $Co(phen)_3^{2+}$	fast	28
$Co(bipy)_3^{3+}$-*bipy	presence $Co(bipy)_3^{2+}$	fast	28
$Co(NH_3)_5H_2O^{3+}$-H_2*O [c]	~0.1, excess, pH 2	24 hr	29
$Co(NH_3)_5NCS^{2+}$-N*CS⁻ [c]	~0.1, 0.4, pH 2.5	hours (90°C)	8
$Co(NH_3)_5CO_3^+$-*CO_3^{2-} [c]	0.006–0.04, 0.003–0.05, pH 8.8–10	70–1200 min (0°C)	30
$Co(NH_3)_4CO_3^+$-*CO_3^{2-} [c]	0.005–0.09, 0.007–0.036, pH 9.4–10.1	3–16 hr	31
$Co(en)_2CO_3^+$-*CO_3^{2-} [c]	0.01–0.06, 0.005–0.03, pH 9.2	3–8 hr	32
cis-$Co(en)_2Cl_2^+$-*Cl⁻ [c]	0.002, 0.038, methanol	83 min (35.8°C)	33
trans-$Co(en)_2Cl_2^+$-*Cl⁻ [c]	0.002, 0.03, methanol	35 hr (25°C)	34
$Co(aeoc)_3^-$-*$Co(H_2O)_6^{2+}$	0.008, 0.008, pyridine	~80 days (30°C)	27
$Co(aeoc)_2(H_2O)_2$-*$Co(C_2H_3O_2)_2$	0.008, 0.008, pyridine	C, 50 sec	27
$Co(salicylaldehydo)_2$-*$Co(C_2H_3O_2)_2$	0.008, 0.008, pyridine	C, 40 sec	27
$Co(N,N'$-ethylenebis(salicylaldimine))-*$Co(C_2H_3O_2)_2$	0.0001, 0.0001, pyridine	20 min (15°C)	27
$Co(phthalocyanine)$-*$Co(C_2H_3O_2)_2$	0.004, 0.008, pyridine	N, 5 days (30°C)	27
Vitamin B_{12}-*$Co(H_2O)_6^{2+}$	pH 2–12	N, 14 days (55°C)	35
$Co(CN)_5^{3-}$-*CN⁻	0.02, 0.03	C, 2 min	36
$Co(CN)_6^{3-}$-*CN⁻ [d]	0.05, 0.05, pH 11	N, 8 days	4, 11
$Co(CO_3)_3^{3-}$-*CO_3^{2-}	1.0, 1.0	N, 15 hr	37
$Co(C_2O_4)_3^{3-}$-*$C_2O_4^{2-}$	0.06, 0.01	N, 25 min (50°C)	3
$Co(EDTA)^{2-}$-*$Co(H_2O)_6^{2+}$	0.005, 0.005, pH 2–5	fast	38
$Co(EDTA)^-$-*$Co(H_2O)_6^{2+}$	0.005, 0.005, pH 2.8	very slow	38
$Rh(en)_3^{3+}$-*$Rh(H_2O)_6^{3+}$		slow	39

Reaction	Conditions	Time	Ref.
$Ir(en)_3^{3+}$-*$Ir(H_2O)_6^{3+}$		slow	39
$IrBr_6^{2-}$-*Br^-	0.01, 0.01	slow	13
$IrCl_6^{2-}$-$Ir(py)_2Cl_4^-$	0.005, 0.009	N, 34 hr	40
Nickel group:			
$Ni(en)_3^{2+}$-*$Ni(H_2O)_6^{2+}$		C, 5 min	41
$Ni(en)_3^{2+}$-*en [c]	0.05, 0.01	5 sec (0°C)	42
$Ni(NH_2C(CH_3)_2C(CH_3)_2NH_2)_2$-*$Ni(H_2O)_6^{2+}$ [c]	0.005, 0.015, pH 6.8	67 min	28
$Ni(bipy)_3^{2+}$-*$Ni(H_2O)_6^{2+}$		5 min	41
$Ni(phen)_3^{2+}$-*phen	0.003, 0.01, $pH7$	118 min (45°C)	43
$Ni(salicylaldehydo)_2$-*Ni^{2+}	Methyl Cellosolve	C, 5 min	41
$Ni(8\text{-hydroxyquinolato})_2$-*$Ni^{2+}$	0.005, 0.005, Methyl Cellosolve	C, 5 min	41
$Ni(N,N'\text{-ethylenebis(salicylaldimine)})$-*$Ni^{2+}$	Methyl Cellosolve	N, 50 hr	41
$Ni(N,N'\text{-trimethylenebis(salicylaldimine)})$-*$Ni^{2+}$	Methyl Cellosolve	C, 5 min	41
$Ni(DMG)_2$-*Ni^{2+}	0.005, 0.005, pyridine	~14 hr	41
$Ni(\text{dipropyl dithiocarbamato})_2$-*$Ni^{2+}$	acetone	N, 1 hr	41
$Ni(CN)_4^{2-}$-*CN^-	0.005, 0.02, pH 6.5–10.5	C, 30 sec	11, 45
$Ni(CN)_4^{2-}$-*$Ni(NH_3)_x^{2+}$	0.005, 0.005, 0–3 M NH_3	C, 25 sec	45
$Ni(CN)_4^{2-}$-*$Ni(C_2O_4)_2^{2-}$	0.007, 0.007, pH 6–8	N, 9 min	45
$Ni(EDTA)^{2-}$-*$Ni(H_2O)_6^{2+}$	0.002, 0.002, pH 0.2–9.6	C, 1 min, to N, 24 hr	38
$Pd(CN)_4^{2-}$-*CN^-	0.05, 0.05, pH 10	C, 3 min	11
$PdCl_4^{2-}$-*Cl^-		fast	13
$PdBr_4^{2-}$-*Br^-		fast	13
$Pt(NH_3)_3Cl^+$-*Cl^- [c]	0.0005, 0.01, 0.2 M KNO_3	12.8 hr	46
$trans$-$Pt(NH_3)_2Cl_2$-*Cl^- [c]	0.0005, 0.01, 0.2 M KNO_3	5.5 hr	46
$Pt(NH_3)Cl_3$-*Cl^- [c]		7.2 hr	47
$Pt(CN)_4^{2-}$-*C*N^-	0.04, 0.16	~1 min	48
$Pt(SCN)_4^{2-}$-*SCN^-		fast	13
$PtCl_4^{2-}$-*Cl^-	0.004, 0.06	~14 hr	48, 49, 50

Table 5 (Continued)

Exchanging Species	[Complex], [Reactant], and Conditions	Exchange Rates	References
$PtBr_4^{2-}$ -*Br^-	0.05, 0.20	~6 min	13, 48, 51
PtI_4^{2-} -*I^-	0.1, 0.4	~4 min	48
$PtCl_6^{2-}$ -*Cl^- [c d]	0.02, 0.005, pH 1.5	C, seconds	50, 52
*$PtCl_6^{2-}$ -cis-$Pt(NH_3)_2Cl_4$		N	40
$PtCl_6^{2-}$ -*$PtCl_4^{2-}$ [d]	0.008, 0.014, pH 2	~1 hr	40, 50
$PtBr_6^{2-}$ -*Br^- [d]	0.15, 0.35	C, 30 min (100°C); N, 2 hr (dark)	13, 40, 53
PtI_6^{2-} -*I^- [d]	0.005, 0.005, pH 2	30 min (18°C)	52
Copper group:			
$Cu(en)_2^{2+}$ -*en	0.001, 0.002	C, 3 sec (0°C)	42
$Cu(aeoc)_2$ -*$Cu(C_2H_3O_2)_2$	chloroform	C, 2 min	54
$Cu(N$-methylsalicylaldimine$)_2$ -*$Cu(C_2H_3O_2)_2$	0.015, 0.015, pyridine	C, 15 sec	55
$Cu(N,N'$-ethylenebis(salicylaldimine$))$- *$Cu(C_2H_3O_2)_2$ [c]	0.015, 0.015, pyridine	2.1 hr	55
$Cu(N,N'$-ethylenebis(4-imino-2-pentanone$))$- *$Cu(C_2H_3O_2)_2$	0.004, 0.004, pyridine	37 hr	55
Cu(pheophytin)-*Cu^{2+}	80% acetone	N, 48 hr	19
$Cu(CN)_2^-$ -*CN^-	0.026, 0.026, pH 9.8	C, 2 min	4
$CuBr_2^-$ -*Br^-		fast	56
$Ag(CN)_2^-$ -*CN^-	0.026, 0.026, pH 10.3	C, 2 min	4
$AuCl_4^-$ -*Cl^- [c]	0.003–0.012, 0.003–0.076, pH 0–3	0.77–4.2 min (0°C)	57
Zinc group:			
$Zn(H_2O)_4^{2+}$ -H_2*O	0.2, excess, 0.4 M $HClO_4$	C, 2 min	5
$Zn(en)_3^{2+}$ -*en	0.02, 0.16	C, 6 sec (0°C)	42

$Zn(aeoc)_2$–*$Zn(C_2H_3O_2)_2$	0.01, 0.01, pyridine	C, 30 sec (0°C)	58
$Zn(8$-hydroxyquinolato$)_2$–*$Zn(C_2H_3O_2)_2$	0.01, 0.01, pyridine	C, 30 sec (0°C)	58
$Zn(N,N'$-ethylenebis(salicylaldimine))–*$Zn(C_2H_3O_2)_2$	0.01, 0.01, pyridine	C, 30 sec (0°C)	58
$Zn(N,N'$-ethylenebis(4-imino-2-pentanone))–*$Zn(C_2H_3O_2)_2$	0.01, 0.01, pyridine	C, 30 sec (0°C)	58
Zn(phthalocyanine)–*$Zn(C_2H_3O_2)_2$	0.002, 0.002, pyridine	N, 35 days	58
$Zn(EDTA)^{2-}$–*Zn^{2+}	pH 3–11	C, 1 min	59
$Zn(CN)_4^{2-}$–*CN^-	0.026, 0.026, pH 10.3	C, 2 min	4
$Hg(H_2O)_4^{2+}$+H_2*O		not rapid	60
$Hg(en)_2$–*en	0.006, 0.01	C, 6 sec (0°C)	42
$HgCN^+$–*Hg^{2+} c	0.007, 0.001, pH 2.6	15 min	61
$Hg(CN)_2$–*CN^-	0.05, 0.05, pH 10	C, 15 sec	11
$Hg(CN)_4^{2-}$–*CN^-	0.02, 0.02, pH 10	C, 5 min	11
$HgCl_2$–*Cl^-	0.001, 0.002	C, 1 min	57
$HgCl_4^{2-}$–*Cl^-	0.3, 1.0	C, 1 min	57
HgI_2–*I^-		C, 2.5 min	62
HgI_4^{2-}–*I^-	0.0005, 0.3	C, 30 sec	44, 62

[a] This table is taken from the more complete table furnished by Stranks and Wilkins.[1]
[b] The following symbols are used in the table: N signifies ≤5% exchange in the time indicated at the highest concentrations and temperature. C signifies >90% exchange in the time indicated at the lowest concentration and temperature. Time designated without N or C signifies half-life, $t_{1/2}$. Temperature unless otherwise indicated is 20–30°C or room temperature. Exchange conditions include [complex], [reactant], pH, and solvent (unless otherwise indicated solvent is water). Ligands: for symbols of ligands see p. 29.
[c] Exchange has been studied kinetically.
[d] Exchange is photocatalyzed.

6. The systems of higher coordination number are less labile than corresponding complexes of lower coordination number, e.g., compare the inertness of six- and eight-coordinated cyanometal systems with two- and four-coordinated compounds.

7. The greater the positive charge on the central atom, the slower its reactions providing crystal field factors, etc., do not change greatly, e.g., $Fe(EDTA)^-$ is slow to exchange but $Fe(EDTA)^{2-}$ is labile.

REFERENCES

1. D. R. Stranks and R. G. Wilkins, *Chem. Revs.*, **57**, 743 (1957).
2. J. P. Hunt and H. Taube, *J. Chem. Phys.*, **19**, 602 (1951).
3. F. A. Long, *J. Am. Chem. Soc.*, **63**, 1353 (1941).
4. A. G. MacDiarmid and N. F. Hall, *ibid.*, **76**, 4222 (1954).
5. J. P. Hunt and H. Taube, *J. Chem. Phys.*, **18**, 757 (1950); R. A. Plane and H. Taube, *J. Phys. Chem.*, **56**, 33 (1952); J. P. Hunt and R. A. Plane, *J. Am. Chem. Soc.*, **76**, 5960 (1954).
6. R. G. Wilkins and D. S. Popplewell, *Rec. trav. chim.*, **75**, 815 (1956) and unpublished observations.
7. H. Taube and E. L. King, *J. Am. Chem. Soc.*, **76**, 4053 (1954).
8. A. W. Adamson and R. G. Wilkins, *J. Am. Chem. Soc.*, **76**, 3379 (1954).
9. H. van der Straaten and A. H. W. Aten, Jr., *Rec. trav. chim.*, **73**, 157 (1954).
10. Y. A. Fialkov and Y. P. Nazarenko, *Doklady Akad. Nauk S.S.S.R.*, **101**, 1059 (1955).
11. A. W. Adamson, J. P. Welker, and M. Volpe, *J. Am. Chem. Soc.*, **72**, 4030 (1950).
12. H. E. Menker and C. S. Garner, *ibid.*, **71**, 371 (1949).
13. A. A. Grinberg, *Conference of the Academy of Sciences of the U.S.S.R. on the Peaceful Uses of Atomic Energy*, July, 1955. Consultants Bureau, New York (English translation).
14. F. A. Long, *J. Am. Chem. Soc.*, **61**, 571 (1939).
15. E. L. Goodenow and C. S. Garner, *ibid.*, **77**, 5268 (1955). H. Baadsgaard and W. D. Treadwell, *Helv. Chim. Acta*, **38**, 1669 (1955).
16. U. Drekmann, *Z. physik. Chem.*, **53B**, 227 (1943).
17. A. W. Adamson, J. P. Welker, and W. B. Wright, *J. Am. Chem. Soc.*, **73**, 4786 (1951).
18. M. J. Polissar, *ibid.*, **58**, 1372 (1936).
19. S. Ruben, M. D. Kamen, M. B. Allen, and P. Nahinsky, *ibid.*, **64**, 2297 (1942).
20. I. B. Whitney, G. K. Schweitzer, and C. L. Comar, *ibid.*, **77**, 1390 (1955).
21. H. C. Clark, N. F. Curtis, and A. L. Odell, *J. Chem. Soc.*, **1954**, 63.
22. R. C. Thompson, *J. Am. Chem. Soc.*, **70**, 1045 (1948); C. Haenny and G. Rochat, *Helv. Chim. Acta*, **32**, 2441 (1949); C. Haenny and E. Wikler, *ibid.*, **32**, 2444 (1949).
23. S. S. Jones and F. A. Long, *J. Phys. Chem.*, **56**, 25 (1952).
24. L. L. Larson and C. S. Garner, *J. Am. Chem. Soc.*, **76**, 2180 (1954).

25. H. L. Friedman, H. Taube, and J. P. Hunt, *J. Chem. Phys.*, **20**, 1016 (1952).
26. S. A. Hoshowsky, O. G. Holmes, and K. J. McCallum, *Can. J. Research*, **27B**, 258 (1949); P. Sue and G. Kayos, *J. chim. phys.*, **45**, 188 (1948); J. F. Flagg, *J. Am. Chem. Soc.*, **63**, 557 (1941).
27. B. O. West, *J. Chem. Soc.*, **1952**, 3115; **1954**, 395, 578.
28. R. G. Wilkins, P. Ellis, and M. J. G. Williams, *ibid.*, **1957**, 4056.
29. A. C. Rutenberg and H. Taube, *J. Chem. Phys.*, **20**, 825 (1952).
30. D. R. Stranks, *Trans. Faraday Soc.*, **51**, 505 (1955).
31. G. M. Harris, *J. Chem. Phys.*, **18**, 764 (1950); G. M. Harris and D. R. Stranks, *Trans. Faraday Soc.*, **48**, 137 (1952).
32. J. S. Holden and G. M. Harris, *J. Am. Chem. Soc.*, **77**, 1934 (1955).
33. D. D. Brown and C. K. Ingold, *J. Chem. Soc.*, **1953**, 2680
34. R. G. Pearson, P. M. Henry, and F. Basolo, *J. Am. Chem. Soc.*, **79**, 5379 (1957).
35. K. H. Fantes, J. E. Page, L. F. J. Parker, and L. E. Smith, *Proc. Roy. Soc. London*, **B136**, 592 (1949); R. R. Baldwin, J. R. Lowry, and R. V. Harrington, *J. Am. Chem. Soc.*, **73**, 4968 (1951); R. N. Boos, C. Rosenblum, and D. T Woodbury, *ibid.*, **73**, 5446 (1951).
36. A. W. Adamson, *ibid.*, **73**, 5710 (1951).
37. D. Marx, *Compt. rend.*, **233**, 865 (1951).
38. C. M. Cook, Jr., and F. A. Long, *J. Am. Chem. Soc.*, **80**, 33 (1958).
39. J. Stiegman, *Phys. Rev.*, **59**, 498 (1941).
40. A. A. Grinberg and P. Filinow, *Compt. rend. acad. sci. U.R.S.S.*, **23**, 912 (1939); **31**, 453 (1941).
41. J. E. Johnson and N. F. Hall, *J. Am. Chem. Soc.*, **70**, 2344 (1948); N. F. Hall and B. R. Willeford, Jr., *ibid.*, **73**, 5419 (1951).
42. D. S. Popplewell and R. G. Wilkins, *J. Chem. Soc.*, **1955**, 4098.
43. R. G. Wilkins and M. J. G. Williams, *J. Chem. Soc.*, **1957**, 1763.
44. S. Chatterjee and P. Rây, *J. Indian Chem. Soc.*, **17**, 524 (1940).
45. F. A. Long, *J. Am. Chem. Soc.*, **73**, 537 (1951).
46. D. Banerjea, F. Basolo, and R. G. Pearson, *ibid.*, **79**, 4055 (1957).
47. T. S. Elleman, J. W. Reishus, and D. S. Martin, Jr., *ibid.*, **80**, 536 (1958).
48. A. A. Grinberg and L. E. Nikol'skaya, *Zhur. Priklad. Khim.*, **24**, 893 (1951).
49. L. F. Grantham, T. S. Elleman, and D. S. Martin, Jr., *J. Am. Chem. Soc.*, **77**, 2965 (1955).
50. R. L. Rich and H. Taube, *ibid.*, **76**, 2608 (1954).
51. A. A. Grinberg, L. E. Nikol'skaya and G. A. Shagisultanova, *Doklady Akad. Nauk S.S.S.R.*, **101**, 1059 (1955).
52. A. A. Grinberg, L. I. Kozlova, L. E. Nikol'skaya, and G. A. Shagisultanova, *J. Appl. Chem. U.S.S.R.*, **28**, 5 (1955).
53. A. W. Adamson and J. M. Grunland, *J. Am. Chem. Soc.*, **73**, 5508 (1951).
54. S. Ruben, O. Seaborg, and J. Kennedy, *J. Appl. Phys.*, **12**, 308 (1941).
55. R. B. Duffield and M. Calvin, *J. Am. Chem. Soc.*, **68**, 557 (1946).
56. R. Daudel, *Compt. rend.*, **215**, 301 (1942).
57. R. L. Rich and H. Taube, *J. Phys. Chem.*, **58**, 1, 6 (1954).
58. L. Leventhal and C. S. Garner, *J. Am. Chem. Soc.*, **71**, 371 (1949); D. C. Atkins and C. S. Garner, *ibid.*, **74**, 3527 (1952).

406 MECHANISMS OF INORGANIC REACTIONS

59. A. Turco, G. Sordillo, and M. Scatena, *Ricerca Sci.*, **25**, 2361 (1955).
60. R. B. Bernstein and H. G. Pars, *J. Am. Chem. Soc.*, **77**, 4433 (1955).
61. R. L. Wolfgang and R. W. Dodson, *ibid.*, **76**, 2004 (1954).
62. A. Polessitskij, *Compt. rend. acad. sci. U.R.S.S.*, **24**, 540 (1939); R. Daudel, *Compt. rend.*, **215**, 177 (1942).

Author index

407

Subject index